Intellectual and
Developmental Disabilities

Intellectual and Developmental Disabilities

Toward Full Community Inclusion

THIRD EDITION

Paul Wehman
Phillip J. McLaughlin
Therese Wehman

pro·ed
An International Publisher

8700 Shoal Creek Boulevard
Austin, Texas 78757-6897
800/897-3202   Fax 800/397-7633
www.proedinc.com

© 1992, 1996, 2005 by PRO-ED, Inc.
8700 Shoal Creek Boulevard
Austin, Texas 78757-6897
800/897-3202   Fax 800/397-7633
www.proedinc.com

Library of Congress Cataloging-in-Publication Data

Intellectual and developmental disabilities : toward full community inclusion / [edited by]
    Paul Wehman, Phillip J. McLaughlin, Therese Wehman.—3rd ed.
        p.   cm.
        Rev. ed. of: Mental retardation and developmental disabilities. 2nd ed. 1996.
        Includes bibliographical references and indexes.
        ISBN 0-89079-990-3 (alk. paper)
        1. Developmentally disabled—Services for.   2. Developmental disabilities.   I. Wehman,
    Paul.   II. McLaughlin, Phillip J.   III. Wehman, Therese.   IV. Mental retardation and
    developmental disabilities.

        HV1570.I68 2005
        362.196'8—dc22

                                                                    2004048758

Art Director: Jason Crosier
Designer: Nancy McKinney-Point
This book is designed in Minion and Knockout.

Printed in the United States of America

1 2 3 4 5 6 7 8 9 10   09 08 07 06 05

CONTENTS

PREFACE

It is a pleasure to present a significantly expanded and more contemporary third edition of this book on developmental disabilities. The previous text is now over 9 years old and does not reflect the many changes that have occurred in laws, legal actions, and changes in policy and practices throughout the field. The term *mental retardation* is rapidly disappearing in many circles and is being replaced by the term *intellectual disabilities*. There is an increasing emphasis on the use of supports, person-centered planning, self-determination, consumer-driven controls over funds, and, more than ever, full community inclusion. We have reflected these changes in the title, which suggests that the major theme through the book is community inclusion, whether it is in education, living, or school environments.

The book continues to be arranged in terms of a life-span perspective on developmental disabilities, a survey of developmental disabilities, and a section on service and program issues. We also have included personal perspectives from three individuals with disabilities or family members of individuals with disabilities. Jay McLaughlin, Ray Graesser, and Ed Turner all graciously agreed to share some of their personal and family issues of managing disability. (Tragically, Ray Graesser has since passed away, a terrible loss for his family, for the field, and for other people with disabilities.)

In Section I, "Life Span," the chapters relate to key aspects of service delivery, early childhood intervention, going to school, transition from school to adulthood, and aging. Together, the chapters set the foundation for the book, but more important, they move us away from a focus on individual disability categories and more into the generic community service issues that are critical for full community inclusion.

In Section II, "Developmental Disabilities," mild and severe intellectual disabilities, cerebral palsy, seizure disorders, emotional disturbances, autism, and learning disabilities are described in detail with up-to-date references and reflecting new language and new approaches in the field. In this section, we have recognized the changes expressed in the current American Association on Mental Retardation (2002) definition of mental retardation, as well as the name changes reflected in the President's Committee on Intellectual Disabilities.

In the third section, "Services and Programs," information is presented on service and program issues that are critical with intellectual and developmental disabilities. These chapters include information on community-based vocational training, positive behavior support, supported employment, independent living, social security and the Ticket to Work and Work Incentives Act, One-Stop Career Centers, postsecondary education, and legal rights and benefits.

A number of these chapters are new since the previous edition, and those chapters that have been updated reflect new information that will be very useful to students in training, as well as practitioners in the field. A great deal of work is required to make full community inclusion a reality for people with intellectual and developmental disabilities. Foremost among the challenges, however, is the need for trained professionals in the field and knowledgeable advocates who can argue for the best quality services in their communities. This book directly addresses the spectrum of information that service providers, teachers, counselors, and students in the fields of developmental disabilities, special education, rehabilitation, and psychology need to have. We have gone to great lengths to integrate this information in a way that will make it easily accessible to professionals, families, and students who are working in the thousands of community settings throughout the country and world. We believe we have covered all of the major issues and service delivery challenges that are faced daily by those who work in the trenches. The personal perspectives of consumers and family members in this book, along with the plethora of case studies, will give the reader a great deal of down-to-earth information that we hope will be extremely useful.

REFERENCE

American Association on Mental Retardation. (2002). *Mental retardation: Definition, classification, and systems of supports* (10th ed.). Washington, DC: Author.

LIFE SPAN

PERSONAL PERSPECTIVE

When I was 26 years old, I was struck by a car going 65 miles per hour as I rode my bicycle. The impact shattered my left leg below the knee, and the jagged ends of the bones severed my nerves as they went through my skin. Fourteen years later, I have metal rods in each of the two bones in my lower leg, and I wear a brace every day. In my right arm, a plate and seven screws hold the pieces of splintered bone in place. Although these injuries have presented their own challenges, the most significant injury I sustained turned out to be the "invisible" one—the trauma to my brain that left me in a coma for 5 days.

Crutches, casts, stitches, bruises, swelling, wheelchairs, canes, and the like all provide significant and obvious visible evidence of a severe injury. These markers encourage others to help the person with the injury, to relax the pace, to make allowances—whether the person needs it or not. But once those visible reminders are gone and only the cognitive sequelae remain, the survivor of a brain injury has to go it alone. The struggles of day-to-day life, the simple ordering of tasks, remembering not to lock your keys in the car, to balance your checkbook, to pay your bills

on time, to feed the dogs, to keep groceries in the refrigerator—these become all-consuming tasks, exhausting the short supply of energy you have to get through each day.

Finding solutions to these problems and determining effective ways to live a productive life become the task of the brain injury survivor. This can be difficult and time-consuming, and it can erode and undermine your self-image. The demands are often overwhelming.

Early in my recovery I became frustrated over many things. I was very short-tempered and angered easily. I often found myself saying unkind words to my wife, my friends, my coworkers, many people I came into contact with. In hindsight it was merely a manifestation of my frustration with my own inability to accomplish things in an effective manner and a reasonable amount of time. But that doesn't make it any less rude when you're being harsh to people. As my cognitive abilities returned, I would realize some time later that I had been unfair, and I would apologize, but the damage was done. Early on, it was a week or 10 days after the incident that I would realize my indiscretion and apologize for it.

1

My realization and apologies gradually came closer to the incident—4 or 5 days after, then 2 or 3 days, and so forth. My father pointed this out to me and suggested I put my energy into trying to make the realization and the unfortunate incident switch places. In other words, I began to try to realize I was going to say or do something rude *before* I did it rather than after—and I could stop myself before it happened. I often look back at that realization as one of the many critical turning points in my recovery.

Very early in my recovery—while I was still an inpatient at the Medical College of Virginia (MCV)—I recall a nurse talking to me about disabilities and the ways they might change your life but, more important, the ways your life would remain the same. He was talking about people with disabilities in general, and he told me that "we're a lot more the same than we are different." That was 14 years ago, and I remember it as if it were yesterday. When I work with people with disabilities now, I work constantly to emphasize our similarities, because they're much more significant and helpful than our differences.

I remember as my recovery progressed the things people would do that made me feel "special"—but it was special in a way I resented. I'm sure that people meant well, but as my cognitive capacities more and more closely approximated my preinjury levels, and my awareness rose, I didn't want to be special anymore. I wanted to be normal. I wanted to be just like everyone else; I wanted to do the things everyone else was doing, like drive a car, go on a trip, have a beer with my friends, just have fun. If a person wants to feel special—and many of us do—it needs to be *that person's* choice, not someone else's. The ability to make choices is one of the things that makes us more fully human, makes us unique individuals, and being special should just be another of life's many choices, not a label thrust upon an unwilling person in an unfortunate situation.

The current manifestation of this experience is my distaste for activities labeled spe-

cial, as in Special Olympics and special education. I think that the intentions of the people who organize the Special Olympics are very good, as were the intentions of the people who tried to make me feel special. But the road to Hell, as they say, is paved with good intentions, and when I put in extra effort in my work with people with disabilities, it's to make them feel *less* special rather than more. When I push friends in their wheelchair, if it's at all possible, I try to walk beside them rather than behind them. I never liked people pushing me from behind when I was in a wheelchair. Think about the last time you walked somewhere with one of your friends—did you walk behind them? Did they walk behind you? Having a conversation with a person behind you is unnatural, and it was one of the ways that I really didn't like to feel special.

When a person has a visible injury, others are quick to hold doors, pick up dropped objects, and get things down from high shelves. It's easy for other people to envision themselves in such a situation—we've all known people who have had such temporary setbacks, and we may have even had one ourselves. We know that we would like to have others help us in such a situation, so most people are willing to help out. Even when your challenges are significant, the help that other people offer makes it much easier to get by from day to day.

An injured brain is much slower to heal than an injured arm or leg or ankle—the mechanisms for repair are much more complex, and it may be many years before a person recovers from a brain injury. People who know that you've had a brain injury will make allowances for you and slow down the pace. Once you get back into the real world, however, back into competitive employment and back to your old lifestyle, your injury is invisible and you have to perform at the same level as everyone else. That's why it takes practice, practice, practice so that you can work at full speed.

People often want to assist a person with any severe or obvious injury or disability, and this sentiment is gracious, generous, and easy to understand. In certain instances, the person does need assistance. However, I feel I was helped more over the long term when I was forced to strive just a little bit more, to reach a little bit higher, to do just a little bit extra to get something I wanted. This gave me a stronger sense of mastery and more feelings of competence than I would have had if someone had done everything for me. People need to learn to do things for themselves to the extent they're able. When a child is growing up, his parents don't tie his shoes for him until he's 15 years old. The child has to learn to do things for himself.

At some point, the highly motivated survivor realizes, you're going to have to start doing things for yourself, and it would be a good idea to start practicing now. After surviving my accident, I became very dependent for many months—dependent on doctors, nurses, therapists, friends, family members, and so on. But I place an extremely high value on independence, and I began striving for that goal the moment I realized it was out there. I was training for what was to be my third triathlon when I had my accident, riding my bicycle. My focus in recovery was to return to the level of health I had enjoyed before my accident, but I was frustrated in that pursuit by the cast I wore on my left leg for 6 months. However, I realized there were things I could do even though I was wearing a cast, and the first time the grass needed cutting, I got out there and started pushing the lawn mower. It was exhausting and I could only do small sections of the yard before taking long breaks, but eventually I got it done. This helped me build my endurance once again. I would get on my crutches and go around the block near our house. The second time I cut the grass it was a little bit easier, and the more I pushed myself, the easier it became.

Soon I experienced the "double-edged sword" of a good recovery. The more "normal" you appear, the more people will ask of you. But with hard work it became self-fulfilling—when you "fake it till you make it," you're eventually *going* to make it. Because each time a person asks for a little bit more, and you in turn deliver a little bit more, you get a little bit stronger, you have another success under your belt. And that pushes the bar higher. Cutting the grass or working for another person, the same rules apply—the more you do it, the easier it becomes. Samuel Johnson, author of the first American dictionary, said in 1779, "That which we hope to do with ease we must first do with diligence." The more diligently I did things after my accident, the easier they became.

Recovery from any injury presents new challenges. If you've been out of commission and out of your day-to-day routines for a very long time, as people with severe injuries normally are, it can take some time just to return to your preinjury level of functioning. I was in the hospital and in rehabilitation programs for over 6 months, and that's probably pretty typical of a person with a severe injury or illness. Six months is a long time for your body and your mind. You lose a lot of energy, a lot of strength, a lot of your natural problem-solving ability. And they take a long time to return. Finding that you don't have the energy or the natural problem-solving speed and capability you had 6 months earlier adds to the frustrations you experience on return to work.

This happens in your personal life as well as your professional and academic life. I was relatively newly married at the time of my accident—we had been married for about 9 months. In addition, we had moved from an apartment into our first house only 4 days before my accident. My wife had certain expectations of me, just as I had expectations of myself. My employers and friends had certain expectations, as well. Fortunately, my friends are good ones, and they remained with me through the difficult months and years that followed my accident.

I had been working successfully at a job for approximately 7 years at the time of my accident, earning a decent wage and moving ahead in my company. The combination of my physical injuries and my brain injury kept me out of work for over 6 months. When I returned to work, all of us—me, my wife, and my employers—expected pretty much the same person, maybe with a limp. After all, I *appeared* to be the same as I had been the day before the accident. But I had extreme difficulty staying organized, staying focused, continuing tasks through to completion.

In my experience, among the most significant challenges as I recovered was dealing with my mood swings, toward myself and others. My temper was short, and I struggled to maintain it. At the same time, my patience with myself was very short—I never gave myself a break, never cut myself any slack. This, again, is a double-edged sword in recovery. It causes you to push harder and reach higher, but it can be emotionally and physically draining. Eventually, I was overwhelmed—I could never live up to the unrealistic expectations I placed on myself. The combination of unrealistic expectations and slow processing speed frustrated me so completely I fell into a severe depression and ended up in the psychiatric unit at MCV for a 3-week stay.

When I got out, I had to rebuild from the ground up. It was a bitter pill to swallow, but I knew that the only way I could build myself back up was to lower the bar and start over from the beginning. I took jobs that were much less demanding in much less stressful environments and started from there.

The first job I took after leaving my "real" job was at the YMCA, cleaning mats, sweeping tennis courts, and doing other light janitorial work. The Y was an outstanding place to return to work; I knew almost everyone there, they were supportive and helpful, and the atmosphere was extremely healthy. I had been trying to convince myself that I was up to the demands of a stressful job, but that simply wasn't true. I needed to start off a little bit slower and work my way back.

Eventually, I decided I was ready for something a little bit more demanding, and I went to a very large local hunting and fishing store called Green Top Sporting Goods and applied there. I had hunted and fished for most of my life, so the field was familiar to me; but it was my first experience in retail, and it came as something of a shock. But the business was family owned, and I once again found myself in a very supportive environment. As I got the hang of the job and my endurance slowly came back, I was able to gradually increase my hours. Hauling boxes of shotgun shells all day was physically demanding, but it was a great way to enhance my endurance.

Organization presented a constant challenge for me at Green Top. In addition to the physical demands of hauling around heavy merchandise, the cognitive demands were significant, as I had to organize and restock several hundred items ranging from packets of BBs to folding duck blinds and large dog crates. I had worked with a job coach in the past, and Green Top was offered a job coach to work with me at the store. However, being a family business, they preferred to take their chances on me and keep all of the training inhouse. The organizational problems were many but not complex; I was eventually able to solve them on my own, and the experience served to enhance my problem-solving capabilities, my organizational strengths, and my self-confidence.

After about 2 years at Green Top, I was asked to give a talk about recovery from brain injury at a conference in Norfolk, Virginia. Dr. Paul Wehman attended that conference, and he offered me an opportunity to work as a job coach at the Rehabilitation Research and Training Center at MCV. This was the first time I felt I would really be challenging myself cognitively, and I was reluctant to leave the security and predictability of the job I had. However, I realized I was "at the edge of the envelope" once again, and it was time to move forward. I was fortunate to have good training and support there, and it enabled me to be successful as a job coach. From there I went back to Virginia Commonwealth University, finished my degree in psychology, and went on to get a master's degree in rehabilitation counseling.

If there is one idea that has guided me and continues to guide me in my recovery and in my work, it is to "treat others the way I would have them treat me." If there is only one concept that I could pass on that I think might help others in the future, it would be that. I feel that the Golden Rule, far more than any other idea or concept that is taught at the greatest universities in the world, is the most valuable lesson of all. If you don't take anything else away from what I've said, take that—and treat your clients, your patients, your students, your family members, and anyone else you might come into contact with professionally and personally just as you'd want them to treat you.

—*Jay McLaughlin*

CHAPTER I

Service Delivery

Pamela S. Wolfe, Valerie Postal,
Therese Wehman, Paul Wehman, and Ed Turner

LEARNING GOALS

Upon completion of this chapter, the reader will be able to

- describe who may have a developmental disability
- describe the differences between consumer empowerment and normalization philosophies
- describe how to teach self-advocacy
- describe the educational and community integration needs of people with developmental disabilities
- discuss cultural differences in persons with disabilities
- list and discuss five major challenges for service providers in working with persons with developmental disabilities

ndividuals with disabilities represent a heterogeneous group. Like everyone, they have strengths and challenges that make them unique. Because of their varied needs, persons with disabilities often interact with professionals in the human service delivery system. Professionals with whom they interact may include educators, counselors, advocates, case managers, and other related personnel. Due to the wide variety of service delivery systems, individuals with disabilities and their families often must contend with different service delivery models, eligibility criteria, and procedures. Variations in service delivery systems can make it difficult for individuals with disabilities to know what services are available, how to access them, and how to be empowered to make their own decisions. This is especially true for individuals with developmental disabilities who require a wide range of services. This chapter will outline who has a developmental disability and how such individuals can be empowered when interacting with service delivery systems. Further, the needs of persons with developmental disabilities will be addressed, as well as issues that service providers may face when meeting those needs. To highlight issues related to service delivery, three individuals will be introduced who have been identified as having developmental disabilities. Each individual is receiving one or more specialized services and is facing an issue of service provision. As these cases illustrate, the service delivery system for individuals with developmental disabilities is diverse and can change over time.

 ## CASE EXAMPLE: SAM

Sam is a 3-year-old boy who loves trains. He lives with his mother, Lily, in an apartment in a large midwestern city. Lily is a 20-year-old single mother who recently immigrated to the United States from Thailand. She has had little experience with children but felt lucky that Sam was such an easy baby compared to others she saw around the apartment complex. Sam seemed content and began walking and talking like other children of the same age. However, Lily became concerned when Sam stopped talking at 15 months of age. He began to cover his ears with his hands and screamed for up to 2 hours each evening. Lily took Sam to a clinic and was told that he might have an ear infection; he was prescribed antibiotics for 2 weeks. When he returned to the clinic to be reexamined, Sam screamed and ran around the waiting room, tearing the magazines. As a result, he was referred to the Developmental Unit at the Children's Hospital, where he was examined by a team of doctors and therapists. After 3 hours of testing, Sam was diagnosed as having autism and expressive language delays. Once he received his initial diagnosis, he was referred to an early intervention program, which he attends 4 mornings a week. Lily is unfamiliar with the services available to children with disabilities in the United States and is grateful to finally have a service coordinator who understands her language and interprets reports and meeting discussions for her. Sam is learning to use the Picture Exchange Communication System (PECS) at preschool and can use picture cards to request favorite foods, drinks, toys, and activities. Lily also uses PECS at home and has noticed that Sam does not scream as much as before. However, Sam always screams if anyone touches or moves his trains; he spends hours each day arranging the pattern of cars he selects for the day. Any infringement on this activity at home or at preschool results in an incident of screaming, hitting, or biting.

CASE EXAMPLE: GARY

Gary is widely recognized as the biggest football fan in town; he hasn't missed a Tigers' game in his small West Coast town in 6 years. He is 34 years old and works as a custodian at the community college where the Tigers play on Saturday afternoons. Gary has been diagnosed as having severe intellectual disability and depression. He lives in a group home located near the center of town and within walking distance of his job, church, and favorite diner. All of the local townspeople know Gary and wait for his arrival at the same time each day. With no family in the area, Gary relies on friends and group home staff for transportation to the grocery store, shopping mall, doctor's office, and pharmacy. He often needs assistance when coordinating appointments with his work schedule and daily routine. He is taking medication to help control his severe depression. The pharmacist is Gary's friend and calls to remind him to refill his prescriptions each month. When the pharmacist was on vacation last year, Gary's prescription lapsed and he experienced severe symptoms of depression requiring overnight hospitalization.

 ## CASE EXAMPLE: JESSICA

Jessica is Sophie's best friend. Jessica and Sophie are seventh graders at George Washington Middle School, located in a suburb of a large city. Jessica lives with her mom, dad, and two younger brothers in a house across the street from her school. She has been diagnosed as having a moderate developmental disability, cerebral palsy, and a seizure disorder. She is enrolled in a life skills classroom for half of the day; in the afternoons, she takes part in integrated class activities. The school personnel have been trained to handle seizures and support her movement in a wheelchair throughout the school. Sophie is usually the one who volunteers to accompany Jessica throughout the school and community; the two girls are inseparable.

WHO ARE PEOPLE WITH DEVELOPMENTAL DISABILITIES?

Sam, Gary, and Jessica have been labeled as having developmental disabilities. However, as evidenced in the cases, each has very different strengths and challenges. People with developmental disabilities represent a wide range of individuals; precisely who has a developmental disability is often difficult to ascertain. An examination of how the term was first introduced is helpful in understanding who may have a developmental disability. In the 1960s, President John F. Kennedy began to highlight issues related to disabilities. Specifically, he appointed a panel to report on aspects of mental retardation, now often referred to as *intellectual disability*. Based on the findings of the panel, Kennedy called for a comprehensive approach to mental retardation and mental health services. Federal legislation was enacted in 1963 (the Maternal and Child Health and Mental Retardation Planning Amendments, Public Law [P.L.] 88-156; and the Mental Retardation Facilities and Community Mental Health Centers Construction Act, P.L. 88-164). However, leaders in the field of special education noted that the focus on mental retardation was too narrow and that disabilities such as cerebral

palsy and epilepsy often accompanied mental retardation and had similar related service needs and issues. In 1970, the Developmental Disabilities Services
and Facilities Construction Act (P.L. 91-517) introduced the term *developmental
disabilities* and was intended to meet the needs of a broader constituency. The
Developmental Disabilities Assistance and Bill of Rights (DD) Act of 1990
(P.L. 100-146) reauthorized the 1970 DD Act and added an emphasis on the empowerment of individuals with disabilities. Table 1.1 provides an overview of

TABLE 1.1
Major Legislation Affecting Individuals with Developmental Disabilities

Date	Legislation	Provision
1970	Developmental Disabilities Services and Facilities Construction Act (P.L. 91-517)	First introduced the concept of "developmental disabilities."
1971	Title XIX of the Social Security Act (P.L. 92-223)	Required intermediate care facilities for individuals with mental retardation (ICF/MRs) to provide "active treatment."
1975	Education for All Handicapped Children Act (P.L. 94-142)	Guaranteed a free and appropriate education to all children.
1978	Rehabilitation, Comprehensive Services, and Developmental Disabilities Amendments (P.L. 95-602)	Revised the definition of developmental disabilities to emphasize "functionality."
1984	Developmental Disabilities Act Amendments (P.L. 98-527)	Included employment-related activities as a priority.
1990	Developmental Disabilities Assistance and Bill of Rights Act (P.L. 100-146)	Reauthorized the Developmental Disabilities Assistance and Bill of Rights Act for 3 years and emphasized the empowerment of individuals with disabilities; placed particular emphasis on protection and advocacy.
1990	Individuals with Disabilities Education Act (P.L. 101-476)	Reauthorized parts of the Education for All Handicapped Children Act. Changed the name of the law to Individuals with Disabilities Education Act (IDEA) to reflect people before disability; expanded the definition of disability to include children with autism and traumatic brain injury; increased emphasis on transition planning; provided support for projects for students with serious emotional disturbances.

(continues)

major legislation affecting service provision for individuals with developmental disabilities. Legislative changes have occurred in virtually every area of service provision ranging from education to residential and vocational services. Further, legislation such as the Americans with Disabilities Act of 1990 (P.L. 101-336) has provided basic and far-reaching protection and advocacy for individuals with disabilities.

The DD Act defines who has a developmental disability. Major components of the definition are listed in Table 1.2. An individual who is identified as having a developmental disability can be both mentally and physically impaired,

TABLE 1.1 *Continued.*
Major Legislation Affecting Individuals with Developmental Disabilities

Date	Legislation	Provision
1990	Americans with Disabilities Act (ADA) (P.L. 101-336)	Offered important civil rights for individuals with disabilities; extended rights to access in employment settings, public transportation, and public establishments.
1992	Rehabilitation Act Amendments (P.L. 102-569)	Supported the service systems through which employers can find assistance and expertise in identifying and completing the reasonable and appropriate job accommodations called for in the ADA; established a basis in the adult service system for accomplishing the transition preparation, planning, and implementation activities in the IDEA; put the abilities and choices of people with a disability first and challenged the services system and the greater community to support their efforts to work, live, and participate in the community.
1997	IDEA Amendments of 1997 (P.L. 105-17)	Strengthened the role of families in educational programming and mandated that states must collect data to determine whether students from culturally and linguistically diverse backgrounds are overrepresented or underrepresented in special education; noted that students ages 3 to 9 can be identified as developmentally delayed.

TABLE 1.2
Federal Definition of Developmental Disabilities

The term *developmental disability* means a severe, chronic disability of a person 5 years of age or older which

- is attributable to a mental or physical impairment or combination of mental and physical impairments;
- is manifested before the person attains age 22;
- is likely to continue indefinitely;
- results in substantial functional limitations in three or more of the following areas of major life activity:
—self-care
—receptive and expressive language
—learning
—mobility
—self-direction
—capacity for independent living
—economic self-sufficiency
- reflects the person's need for a combination and sequence of special interdisciplinary or generic care, treatment, or other services which are of lifelong or extended duration and are individually planned and coordinated except that such term, when applied to infants and young children means individuals from birth to age 5, inclusive, who have substantial developmental delay or specific congenital or acquired conditions with a high probability of resulting in developmental disability if services are not provided.

Note. From the Developmental Disabilities Assistance and Bill of Rights Act of 1990, Title 42, U.S.C. 6000–6083. *U.S. Statutes at Large, 104,* 1191–1204.

with disabilities originating before the age of 22; the disability is thought to continue indefinitely. Typical categories of disability include epilepsy, cerebral palsy, intellectual disability, and autism.

Table 1.3 lists some of the categories that might be included in the definition of developmental disabilities. Obviously, the listing is not exhaustive and could include other disabilities depending on the functional limitations the disability imposes. Functional limitations are an important concept in understanding who might have a developmental disability. According to the definition included in the DD Act, individuals who have a developmental disability show deficits in three of seven life activities: self-care, language, learning, mobility, self-direction, capacity for independent living, and economic self-sufficiency. The act defines disability in terms of what an individual is and is not able to do rather than in terms of clinical diagnosis. The change in emphasis from cause and effect to adaptive life activities can help human service professionals identify areas where they may be asked to provide assistance. Consider the contrast in utility of the following two descriptions in pinpointing service provision needs for Gary:

TABLE 1.3
Range of Developmental Disabilities

Learning disorders	Myelomeningocele/spina bifida
Attention-deficit/hyperactivity disorder (ADHD)	Hearing impairment
Mental retardation	Vision disorder
Autism/pervasive developmental disorder (PDD)	Behavior disorder
Communication disorder	Developmental coordination disorder
Cerebral palsy	Developmental delay

Note. From *Handbook of Developmental Disabilities: Resources for Interdisciplinary Care* (pp. 4–10), by L. A. Kurtz, P. W. Dowrick, S. E. Levy, and M. L. Batshaw, 1996, Austin, TX: PRO-ED. Copyright 1996 by PRO-ED, Inc. Adapted with permission.

- Gary is mentally handicapped because of trisomy 21 and has a recorded IQ of 45 on the *Wechsler Adult Intelligence Scales–Third Edition.*
- Gary is developmentally disabled and experiences significant difficulties in self-care, learning, and capacity for independent living.

Note how the second definition brings professionals much closer to knowing how they can assist Gary through programming. For example, Gary might need assistance in dressing appropriately for the weather, preparing meals, and reading functional signs such as a local bus schedule or his TV guide.

Greater emphasis on adaptive and functional skill areas has also been noted in the revised definition of mental retardation from the American Association on Mental Retardation (AAMR). The revised definition states that mental retardation is characterized by significantly subaverage intellectual functioning, existing concurrently with related limitations in two or more of the following adaptive skill areas: communication, self-care, home living, social skills, community use, self-direction, health and safety, functional academics, leisure, and work (AAMR, 1992). Note that both the AAMR and DD definitions emphasize adaptive skill areas; the developmental disability definition requires three adaptive skill area deficits, whereas the AAMR definition requires two. Although they are similar, the developmental disability definition is broader in scope. A person does not have to have mental retardation to be labeled as having a developmental disability.

A further examination of the definition of developmental disabilities reveals that an individual must show deficits in three life areas and must manifest the disability before age 22. An individual who has sustained a severe head injury at age 19 might be considered developmentally disabled if the injury limited life activities such as language, learning, capacity for independent living, and economic self-sufficiency. Conversely, an individual who was born with a congenital hearing loss might not be considered developmentally disabled if he or she experienced only a deficit in language (Summers, 1986). The DD Act notes that when the term *developmentally disabled* is applied to children from birth through 4 years, there may be a "developmental delay." That is, they may not have permanent functional limitations but only be delayed in their functioning.

Although the definition may not provide an easy answer as to who has a developmental disability, it does place an important emphasis on adaptive skill areas and highlight the need for diverse services. A precise record of the prevalence of developmental disabilities is difficult to obtain due to definitional issues (knowing what disability categories to include); however, current estimates are that 5% of the total population may have a developmental disability (Kurtz, Dowrick, Levy, & Batshaw, 1996).

CONSUMER EMPOWERMENT FOR PEOPLE WITH DEVELOPMENTAL DISABILITIES

Concept of Normalization

For the past 30 years, the concept of normalization has been the philosophical and ideological cornerstone of human service programs for people with developmental disabilities. Nirje (1969) conceptualized the normalization principle as making available to individuals with disabilities "patterns and conditions of everyday life which are as close as possible to the norms and patterns of the mainstream of society" (p. 181). Wolfensberger (1972) expanded the concept to include not only the outcomes or goals of human service programs, but also the means (strategies, techniques, technologies) used to achieve these goals. Wolfensberger further refined the meaning of the term to remove the notion that individuals with disabilities should somehow be "shaped" through appearance and experiences to fit the statistical norm of their community. Rather, normalization focuses on enabling individuals to lead lives that are valued by other members of their community.

During the 1970s and 1980s, normalization quickly became accepted as the guiding philosophy of the majority of human service programs, which has had a tremendously positive effect on the lives of millions of individuals. Normalization can be seen as directly responsible for, or significantly contributing to, the increase in community residential alternatives, the development of community-based employment programs, the rise in the self-advocacy movement, and the trend toward inclusive educational opportunities. However, normalization as the philosophical basis underlying human services is currently being replaced with another philosophical tenet: consumer empowerment. This tenet places decision-making power in the hands of consumers of human service programs: individuals with disabilities.

Defining Consumer Empowerment

Many terms have been used to describe the concept of consumer empowerment, an individual's exertion of power over his or her own life: self-determination, self-direction, consumer decision making, choice, autonomy, and self-advocacy. Although many of the terms are similar, three can assist in defining the construct of consumer empowerment: self-determination, control, and self-advocacy. Each term emphasizes an individual's opportunity and ability to make choices in daily life, exert control over decisions, and assert personal rights.

Self-Determination

Wehmeyer (1996) defines self-determination as "acting as the primary causal agent in one's life and making choices and decisions regarding one's quality of life free from undue external influence or interference" (p. 124). Self-determination refers to an individual's ability to express preferences and desires, to make decisions, and to initiate actions based on those decisions. According to Wehmeyer, an act or event is self-determined if the individual's actions reflect four characteristics: (a) the individual acted autonomously; (b) the behaviors were self-regulated; (c) the person initiated and responded to events in a "psychologically empowered" manner; and (d) the person acted in a self-realizing manner. In essence, self-determination emphasizes personal goal setting and then engagement in activities designed to achieve those goals.

Control

The concept of control expands and extends the principles of self-determination. Control focuses on the extent to which individuals are independent and self-sufficient and refers to an individual's ability to access the resources necessary to freely act on choices and decisions. Whereas self-determination emphasizes goal setting and actions designed to achieve goals, control focuses on the extent to which decisions are made free from excessive external influence.

Individuality and personal responsibility are highly valued in U.S. society. However, citizens with disabilities historically have had limited opportunities to learn and use decision-making skills, to develop individuality and autonomy, and to assume responsibility for their own lives (Robertson et al., 2001; Wehmeyer, Agran, & Hughes, 1999). Students with disabilities are often excluded from educational planning or have their choices and preferences ignored (Wehmeyer et al., 1999). Lack of choice also has been evident within the adult service system, in vocational and residential programs, for example. Robertson et al. (2001) found that the majority of persons with intellectual disability had little or no opportunity to exercise self-determination over major life decisions such as where or with whom to live. Further, they found that choice was restricted even for mundane decisions such as when, where, and with whom to eat. As Wehmeyer et al. (1999) suggest, more opportunities for choice making should be incorporated into service delivery programs and must be systematically taught to individuals with disabilities.

Self-Advocacy

Self-advocacy refers to the skills needed to advocate on one's own behalf (Wehmeyer et al., 1999). Self-advocacy may occur when an individual acts alone to promote his or her self-interest or when the individual is participating in a group. To be an effective self-advocate, individuals with disabilities need to know how and what to advocate. Necessary skills include assertiveness; effective communication strategies for use in individual, small group, and large group settings; listening skills; and knowledge about how to navigate through various service systems (Wehmeyer et al., 1999).

Consumer Empowerment and Service Delivery Programs

Although most professionals agree that consumer empowerment should be encouraged, many service delivery systems impede opportunities for self-determination, choice making, and self-advocacy. Often, service delivery systems are predicated on a medical model, in which individuals with disabilities are viewed as "sick" and in need of repair by professionals, who are in control of services. In contrast, the ecological perspective posits that consumer empowerment must be viewed as a product between the individual and the multiple environments in which the individual functions. Heller, Factor, Sterns, and Sutton (1996) suggest that many issues that persons with disabilities face can be attributed to problems in the social system. According to this perspective, consumer empowerment is viewed within the broader context of the social system and not simply within the purview of the individual with a disability. Some authors have suggested that self-determination be viewed in the context of an ecosystem (Abery & Stancliffe, 1996). Table 1.4 outlines the four environments of such an ecosystem.

The focus of the exosystem is service delivery. As Abery and Stancliffe (1996) note, the empowerment of persons with disabilities is influenced by the decisions and actions that occur within contexts that do not include them as active participants. That is, schools and organizations have unique, and in some cases, well-established ways that decisions are made and activities carried out. If consumer empowerment is to occur, current delivery systems must undergo a "system change" and place decision making in the hands of persons with disabilities rather than professionals (Abery & Stancliffe, 1996). Abery and Stancliffe have developed a series of steps to be taken by agencies interested in creating a system change toward greater consumer empowerment. As shown in Table 1.5, systems and agencies must (a) examine their own strengths and weaknesses, (b) develop a unifying vision, (c) generate a vision of service provision, (d) identify priorities and strategies, (e) identify structures needed for change to occur, (f) identify the skills and resources necessary for change, and (g) develop an assessment process to support self-determination.

Person-centered planning (PCP) has emerged as a means to empower individuals with disabilities in their interactions with service delivery systems. An extension of the normalization principle, PCP was first developed in the mid-1980s and now guides much of the ideology underlying human service delivery (Wagner, 1999). In PCP, individuals with disabilities take control over decisions that affect their lives. It contrasts with traditional service delivery models that are more "system centered" than consumer centered (Holburn, Jacobson, Vietze, Schwartz, & Sersen, 2000). According to O'Brien (1987), there are five essential outcomes of PCP: community presence, community participation, positive

TABLE 1.4
Ecological Framework for Self-Determination

Microsystem: Concerned with the immediate settings in which the person spends his or her daily life. Involves the family or other residential setting, school, and work context. Self-determination can be enhanced by environment change such as providing skill-based intervention programs, more opportunities for choice-making, and training of staff to learn how to assess choice.

Mesosystem: Concerned with the linkages that exist between the multiple settings in which the person participates. Includes school–family linkages and interagency collaboration. Self-determination can be enhanced by improving family–service provider connections and communication, stimulating family involvement, achieving consistency across settings, and encouraging family advocacy.

Exosystem: Concerned with the decisions and actions that occur within contexts that do not include the person as an active participant. Considers the effect of external contexts on an individual such as program structure and content. Self-determination can be enhanced by undertaking person-centered planning and restructuring services to emphasize individual choice.

Macrosystem: Concerned with the beliefs, attitudes, and values held by society. Social movements such as deinstitutionalization, legislation such as the Americans with Disabilities Act, guardianship and conservatorship, and societal values regarding self-determination all affect the macrosystem. Self-determination can be enhanced by encouraging self-advocacy opportunities and increasing public knowledge about persons with disabilities.

Note. Adapted from "The Ecology of Self-Determination," by B. H. Abery and R. J. Stancliffe, in *Self-Determination Across the Life Span* (pp. 111–145), by D. J. Sands and M. L. Wehmeyer (Eds.), 1996, Baltimore: Brookes. Copyright 1996 by Paul H. Brookes. Adapted with permission.

relationships, respect, and competence. Some approaches that involve person-centered planning include Personal Futures Planning (Mount, 1994), McGill Action Planning System (MAPS; Vandercook, York, & Forest, 1989), Planning Alternative Tomorrows with Hope (PATHS; Pearpoint, O'Brien, & Forest, 1993), Essential Lifestyles Planning (Smull & Harrison, 1992), and Lifestyle Planning (O'Brien & Lovett, 1992). Table 1.6 lists the key characteristics of PCP as outlined by the AAMR (2002).

Obviously, merging opportunities for consumer empowerment into traditional service delivery systems presents a challenge. Employment of person-centered planning requires a philosophical shift away from the professional as expert. PCP in essence "de-professionalizes and de-emphasizes professional decision making" (Holburn & Vietze, 1998, 1999). Further, PCP is not system friendly (Holburn & Vietze, 1998) and requires organizational flexibility. Perhaps the greatest barrier to PCP is regulatory constraint. As Holburn and Vietze (1999) indicate, reimbursement in traditional models of service delivery is contingent on adherence to a medical model. Critics also have argued that PCP

TABLE 1.5
Steps in Systems Change Process

1. *Examination of programmatic strengths and weaknesses.* An examination of the strengths and weaknesses of participating programs is first undertaken to provide staff with feedback about structural and organization features of their service that enhance or inhibit self-determination experienced by persons with disabilities.

2. *Development of a unifying vision.* The development of a unifying vision of what programs that serve persons with disabilities should be like is a second step in the systems change process. Without the creation of a consensual vision that is broadly understood and easily translated into criteria for assessing results, organizational change efforts will quickly bog down.

3. *Generation of a coherent vision of service provision.* Through conducting consensus-building activities, participating service staff are encouraged to come to agreement on a core body of knowledge, skills, and capacities for the persons with disabilities whom they serve and on goals for organizational change.

4. *Identification of priorities and strategies for systems change.* Different organizations will evolve different priorities for change depending upon what they perceived as their most urgent needs. The identification of two or three priorities and strategies for systems change that will enhance the opportunities for self-determination available to persons with disabilities serves as the fourth step.

5. *Identification of structures necessary for desired change.* Only after goals, priorities, and steps for change have been defined can an intelligent discussion occur about new structures that will support and maintain desired changes. Working with small groups, including both administrative and direct-service personnel from participating services, the manner in which individuals desire to work together, and what they need to get the job accomplished, is explored.

6. *Identification of skills and resources necessary for change.* At this stage of the organizational change process, staff are encouraged to explicitly define the specific types of training and technical assistance they need to enhance the self-determination of those whom they serve. Based upon feedback from staff, programs to provide the necessary skill development need to be identified or created and implemented.

7. *Development of assessment processes to support enhanced self-determination.* For systems change to occur, all aspects of an organization must move forward. In this stage, personnel from service agencies develop and implement strategies to ensure that those within the system can adequately track organizational change and the impact of this change upon the self-determination of those individuals whom they serve.

Note. Adapted from "The Ecology of Self-Determination," by B. H. Abery and R. J. Stancliffe, in *Self-Determination Across the Life Span* (pp. 111–145), by D. J. Sands and M. L. Wehmeyer (Eds), 1996, Baltimore: Brookes. Copyright 1996 by Paul H. Brookes. Adapted with permission.

cannot exist in the context of large agencies and, if completed for all clients, is no longer personalized and individualized (Holburn & Vietze, 1998, 1999).

A human service program designed according to the principle of consumer empowerment would be very different from most programs existing today. For example, agency missions would need to change to reflect the provision of supports and services needed to assist people with disabilities to meet their individual goals. Services would not be limited by available options or funding

TABLE 1.6

Key Characteristics of Person-Centered Planning (PCP)

1. The person who is at the focus of the planning and those who love the person are the primary authorities on the person's life direction.
2. The primary purpose of PCP is to learn through shared action (i.e., the process is more than producing paperwork; it is about taking action to reach goals) and reflection on and evaluation of that action.
3. PCP aims to change common patterns of community life (e.g., segregation and congregation of people with disabilities, devaluing stereotypes, inappropriately low expectations, denial of opportunity).
4. PCP requires collaborative action and fundamentally challenges practices that separate people and perpetuate controlling relationships.
5. PCP requires respect for the dignity and completeness of the focus person.
6. PCP calls for a sustained search for effective ways to overcome difficult barriers and conflicting demands.
7. PCP promotes and values accurate individual services and supports, and clarifies individual interests and needs.
8. PCP shapes services to support a person's vision of a valued lifestyle.
9. PCP facilitates change in services to be more responsive to interests of people.
10. PCP promotes a search for capacities within organizations and individuals.
11. PCP organizes efforts in the community to include person, family, and direct support professionals.
12. PCP focuses on quality of life and emphasizes dreams, desired outcomes, and meaningful experiences.

Note. Adapted with permission from *Fact Sheet: Person-Centered Planning,* 2002, by American Association on Mental Retardation. Retrieved February 14, 2002, from http://www.aamr.org/Policies/faq_planning.shtml

issues and would be driven by each person. Further, services would not focus on diagnostic labels, functional deficits, perceived lack of motivation on the part of the individual, or a suspected lack of enthusiasm on the part of the individual's family. A consumer empowerment approach would focus on changes needed by members of society or the human service system. Before meaningful change can occur in organizations, agencies must tackle practical issues such as role clarity, language, regulation compliance, and funding. Table 1.7 lists Holburn and Vietze's (1999) strategies for resolving conflict between system-centered and person-centered approaches.

Human service personnel working with Sam, Gary, and Jessica have worked to ensure that the individuals are empowered in their interactions with their service delivery systems. For example, Sam, who is enrolled in early intervention, receives services aimed at assisting the family as well; the team working with Sam acknowledges that his service needs will change over time as he transitions from one setting to the next. In addition, his team is concerned with more than what goes on in the school. Sam's mother has requested respite care for after-school hours. The team is working with her to identify some potential sources.

TABLE 1.7
Resolving Conflict Between System-Centered and Person-Centered Approaches

Conventional Agency Approach	Person-Centered Planning Approach	Examples of Failure To Resolve Conflict	Examples of Constructive Ways To Address Conflict
Fair, egalitarian (everyone gets help or no one does)	"One person at a time"	Person-centered planning has begun with all consumers, but system resources are overwhelmed	Focus on smaller number of people for person-centered planning while working on system changes that will affect all consumers
Loyalty to the traditional interdisciplinary team process	Loyalty to the person-centered planning process	Interdisciplinary team plans to lift restrictions when behavior improves, but denied preference leads to worsening of challenging behavior	Permit full access to preferred activities and situations and arrange contingencies within those contexts
Professional language, technical jargon	Plain English, everyday language	Ground rules are established for using people-first language during meetings, but this stifles discussion	Accept all vernacular during meeting, but acknowledge different language forms and purposes
Regulatory constraints and workload. Heavy reliance on policies and directives from the top down to regulate employee behavior.	Takes more time, personal investment, and creativity	Agency develops person-centered mission statement, but employee activities still absorbed by internal quality assurance and regulatory compliance	Collaborative problem-solving to explore agency resource reallocation, interpreting rules to fit individual lifestyles, alternative agency funding sources
Fixed patterns of resource use around categories of service (slots)	Individualized funding to support action toward a personal vision of a more desirable future	Vision is compromised with traditional funding, and skepticism grows	Funders and person-centered planners locate and merge available local, state, and federal resources

Note. From "Acknowledging Barriers in Adopting Person-Centered Planning," by S. Holburn and P. Vietze, 1999, *Mental Retardation, 37,* p. 123. Copyright 1999 by Allen Press. Reprinted with permission.

Gary participated in a formal person-centered planning meeting. Because he is so involved in a number of activities, many members of the community participated in the planning meeting. The team made sure that they "thought outside of the box" when finding employment for Gary and outlining his leisure options.

Finally, Jessica also is empowered as she participates in her educational programming. Jessica's IEP team has addressed issues of sibling support and worked to help her secure benefits to make environmental adaptations to her parents' home so she can move about more freely despite her physical limitations.

TEACHING SELF-ADVOCACY

What are the best ways to teach consumers how to select services and to become involved in life-planning activities? For true consumer empowerment, individuals must become self-advocates and be given a meaningful role in the process. For this to happen, service providers should not be afraid to encourage consumers to speak up for what they need as effective self-advocates. Some service providers look at that as giving up control and are hesitant to do it. Others feel they must offer guidance that will prevent their consumers from failing. Although that practice is understandable, it really can be a disservice to consumers in the normal learning process because some of the greatest learning experiences in one's life are due to failing and then learning to do better next time. It also amounts to a lack of respect for a person's right to make mistakes and learn from those mistakes. Service providers who truly believe in the concept of customer-driven services will be eager to give the people they serve opportunities to succeed, fail, and learn, because these are all necessary in becoming effective self-advocates.

To be effective self-advocates, consumers must understand exactly what self-advocacy is and what it is not. Some consumers hesitate to use self-advocacy because they view it as having to confront parents or others in authority. This can be intimidating for people, especially those with developmental disabilities. Therefore, self-advocacy should be presented as a tool to get things done in one's life. Table 1.8 lists, in simple but age-appropriate terms, good and bad self-advocacy practices.

Levels of Self-Advocacy

Once consumers understand the meaning of self-advocacy and how to use it positively, they must become comfortable using it while interacting with others.

TABLE 1.8
Good and Bad Self-Advocacy Practices

Good Self-Advocacy Practices	Bad Self-Advocacy Practices
Being responsible	Being too aggressive
Taking charge	Being controlled
Knowing needs	Knowing it all
Getting information	Depending on others
Making good decisions	Blaming others for bad decisions

This can be accomplished by showing some examples of how most people use it all their life. The use of self-advocacy begins early in life when one tells parents what one wants. Its use slowly progresses as one begins to interact with friends, teachers, and employers. When consumers begin looking at using self-advocacy in these ways, it becomes a little less intimidating; by using it in every aspect of their daily life, it becomes easier. Table 1.9 shows the progression in the use of self-advocacy throughout one's life. It is another tool service providers can use to increase the comfort level of their consumers, who can use self-advocacy to participate in life-planning activities.

Practicing Effective Self-Advocacy Skills

When consumers know what self-advocacy is and begin to feel comfortable using it, they are ready to learn what tools to use when practicing it. Service providers must train those they serve to be consumers of any service they are seeking. Often the first step in acquiring that service, believing they are entitled to it, is half the battle. The first key to becoming effective self-advocates is simply

TABLE 1.9
Using Self-Advocacy Across One's Life Span

Level I: Expressing wants, needs, and desires to parents by

- staying up to watch TV
- having friends over to spend the night
- asking for a favorite food for dinner

Level II: Expressing oneself to friends by

- choosing your favorite game to play
- telling friends about a movie you would like to see
- asking a special friend for a date

Level III: Expressing yourself to education professionals by

- telling a teacher why you want to take a particular subject
- expressing your concerns in an Individualized Education Program meeting
- choosing your own high school academic program

Level IV: Expressing yourself to rehabilitation professionals by

- choosing your own career goal
- asserting your input in the development of your Client Employment Profile
- expressing your preference about rehabilitation services

Level V: Expressing yourself to your employer by

- requesting accommodation needs assertively
- explaining accommodation needs confidently
- negotiating accommodation needs successfully

learning to be well-informed, assertive customers of any service delivery system. Second is understanding what service and supports will be needed to accomplish life's goals and challenges. Third is believing that they have the right to choose services to enable them to live a full, rich life. Consumers who become strong self-advocates will be more effective partners when deciding what services they need to achieve goals they have set.

A Plan of Action

Even consumers who have been trained to be self-advocates need a plan that will assist them in reaching their goals. This is especially true for people who have developmental disabilities because typically they have had few opportunities to make their own decisions about how they want to live their life. Well-meaning professionals and overprotective parents have made such decisions for them. Service providers should involve their consumers in the development of action plans because it will ensure investment in and commitment to the goals that are identified in the plan. A good action plan should include easy-to-accomplish steps, supports, and resources that will be needed to reach the goals. Identifying steps that are easily obtainable builds self-confidence and can add momentum as consumers move toward the goals. Clearly identifying possible resources and needed supports in the plan lets customers know who might be enlisted to assist them in reaching their goals. This also reassures them that they are not alone when they encounter barriers. Such a plan will enable consumers to see for themselves the progress they are making toward their goals. Appendix 1.A is a form that can be used by people with disabilities in planning and achieving their lifetime goals. By answering the questions, individuals can come up with ways to meet the goals they set for themselves.

Facilitating consumer involvement will improve outcomes. Using strategies designed to ensure that consumers are a part of the process will help them to be invested in and committed to accomplishing their goals. This will undoubtedly be more time-consuming, but the rewards for both service providers and consumers will be well worth the effort. Developing goals that consumers truly are invested in accomplishing will give you, as a service provider, a real sense of satisfaction because you know these are things that will really benefit your customer. If you work for an agency that really believes this is the right way to do business, your manager will understand that procedures will take a little more time. When you, as a direct service provider, are committed to involving your customer in the service delivery process, you will be able to help your manager understand why procedures are taking longer to complete. If you do not work for that type of agency, you might ask yourself if you are working at the right place. As more and more agencies begin to understand laws and regulations and become serious about giving consumers the right to choose their services and develop their service plans, they will adopt this new way of doing business. Achieving quality outcomes is a win–win situation for all concerned. For consumers, it means getting services they really need to enhance their quality of life. For direct service providers, it means supporting their consumers to achieve outcomes that will make long-term positive changes in their lives. For agencies, it means developing a reputation of honoring the customer's right to make choices, and, more than likely, those who fund services and other consumers will choose them in the future.

MEETING THE NEEDS OF PEOPLE WITH DEVELOPMENTAL DISABILITIES

As noted in the Developmental Disabilities Assistance and Bill of Rights Act of 1990, the needs of individuals with disabilities may be unique, varied, and extensive. Individuals with developmental disabilities may have educational, independent-living, economic self-sufficiency, psychosocial, and behavioral needs.

Education

Perhaps nowhere has service provision for individuals with developmental disabilities been more comprehensive than in the educational setting. The Individuals with Disabilities Education Act of 1990 (IDEA) set forth the right not only to a free and appropriate education but also to any services deemed necessary to meet the needs of students with disabilities. IDEA serves many children in a variety of disability categories. Table 1.10 notes the percentage of students ages 6 through 21 who were served by IDEA in 1989–1990 and 1998–1999. It should be noted that children with autism, traumatic brain injury, and developmental delay were added after 1989–1990. As shown in the table, from 1998 to 1999, individuals having mental retardation made up 11% of all students served under IDEA; individuals with autism made up 1%. Table 1.11 shows the growth of the number of individuals in disability categories over time and the percentage of change. As noted in the table, the category of mental retardation changed 8.4% from 1989–1990 to 1998–1999. In contrast, the category of autism has experienced significant growth. Although the category of autism was not reported until 1992–1993, from then until 1998–1999, there was a 243.9% increase in students who were identified as having autism.

The education of students with developmental disabilities has taken on a new and comprehensive meaning. As noted previously, the emphasis on function included in the definition of developmental disabilities should serve to make educational programming more meaningful. Functionality is a construct that should guide all educational programming by requiring personnel to ask themselves whether the concepts and skills they are teaching will be important for the students in their future lives. For example, Jessica's teachers have made certain that her goals, objectives, and skills are functional as she participates in an inclusive seventh-grade setting. Jessica spends part of her educational day in the community. A community-based outing to a fast-food restaurant provides her with opportunities to increase her competency in skills such as money handling and word recognition, as well as her social skills.

TABLE 1.10

Percentage of Students Ages 6 Through 21 Served Under IDEA
by Disability Category, 1989–1990 and 1998–1999

Disability Category	1989–1990	1998–1999
Specific learning disabilities	48.5	50.8
Speech and learning impairments	22.9	19.4
Mental retardation	13.3	11.0
Emotional disturbance	9.0	8.4
Multiple disabilities	2.1	1.9
Hearing impairments	1.4	1.3
Orthopedic impairments	1.1	1.3
Other health impairments	1.2	4.0
Visual impairments	0.5	0.5
Autism	NA	1.0
Deaf–blindness	>0.1	>0.1
Traumatic brain injury	NA	0.2
Developmental delay	NA	0.2

Note. From the U.S. Department of Education, Office of Special Education Programs, *Data Analysis System (DANS)*, 2002.

Independent Living

The deinstitutionalization movement has dramatically decreased the number of individuals residing in institutions and placed many individuals with disabilities into community residential settings. L. L. Anderson, Lakin, Mangan, and Prouty (1998) report that between 1987 and 1997, every state reduced its population of people with intellectual disabilities and developmental disabilities living in state institutions. Thus, for many individuals with disabilities, institutional living has given way to residence in smaller, more normalized settings in the community. Residential options can include living with family members or alone, foster family care, semi-independent and supported living, state and nonstate group residences, state and nonstate institutions, and nursing homes. Table 1.12 provides the percentage of individuals with developmental disabilities in a variety of residential options.

One of the greatest challenges facing residential service delivery systems is the expansion of services. For example, Lakin, Anderson, Prouty, and Polister (1999) report that states would need to expand their current delivery systems by an average of 72.3% to meet the service needs of all people with intellectual or developmental disabilities who receive services outside of an institution. Further,

TABLE 1.11

Number of Students Ages 6 Through 21 Served Under IDEA[a]
in the 1989–1990 and 1998–1999 School Years

Disability Category	1989–1990	1998–1999	Percent Change
Specific learning disabilities	2,062,076	2,817,148	36.6
Speech and language impairments	974,256	1,074,548	10.3
Mental retardation	563,902	611,076	8.4
Emotional disturbance	381,639	463,262	21.4
Multiple disabilities	87,957	107,763	22.5
Hearing impairments	57,906	70,883	22.4
Orthopedic impairments	48,050	69,495	44.6
Other health impairments	52,733	220,831	318.7
Visual impairments	22,866	26,132	14.3
Autism[b]	NA	53,576	—
Deaf–blindness	1,633	1,609	−1.5
Traumatic brain injury[b]	NA	12,933	—
Developmental delay[c]	NA	11,910	—
All disabilities	4,253,018	5,541,166	30.3

Note. From the U.S. Department of Education, Office of Special Education Programs, *Data Analysis System (DANS)*, 2002.

[a]Data from 1989–90 through 1993–94 include children with disabilities served under Chapter 1 of the Elementary and Secondary Education Act. Beginning in 1994–95, all services to students with disabilities were provided under IDEA only.

[b]Autism and traumatic brain injury were first required to be reported in 1992–93. The percentage increases for these disability categories between 1992–93 and 1998–99 were 243.9% and 226.6%, respectively.

[c]Developmental delay was first reported in 1997–98. The percentage increase between the 2 years was 214.1%.

in 1998 approximately 71,000 individuals who were not receiving residential services were waiting for services (Lakin et al., 1999).

Gary is receiving residential services. Specifically, he lives in a small group home in his community with two other men who have disabilities. Their home is located in a typical neighborhood and is indistinguishable from other homes except for the wheelchair ramp leading to the front door. Gary has his own room but is supervised by a staff member who is available evenings, overnight, and on weekends to help him with his daily needs. The three men cook some meals together, but each has his own network of friends who visit. Gary was fortunate to receive residential services. Like those highlighted in national statistics, there is a waiting list for entrance to group homes in Gary's town. Students with disabilities graduating from school at present are typically faced with a wait of 1½ years.

TABLE 1.12

Residential Placements for Individuals with Developmental Disabilities in 1998

Type of Placement	Reported	Estimated
Group residence of 1–6	198,200	202,915
Group residence of 7–15	53,529	54,872
Group residence of 16 or more	88,233	89,857
Psychiatric	1,004	1,004
Nursing	23,377	23,531
Residents in all settings	368,267	372,179
% of residents in community settings	68.4	69.3
Persons waiting for residential services	56,639	71,831

Note. Adapted from "Community Residential Services Would Require Expansion of 72% To Serve Everyone in Community Settings: Trends and Milestones," by K. C. Lakin, L. Anderson, R. Prouty, and B. Polister, 1999, *Mental Retardation, 37,* pp. 251–254. Copyright 1999 by American Association on Mental Retardation. Adapted with permission.

Economic Self-Sufficiency

The right to work is an important concept in U.S. society. However, securing suitable employment has been an ongoing challenge for people with disabilities. Two thirds of working-age individuals with disabilities in the United States are unemployed, and only 20% are working full time (Braddock, Hemp, Parrish, & Westrich, 1998). Further, Louis Harris & Associates (2000) report that 79% of unemployed people with disabilities ages 16 through 64 say they would like to have a job. Unfortunately, the bulk of day-program resources are used to maintain people with significant disabilities in segregated work centers (Wehman, Bricout, & Kregel, 2000). It may indeed be true that "not working is perhaps the truest definition of what it means to be disabled" (Louis Harris & Associates, 1986, p. 81).

Vocational options for individuals with developmental disabilities traditionally have consisted of day or activity centers. Available vocational options are expanding from institutions to nonwork programs, workshops, affirmative industries, crews, enclaves, and individualized jobs. For example, Table 1.13 depicts an array of jobs in which individuals with intellectual disabilities were employed in South Carolina. As noted in the table, jobs ranged from work in manufacturing and the lumber industry to fast food to sheltered workshops. In addition, Blanck (1998) found that job opportunities and income levels have increased significantly for people with intellectual disabilities, from $63 per month in 1990 to $538.22 per month in 1997.

Federal policies and legislative actions also have evolved in support of employment of individuals with disabilities. The Rehabilitation Act provides grants

TABLE 1.13

Vocational Placement Options of Persons with Intellectual Disability in South Carolina

Job Types	Percent of All Employed	Job Types	Percent of All Employed
Workshop	2.6	Wal-Mart, Best Buy, Other large store	3.6
Mobile work crew	1.8	Small business	5.7
Enclave	15.4	Manufacturing & lumber	7.0
Combination[a]	5.8	Government[b]	8.5
Grocery store	10.8	Other services[c]	6.4
Fast-food	13.4	Goodwill or other not-for-profit	1.7
Other restaurant	12.5	Combination[d]	1.8
Motel or hotel	3.1		

Note. From "What Individual, Provider, and Community Characteristics Predict Employment of Individuals with Mental Retardation?" by S. McDermott, M. Martin, and S. Butkus, 1999, *American Journal on Mental Retardation, 104,* p. 350. Copyright 1999 by American Association on Mental Retardation. Reprinted with permission.

[a]Workshop, mobile work crew, and enclave.

[b]School district, local government.

[c]Home health, day care.

[d]Enclave, mobile work crew, workshop, and other (grocery store, fast-food, government, other restaurant, large store, manufacturing, other service).

to states for supported employment services, and the Americans with Disabilities Act prohibits job discrimination and requires reasonable accommodations (Blanck, 1998). The term *supported employment* refers to the placement of people with disabilities in integrated jobs in community settings working alongside people without disabilities. An attempt is made to match individual skills, interests, and aptitudes to jobs and to provide individualized supports, such as job coaching, to facilitate long-term success. Gary participates in supported employment. He loves his boss and considers himself lucky to have found such a good job. During the first 2 months on the job, Gary was shown how to perform the job responsibilities by John, the supervisor of the maintenance crew for the college. At first, John coached him every day, but he quickly faded back on the visits because Gary caught on quickly and was very conscientious about his work. Now John stops by about once a week, usually on Friday, and then Gary goes out for pizza with the crew. Supported employment placements like Gary's have grown rapidly from fewer than 10,000 people involved in 1984 to over 140,000 in 1995 (Wehman, Revell, & Kregel, 1996). However, fewer than 7% of those in supported employment have severe or profound intellectual disabilities. People with mild, moderate, or borderline intellectual disabilities, brain injury, mental illness, or physical disabilities constitute the remaining 93% (Mank, Cioffi, & Yovanoff, 1998).

Psychosocial Needs

Although securing and maintaining employment is important for individuals with developmental disabilities, it is not the only desired outcome. To fully serve individuals with developmental disabilities and their families, professionals must be aware of their psychosocial needs. A critical issue to consider in serving individuals with disabilities is the extent to which programming efforts result in the enhancement of people's lives. Fleeting gains in adaptive behavior, employment skills, or social competence have limited value if they do not impact the daily quality of life one experiences. Schalock (2000) defines *quality of life* as a "concept that reflects a person's desired conditions of living related to eight core dimensions of one's life: emotional well-being, interpersonal relationships, material well-being, personal development, physical well-being, self-determination, social inclusion, and rights" (p. 347).

Service providers must keep in mind that quality of life is a dynamic and multidimensional concept. Environmental factors interact with personal demographic characteristics to influence a person's quality of life (Hughes, Hwang, Kim, Eisenman, & Killian, 1995). Schalock, DeVries, and Lebsack (2000) suggest that three important aspects must be considered when addressing issues of quality of life. First, quality of life, by its very nature, is subjective. Second, people value various core dimensions differently. Finally, the value attached to each core dimension varies across one's life. For example, children and youth may determine the most important dimensions to be personal development, self-determination, interpersonal relationships, and social inclusion (Schalock, 1996); elderly individuals may identify physical well-being, interpersonal relationships, and emotional well-being as the most important dimensions (Schalock et al., 2000).

Essential to promoting an enhanced quality of life is the opportunity for individuals with disabilities to make choices that direct their daily living. Promotion of choice making by people with disabilities is based on the premises that opportunities to be autonomous lead to positive benefits for individuals and that individuals with disabilities want to make such decisions (Heller, Miller, & Factor, 1999). Greater autonomy from an early age is likely to lead to greater independence, community integration, and quality of life for adults with disabilities (Abery & Stancliffe, 1996). However, as noted previously, opportunities for choice are often severely restricted for persons with developmental disabilities. Restriction of choice-making opportunities can affect quality of life. In a study of adults with intellectual disabilities living in the community, Lakin, Burwell, Hayden, and Jackson (1992) found that the majority had no choices regarding when they went out with friends (54%) or how to spend discretionary money (57%). Important decisions such as consent for medical procedures or choosing a home or a roommate are much less likely to be given to adults with intellectual disabilities (Wehmeyer & Metzler, 1995). Gaudet, Pulos, Crethar, and Burger (2002) compared the ratings of psychosocial concerns of individuals with developmental disabilities with proxy ratings of concerns from family and service providers. The authors report low correlations between the three groups on ratings of cognition, interpersonal relationships, adaptations to daily living, emotions, and sexuality.

Positive Behavior Support

Individuals with disabilities sometimes behave in challenging ways that can limit their participation in integrated living, work, or social activities. Challenging behavior has been identified as one of the most significant issues in the field of developmental disabilities (Hastings & Brown, 2000). In a review of intervention research in behavioral and developmental disabilities from 1980 to 1997, Dunlap, Clarke, and Steiner (1999) found that 25% of the articles reviewed targeted disruptive behaviors. Challenging behaviors may include behavior that is harmful to individuals with disabilities or to others such as caregivers (Hastings & Brown, 2000). Challenging behavior has been reported as a significant source of stress and burnout for families and direct support staff (J. Chan & Sigafoos, 2000; Jenkins, Rose, & Lovell, 1997). What constitutes challenging behavior may vary. However, any action may become a serious behavior problem if it interferes with the individual's quality of life, acquisition of skills, or opportunities for personal interactions. In Chapter 14, Reid and Rotholz provide more detailed information on behavior support guidelines and technologies.

IDEA mandates the use of functional behavioral assessments and positive behavior supports for individuals with disabilities who display serious behavior problems. A functional behavioral assessment (FBA) is a tool for gathering information about antecedents, behaviors, and consequences to determine the function of (reason for) a behavior (Gresham, Watson, & Skinner, 2001). An FBA can include three assessment procedures: (a) an interview with the person who has the problem behavior or with people who have direct contact with or knowledge about that individual, (b) a systematic observation of the individual's problem behavior in typical daily routines, and (c) systematic manipulation of specific variables that are or are not associated with the problem behavior (O'Neill et al., 1997). Table 1.14 lists the primary outcomes of the FBA process.

TABLE 1.14
Primary Outcomes of a Functional Assessment Process

1. A clear description of the problem behaviors, including classes or sequences of behavior that frequently occur together.
2. Identification of the events, times, and situations that predict when the problem behaviors will and will not occur across the full range of typical daily routines.
3. Identification of the consequences that maintain the problem behaviors (that is, what functions the behaviors appear to serve for the person).
4. Development of one or more summary statements or hypotheses that describe specific behaviors, a specific type of situation in which they occur, and the outcomes or reinforcers maintaining them in that situation.
5. Collection of direct observation data that support the summary statements that have been developed.

Note. From *Functional Assessment and Program Development for Problem Behavior* (2nd ed., p. 3), by R. E. O'Neill et al., 1997, Pacific Grove, CA: Brooks/Cole. Copyright 1997 by Brooks/Cole Publishing. Reprinted with permission.

IDEA also requires the development of positive behavior support (PBS) plans. The goal of PBS is to reduce or eliminate problem behavior and teach a functionally equivalent alternative behavior. For example, Sam screams if anyone touches or disturbs the order of his trains. The function of his screaming behavior was determined by his team to be a means of deterring others from intruding on his preferred arrangement of his toys. The team devised a plan in which Sam is learning to use the PECS cards to "tell" people to stay away from his trains. When Sam sees a person in the immediate vicinity of his trains, he hands the person a card that states, "DON'T TOUCH." As Sam has become more adept at using the card to deter intruders from the trains, his screaming has decreased from an average of four incidents per day to three incidents per week.

One area of challenging behavior that is often neglected by educators and service providers is sexual behavior. In a national survey of community agencies, Ward, Trigler, and Pfeiffer (2001) found inappropriate sexual behaviors to be the most challenging behaviors for community service providers. Given that appropriate sex education can increase the probability of successful adult adjustment of any adolescent, efforts should be made to address sociosexual concerns. A particularly appropriate time to address such concerns is during transition planning, when the goal of the team is to prepare students for adult roles and responsibilities (Wolfe & Blanchett, 1997).

Case Management

Another service need of some people with developmental disabilities is case management. Case management can be defined as a method of providing comprehensive and coordinated services through a primary agent who, together with the consumer, takes responsibility for providing or obtaining services (Kemp, 1981). Roessler and Rubin (1998) suggest that case management centers on three areas: intake interviewing, service coordination, and case recording and reporting. Intake interviewing includes identifying what services are needed. Table 1.15 lists the service coordination responsibilities of a case manager developed by Roessler and Rubin, who drew on the work of a number of researchers (e.g., Beardsley & Rubin, 1988; Emener & Rubin, 1980; Rubin et al., 1984; Wright, Leahy, & Shapson, 1987). As noted in the table, service coordination requires the case manager to act as a liaison between various agencies and the consumer with disabilities. Because an individual with developmental disabilities may have a variety of needs, a case manager may be needed to help identify and secure services. Further, because service needs are generally lifelong or of an extended duration, a case manager must individualize and modify service planning as needs change over the life span of the consumer. It should be noted that case management has as its ultimate goal consumer empowerment; case managers should strive to teach the needed skills so that consumers and their families can take control of their services (Fiene & Taylor, 1991).

Sam, Gary, and Jessica all receive case management services. For example, a case manager is helping Sam and his mother coordinate a variety of services to meet both Sam's and his family's needs. A specific service provided to Sam and

TABLE 1.15
Service Coordination Activities of a Case Manager

- Identifies rehabilitation facilities, centers, agencies, or programs that provide services to persons with disabilities.
- Reviews the client's progress in a training program with the client and his or her instructor.
- Briefs cooperating services or agencies when referring clients.
- Refers clients to training facilities for development of vocational skills.
- Establishes working relationships with community organizations and leaders to secure referrals.
- Refers clients for work evaluation.
- Refers clients to rehabilitation facilities to assess clients' physical limitations, work tolerance, motivation, and level of vocational functioning.
- Refers clients for work adjustment training.
- Refers clients for medical evaluation.
- Refers clients for psychological evaluation and testing.
- Refers individuals who are ineligible for or unsuited to the agency's services to other agencies.
- Coordinates activities of all agencies involved in a rehabilitation plan.
- Refers clients for psychiatric treatment.
- Provides information regarding organization's programs to current and potential referral services.
- Collaborates with other providers so that services are coordinated, appropriate, and timely.
- Consults with medical professionals regarding functional capacities, prognosis, and treatment plans for clients.
- Participates in diagnostic staffings on clients.
- Establishes timetables for performing assorted rehabilitation services.
- Collaborates with cooperating rehabilitation workers in planning and executing the client's rehabilitation plan.
- States clearly the nature of clients' problems for referral to service providers.
- Refers clients to appropriate specialists or special services.
- Facilitates clients' cooperation in diagnostic procedures.
- Monitors clients' progress toward attaining the vocational goal specified in the written rehabilitation plan.
- Makes sound and timely financial decisions.
- Negotiates financial responsibilities with the referral sources or sponsor for a client's rehabilitation.
- Evaluates effect of services on individual clients.

Note. Adapted from *Case Management and Rehabilitation Counseling* (3rd ed.), by R. T. Roessler and S. E. Rubin, 1998, Austin, TX: PRO-ED. Copyright 1998 by PRO-ED, Inc. Adapted with permission.

Lily is the caseworker's bilingual skills, which are critical to facilitating Lily's understanding of service delivery options in the United States. As noted previously, Gary forgot to take his medication when his friend the pharmacist was on vacation. Gary's case manager is working to ensure that another similar incident does not occur. His case manager, along with his doctors, has developed a plan to remind Gary to take his medication and when to reorder more.

CULTURALLY COMPETENT SERVICE DELIVERY

What is unique about the 21st century is that, eventually, no single racial or ethnic group will constitute a majority of the U.S. population. Dramatic demographic changes are making the United States increasingly diverse in its racial and ethnic makeup. During the 1980s the number of Asian–Pacific Islanders increased by almost 108%, Hispanics by 54%, Native Americans by 38%, and African Americans by 13.2% (U.S. Bureau of the Census, 1996). By the year 2010, approximately 68% of the U.S. population will be African American, Hispanic, or Asian American; and by 2050, non-Hispanic Whites will be 53% of the population (Violand-Sanchez, Sutton, & Ware, 1991). In 1990, approximately 32 million people or almost 14% of the U.S. population over 5 years of age were nonnative speakers of English, and 21% reported that they spoke English less than well. The majority (54%) spoke Spanish, followed by speakers of French, German, Italian, and Chinese (U.S. Bureau of the Census, 1990). This linguistic diversity is expected to continue given that 90% of recent immigrants come from non–English-speaking countries (Han, Baker, & Rodriguez, 1997). Considering these population shifts, it is not surprising that public schools report an upward trend in minority student enrollments. Already, African Americans and Hispanics constitute the majority of students in most of the nation's largest public schools.

A major implication of these shifting demographic trends is that human service providers will be faced with a growing number of families who will hold cultural values, attitudes, beliefs, and preferences that are different from their own. Therefore, it is important that personnel working with individuals who have disabilities and their families be capable of delivering services in ways that are culturally relevant and responsive (Ford, 1992; Harry, 1992; Harry, Allen, & McLaughlin, 1995). To successfully accomplish this, professionals need to have a clear understanding of what culture is, know what it means to be cross-culturally competent, and possess and develop strategies for engaging in culturally sensitive interactions with families in service delivery systems. A brief discussion of each of these follows.

What Is Culture?

Culture has been defined in many different ways. It is the evolving experience of living within a group of people as expressed in their language, value system, customs, decision-making processes, and identity development. Many factors shape one's sense of group identity, including race, ethnicity, geographic location, income status, gender, religion, sexual orientation, occupation, and disability status (Turnbull & Turnbull, 1996). Culture has also been referred to as the framework within which individuals, families, and groups interpret their experiences and develop their visions of how they want to live their lives (P. P. Anderson & Fenichel, 1989). Gollnick and Chinn (1990) refer to the dominant culture as a *macroculture.* Our macro-American culture is characterized by the following values (S. Q. Chan, 1998; Gollnick & Chinn, 1998; Zuniga, 1998):

- individualism and privacy
- equity
- industriousness
- ambition
- competitiveness
- self-reliance
- independence
- appreciation of the good life
- perception that humans are separate and superior in nature

The macroculture in the United States is described as an "individualistic culture," whereas some other cultures are considered to be "collectivistic." Cultures with an individualistic focus emphasize the potential, goals, achievements, and self-fulfillment of individuals. Collectivistic cultures tend to view the needs of the group as having priority over those of the individual; they stress interdependence and cooperation for the collective good (S. Q. Chan, 1998; Kohis, 1994; Zuniga, 1998). People living in the United States are influenced by the macroculture whether or not they choose to adopt all of its values and belief systems. Each individual is also influenced by his or her membership in several *microcultures.* A microculture is a group of individuals who share some, but not all, of the cultural patterns of a macroculture and a common set of cultural patterns distinct from those of the macroculture (Gollnick & Chinn, 1998). An individual may be a member of several microcultural groups based on gender, ethnicity, social class, religion, age, primary language, and geographic location (Gollnick & Chinn, 1998). Consider, for example, the differences between the customs and mores of the Deep South and those of New England, or the differences in cultural patterns among Mexican Americans, Native Americans, and Polish Americans. The number of microcultures in the United States has increased in recent decades because of the influx of immigrants from other countries. Understanding that cultural identity is extremely complex helps us appreciate the diversity of our country as well as the circumstances of the families and children in our programs. It also requires that service delivery systems and the professionals who work in them develop cultural sensitivity and cultural awareness and become culturally competent.

What Is Cultural Competence?

Cultural sensitivity, cultural awareness, and *cultural competence* are all terms that have been used to suggest the need to increase understanding of the differences among cultural groups in the United States. Randall-David (1989) defines cultural sensitivity in the following quote: "In order to provide the most effective services to any community of people, professionals must be sensitive to cultural values of the group while recognizing and respecting individual differences" (p. 4). Cultural competence has been defined in several ways. Cross, Bazron, Dennis, and Isaacs (1989) described it as "a set of congruent behaviors, attitudes, and policies that come together in a system, agency, or among professionals to work effectively in cross-cultural situations" (p. iv). Another definition was provided by Roberts et al. (1990), who described cultural competence as follows:

> a program's ability to honor and respect those beliefs, interpersonal styles, attitudes, and behaviors, of both the families who are clients and the multicultural staff who are providing services. The use of the word "competence" has gained acceptance in the field because it is felt that competence implies more than beliefs, attitudes and tolerance, though it also includes them. Competence also implies skills which help to translate beliefs, attitudes, and orientation into action and behavior. (p. 1)

Elements of cross-cultural competence have been described by Cross as cited by S. Q. Chan (1990). Chan listed three important elements in building cross-cultural competence: (a) cultural self-awareness, (b) knowledge of information specific to each culture, and (c) skills that enable the individual to engage in successful cross-cultural communications and interactions. These elements are discussed next.

Strategies for Becoming More Culturally Competent

Enhancing Cultural Self-Awareness
Lynch and Hanson (1992) suggest that self-awareness begins with the examination and exploration of one's own heritage. Learning about one's roots and cultural heritage are the first steps in understanding how one's values, customs, beliefs, and behaviors have been shaped by culture. Lynch and Hanson also suggest several strategies for becoming more culturally self-aware:

- seeking out an oral history of the family by listening to recollections and stories about the lives of the oldest living family members
- looking at old family albums, photographs, journals, or lists of important events
- engaging in a document search in the county courthouse to obtain clues to the family's past through marriage records, birth and death records, and land titles
- doing a computer-based search through electronic genealogy forums and bulletin boards

Enhancing Knowledge of Specific Cultural Groups
Once individuals have become familiar with their own culture, the next step toward becoming culturally competent is to learn about other cultures through

readings, interactions, and direct involvement. Barnwell and Day (1996) suggested several strategies for learning about cultural groups in a community:

- identifying the different cultural groups in your region
- reading about these cultural groups
- consulting with a bicultural team member or professional who has worked with the community
- participating as an observer in religious events, community meetings, and gatherings of a cultural group and noticing similarities as well as differences from the mainstream culture in how the community participates in those events
- visiting local businesses patronized by different cultural groups in the community
- developing relationships with key people (community leaders, clergy, teachers) and cultural organizations within a community
- trying to learn the language or at least a few sentences spoken by the families of diverse cultural groups in the community
- taking time to reflect on the cultural information that is obtained and avoid making assumptions (stereotyping) about specific cultural groups

Enhancing Cross-Cultural Communications and Interactions

Communication is an important issue when working with families because it links to all aspects of service delivery. It is especially crucial when working with families who speak different languages and have limited English abilities. Randall-David (1989) suggests the following strategies for professionals to facilitate cross-cultural communication and interactions:

- Follow the family's lead to determine proper social etiquette regarding appropriate eye contact.
- Allow families to choose seating to establish comfortable body space. In the family's home, professionals should wait to sit down until a family member indicates where to sit.
- Avoid overt gestures and body language that may be misunderstood.
- Determine the fluency of the family members who speak English by asking simple open-ended questions.
- Avoid using slang, professional jargon, and complex sentences to facilitate communication.
- Adjust speaking rate and style to facilitate understanding.
- Learn the proper form of address in the family's language. This often helps establish a good relationship.
- Acknowledge the important roles that key family members (such as grandparents) may play by making eye contact with them when speaking. (This strategy is only appropriate depending on the extent to which eye contact is viewed as respectful in a particular culture.)
- State important information more than once.
- Always give a reason for suggestions to the family.

- Reinforce verbal interactions with written material in the family's language and with visual aids.

Service delivery systems and the professionals working in them are constantly meeting families of individuals with disabilities whose cultures, values, and beliefs are different from their own. This section has identified ways that culture may be important to service providers and has provided strategies for working more effectively with culturally diverse families of individuals with disabilities.

ISSUES FOR SERVICE PROVIDERS

People with developmental disabilities may interact with a variety of providers in service delivery systems. Service providers may face a number of challenges when working with individuals with disabilities, including collaboration, family involvement, transition, and training of professional staff.

Collaboration

Teamwork is readily recognized as a method of accomplishing more than one individual can accomplish alone. Team members who share information, resources, and responsibility usually attain better results. Terminology used to denote group planning and problem solving has included "interdisciplinary," "multidisciplinary," and "transdisciplinary" models or approaches. Collaboration is now used to describe the process of collective responsibility of service delivery. *Interpersonal collaboration* is defined as "a style for direct interaction between at least two coequal parties voluntarily engaged in shared decision making as they work toward a common goal" (Friend & Cook, 2000, p. 6). The professional literature in medicine, mental health, and social services is overflowing with information on the subject (Dettmer, Dyck, & Thurston, 1999). The need for collaboration in service provision is apparent in the passage of IDEA and is emphasized even more strongly in the 1997 IDEA Amendments. Given the diverse needs of individuals with disabilities, many different disciplines must converge to provide optimal service delivery. Collaboration is no longer a recommendation for best practice but, rather, the foundation of all service delivery.

Every group that meets is not a collaborative team. Collaboration requires commitment on the part of each team member to a shared goal. Further, it requires careful attention to communication skills and obliges participants to maintain parity in their interactions (Friend & Cook, 2000). Successful collaboration rests on the strengths and skills of team members and is enhanced by the diversity of the interests, values, abilities, and experiences of team members. Just as professionals receive training in their area of expertise, so too should they be prepared for collaboration.

Collaboration with people from different fields is often difficult, given diverse goals, expectations, and policies. Mattessich and Monsey (1992) list five principles on which to base collaborative relationships: (a) identify mutual goals, (b) understand and work within each program's operating procedures, (c) share responsibility, (d) share successes and failures, and (e) share resources.

For Sam and his family, collaboration will be key in developing a successful Individual Family Service Plan (IFSP). Sam's team might include his mother, mental health/mental retardation service coordinator, physician, early childhood special education teacher, speech–language pathologist, occupational therapist, behavior specialist, autism consultant, babysitter, and others as decided by team members. Each member of Sam's team will need to share information and ideas to create the optimal service plan. Sam's team will be responsible for discussing what services he needs now as well as in the future when he transitions into kindergarten.

Challenges for Service Providers
- Monitor the use of professional jargon and remember to "translate" jargon for unfamiliar team members.
- Work to foster communication skills, including listening, brainstorming, and open sharing of ideas.
- Encourage all participants to play an active role in the team's work.
- Arrange team meetings to accommodate family and client preferences.
- Keep an open mind. Value all ideas, even those that differ from your own.
- Share responsibility for outcomes whether they are successes or continuing challenges.

Family Involvement and Support

IDEA has prioritized family involvement in the educational decision-making process (Turnbull & Turnbull, 1998). Parents have been given the rights of informed consent, due process, and involvement in the educational planning of their child's curriculum. The focus on the family in service delivery is a reflection, in part, of the changing demographics of the family. The two-parent family with a house, a car, a dog, and 2.3 children is no longer the norm. Service providers must be prepared to support the complex needs of various family configurations. Further, a shift in the U.S. population demographics underscores the need for service providers to understand and value diversity when working with families. Service personnel should be "culturally competent" to work effectively with all clientele. Cultural competence means accepting, honoring, and respecting cultural diversity and differences (Dettmer et al., 1999). Effective service personnel must strive to understand each family's interests, desires, and priorities and maintain open communication to monitor success and adjust to changing family situations.

Family support is recognized as an important way for service personnel to provide assistance. Family support may include respite care, cash subsidy payments, family counseling, structural adaptations to the home, in-home training, sibling support programs, behavior support services, and the purchase of specialized equipment. Service providers should address the family system when determining desired resources and supports. For example, Sam's family identified two main avenues of support from service personnel: (a) the services of the educational team in addressing his academic, communication, adaptive, and behavioral needs, and (b) team support for exploring financial assistance, respite care, behavioral support services, community orientation, and availability of resources.

Challenges for Service Providers
- Welcome and encourage family participation in all aspects of decision making.
- Work to understand and respect the complexity of family interactions and priorities.
- Make no value judgments when family or other staff opinions differ from your own.
- Understand that needs change over time and adjust to meet those changing needs.
- Work to become increasingly culturally competent.
- Understand that families have a history of interactions with service providers and may approach professional input differently based on the success of past experiences.
- Be aware of the impact your service suggestions (or demands) may place on the family.
- Be an advocate for the rights of parents and family to institute change in the child's life.
- Be aware that culturally and linguistically diverse families may not see disabilities in the same manner as service providers.

Transition

The term *transition* conjures up many different meanings. Wehman (2001) defines it as "the life changes, adjustments, and cumulative experiences that occur in the lives of young adults as they move from school environments to independent living and work environments" (p. 7). As noted in Wehman's definition, transition can include movement from one setting to another and from one stage of life to another. Like all individuals, people with developmental disabilities will experience many transitions during their lifetimes.

Many children, like Sam, are eligible for service delivery in the first years of life. Young children receiving services may experience two periods of formal transition planning. First, as the child approaches age 3, the state-appointed agency providing services for infants and toddlers (birth through age 2), in cooperation with the providers of service to preschoolers (ages 3–5), orchestrate a transition to the system of service provision for preschoolers. Then, as the child approaches school age (usually 5 years for kindergarten), responsibility for service provision shifts to the local school district. For young children and their families, dramatic changes in personnel (teachers, service coordinators, therapists) and administrative practices can be challenging. Professional staff must work to make the transitions between systems of service delivery as seamless as possible.

Young adults with disabilities also undergo formal transition planning in their adolescent years when the transition from school to the adult world begins. IDEA mandates that a transition plan be developed, if determined as appropriate, by the age of 16 or, in some cases, by age 14. A comprehensive Individual Transition Plan (ITP) for a student leaving high school should focus on eight key areas: employment opportunities, postsecondary educational opportunities, living opportunities, financial and income needs, friendship and socialization needs, transportation needs, health and medical needs, and legal and advocacy needs (Wehman, 2001). Obviously, transition to adulthood is a complex process involving the cooperation and resources of many support agencies and service personnel. Although it is the responsibility of the education planning team to initiate the transition planning process, successful and smooth passage from adolescence to adulthood will depend on the diligent work of the ITP team. All transition planning must be concerned with quality-of-life outcomes, particularly opportunity for choosing lifestyle priorities. Individuals with disabilities must participate in the selection of transition goals and plans to achieve those goals. Self-determination is paramount at this critical life stage. For Jessica, formal transition planning will begin next year. Although Jessica and the team have been thinking about her future, at the planning meetings they will address her future vocational, education, leisure, and residential needs. The team will ensure that Jessica is working on acquiring the skills she will need to be successful in her future environments. Because the planning revolves around Jessica, she will be the most important member of the team and will advocate for herself with regard to her future placements and decisions.

Challenges for Service Providers

- Understand that transition will be ongoing and will occur many times in an individual's life.
- Be aware that successful transition requires the cooperation of many different service agencies.
- Be aware that transition requires preplanning and projection of needed services from one service system to another.
- Understand the value and need for quality communication between and among service delivery disciplines.
- Understand the roles and responsibilities of other professionals and how to work with other agencies.
- Have empathy for clients undergoing transition and their families; change is often difficult and may require time to adjust.
- Be patient with clients and their families as they strive to make decisions with long-reaching implications for the future.
- Understand that transition may result in new and unique service needs for clients; service providers must remain flexible and attuned to new needs.
- Focus on transition outcomes that include aspects of quality of life.

Training of Professional Staff

The key component to successful service delivery is the quality of the workforce. From the novice who enters the field with little or no experience but much enthusiasm, to the seasoned professional, there is a need for continual staff development. More than 4 million people with developmental disabilities live in the United States (Hewitt, 2001). These individuals and their families receive varied types of services and supports from an estimated 750,000 direct support professionals (DSPs). DSPs face a number of challenges, including staff turnover. Variables contributing to high turnover rates of DSPs include greater support needs of clients, lower starting pay, less tenured supervisors, and eligibility for paid leave (Larson & Lakin, 1999).

Rapid changes in the field of developmental disabilities have resulted in many new roles for service providers. Changing roles mean that service providers must stay abreast of changes and translate new changes into satisfactory services for the consumers they serve. During their professional careers, service providers may be called upon to fulfill the roles of communicator, facilitator, teacher, evaluator, advocate, and friend. One concern is that educators may not be adequately prepared for delivering team-oriented kinds of service (Dettmer et al., 1999). Further, given the varied needs of clientele, DSPs may need a variety of specialized skills. For example, DSPs in Gary's home need training on medication prescribed for depression and other mental health needs. To meet the training needs of DSPs, both in-service and staff development training is needed. Dettmer and Landrum (1997) list five overarching purposes of staff development training: (a) job maintenance, (b) professional development, (c) role modification, (d) personal growth, and (e) inspiration.

Challenges for Service Providers
- Understand the need for flexibility of professional roles and responsibilities.
- Understand that as needs arise, roles and responsibilities of service providers change and are redefined.
- Learn to collaborate and work efficiently as a member of a service delivery team.
- Advocate for individuals with disabilities in general and individual clients in particular. Be mindful of the mission statements of agencies.
- Work toward continued professionalism in the field by action and advocacy.
- Translate new challenges in the field into current best practices for clients.

FINAL THOUGHTS

Each person who has a developmental disability is unique. Service providers working with them may be called upon to provide assistance in areas such as education, residential services, economic self-sufficiency, psychosocial issues, behavioral concerns, and case management. Further, service personnel may face a number of challenges when providing quality services such as collaboration, working with families, transition, and the training of professional staff. The challenges outlined should serve not to discourage professionals but rather as an impetus for continuing change and improvement. Individuals such as Sam, Gary, and Jessica count on service providers to undertake the professional challenges facing them and work toward system change efforts that empower them to take responsibility for and control of their lives.

Action Plan Form

1. What are your current life improvement goals?	Time frame to reach goals.
2. What are the action steps you will take to reach your goals?	Time frame for taking action steps.

Resources to use in meeting goals.

3. Individuals who can help.	Agencies that can help.	What will the individual or agency contribute?

4. Barriers to overcome to reach goals.	Strengths to overcome barriers.
5. What lessons have you learned in working toward your goals?	How will these lessons assist you to reach other goals?

6. Assessing your progress	Yes or No	Actions or explanations
Did you reach your goals?		
Did you celebrate achieving your goals?		
Will you continue to work on the same goals?		
Will you modify your goals?		
Will you develop new goals?		
Will you develop your new goals differently?		
Are your new goals related to your old goals?		

REFERENCES

Abery, B. H., & Stancliffe, R. J. (1996). The ecology of self-determination. In D. J. Sands & M. L. Wehmeyer (Eds.), *Self-determination across the life span* (pp. 111–145). Baltimore: Brookes.

American Association on Mental Retardation. (1992). *Mental retardation: Definition, classification, and systems of supports* (9th ed.). Washington, DC: Author.

American Association on Mental Retardation. (2002). Fact sheet: Person-centered planning. Retrieved February 14, 2002, from http://www.aamr.org/policies/faq_planning.shtml

Americans with Disabilities Act of 1990, 42 U.S.C. § 12101 *et seq.*

Anderson, L. L., Lakin, K. C., Mangan, T. W., & Prouty, R. W. (1998). State institutions: Thirty years of depopulation and closure. *Mental Retardation, 36,* 431–443.

Anderson, P. P., & Fenichel, E. S. (1989). *Serving culturally diverse families of infants and toddlers with disabilities.* Arlington, VA: National Center for Clinical Infant Programs.

Barnwell, A., & Day, M. (1996). Providing support to diverse families. In P. J. Beckman (Ed.), *Strategies for working with families of young children with disabilities* (pp. 47–68). Baltimore: Brookes.

Beardsley, M., & Rubin, S. (1988). Rehabilitation service providers: An investigation of generic job tasks and knowledge. *Rehabilitation Counseling Bulletin, 37,* 122–139.

Blanck, P. (1998). *The Americans with Disabilities Act and the emerging workforce: Employment of people with mental retardation.* Washington, DC: American Association on Mental Retardation.

Braddock, D., Hemp, R., Parrish, S., & Westrich, J. (1998). *The state of the states in developmental disabilities* (5th ed.). Washington, DC: American Association on Mental Retardation.

Chan, J., & Sigafoos, J. (2000). A review of child and family characteristics related to the use of respite care in developmental disability services. *Child and Youth Care Forum, 29,* 27–37.

Chan, S. Q. (1990). Early intervention with culturally diverse families of infants and toddlers with disabilities. *Infants and Young Children, 3*(2), 78–87.

Chan, S. Q. (1998). Families with Asian roots. In E. W. Lynch & M. J. Hanson (Eds.), *Developing cross cultural competence: A guide for working with young children and their families* (2nd ed., pp. 251–354). Baltimore: Brookes.

Cross, T., Bazron, B., Dennis, K., & Issacs, M. (1989). *Towards a culturally competent system of care: A monograph on effective services for minority children who are severely emotionally disturbed.* Washington, DC: Georgetown University Child Development Center.

Dettmer, P., Dyck, N., & Thurston, L. (1999). *Consultation, collaboration, and teamwork.* Boston: Allyn & Bacon.

Dettmer, P., & Landrum, M. (1997). *Staff development: The key to effective gifted education programs.* Waco, TX: Prufrock.

Developmental Disabilities Assistance and Bill of Rights Act of 1990, Title 42, U.S.C. 6000–6083. *U.S. Statutes at Large, 104,* 1191–1204.

Dunlap, G., Clarke, S., Steiner, M. (1999). Intervention research in behavioral and developmental disabilities. *Journal of Positive Behavior Interventions, 1,* 170–180.

Emener, W., & Rubin, S. E. (1980). Rehabilitation counselor role and functions and sources of role strain. *Journal of Applied Rehabilitation Counseling, 11,* 57–59.

Fiene, J. I., & Taylor, P. A. (1991). Serving rural families of developmentally disabled children: A case management model. *Social Work, 36*(4), 323–327.

Ford, B. A. (1992). Multicultural education training for special educators working with African-American youth. *Exceptional Children, 59,* 107–114.

Friend, M., & Cook, L. (2000). *Interactions: Collaboration skills for school professionals* (3rd ed.). New York: Addison Wesley Longman.

Gaudet, L., Pulos, S., Crethar, H., & Burger, S. (2002). Psychosocial concerns of adults with developmental disabilities: Perspectives of the self, family member, and provider. *Education and Training in Mental Retardation and Developmental Disabilities, 37,* 23–26.

Gollnick, D. M., & Chinn, P. C. (1990). *Multicultural education in a plurastic society* (3rd ed.). New York: Merrill/Macmillan.

Gollnick, D. M., & Chinn, P. C. (1998). *Multicultural education in a plurastic society* (5th ed.). Upper Saddle River, NJ: Merrill/Prentice Hall.

Gresham, F., Watson, T., & Skinner, C. (2001). Functional behavior assessment: Principles, procedures, and future directions. *School Psychology Review, 30,* 156–172.

Han, M., Baker, D., & Rodriguez, C. (1997). *A profile of policies and practices for limited English proficient students: Screening methods, program support and teacher training (SASS1993–94).* Washington, DC: U.S. Department of Education, National Center for Education Statistics.

Harry, B. (1992). Restructuring the participation of African-American parents in special education. *Exceptional Children, 59,* 123–131.

Harry, B., Allen, N., & McLaughlin, M. (1995). Communication versus compliance: African-American parent involvement in special education. *Exceptional Children, 61,* 364–377.

Hastings, R., & Brown, T. (2000). Functional assessment and challenging behaviors: Some future directions. *Journal of the Association for Persons with Severe Handicaps, 25,* 229–240.

Heller, T., Factor, A., Sterns, H., & Sutton, E. (1996). Impact of person-centered later life planning training program for older adults with mental retardation. *Journal of Rehabilitation, 62,* 77–83.

Heller, T., Miller, A., & Factor, A. (1999). Autonomy in residential facilities and community functioning of adults with mental retardation. *Mental Retardation, 37,* 449–457.

Hewitt, A. (2001). Educational opportunities for direct support professionals. *The Exceptional Parent, 31,* 48–50.

Holburn, S., Jacobson, J. W., Vietze, P. M., Schwartz, A. A., & Sersen, E. (2000). Quantifying the process and outcomes of person-centered planning. *American Journal on Mental Retardation, 105,* 402–416.

Holburn, S., & Vietze, P. (1998). Has person-centered planning become the alchemy of developmental disabilities? A response to O'Brien, O'Brien, and Mount. *Mental Retardation, 36,* 485–488.

Holburn, S., & Vietze, P. (1999). Acknowledging barriers in adopting person-centered planning. *Mental Retardation, 37,* 117–124.

Hughes, C., Hwang, B., Kim, J., Eisenman, L., & Killian, D. (1995). Quality of life in applied research: A review and analysis of empirical measures. *American Journal on Mental Retardation, 99,* 623–641.

Individuals with Disabilities Education Act of 1990, 20 U.S.C. § 1400 *et seq.*

Individuals with Disabilities Education Act Amendments of 1997, 20 U.S.C. § 1401.

Jenkins, R., Rose, J., & Lovell, C. (1997). Psychological well being of staff working with people who have challenging behavior. *Journal of Intellectual Disability Research, 41,* 502–511.

Kemp, B. J. (1981). The case management model of human service delivery. In E. L. Pan, T. E. Bashe, & C. Vash (Eds.), *Annual review of rehabilitation* (Vol. 2, pp. 212–238). New York: Springer.

Kohis, L. R. (1994). *The values Americans live by.* Washington, DC: Merifian House International.

Kurtz, L. A., Dowrick, P. W., Levy, S. E., & Batshaw, M. L. (1996). *Handbook of developmental disabilities: Resources for interdisciplinary care.* Austin, TX: PRO-ED.

Lakin, K. C., Anderson, L., Prouty, R., & Polister, B. (1999). Community residential services would require expansion of 72% to serve everyone in community settings: Trends and milestones. *Mental Retardation, 37,* 251–254.

Lakin, K., Burwell, B., Hayden, M., & Jackson, M. (1992). *An independent assessment of Minnesota's Medicaid Home and Community Based Services Waiver Program* (Rep. No. 37). Minneapolis: University of Minnesota, Center for Residential Services and Community Living, Institute on Community Integration.

Larson, S., & Lakin, K. (1999). Longitudinal study of recruitment and retention in small community homes supporting persons with developmental disabilities. *Mental Retardation, 37,*
267–280.

Louis Harris & Associates. (1986). *The International Center for the Disabled survey of disabled
Americans: Bringing disabled Americans into the mainstream.* New York: Author.

Louis Harris & Associates. (2000). *The N.O.D./Harris survey program on participation and attitudes: Survey of Americans with disabilities.* New York: Author.

Lynch, E. W., & Hanson, M. J. (1992). *Developing cross-cultural competence: A guide for working
with young children and their families.* Baltimore: Brookes.

Mank, D., Cioffi, A., & Yovanoff, P. (1998). Employment outcomes for people with severe disabilities: Opportunities for improvement. *Mental Retardation, 36,* 205–216.

Mattessich, P. W., & Monsey, B. R. (1992). *Collaboration: What makes it work.* St. Paul, MN:
Amhert H. Wilder Foundation.

McDermott, S., Martin, M., & Butkus, S. (1999). What individual, provider, and community characteristics predict employment of individuals with mental retardation? *American Journal
on Mental Retardation, 104,* 346–355.

Mount, B. (1994). Benefits and limitations of personal futures planning. In V. J. Bradley, J. W.
Ashbaugh, & B. C. Blaney (Eds.), *Creating individual supports for people with developmental
disabilities: A mandate for change at many levels* (pp. 97–108). Baltimore: Brookes.

Nirje, B. (1969). The normalization principle and its human management implications. In R. B.
Dugel & W. W. Wolfensberger (Eds.), *Changing patterns in residential services for the mentally retarded* (pp. 179–188). Washington, DC: U.S. Government Printing Office.

O'Brien, J. (1987). A guide to life-style planning: Using the Activities Catalogue to integrate services and natural support systems. In G. T. Bellamy & B. Wilcox (Eds.), *A comprehensive
guide to the Activities Catalogue: An alternative curriculum for youth and adults with severe
disabilities* (pp. 175–189). Baltimore: Brookes.

O'Brien, J., & Lovett, H. (1992). *Finding a way toward everyday lives: The contribution of person-
centered planning.* Harrisburg: Pennsylvania Office of Mental Retardation.

O'Neill, R. E., Horner, R., Albin, R., Sprague, J., Storey, K., & Newton, J. (1997). *Functional
assessment and program development for problem behavior* (2nd ed.). Pacific Grove, CA:
Brooks/Cole.

Pearpoint, J., O'Brien, J., & Forest, M. (1993). *PATH: A workbook for planning positive possible
futures and planning alternative tomorrows with hope for schools, organizations, businesses,
and families* (2nd ed.). Toronto: Inclusion Press.

Randall-David, E. (1989). *Strategies for working with culturally diverse communities and clients.*
Washington, DC: Association for the Care of Children's Health.

Roberts, R. N., Barclay-McLaughlin, G., Cleveland, J., Colston, W., Malach, R., Mulvey, L., Rodriguez, G., Thomas, T., & Yonemitsu, D. (1990). *Developing culturally competent programs
for families of children with special needs.* Logan: Utah State University, Early Intervention
Research Institute, Developmental Center for Handicapped Persons (prepared by Georgetown University Child Development Center, Washington, DC).

Robertson, J., Emerson, E., Hatton, C., Gregory, N., Kessissoglou, S., Hallam, A., & Walsh, P. N.
(2001). Environmental opportunities for supports for exercising self-determination in
community-based residential settings. *Research in Developmental Disabilities, 22,* 487–502.

Roessler, R. T., & Rubin, S. E. (1998). *Case management and rehabilitation counseling* (3rd ed.).
Austin, TX: PRO-ED.

Rubin, S. E., Matkin, R., Ashley, J., Beardsley, M., May, V. R., Onstott, K., & Puckett, F. (1984).
Roles and functions of certified rehabilitation counselors. *Rehabilitation Counseling Bulletin, 27,* 199–224, 239–243.

Schalock, R. (1996). The quality of children's lives. In A. H. Fine & N. M. Fine (Eds.), *Therapeutic
recreation for exceptional children: Let me in, I want to play* (2nd ed., pp. 83–94). Springfield,
IL: Thomas.

Schalock, R. (2000). Three decades of life. In M. L. Wehmeyer & J. R. Patton (Eds.), *Mental retardation in the 21st century* (pp. 335–356). Austin, TX: PRO-ED.

Schalock, R., DeVries, D., & Lebsack, J. (2000). Rights, quality measures, and program changes. In S. Herr & G. Weber (Eds.), *Aging, rights and quality of life of older persons with developmental disabilities.* Baltimore: Brookes.

Smull, M. W., & Harrison, S. B. (1992). *Supporting people with severe retardation in the community.* Alexandria, VA: National Association of State Mental Retardation Program Directors.

Summers, J. A. (1986). Who are developmentally disabled adults? A closer look at the definition of developmental disabilities. In J. A. Summers (Ed.), *The right to grow up. An introduction to adults with developmental disabilities* (pp. 3–16). Baltimore: Brookes.

Turnbull, A., & Turnbull, H. (1998). *Free appropriate public education: Law and children with disabilities.* Denver, CO: Love.

Turnbull, A. P., & Turnbull, H. R. (1996). Self-determination within a culturally responsive family systems perspective: Balancing the family mobile. In L. E. Powers, G. H. S. Singer, & J. Sovers (Eds.), *On the road to autonomy: Promoting self-competence among children and youth with disabilities* (pp. 195–220). Baltimore: Brookes.

U.S. Bureau of the Census. (1990). *1990 census of population.* Washington, DC: U.S. Government Printing Office.

U.S. Bureau of the Census. (1996). *Resident population of the United States: Middle series projections, 2035–2050 by sex, race, and Hispanic origin with median age. 1996 census of population.* Washington, DC: U.S. Government Printing Office.

U.S. Department of Education. (1998). *Twentieth annual report to Congress on the implementation of the Individuals with Disabilities Education Act.* Washington, DC: Department of Education, Office of Special Education and Rehabilitative Services.

U.S. Department of Education. (2001). *Twenty-second annual report to Congress on the implementation of the Individuals with Disabilities Education Act.* Washington, DC: Department of Education, Office of Special Education and Rehabilitative Services.

U.S. Department of Education, Office of Special Education Programs. (2002). *Data Analysis System (DANS).*

Vandercook, T., York, J., & Forest, M. (1989). The McGill action planning system (MAPS): A strategy for building the vision. *Journal of the Association for Persons with Severe Handicaps, 14,* 205–215.

Violand-Sanchez, E., Sutton, C. P., & Ware, H. W. (1991). *Fostering home-school cooperation: Involving language minority families as partners in education.* Washington, DC: National Clearinghouse for Bilingual Education.

Wagner, G. A. (1999). Further comments on person-centered approaches. *The Behavior Analyst, 22,* 53–54.

Ward, K., Trigler, J., & Pfeiffer, K. (2001). Community services, issues, and service gaps for individuals with developmental disabilities who exhibit inappropriate sexual behaviors. *Mental Retardation, 39,* 11–19.

Wehman, P. (2001). *Life beyond the classroom: Transition strategies for young people with disabilities* (3rd ed.). Baltimore: Brookes.

Wehman, P., Bricout, J., & Kregel, J. (2000). Supported employment in 2000: Changing the locus of control from agency to consumer. In M. L. Wehmeyer & J. R. Patton (Eds.), *Mental retardation in the 21st century* (pp. 115–150). Austin, TX: PRO-ED.

Wehman, P., Revell, W. G., & Kregel, J. (1996). *Supported employment from 1986–1993: A national program that works.* Manuscript submitted for publication.

Wehmeyer, M. L. (1996). Self-determination in youth with severe cognitive disabilities: From theory to practice. In L. Powers, G. H. S. Singer, & J. Sowers (Eds.), *On the road to autonomy: Promoting self-competence in children and youth with disabilities* (pp. 115–133). Baltimore: Brookes.

Wehmeyer, M. L., Agran, M., & Hughes, C. (1999). *Teaching self-determination to students with disabilities. Basic skills for successful transition.* Baltimore: Brookes.

Wehmeyer, M., & Metzler, C. (1995). How self-determined are people with mental retardation? The national consumer survey. *Mental Retardation, 33,* 111–119.

Wolfe, P. S., & Blanchett, W. J. (1997). Infusion of sex education curricula into transition planning: Obstacles and solutions. *Journal of Vocational Rehabilitation, 8,* 143–154.

Wolfensberger, W. (1972). *The principle of normalization in human services.* Toronto: National Institute on Mental Retardation.

Wright, G. N., Leahy, M. J., & Shapson, P. R. (1987). Rehabilitation Skills Inventory: Importance of counselor competencies. *Rehabilitation Counseling Bulletin, 31*(2), 107–118.

Zuniga, M. E. (1998). Families with Latino roots. In E. W. Lynch & M. J. Hanson (Eds.), *Developing cross cultural competence: A guide for working with young children and their families* (2nd ed., pp. 209–250). Baltimore: Brookes.

CHAPTER 2

Early Childhood Intervention

D. Michael Malone and Mary Boat

LEARNING GOALS

Upon completion of this chapter, the reader will be able to

- discuss the rationale for early intervention and education including central philosophical and theoretical foundations
- define the population of children who are eligible for services under the Individuals with Disabilities Education Act (IDEA)
- identify central themes that currently characterize early childhood intervention, including professional ethics and standards, service delivery in natural environments, inclusion, the concept of family centeredness, diversity, collaboration, and early transition planning

CASE EXAMPLE: AMY

Within a month of her birth, Amy's parents noticed that she was having some difficulty with bowel functions. Initial conversations with her pediatrician provided them with some relief, however. Maybe they were, as was suggested, just being overanxious new parents. Time passed, the bowel problems persisted, and concerns expressed by Amy's parents continued to be dismissed as unwarranted. Amy's problems peaked when she was 2½ years old and her regular constipation resulted in a condition labeled as *acquired megacolon*. At the pediatrician's office, the explanation given for this situation was that Amy was just reluctant to "use the potty" and that she could pass a stool if she wanted. Because Amy had already demonstrated her willingness to be potty trained, her parents didn't consider this explanation satisfactory, and they explored a number of behavioral and dietary interventions to enable Amy to have more regular bowel movements. These interventions failed (serving only to frustrate both child and parents) and one morning at 2 A.M., Amy was rushed to the hospital emergency room. With the fear that the constant and extreme constipation could lead to a ruptured intestine, Amy's parents insisted that something was not right and that the problems needed to be seriously explored. It was at this time that X-rays were taken that led to a diagnosis of spina bifida occulta. Although subsequent MRIs seemed to rule out neurological impairment, Amy's abnormal bowel functions continued. Four years later, Amy is on a twice-a-day schedule of medication to ensure that her bowel functions remain regular, and questions remain unanswered.

 ## CASE EXAMPLE: ZACH

Zach is a 3-year-old boy with autism who has been receiving home-based intervention services for almost a year and a half. His family lives in a rural environment and includes his mom, dad, and 2-month-old twin brothers. At a recent IEP meeting, Zach's parents expressed a desire to have Zach attend a classroom-based program, citing a lack of opportunities for him to interact with others and time constraints due to the birth of the twins as primary factors in their interest. Zach's parents also think that his extensive behavioral and communication needs cannot be addressed until he is able to observe age-appropriate behavior. Currently, the county in which Zach's family lives has a child development center 2 to 3 miles from the family's home that provides inclusive education for all young children. This program, however, typically has been discouraged as a placement for children with significant behavioral and social–emotional needs due to a perceived lack of support from the staff for the inclusion of these children. There is a school-based preschool program in the county that provides a continuum of related services and a range of options for inclusion. Enrollment in this program would require a 1½-hour round-trip drive for Zach and his parents or a 2½-hour round-trip bus ride for Zach. Zach's parents are frustrated by what they believe to be a lack of appropriate options for their child.

 ## CASE EXAMPLE: KIM

Kim is a 5-year-old boy with Down syndrome. He attends a kindergarten program at the local public school, where he is an inclusive classroom. His education team consists of his kindergarten teacher, an educational assistant, an early childhood special education specialist, an occupational therapist, and a speech–language pathologist. The specialist and therapists consult with Kim's teacher and come into the classroom to work with Kim and the staff. Kim's family emigrated from Korea to a midwestern state in the United States 2 years before his birth. The family presently consists of Kim, an 8-year-old brother, mother, father, a grandmother, and an aunt and uncle. In addition, the family often has relatives from Korea visiting for extended periods. Kim's father, who owns a floral shop, was diagnosed with Parkinson's disease 2 years ago, and Kim's brother has undergone two surgeries over the past year to remove a nonmalignant brain tumor. Kim's mother works part time at the floral shop and attends to the family's extensive health needs. Recently, she received a letter from Kim's teacher regarding the need to set up a meeting to discuss some of Kim's behavior challenges. Specifically, the team is concerned about his difficulty following directions (particularly when they involve sitting and listening) and his limited peer interaction skills (he often resorts to hitting and biting when he doesn't get what he wants). The team believes that Kim won't be able to move on to first grade if these issues are not addressed.

Several weeks after the letter, Kim's mother received a phone message from the teacher, who stated that she had not heard back from her, that the team had set a meeting date, and that they hoped she could attend. However, the meeting date and time conflicted with a doctor's appointment, and Kim's mother could not attend. Kim's mother wonders why the team is so concerned about Kim's behavior in the classroom when they have yet to teach him to speak. Kim's communication repertoire consists of a handful of basic ASL signs and a handful of words. When asked during IEP meetings about her goals for Kim, his mother has always stated that she wants him to be able to communicate by talking. She is frustrated that the team does not acknowledge the importance of communication to her family, but she doesn't want to make waves because she is grateful that her son has the option to attend a "real" school. She has stated that if the family still lived in Korea, her son would not have this opportunity.

The cases of Amy, Zach, and Kim highlight the need for early childhood intervention in both the medical and educational realms. The challenges faced by both children and parents further illuminate the need for that intervention to be family centered. Put simply, the purpose of early childhood intervention is to provide young children (from birth through 8 years of age) who are at risk for or have identified disabilities and their families the supports and services necessary to enable those children and families to access and benefit from their environments—whether at home, in hospitals, at school, or in other community settings. These supports and services must facilitate inclusion, independence, and productivity to the greatest degree possible, improving the quality of life of the children and families who are recipients. The purpose of this chapter is to discuss the rationale for early childhood intervention, including philosophical and theoretical foundations; define the population of children who are eligible for services under IDEA; and identify central themes that currently characterize early childhood intervention, including professional ethics, challenges related to preparing personnel, the concept of family-centeredness, service delivery in natural environments, inclusion, diversity, collaboration, and early transition planning.

FOUNDATIONS OF EARLY CHILDHOOD INTERVENTION

Over the past 4 decades, significant philosophical changes have occurred in the national agenda relative to the provision of services and supports to young children with disabilities and their families. These changes have been reflected in the legislative chronology leading up to the current authorization of IDEA. The terminology used to identify children with disabilities has evolved; the focus has shifted from institutionally based services to inclusive, community-based services; attention has been redirected from exclusively child-centered care to include family-centered care; and direct service models have moved from a single discipline base to a collaborative base. Without a doubt, a number of fundamental challenges have been associated with the policy changes represented by the provisions of IDEA, including the identification, coordination, and, ultimately, provision of services and supports that are most appropriate for young children with disabilities and their families.

While the history of individuals, groups, and programs freely providing some form of intervention to the nation's youngest children and their families is long and distinguished, the universal public provision of early childhood intervention services and supports owes much to the evolution of federal initiatives (e.g., the U.S. Children's Bureau/Administration for Children, Youth and Families' publication of *Infant Care* from 1914 to 1984; the 1954 Department of Health, Education, and Welfare [HEW] Children's Bureau Report to Congress, "Conditions of Mothers and Children in This Nation"; P.L. 89-10, the Elementary and Secondary Education Act of 1965; P.L. 94-142, the Education for All Handicapped Children Act of 1975; P.L. 99-457, the Education of the Handicapped Act Amendments of 1986; and P.L. 105-17, the Individuals with Disabilities Education Act Amendments of 1997). The current context for early childhood intervention in the United States is grounded in the history of these federal initiatives, the current authorization of IDEA, the Council for Exceptional Children's Division for Early Childhood Recommended Practices, the National Association for the Education of Young Children/CEC Division for Early Childhood Professional Standards, and an expanding base of research. The basic concept of early childhood intervention is outlined in Table 2.1.

The fundamental principles and values of early childhood intervention are grounded in both social policy and developmental theory. First, many families, health and human service professionals, and policymakers believe that it is a societal responsibility to provide needed intervention programs. Although the welfare of children is primarily the responsibility of parents, we understand that social policy and services are needed to support many parents in their effort to provide for their children (Malone & Orthner, 1988). Second, we recognize that the early childhood years represent a critical period for influencing child and family outcomes (Farran, 2001; Guralnick, 1997a; McCall & Plemons, 2001). The greater the risk experienced by children and families, the greater the need for direct, comprehensive, and sustained intervention. Third, early childhood intervention reflects a philosophy of prevention. Although the challenges experienced by many children and families are "preexisting" and so must be addressed in terms of treatment or remediation, we would hope to prevent continued negative outcomes and the development of secondary and unanticipated effects. Finally, early childhood intervention is grounded in the belief that programs must be (a) focused on the needs of families, (b) based in natural environments,

TABLE 2.1
Early Childhood Intervention

What: Identification and screening, referral, diagnosis, direct intervention

> **Critical Features:** Age of child at time of intervention, degree of parent involvement, intensity and amount of intervention, breadth and duration of intervention, amenability of parent and child to intervention

Who: Children with delays in central areas of development, including cognition, motor and physical growth, communication and language, psychosocial and self-help skills; children with physical or mental conditions that are likely to result in delays; children who are at risk medically or environmentally for substantial delays

Why: Facilitate child development; support family; promote independence, inclusion, and productivity

When: Birth to 8 years (often considered by age groups: birth–3, 3–5, and 6–8)

Where: Center-based programs, home-based programs, hospital-based programs, most natural environment possible

How: Statewide, comprehensive, multidisciplinary, interagency service programs

---

(c) willing to acknowledge and make use of contributions of stakeholders from multiple disciplines, and (d) able to plan and coordinate supports and services within a systems framework.

The benefits of early childhood intervention can be significant (for a detailed analysis of child, family, and program outcomes, see Guralnick, 1997b; Bailey, Bruer, Symons, & Lichtman, 2001; and Shonkoff & Meisels, 2000). Generally speaking, the benefits can be described as improved development; the prevention or suppression of secondary risk factors; the reduction of family stress; the promotion of independence, inclusion, and productivity; the reduction of need for specialized services; and the reduction of health care and educational costs. McCall and Plemons (2001) provide a more specific presentation of the benefits of high-quality early childhood intervention (pp. 279–280):

- increases in IQ scores, language fluency, and other early mental and academic skills
- reduction in academic problems through high school, including class failure, dropout rates, rates of grade retention, and use of remedial and special education
- promotion of social maturity and independence
- reduction of noncompliance and delinquent behavior, reduction of teen pregnancy, increased graduation rates, improved employment rates, and less reliance on welfare programs after high school

The need for early childhood intervention services, programs, and supports has always existed, and research on critical early childhood intervention issues has been conducted for decades. However, broader social awareness and accountability were prompted by changes in social policy that began mandating these services, programs, and supports. Such policy changes lent strength to and created momentum for professional agencies supporting early childhood intervention. Are early childhood intervention efforts successful in producing desired outcomes for children and families? The answer depends on a myriad of contextual factors, including, but not limited to, child characteristics, characteristics of the family system, programmatic characteristics, and measurement characteristics. In general, however, the benefits of early childhood intervention as a societal endeavor have justified the costs in time, effort, and funding provided.

OVERVIEW OF THE INDIVIDUALS WITH DISABILITIES EDUCATION ACT

The Individuals with Disabilities Education Act is the most comprehensive law supporting the developmental and educational experiences of children and families (an overview of other disability laws is provided in Chapter 20). The current authorization of IDEA, as a successor of the Education for All Handicapped Children Act (P.L. 94-142), is designed to support and protect the education-related rights of children with disabilities and their families by

- assisting localities, educational service agencies, states, and federal agencies in providing for children's education
- assisting states to implement statewide, comprehensive, coordinated, multidisciplinary, interagency systems of early intervention services for infants and toddlers with disabilities and their families
- ensuring that educators and parents have the tools needed to improve educational results for children through systemic-change activities; coordinated research and personnel preparation; coordinated technical assistance, dissemination, and support; and technology development and media services
- assessing efforts to educate children with disabilities

IDEA provides for children and young adults from birth to 21 years of age who experience physical or mental disabilities. Part C of the law provides for children under 3 years of age who need early intervention services because they are either (a) experiencing developmental delays in cognitive, physical, communicative, social or emotional, or adaptive development or (b) have a diagnosed physical or mental condition that has a high probability of resulting in developmental delay. Delays must be determined using appropriate diagnostic instruments and procedures. With respect to the 3- to 21-year-old age group, a child with a disability is defined as someone with intellectual disability, hearing impairment, deafness, speech or language impairment, visual impairment or blindness, serious emotional disturbance, orthopedic impairment, autism, traumatic brain injury, other health impairment, specific learning disability, deaf-blindness, or multiple disabilities. Other conditions can be included if they are likely to result in the need for special education or related services. States and local educational agencies can use the definition provided above for children under age 3 to consider the eligibility of children who are 3 to 9 years of age.

IDEA provides for a host of services and supports including a free and appropriate public education (FAPE, which includes special education *and* related services such as transportation and speech and occupational therapy); the least restrictive environment (LRE); team-based determination of eligibility and services; the development and use of an Individualized Family Service Plan (IFSP, typically for children from birth through 3 years of age) or Individualized Education Program (IEP, for children 3 through 8 years of age); and transition services (infant–toddler programs to preschool, preschool to kindergarten, middle school to high school, and high school to postschool opportunities). IDEA includes provisions for procedural safeguards (written notice to parents regarding identification, evaluation, and placement of children); team and multisource evaluation and placement procedures; periodic review; and due process (impartial hearings for parents who disagree with the identification, evaluation, or placement of a child). Federal funds are provided to states and local education agencies to help them implement and monitor IDEA requirements.

IDEA is based on the assumption that a child's initial placement should be in the setting that would be most natural to the child if the child did not have a disability. Thus, a preference is given to fully inclusive placements. However, a continuum of placement settings is presented in IDEA, acknowledging that a fully inclusive environment may not be in the best interest of all children with disabilities:

- General education: Students receive special education and related services outside of the general education classroom for less than 21% of the school day.
- Resource room: Students receive special education and related services outside of the general education classroom for 21% to 60% of the school day.
- Separate class: Students receive special education and related services outside of the general education classroom for more than 60% of the school day.
- Separate school: Students receive special education and related services in separate day schools (more than 50% of the school day), residential facilities (more than 50% of the school day), or homebound or hospital environments.

These options are designed with school-age (e.g., kindergarten through third-grade) children in mind and may not be applicable for infant–toddler and preschool programs. Further, variations on these options exist within school-age programs, allowing schools to tailor programs to children's needs (e.g., Lewis & Doorlag, 1999). A full copy of IDEA can be accessed at www.idea practices.org and www.ed.gov (search on "IDEA").

CENTRAL THEMES OF EARLY CHILDHOOD INTERVENTION

Professional Ethics

All efforts to support the needs of young children and their families should be grounded in the ethical standards established by professional and local agencies. Thus, it is critical that professionals become familiar with and adhere to these standards. The following definitions taken from Webster's *New Collegiate Dictionary* provide us with a general compass for ethical behavior:

- Ethic: any set of moral principles or values; the moral quality of a course of action.
- Moral: concerned with the judgment of the goodness or badness of human action and character.
- Principle: a fundamental or universal truth, law, or assumption; a rule or standard.
- Value: a social end or goal considered desirable of achievement, utility, or merit.

Thus, ethical standards are intended to guide and regulate appropriate and responsible behavior in professional contexts (Schwolwinski, Barsalou, & Wehner, 1999). They require a commitment to a shared set of core values related to working with and promoting the welfare and dignity of children, families, and professionals. Although a large number of professional organizations supporting early childhood intervention exist, three of these organizations stand in the forefront: National Association for the Education of Young Children (NAEYC), Council for Exceptional Children (CEC), and the CEC Division for Early Childhood (DEC). The mission statements for these three groups are provided in Table 2.2. The belief statements or core values and professional code of ethics for each organization can be accessed via the Internet address included with each mission statement.

As noted in the preamble to the NAEYC *Code of Ethics*, many of the decisions made by professionals providing early childhood intervention are moral

TABLE 2.2
Mission Statements

- The National Association for the Education of Young Children (www.naeyc.org) exists for the purpose of leading and consolidating the efforts of individuals and groups that work to achieve healthy development and constructive education for all young children.
- The worldwide mission of the Council for Exceptional Children (www.cec.sped.org) is to improve educational outcomes for individuals with exceptionalities.
- The Division for Early Childhood (www.dec-sped.org), a division of the Council for Exceptional Children, is dedicated to promoting policies and practices that support families and enhance the optimal development of children. Children with special needs include those who have disabilities or developmental delays, are gifted/talented, or are at risk of future developmental problems.

---

and ethical in nature. Dilemmas will inevitably arise as decisions are made regarding the best and most appropriate course of action. The best and most appropriate answer may not always be obvious. The preamble states,

> There may be no readily apparent, positive way to handle a situation. One important value may contradict another. When we are caught "on the horns of a dilemma," it is our professional responsibility to consult with all relevant parties in seeking the most ethical course of action to take. (NAEYC, 1997)

The following statements form the basis for the NAEYC *Code of Ethics* and reflect principles of child and family development captured in both the CEC and DEC ethical standards:

- Ethical responsibilities to children: Childhood is a unique and valuable stage in the life cycle. Our paramount responsibility is to provide safe, healthy, nurturing, and responsive settings for children. We are committed to support children's development; respect individual differences; help children learn to live and work cooperatively; and promote health, self-awareness, competence, self-worth, and resiliency.
- Ethical responsibilities to families: Families are of primary importance in children's development (the term *family* may include others besides parents who are responsibly involved with the child). Because the family and the early childhood practitioner have a common interest in the child's welfare, we acknowledge a primary responsibility to bring about collaboration between the home and school in ways that enhance the child's development.
- Ethical responsibilities to colleagues: In a caring, cooperative workplace, human dignity is respected, professional satisfaction is promoted, and positive relationships are modeled. Based on our core values, our primary responsibility in this arena is to establish and maintain settings and relationships that support productive work and meet professional needs. The same ideals that apply to children are inherent in our responsibilities to adults.
- Ethical responsibilities to community and society: Early childhood programs operate within a context of an immediate community made up of families and other institutions concerned with children's welfare. Our responsibilities to the community are to provide programs that meet its needs, to cooperate with agencies and professions that share responsibility for children, and to develop needed programs that are not currently available. Because the larger society has a measure of responsibility for the welfare and protection of children, and because of our specialized expertise in child development, we acknowledge an obligation to serve as a voice for children everywhere.

Due to the potential impact that intervention may have on children and families, professionals must be particularly informed about the ethical considerations related to confidentiality. Indeed, professionals will have access to and the opportunity to discuss with others information about children and families that should be protected. Confidential information an be defined as any information that is considered personally identifiable (of an individual or family) in nature, including (a) the name of the child, parent, or other family member; (b) the address of the child or family; (c) a personal identification number (such as the child's social security number or student number); (d) list of personal characteristics or other information that would allow the child or family to be identified with reasonable certainty; and (e) any other information that is of a private or sensitive nature.

Such information may be transmitted or recorded via oral communication, written notes, audio- or videotapes, film, and computer disks. One should always handle and transmit confidential information with care. Professionals are expected to behave in ethical, diplomatic, and discrete ways regarding the stewardship and sharing of confidential information. In addition to the basic standards established by the professional organizations identified above, one should always ask about and become familiar with specific program policies regarding the release of information. It is important to discuss any questions or concerns regarding confidentiality with an immediate supervisor. In short, ethical standards and codes of conduct are designed to protect the rights of all involved. The protection of rights presupposes professionals' acceptance of responsibility. As in most aspects of life, it is wise to be guided by sound principles, honesty, courtesy, discretion, and common sense.

Challenges Related to Preparing Personnel

One of the most fundamental and formidable challenges to early childhood intervention in general, and the full implementation of the provisions of IDEA in particular, has been the adequate and timely preparation and retention of high-quality personnel (Kilgo & Bruder, 1997; U.S. Department of Education, 1998; Wagner, 2001; Winton & McCollum, 1997; Yates & Higgins-Hains, 1997). Indeed, the provision of appropriate intervention services and supports is in part a function of the availability of a fully staffed and competent workforce. In *Teacher Quality: A Report on Teacher Preparation and Qualifications,* Riley (1999) reported that only one in five new and veteran teachers felt well prepared for the modern classroom with respect to teaching students with disabilities, working with students from diverse cultural backgrounds, raising standards in the classroom, and using technology. This data is echoed in the report *Teacher Quality Initiative: Eliminating Barriers to Improving Teaching* (Dozier & Berlotti, 2000). The challenges presented above are exacerbated by concerns about the quality of the personnel preparation in areas such as current state and federal laws and regulations, inclusion, new and emerging assessment and instructional practices, family systems and involvement, and teamwork (Campbell & Fyfe, 1995; Gallagher, Malone, Cleghorne, & Nelson, 1997; Malone, Gallagher, & Long, 2001; Riley, 1999; State Superintendent's Task Force for Preparing Special Education Personnel, 2001).

As children with disabilities are increasingly educated in general education classrooms (at a current rate of 80% [McLeskey, Henry, & Hodges, 1999]), the need for fully qualified teachers and related service personnel assumes even greater importance. Unfortunately, the vacancies in early childhood intervention positions are significant, and the professionals employed in this area are often underprepared to meet contemporary challenges (DePoy & Miller, 1996; Dozier & Berlotti, 2000; Gallagher et al., 1997; Malone & Manders, 1995; Malone, McKinsey, Thyer, & Straka, 2000; Riley, 1999; Scruggs & Mastropieri, 1996; U.S. Department of Education, 1996, 2000). Not only is it becoming more difficult to recruit people into early childhood intervention–related jobs, but these personnel are more likely than personnel in other health and human service jobs to leave their chosen profession (e.g., Wagner, 2001). Urban areas with diverse educational contexts have the highest rates of staff turnover; consequently, large numbers of school districts are forced to employ personnel lacking full certification or licensure to meet service needs (Wagner, 2001). A factor in staff turnover is the quality of training professionals sometimes receive. Professionals who enter the workforce fully prepared to meet the challenges of working with children with disabilities and their families will experience less job-related stress and anxiety and be less likely to seek employment out of the field. Finally, the demands for a qualified workforce are exacerbated in states where revised state teacher education and licensure standards reflecting inclusive education have resulted in shortages of teachers with appropriate credentials. Although certification or licensure is used as a general indicator of personnel quality (Boe, Cook, Bobbitt, & Terbanian, 1998; U.S. Department of Education, 1998), other factors such as program of study completed, experience, attitudes, and knowledge of and skills in collaboration, critical thinking, leadership, early intervention and prevention, and professional ethics are likely to enhance one's sense of personal and professional efficacy and quality (Kennedy, 1992). Indeed, certification or licensure is a necessary, but not a sufficient, indicator of teacher quality (Hebbeler, 1994; Kennedy, 1992). The personnel-related challenges to early childhood intervention underscore the importance of and need for a sincere and serious focus on professional ethics and standards as reflected in the *Guidelines for Preparation of Early Childhood Professionals* (NAEYC, 1996) and the *DEC Recommended Practices in Early Intervention/Early Childhood Special Education* (Sandall, McLean, & Smith, 2000). University personnel who prepare students to be early childhood interventionists must move beyond acknowledging these standards in accreditation portfolios to designing curricula that clearly reflect the standards and make them explicit to students.

Family-Centered Practice

Family-centered practice is a critical component of services to children with disabilities and their families. A family-centered approach involves recognizing the importance of families as primary decision makers. To create a system of family-centered practices, professionals must be familiar with family "values, structures, and interaction patterns" (Bailey, 1991, p. 34). While family-centered practice is considered particularly critical to the service delivery process for infants and toddlers (see Part C of IDEA), this philosophical orientation is also embedded within policy and standards for children 3 to 8 years of age. Indeed, IDEA supports family-centered practice by clearly describing families as partners in the process of education decision making and mandating families as members of their child's education team, whether it be an IFSP team or an IEP team.

The concept of family-centered practice grew out of the infusion of systems theory into the understanding of human development. Systems theory proposes that individuals are members of subsystems (e.g., family, work, local community, the broader society) that directly and indirectly influence one another (Bronfenbrenner, 1979; Sameroff & Chandler, 1975). According to systems theory, outcomes for individuals cannot be considered outside of the experiential and environmental contexts in which they exist. Thus, young children are inseparable from their family contexts. Family-centered practice recognizes that children are part of a family system and proposes that in order to affect outcomes for children with disabilities, the course of intervention must be determined collaboratively with the families. Figure 2.1 highlights critical variables identified in the literature (Dunst, Trivette, & Deal, 1988; Glasser, 1996; Guralnick, 1997b; Turnbull, Summer, & Brotherson, 1984) and depicts the complexity of considering family-centered practices.

In the *DEC Recommended Practices in Early Intervention/Early Childhood Special Education* (Sandall et al., 2000; available via www.sopriswest.com), Trivette and Dunst (2000) suggest using the term *family-based* to refer to practices that reflect genuine involvement by and collaboration with families. The authors define such practices as those that build individual and family competence and strengthen the family unit. Specific recommended family-based practices are categorized into four broader themes: shared responsibility and collaboration, strengthening family functioning, individualized and flexible practices, and strengths- and assets-based practices (Trivette & Dunst, 2000, p. 41). Similarly, the themes of collaboration, teamwork, communication, sensitivity, and diversity are underscored in the NAEYC and DEC professional standards for family and community relationships identified in the *Guidelines for Preparation of Early Childhood Professionals* (NAEYC, 1996).

Consider the case example of Zach's family. In this case, the family structure and needs have changed over time. The birth of the twins has decreased the parents' capacity to provide intervention at home and has limited their ability to provide transportation for Zach. In addition, the family's thinking regarding important experiences for Zach has changed. Zach's parents believe that, at this stage in his life, experiences with peers are an important part of his continued development. Prior to the birth of the twins and during Zach's infancy and toddlerhood, the appropriateness of various preschool options for Zach was less of a concern for the family. Now it is a critical factor in the decision-making process. This scenario illustrates how family concerns, needs, and priorities can change over time. A family-centered system would empower Zach's family by responding to their changing needs and respecting their priorities. Furthermore, a family-centered system would support Zach's family in identifying resources using their existing options and naturally occurring environments.

The implications of family-centered practice for professional development and service provision are extensive. If families are the foundation of the early

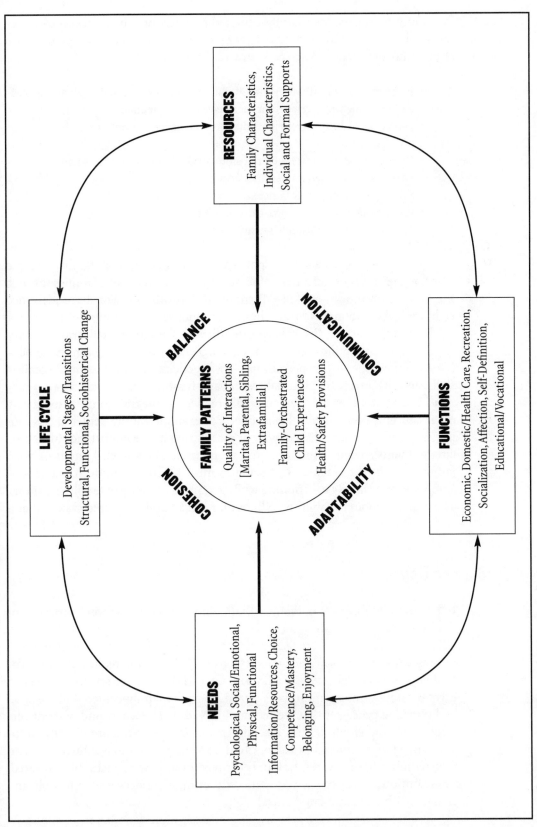

FIGURE 2.1. Model of family system influences.

intervention process, then family-centered practice must be at the core of professional training and service delivery. IDEA provides basic guidelines that clearly inform practice (Allen & Schwartz, 2001):

- Families of young children with disabilities must be involved in planning and implementing services for themselves and their child.
- Parents have due process rights that provide them with options in the process.
- Services must minimize the imposition of professional practices and system practices on families.
- Services must empower families.
- Families are entitled to service coordination.
- Services must be culturally sensitive.

For professionals to be responsive to the mandates of family-centered practice, they must be able to develop quality relationships with families through excellent communication skills. Turnbull and Turnbull (1997) have identified eight critical components of developing productive relationships with families: (a) knowing yourself, (b) knowing families, (c) honoring cultural diversity, (d) affirming and building on family strengths, (e) promoting family choices, (f) encouraging great expectations, (g) practicing positive communication skills, and (h) warranting mutual respect and trust.

The concept of family-centered practice is integrally intertwined with other concepts presented in this chapter. For example, family-centeredness cannot exist without cultural sensitivity or recognition of the importance of natural environments. Being family centered requires clear acknowledgment of what families bring to the table. Professionals must be able to understand general components of family functioning while accepting diversity in family situations. The best outcomes for children will result from a family-centered system that is responsive and flexible.

Service Delivery

IDEA provides multiple guidelines that define the service delivery process. For example, the law identifies the types of services that may be provided (§§ 602, 632), the importance of the least restrictive and natural environments in determining where services are delivered (§§ 612, 635), and the requirement for coordinated service delivery (§§ 612, 613, 641, 644). Effective service delivery in early childhood intervention is the product of the family-centered assessment and planning processes that are required by IDEA. The where and what of services for young children with disabilities and their families are directly influenced by family-centered practice. Children with disabilities age birth to 5 and their families have a variety of options regarding how services are delivered. These options are often viewed as a continuum of services that is flexible and changes with child and family needs.

Service Coordination

The coordination of services for young children with disabilities and their families involves agencies and programs working collaboratively to support families and avoid duplication of services. IDEA sets basic guidelines for the coordination of services for children with disabilities. In general, federal, state, and local agencies must work together to "promote the coordination and timely and appropriate delivery of services" (§ 612 [C]).

Service coordination is more specifically defined in part C (§§ 631, 641, 644). Service delivery in early intervention (birth to age 3) is a complicated process designed to draw on existing resources and programs in a coordinated and collaborative way. Unlike programs administered through the public schools, most early intervention programs must coordinate services from multiple systems. Furthermore, there is much greater diversity in the settings in which services are provided for young children with disabilities and their families. IDEA recognizes the importance of service coordination in early intervention by requiring that families have a single point of contact (a service coordinator) in the service delivery process.

Natural Environments

In keeping with family-centered practice and the doctrine of inclusion, Part C of IDEA requires that services be provided "to the maximum extent appropriate ... in natural environments, including the home, and community settings in which children without disabilities participate" (IDEA, § 632 [G]). Thus, young children with disabilities and their families may receive early intervention services in a variety of settings.

Settings for Early Childhood Intervention Services

Where services are provided should depend on family needs and preferences. Service delivery settings often are divided into the categories of home-based, classroom-based, and hospital-based programs. In determining settings for service delivery, it is critical to keep in mind that services are a dynamic set of interventions that result from a family-centered process. Thus, service delivery can never be defined as a program; rather, programs must exist to meet intervention requirements. All intervention programs must adhere to the federal mandate for services in the least restrictive and most natural environment.

Families may access a combination of service locations or access different locations at different points in time. For example, a 4-year-old with disabilities may attend a school-based preschool program part time and receive services in both the school and home settings. Similarly, a 1-year-old with disabilities may receive support in a childcare setting while the parents access resources through a variety of agencies.

Home-Based Services

The home environment exerts a powerful influence on the development of young children (see Figure 2.1; Bronfenbrenner, 1979; Guralnick, 1997b). Because of this, home-based services can be critical in efforts to effect positive outcomes for children who experience biological or environmental risk, especially during the infant and toddler years (Farran, 2000). In a home-based service delivery model, service providers work with families and children to support child and family development using the home environment. Although service providers may (and often do) work directly with children, the focus is typically on helping families to incorporate intervention into family routines to the greatest extent possible. As such, parent education is often a primary component of home-based services. Are home-based programs necessarily better for or preferred by families compared to center- or classroom-based services? It depends on what aspect of the service one is examining. In one study of service provider and parent views of home-based and center-based services, benefits associated with home-based services included a more natural environment, one-on-one supports, comfort and convenience, relationships, and trust. In comparison, benefits associated with center-based programs included curriculum, socialization, networking, and routine and consistency (Hoffman, 2001). Home-based services require providers to be comfortable and competent working one on one with families. Interventionists should avoid projecting their own values, supplanting family actions and functions with their own scripts, diagnosing family faults and prescribing remedies, stereotyping families, trying to "fix" the family's "problems," expecting too much too soon, and promoting dependency (Klaas, 1996). Interventionists must possess attitudes, knowledge, and communication skills that enable them to be sensitive and responsive to the family's structure, experiences, functions, perceptions, and demands.

Classroom-Based Programs

Classroom-based programs are the most common settings for services to preschool children (Bailey & Wolery, 1992), although initiatives designed to provide quality classroom-based settings for infants and toddlers with or at risk for disabilities have increased dramatically. Classroom-based programs may be public or private, or combine resources from both. Public funds for early childhood include Title I, Head Start, and funds for preschool children with disabilities (Part B, § 619). Classrooms may operate in a variety of settings, including churches, childcare centers, child development programs, and schools. In some states, particularly those in which education is the lead agency for infant–toddler programs, school-based classrooms may serve children in the birth-to-3 age group. These classrooms almost always target children with disabilities. All of these programs may be used full time or part time. Families should have a continuum of service setting options available to them to realize the mandate for natural environments (see "Overview of IDEA" earlier in the chapter).

Regardless of the type of classroom-based program, personnel responsible for the IFSPs and IEPs of children with disabilities must meet state-identified requirements for certification or licensure designating competency in early intervention or early childhood special education. Providing services to young children in classroom-based programs requires that professionals work collaboratively with families, program staff, and related service staff.

Hospital-Based Programs

Programs designed to provide support for children and families in hospital-based settings run the gamut from those that promote developmental care in the neonatal intensive care unit (NICU) to education and child-life programs intended to support children who must endure lengthy and occasionally permanent hospital stays. Increasingly, early childhood intervention personnel are employed by hospitals to provide services to children and families and to facilitate transition to and from the hospital setting. These personnel working in or with the hospital setting must have extensive knowledge of hospital programs and the medical system and be able to support family empowerment and positive child outcomes within that system.

What Do These Services Look Like?

The "what" aspect of service delivery for young children with disabilities and their families addresses the specific services and curriculum approaches used to meet family and child needs. Once again, these services must be considered on a continuum of options, which can be adjusted as appropriate. For example, services may be provided directly to a child and family, or services may be provided on a consultative basis. Services may involve directly teaching skills to a child or family member or be limited to providing information. Regardless of the types of services provided to families, the process of determining appropriate services must be ongoing, flexible, and responsive to child and family needs.

Inclusion

Framework and Definition

The term *inclusion,* when used to describe the educational placement of children with disabilities, has been assimilated into the collective consciousness of the educational community at large. Indeed, it has become a common part of educational discourse. Despite this breadth of awareness, the definition and application of the term are as varied as the emotions and reactions it evokes among educators, parents, and students. Although IDEA does not provide a specific definition of inclusion, it does create a framework supporting the inclusion of children with disabilities in the "general curriculum" via definitions, requirements for the least restrictive environment (LRE), procedural safeguards, program and placement options, IEP and IFSP guidelines, evaluation guidelines, technical assistance and training activities, and monitoring activities. The Final Regulations of IDEA, on which the federal and state laws are based, related to including children with disabilities in the general curriculum are provided in Appendix 2.A. With respect to the concept of the LRE, IDEA (§ 300.550) states,

> In general, to the maximum extent appropriate, children with disabilities, including children in public or private institutions or other care facilities, are educated with children who are not disabled, and special classes, separate schooling, or other removal of children with disabilities from the regular

educational environment occurs only when the nature or severity of the disability of a child is such that education in regular classes with the use of supplementary aids and services cannot be achieved satisfactorily.

IDEA defines natural environments as "settings that are natural or normal for the child's age peers who have no disabilities" (used in reference to children birth to 3 years of age) and the general curriculum as "the same curriculum as for nondisabled children" (referring to children 3–21 years of age). Thus, a simple definition of inclusion is the education of children with disabilities in natural environments via the general curriculum with peers without disabilities. Such a definition is limited, however, in that placement in the general education classroom alone is not sufficient for successful inclusion. A more complete definition of inclusion is

> a commitment to supporting the academic, physical, social, emotional, and behavioral needs of children with disabilities in the general education classroom via appropriate attitudes and a variety of instructional and curricular strategies designed to fit students' needs. (Adapted from Rogers [1993] and Wood [2002])

Children's needs are to be supported to the maximum extent appropriate, support services are to be brought to the children with disabilities (rather than pulling the children out of the classroom to be taken to the services), and children with and without disabilities are to be supported alongside one another. Children are not to be selectively placed in general education classes only after earning that opportunity by demonstrating the ability to meet the expectations of the general curriculum (as was the case with the concept and practice of mainstreaming). Finally, the position on inclusion developed by the Council for Exceptional Children's Division for Early Childhood (endorsed by the NAEYC) supports and expands the context for including children with disabilities in the general education environment (see Table 2.3).

Contextual Factors

The emphasis of IDEA on meeting the needs of children with disabilities in natural environments has resulted in an unprecedented number of children with disabilities receiving their education in general education classrooms (McLeskey et al., 1999). Although this trend is extremely encouraging, significant challenges to universal inclusion still exist. The following concerns about including children with disabilities in general education classrooms have been expressed by teachers and parents:

- feelings of fear, anxiety, and lack of confidence related to outcomes for children with and without disabilities
- lack of collaboration among professionals with differing disciplinary backgrounds and philosophical orientations
- belief that children with disabilities will demand so much time that the teacher will not be able to adequately address other children's needs ("some children will lose")

TABLE 2.3

The Division on Early Childhood's Position Statement on Inclusion[a]

Inclusion, as a value, supports the right of all children, regardless of their diverse abilities, to participate actively in natural settings within their communities. A natural setting is one in which the child would spend time had he or she not had a disability. Such settings include but are not limited to home and family, play groups, child care, nursery schools, Head Start programs, kindergartens, and neighborhood school classrooms.

DEC believes in and supports full and successful access to health, social service, education, and other supports and services for young children and their families that promote full participation in community life. DEC values the diversity of families and supports a family guided process for determining services that are based on the needs and preferences of individual families and children.

To implement inclusive practices DEC supports: (a) the continued development, evaluation, and dissemination of full inclusion supports, services, and systems so that options for inclusion are of high quality; (b) the development of preservice and inservice training programs that prepare families, administrators, and service providers to develop and work within inclusive settings; (c) collaborations among all key stakeholders to implement flexible fiscal and administrative procedures to support inclusion; (d) research that contributes to our knowledge of state of the art services; and (e) the restructuring and unification of social, education, health, and intervention supports and services to make them more responsive to the needs of all children and families.

[a]This position statement is endorsed by the National Association for the Education of Young Children.

- lack of training in, experience with, and provision of diverse and individualized instructional strategies
- lack of training in or ability to manage atypical and aggressive behaviors
- lack of sufficient knowledge to explain the rationale for inclusion to parents of children without disabilities
- inadequate administrative and curricular supports
- belief that the philosophies of special education and early childhood education are too different to make a good match ("Can people trained in different areas really work together?")

Guralnick (2001) identified concerns about access to and feasibility of inclusive programs as particularly salient. Although many more children are counted as being included in the general curriculum today than 25 years ago, universal and consistent physical and attitudinal access has not yet been achieved. Researchers with the Early Childhood Research Institute on Inclusion (1998) note that "a challenge for the field of ECSE [early childhood special education] is how we facilitate, support and maintain the meaningful participation of children with disabilities in the activities of inclusive ECE [early childhood education] programs." As noted above, inclusion has not been consistently defined; hence, program parameters vary widely. Access is more readily achieved for children who experience mild to moderate disabilities than for children whose disabilities are more significant (Buysse, Wesley, Keyes, & Bailey, 1996; Malone & Troup, 2002). Variables that promote access to the general curriculum include an understanding of the principles of inclusion, experience with children with disabilities, administrative commitment and support, adequate funding, classroom supports and resources (for both teachers and children), positive teacher attitudes, collaborative planning for children's participation among stakeholders, appropriate preservice preparation, and regular access to information and training on inclusion and children with specific disabilities (Guralnick, 2001; Lieber, Schwartz, Sandall, Horn, & Wolery, 1999; Lipsky & Gartner, 2001; Malone & Troup, 2000).

Successful inclusion requires more than the physical placement of children with disabilities into general education classrooms. It requires a fundamental change in how educational programs are designed and implemented. Thus, concerns regarding the feasibility of inclusion must be considered (Guralnick, 2001). Guralnick defines feasibility as "the ability of a particular program to retain its philosophical and programmatic approach while successfully meeting the individual needs of all the children in the program" (p. 14). The concept of feasibility is grounded in program integrity, commitment to inclusion, and availability of adequate and appropriate resources. For instance, programs that are well grounded in a particular philosophical and administrative orientation are more likely to maintain programmatic integrity while accommodating a diverse student population. For example, the principles of child development and learning presented in *Developmentally Appropriate Practices in Early Childhood Programs* (Bredekamp & Copple, 1997, pp. 9–15) are relevant to the development and learning of all children:

- Domains of children's development (physical, social, emotional, and cognitive) are closely related. Development in one domain influences and is influenced by development in other domains.
- Development occurs in a relatively orderly sequence, with later abilities, skills, and knowledge building on those already acquired.
- Development proceeds at varying rates from child to child as well as unevenly within different areas of each child's functioning.
- Early experiences have both cumulative and delayed effects on individual children's development; optimal periods exist for certain types of development and learning.
- Development proceeds in predictable directions toward greater complexity, organization, and internalization.
- Development and learning occur in and are influenced by multiple social and cultural contexts.
- Children are active learners, drawing on direct physical and social experience as well as culturally transmitted knowledge to construct their own understandings of the world around them.
- Development and learning result from interaction of biological maturation and the environment, which includes both the physical and social worlds that children live in.

- Play is an important vehicle for children's social, emotional, and cognitive development, as well as a reflection of their development.
- Development advances when children have opportunities to practice newly acquired skills as well as when they experience a challenge just beyond the level of their present mastery.
- Children demonstrate different modes of knowing and learning and different ways of representing what they know.
- Children develop and learn best in the context of a community where they are safe and valued, their physical needs are met, and they feel psychologically secure.

Further, the presumption that educational goals of children with and without disabilities differ dramatically is not entirely accurate. Parallel goals identified by Lieber et al. (1999) include

- becoming more confident learners
- learning to interact positively with peers
- learning to respect others
- learning to communicate effectively
- acquiring and using problem-solving skills

Finally, instructional strategies that are often associated with inclusive classrooms but that are, in fact, effective strategies for educating all children and facilitating the attainment of goals include

- direct teaching and instruction (structured teaching, explicit instruction, teacher-managed instruction)
- cooperative teaching (coteaching, collaborative teaching): one teacher–one assistant, station teaching, parallel teaching, alternative teaching, team teaching
- cooperative learning groups
- peer-directed instruction (peer tutoring, peer-mediated instruction): classwide, individualized same-age, individualized cross-aged
- discovery learning (project-based learning groups)
- reciprocal teaching (apprenticeship approach)
- multilevel curriculum
- activity-based instruction
- integrative curriculum
- errorless learning procedures (behavior management techniques = prompts, guidance, reinforcement, discrete trials)
- scaffolding
- naturalistic teaching (play-based instruction, incidental teaching, constructivist strategies)

Strategies such as those presented above are compatible with an array of philosophical and administrative orientations. This compatibility is most readily seen when teachers and administrators demonstrate another component of feasibility: commitment. Commitment to implementing inclusion in the face of inevitable challenges is critical to programmatic feasibility. Commitment will enable personnel to explore different strategies, support and encourage team members, and maintain a positive and proactive attitude. Commitment will energize personnel to find solutions, rather than excuses, to the challenges associated with inclusion.

Finally, the provision of adequate and appropriate resources supports programmatic feasibility. Indeed, satisfaction with inclusion is often linked to the resources available. Malone and Troup (2000) observed that teachers who reported satisfaction with their level of classroom support considered less restrictive classroom options most appropriate for children with disabilities and provided more positive ratings of the inclusion process. Although teachers can be cautious and shy away from actively implementing inclusive programs until adequate and appropriate resources are made available, teachers must consider the alternative that adequate and appropriate resources will not be provided until inclusive programs are actively implemented.

Improved preparation of personnel, direct experience with children with disabilities, and the provision of adequate and appropriate supports (e.g., planning time, inservice training, classroom aids) can work to address the concerns that many teachers have about including children with disabilities in their classrooms. Addressing these concerns and nurturing positive attitudes toward inclusion is critical to promoting benefits of inclusion that have been documented. Child-related benefits associated with effective inclusion include enhanced positive attitudes for children with and without disabilities, gains in academic and social skills, improved preparation for community living, and avoidance of harmful effects of segregation. Teacher-related benefits include provision of collaborative supports, improved social and professional skills, enhanced confidence in teaching ability, and increased participation in and empowerment related to the educational process. Finally, benefits to society include overcoming historical patterns of segregation and bias, removal of misperceptions of competence and ability, and an enhanced sense of value and equality among people.

Cultural Diversity

IDEA specifically addresses the implications of diversity in identifying, assessing, and serving children with disabilities and their families. The congressional findings (§§ 601, 612) articulate the need for the special education system to be responsive to the diversification of U.S. society. The law further dictates procedure related to acknowledging diversity in the evaluation process and recognizing the importance of families in decision-making processes.

Cultural diversity plays a significant role in determining the parameters of service delivery for young children with disabilities and their families. Culture may well be the most consistent influence in a child's life (Turnbull & Turnbull, 1997). However, the influences of cultural diversity on outcomes in the disability system are complex. Cultural diversity, disability, and poverty are interrelated constructs that yield unique outcomes in individual situations within and across cultural groups (Bryant & Maxwell, 1997; Garcia Coll & Magnuson, 2000). Examples of ways in which cultural diversity interacts with disability include causation, assessment, prevention, placement, and intervention (Drew & Hardman, 2000). For example, we know that a disproportionate percentage of cultural minorities live in poverty. We also know that poverty is related to increased incidence of disability (Garcia Coll & Magnuson, 2000; U.S. Department of Education, 2001). Therefore, cultural minorities are disproportionately represented in the disability population. This overrepresentation is further fueled by the assessment and measurement bias related to a lack of cultural sensitivity (Aponte & Clifford, 1995; Lyman, 1998).

The implications of diversity for working with young children with disabilities and their families are tremendous. Policy and practice must respect and build on family diversity by defining family in ways that accommodate diversity and by acknowledging the sociocultural contexts in which families function (Barrera & Kramer, 1997; McGonigel, Kaufmann, & Johnson, 1991). Early childhood intervention professionals must develop competence working across cultures. Rosin (1996) suggests four steps professionals can take toward developing cultural competence. First, they need to investigate and understand the influence of their own cultural contexts. This involves exploring personal values and belief systems to identify ways in which they may help or hinder interactions with those whose values and beliefs differ. Second, professionals must understand the origins of family diversity. Diversity is typically discussed in terms of cultural differences. However, there are other sources of family diversity, such as family structure and socioeconomic status, which may influence or be influenced by cultural diversity. Third, professionals must recognize the ways diversity impacts access to services. For example, language barriers and custom differences may decrease the likelihood that a family will access early childhood intervention services. Fourth, professionals must change the nature of programs and systems that inhibit cultural sensitivity. This step may be the greatest challenge to providing culturally sensitive services. However, any program or system that encourages family-centered practice will make great strides toward supporting family diversity.

Consider the case of Kim and his family. Clearly, the professionals and family do not have the same priorities in addressing Kim's needs. The school is very focused on compliance issues such as sustained attention and following directions, whereas the family is more concerned about Kim's communication skills. Kim's mother is frustrated with the school's lack of acknowledgment of the family's priorities but is hesitant to share her frustrations as a result of her experiences in Korea.

Collaboration

The health and human service system in the United States has traditionally been composed of independent, highly specialized, and politically charged public agencies. The potential effectiveness of this "system" has been compromised by pervasive problems, including (a) inequity in the accessibility of services, (b) discrepancies in services delivered, (c) lack of adequate information on services, (d) inadequate control and administration across the system, and (e) insufficient resources, including funds, personnel, and facilities (Brewer & Kakalik, 1975). The ultimate outcome of such a system is the inability to provide appropriate services, reflecting identified best practices, to individuals and families. This problem may be mediated, however, through effective service coordination at both system-wide and programmatic levels.

Current thinking and federal mandates suggest that successful implementation of early childhood intervention programs requires collaboration among personnel representing diverse disciplines and programs (McWilliam, 2000). The architects of the legislation now known as IDEA acknowledged one of the fundamental assumptions of a systems approach to family-centered intervention: No single discipline or program can address in total the needs of young children with disabilities and their families. They further acknowledged the need to provide a plan for implementing the process of service coordination in detail, which had not been provided in earlier legislation (Harbin & McNulty, 1990).

IDEA includes provisions for a minimum of 14 components that are to compose the statewide system for family-centered early intervention services. The plan for this system includes several mechanisms for facilitating the development and implementation of a statewide, comprehensive, coordinated, multidisciplinary, interagency program of early intervention service delivery, including the state interagency coordinating council, local interagency coordinating council, Individualized Family Service Plan, and position of service coordinator (or case manager). The provisions for the IFSP exemplify the need for interdisciplinary and interagency collaboration:

> Each infant or toddler with a disability and the infant's or toddler's family shall receive: (1) a multidisciplinary assessment of the unique strengths and needs of the infant or toddler and the identification of services appropriate to meet such needs, (2) a family directed assessment of the resources, priorities, and concerns of the family and the identification of supports and services necessary to enhance the family's capacity to meet the developmental needs of their infant or toddler with a disability, and (3) a written individualized family service plan developed by a multidisciplinary team, including the parent or guardian.... (§ 1477 [a])

In addition, the range of services is specified:

> family training, special instruction, speech pathology and audiology, occupational therapy, physical therapy, psychological services, service coordination, medical services (diagnostic and evaluation), early identification, screening and assessment services, specialized health services, vision services, social work services, services associated with assistive technology, and transportation services. (§ 1472 [2][e])

That range of services and the qualified personnel provided for under the law to administer those services require, by their very nature, collaboration. These personnel include

> special educators, speech/language pathologists, audiologists, occupational therapists, physical therapists, psychologists, social workers, nurses, nutritionists, family therapists, orientation and mobility specialists, and pediatricians and other physicians. (§ 1472 [2][f])

Historically, four service models have predominated: (a) the unidisciplinary model, (b) the multidisciplinary model, (c) the interdisciplinary model, and (d) the transdisciplinary model. The unidisciplinary model is characterized by personnel working in isolation of others; each expert focuses on the problems for which he or she was trained without regard to the efforts of others who are also providing services to the child or family. Characteristics of the three team collaborative models are provided in Table 2.4. Each of the three team models has advantages and disadvantages in application. Multidisciplinary teams have the fewest time constraints, but the lack of awareness of one another's activities may result in the duplication of activities and services. Interdisciplinary team members also can work independently and have a more cohesive structure resulting from shared goals and decision making. However, interdisciplinary team processes still may result in the duplication of activities. Transdisciplinary team processes are clearly the most collaborative in that they allow disciplines, programs, and agencies to share resources and result in the most integrated picture of child, family, and intervention. Additionally, this model minimizes duplication of services. A transdisciplinary team model, however, requires an extensive time commitment from participants. It is important to note that no team model will be effective in all situations; thus, skill and flexibility in working across team models is necessary.

In general, the benefits of collaborative teamwork include exchanging ideas, sharing knowledge, gaining insight from other perspectives, learning from people trained in different disciplines, enhancing programming efforts, providing a more complete method of evaluation, promoting parent input, increased continuity from drawing on the expertise of multiple individuals, increased camaraderie, the feeling of being included, the expansion of personal knowledge, and personal benefits related to collegiality (Brown, 1995; Malone et al., 2001; Malone & Koblewski, 1999; McPherson & Malone, 2002).

Challenges to the process include lack of program options from which to select, fiscal restraints, lack of opportunity for follow-up, lack of bilingual staff, lack of time for discussion of cases and interventions, inadequate preparation by team members, lack of formal training in teamwork and leadership, lack of systematic approaches to decision making, lack of interdisciplinary collaboration and trust, lack of clarity regarding team goals, scheduling difficulties, personality differences, conflict, differences in philosophy and approach, lack of consensus, lack of training, and resistance to role release (Bardon, 1983; Fenton, Yoshida, Maxwell, & Kaufman, 1979; Fleming & Fleming, 1983; Huebner &

TABLE 2.4
Characteristics of Team Service Models

Multidisciplinary Team
- Professionals gather for planning meetings.
- Focus is on discipline identity.
- Professionals work independently (with limited sharing of information).
- Information is not truly integrated.
- No efforts are made to arrive at a group consensus regarding decisions.
- No input is obtained from the individual or family receiving services and supports.

Interdisciplinary Team
- Team members gather for planning meetings.
- Focus is on team identity.
- Team members work independently on assessments and interventions, but they collaborate as a team through the regular sharing of information.
- Information is truly integrated.
- An effort is made to arrive at a team consensus regarding decisions.
- Overlapping areas of expertise are recognized.
- Input is provided from the individual or family receiving services and supports.

Transdisciplinary Team
- Team members gather for planning and assessment meetings.
- Focus is on team identity.
- Team members work together during the assessment and intervention process.
- Team members practice role release by sharing information and training others in their areas of expertise.
- Team efforts target intervention across domains.
- Regular meetings are scheduled to discuss team commitment.
- Team members have a strong sense of ownership to the process and to common goals.
- Team is open to and encourages family involvement in assessment and intervention.

Gould, 1991; Malone et al., 2001; Malone & Koblewski, 1999; McPherson & Malone, 2002; Pfeiffer, 1980, 1981; Pfeiffer & Heffernan, 1984; Ysseldyke, Algozzine, & Mitchell, 1982; Ysseldyke, Algozzine, Rostollan, & Shinn, 1981).

Although weighing the benefits and challenges within specific collaborative contexts is complex, characteristics of effective teams put forth by Spencer and Coye (1988) provide a useful foundation:

- having a primary goal or purpose
- recognizing the necessity of each team member (positive interdependence)
- team member commitment to the idea of teamwork
- accountability to an individual, group, or organization
- qualified leadership that is authoritative

Active team members (Malone et al., 2001; Malone & Koblewski, 1999; McPherson & Malone, 2002) have included the following recommendations:

- that time be managed more appropriately (e.g., regular meeting time, more time for meeting, and better use of meeting time)
- that communication be clear and positive
- that personnel be willing to work together, trusting, and open minded
- that team activities be organized (e.g., have ground rules for meetings)
- that team structure include organized, efficient, and flexible leadership, increased parent involvement, and administrative support
- that team members be trained in teamwork (in general), team dynamics and problem solving, and writing intervention plans collaboratively

The presence of such characteristics helps mitigate factors that have the potential to derail the collaborative team process.

Whitehouse's (1951) description of the basic assumptions underlying teamwork, put forth 5 decades ago, is still relevant today:

1. The human organism is dynamic and is an interacting, integrated whole.
2. Treatment must be dynamic and fluid to keep pace with the changing person, and must consider all that person's needs.
3. Teamwork, an interacting partnership of professions specializing in these needs and dealing with the person as a whole, is a valid method of meeting these requirements. (pp. 45–46)

Given these assumptions, the collaborative approach to service delivery may be contemporaneously defined as a viable and interacting partnership composed of all relevant persons, representing a variety of professional disciplines and non-professional roles (family, friends, community), who coordinate their specialized skills and resources to provide appropriate services and supports to individuals with disabilities and their families. Indeed, collaborative teaming is an interactive, reciprocal process (Thomas, Correa, & Morsink, 1995) that reflects the reality that no individual is qualified to meet all the needs of young children with disabilities and their families.

Whitehouse (1951) further noted that decisions made within a team should not be unilateral in design and that team outcomes are the result not of the compilation of individual reports, but of the assimilation of information from contributing disciplinary observations and assessments. Collaboration involves the exchange of information and ideas, the broadening and integration of perspectives, and systematic problem solving (Rosin, 1996; Thomas et al., 1995) to facilitate best practice in early childhood intervention. In this model children and their families are central to the process of service provision, emphasizing the relevance and importance of family input. Disciplinary experts interact with individuals and their families to obtain information through assessment and share this information with other members of the team. The team, with individual members working interdependently, is equipped with the knowledge to make informed collaborative decisions and to develop integrated goals and service programs based on all available information. Team collaboration on the program level is a necessary component to system-wide collaboration.

Although the framework for coordination among agencies and individuals is clearly specified in the legislation, the reality of implementing a system of services to infants and toddlers with disabilities and their families is anything but clear. The process represents a highly complex endeavor that requires all personnel involved, including professionals and parents, to overcome the barriers with which they will be presented. Almost certainly these barriers will include insufficient funds, restrictions on the use of funds that are available, inconsistencies in eligibility criteria, different regulations across agencies, idiosyncratic professional attitudes, excessive caseloads resulting in limited time for other activities, and lack of administrative support (Harbin & McNulty, 1990). However, the benefits to professional personnel, parents, and children are worth the investment of time and energy needed to overcome the challenges associated with the process.

Early Transition Planning

Despite the legislative and practical importance attributed to the process of transitioning children with disabilities across service settings (hospital to home to community-based infant–toddler programs to center-based preschool programs to inclusive school-age programs), relatively little research has been conducted to examine this transition process. As one of the central concepts included in IDEA, *transition* is defined as "a coordinated set of activities for a student, designed within an outcome-oriented process, that promote movement from [one educational setting to the next]." The intent of these activities is not only to promote physical movement to the next setting, but to facilitate a seamless system of services for the child and family that promotes successful developmental and educational outcomes (Repetto & Correa, 1996). Although legally mandated, no formal guidelines are provided in IDEA for early transition planning. This gap has been formally acknowledged in the *Twentieth Annual Report to Congress on the Implementation of the Individuals with Disabilities Education Act* (U.S. Department of Education, 1998). Further, only 2 of 97 blended professional competencies established by the Council for Exceptional Children's Division for Early Childhood (see NAEYC, 1997) directly address the issue of interprogram transition. In short, the limited guidance provided by either legislation or research represents a distinct challenge to personnel charged with the responsibility of developing effective transition plans.

Factors relevant to the successful transition of children with disabilities between programs include identification and support of appropriate skills (e.g., Hains, 1992; LeAger & Shapiro, 1995; Rous & Hallam, 1998; Rule, Fiechtl, & Innocenti, 1990; Sainato & Lyon, 1989); describing instructional environments (Early, Pianta, & Cox, 1999; Graue, 1999; Sainato & Lyon, 1989); identifying parent needs and concerns (Christenson, 1999; Hanline, 1988); and child, family, and teacher roles (Fowler, Chandler, Johnson, & Stella, 1988; Hains, Fowler, &

Chandler, 1988). One of the fundamental challenges of the transition process is matching child performance with expectations of the program into which the child is being transitioned (e.g., preschool to kindergarten transition) (LeAger & Shapiro, 1995; Sainato & Lyon, 1989). Achieving this match can be challenging given the potential for differences between programs in educational philosophy and practice.

The transition process can be stressful for children and families as they anticipate and adjust to a new system that typically differs from that to which they have become accustomed in personnel, educational philosophy, structure, curriculum, and support (Bray, Coleman, & Bracken, 1981; Fewell, 1986; Fowler et al., 1988; Hains, 1992; Hains et al., 1988; Hanline, 1988; Melton, Limber, & Teague, 1999; Rule et al., 1990; Sainato & Lyon, 1989; Wolery, 1989). Thus, communication between settings regarding issues of child characteristics, curriculum, program organization, family needs, and teacher expectations is critical (Hains et al., 1988; LaMontagne, Russell, & Janson, 1998; Pianta & Cox, 1999; Pianta & Walsh, 1996). The process must be carefully and thoughtfully addressed and treated as more than a chronologically dictated physical relocation to the next educational setting. Indeed, the transition process represents a bridging of instructional philosophies and practice of two diverse learning environments and the identification of the supports required to address child and family needs for successfully negotiating the transition. The process must be carefully planned, executed, and evaluated (Pianta & Cox, 1999; Rosenkoetter, Hains, & Fowler, 1994). Teacher expectations, attitudes, and perceptions are also particularly salient (Beckoff & Bender, 1989; Buysse et al., 1996; Giangreco, Dennis, Cloninger, Edelman, & Schattman, 1993; Hannah & Pliner, 1983; Larrivee & Cook, 1979; Scruggs & Mastropieri, 1996; Wolery, Werts, Caldwell, Snyder, & Lisowski, 1995; Zill, 1999). Research on teacher attitudes and perceptions and instructional innovation in general, and transition in particular, indicates such variables are critical to the success of transition efforts and subsequent success in the inclusive classroom (Bender & Ukeje, 1989; Buysse et al., 1996; Chow & Winzer, 1992; Diamond, Spiegel-McGill, & Hanrahan, 1988; Hannah & Pliner, 1983; Malouf & Schiller, 1995; Pajares, 1992). The role that one's attitudes and perceptions play in influencing behavior change has been highlighted in research on self-efficacy and the perceived importance of and competence associated with tasks intended to create change (Bailey, Palsha, & Simeonsson, 1991; Bandura, 1977, 1982; Guskey, 1986, 1988; Johnson & Pugach, 1996; Logan, 1996; Stein & Wang, 1988). Negative attitudes toward, low levels of comfort with, and perceived lack of competence in providing instruction for children with developmental concerns can result in a negative bias toward these children expressed through perceptions about their abilities, lowered expectations for performance, undercrediting actual performance, and lowered motivation and initiative to provide optimal instructional opportunities for the child. Such bias is likely to have a strong effect on how, and to what extent, teachers support transition and inclusive classrooms (Hains et al., 1988; Zill, 1999).

Although progress has been made regarding early transition philosophy and practice, the reality of fully appropriate transitions that result in a seamless bridge across programs is not universal. A balance must be struck between ideals that *should* exist and the reality that *does* exist. Not only is there a need for examination of the actual process of transition, it is important to explore teachers' and parents' perceptions of and attitudes toward the transition of children with disabilities in the early years.

FINAL THOUGHTS

Early childhood intervention is intended to provide supports and services to young children who are at risk for or have identified disabilities, and their families. These supports and services should facilitate the inclusion, independence, and productivity of those children and families. As such, early childhood intervention is a multifaceted and complex process. The cases of Amy, Zach, and Kim provide a sample of challenges faced by children and their families and the need for knowledgeable and caring professionals. In this chapter, we discussed the rationale for early childhood intervention, including philosophical and theoretical foundations. In addition, we defined the population of children who are eligible for services under IDEA and identified central themes that currently characterize early childhood intervention, including professional ethics, challenges related to preparing personnel, service delivery in natural environments, inclusion, the concept of family-centeredness, diversity, collaboration, and early transition planning. Although a host of other issues could easily have been addressed (e.g., cost of intervention, policy considerations, program evaluation), we considered the topics selected to be central to both the law and the process itself. As the base of early childhood intervention research grows and trends for new and improved supports evolve, professionals must keep their focus clear—children and families must realize true benefits. With this in mind, educators will be successful in improving the quality of life of children and their families.

IDEA Reference to Including Children with Disabilities in the General Curriculum

Final Regulations

(P.L. 105:17 Sections and United States Code Authority)

34 CFR PART 300: ASSISTANCE TO STATES FOR THE EDUCATION OF CHILDREN WITH DISABILITIES
(Part B of the Individuals with Disabilities Education Act)

• **Section 300.26, Special Education (Section 602, Definitions; 20 U.S.C. 1401)**— (a)(1) ... the term special education means specially designed instruction, at no cost to the parents, to meet the unique needs of a child with a disability, including—(i) Instruction conducted in the classroom, in the home, in hospitals and institutions, and in other settings.... (3) Specially designed instruction means adapting, as appropriate to the needs of an eligible child under this part, the content, methodology, or delivery of instruction—(ii) To ensure access of the child to the general curriculum, so that he or she can meet the educational standards within the jurisdiction of the public agency that apply to all children.

• **Section 300.28, Supplementary Aids and Services (Section 602, Definitions; 20 U.S.C. 1401)**— ... the term supplementary aids and services means aids, services, and other supports that are provided in regular education classes or other education-related settings to enable children with disabilities to be educated with nondisabled children to the maximum extent appropriate in accordance with Sections 300.550–300.556.

• **Section 300.121, Free Appropriate Public Education (FAPE) (Section 615, Procedural Safeguards; 20 U.S.C. 1415)**—(d) FAPE for children suspended or expelled from school—(3)(i) School personnel, in consultation with the child's special education teacher, determine the extent to which services are necessary to enable the child to appropriately progress in the general curriculum and appropriately advance toward achieving the goals set out in the child's IEP if the child is removed under the authority of school personnel to remove for not more than 10 consecutive school days as long as that removal does not constitute a change of placement under Section 300.519 (Section 300.520(a)(1)). (ii) The child's IEP team determines the extent to which services are necessary to enable the child to appropriately progress in the general curriculum and appropriately advance toward achieving the goals set out in the child's IEP if the child is removed because of behavior that has been determined not to be a manifestation of the child's disability, consistent with Section 300.524.

• **Section 300.305, Program Options (20 U.S.C. 1412, 1413)**—Each public agency shall take steps to ensure that its children with disabilities have available to them the variety of educational programs and services available to nondisabled children in the area served by the agency, including art, music, industrial arts, consumer and homemaking education, and vocational education.

• **Section 300.342, When IEPs Must Be in Effect**—(b)(2) The child's IEP is accessible to each regular education teacher, special education teacher, related service provider, and other service provider who is responsible for its implementation; and (3) Each teacher and provider described in paragraph (b)(2) of this section is informed of—(i) His or her specific responsibilities related to implementing the child's IEP.

• **Section 300.343, IEP Meetings (Section 614, Evaluations, Eligibility, Individualized Education Programs, and Educational Placements; 20 U.S.C. 1414)**—(c) Each public agency shall ensure that the IEP team—(2) Revises the IEP as appropriate to address—(i) Any lack of expected progress toward the annual goals described in Section 300.347(a), and in the general curriculum.

• **Section 300.344, IEP Team (Section 614, Evaluations, Eligibility, Individualized Education Programs, and Educational Placements; 20 U.S.C. 1414)**—(a) The public agency shall ensure that the IEP team for each child with a disability includes—(1) The parents of the child; (2) At least one regular education teacher of the child (if the child is, or may be, participating in the regular education environment); (3) At least one special education teacher of the child, or if appropriate, at least one special education provider of the child; (4) A representative of the public agency who—(i) Is qualified to provide, or supervise the provision of, specially designed instruction to meet the unique needs of children with disabilities; (ii) Is knowledgeable about the general curriculum.

• **Section 300.346, Development, Review, and Revision of IEP (Section 614, Evaluations, Eligibility, Individualized Education Programs, and Educational Placements; 20 U.S.C. 1414)**—(d) The regular education teacher of a child with a disability, as a member of the IEP team, must, to the extent appropriate, participate in the development, review, and revision of the child's IEP, including assisting in the determination of—(1) Appropriate positive behavioral interventions and strategies for the child; and (2) Supplementary aids and services, program modifications or supports for school personnel that will be provided for the child, consistent with Section 300.347(a)(3).

• **Section 300.347, Content of IEP (Section 614, Evaluations, Eligibility, Individualized Education Programs, and Educational Placements; 20 U.S.C. 1414)**—(a) The IEP for each child with a disability must include—(1) A statement of the child's present levels of educational performance, including—(i) How the child's disability affects the child's involvement and progress in the general curriculum (i.e., the same curriculum as for nondisabled children); or (ii) For preschool children, as appropriate, how the disability affects the child's participation in appropriate activities; (2) A statement of measurable annual goals, including benchmarks or short-term objectives, related to—(i) Meeting the child's needs that result from the child's disability to enable the child to be involved in and progress in the general curriculum (i.e., the same curriculum as for nondisabled children), or for preschool children, as appropriate, to participate in appropriate activities; (3) A statement of the special education and related services and supplementary aids and services to be provided to the child, or on behalf of the child, and a statement of the program modifications or supports for school personnel that will be provided for the child—(i) To advance appropriately toward attaining the annual goals; (ii) To be involved and progress in the general curriculum in accordance with paragraph (a)(1) of this section and to participate in extracurricular and other nonacademic activities; and (iii) To be educated and participate with other children with disabilities and nondisabled children in the activities described in this section; (4) An explanation of the extent, if any, to which the child will not participate with nondisabled children in the regular class and in the activities described in paragraph (a)(3) of this section; (5)(i) A statement of any individual modifications in the administration of State or district-wide assessments of student achievement that are needed in order for the child to participate in the assessment; and (ii) If the IEP team determines that the child will not participate in a particular State or district-wide assessment of student achievement (or part of an assessment), a statement of—(A) Why that assessment is not appropriate for the child; and (B) How the child will be assessed; and (6) A statement of—(i) How the child's progress toward the annual goals described in paragraph (a)(2) of this section will be measured; and (ii) How the child's parents will be regularly informed (through such means as periodic report cards), at least as often as parents are informed of their nondisabled children's progress, of—(A) Their child's progress toward the annual goals; and (B) The extent to which that progress is sufficient to enable the child to achieve the goals by the end of the year.

- **Section 300.522, Determination of Setting (Section 615, Procedural Safeguards; 20 U.S.C. 1415)**—(b) Any interim alternative educational setting in which a child is placed under Sections 300.520(a)(2) or 300.521 must—(1) Be selected so as to enable the child to continue to progress in the general curriculum, although in another setting, and to continue to receive those services and modifications, including those described in the child's current IEP, that will enable the child to meet the goals set out in that IEP.

- **Section 300.532, Evaluation Procedures (Section 614, Evaluations, Eligibility, Individualized Education Programs, and Educational Placements; 20 U.S.C. 1414)**—(b) A variety of assessment tools and strategies are used to gather relevant functional and developmental information about the child, including information provided by the parent, and information related to enabling the child to be involved in and progress in the general curriculum (or for a preschool child, to participate in appropriate activities).

- **Section 300.533, Determination of Needed Evaluation Data (Section 614, Evaluations, Eligibility, Individualized Education Programs, and Educational Placements; 20 U.S.C. 1414)**—(a) Review of existing evaluation data. As part of an initial evaluation (if appropriate) and as part of any reevaluation under Part B of the Act, a group that includes the individuals described in Section 300.344, and other qualified professionals, as appropriate, shall—(2) On the basis of that review, and input from the child's parents, identify what additional data, if any, are needed to determine—(iv) Whether any additions or modifications to the special education and related services are needed to enable the child to meet the measurable annual goals set out in the IEP of the child and to participate, as appropriate, in the general curriculum.

• **Section 300.550, General LRE Requirements (Section 612, State Eligibility; 20 U.S.C. 1412)**—(b) Each public agency shall ensure—(1) That to the maximum extent appropriate, children with disabilities, including children in public or private institutions or other care facilities, are educated with children who are nondisabled; and (2) That special classes, separate schooling or other removal of children with disabilities from the regular educational environment occurs only if the nature or severity of the disability is such that education in regular classes with the use of supplementary aids and services cannot be achieved satisfactorily.

• **Section 300.552, Placements (Section 612, State Eligibility; 20 U.S.C. 1412)**—In determining the educational placement of a child with a disability, including a preschool child with a disability, each public agency shall ensure that—(e) A child with a disability is not removed from education in age-appropriate regular classrooms solely because of needed modifications in the general curriculum.

• **Section 300.553, Nonacademic Settings (Section 614, Evaluations, Eligibility, Individualized Education Programs, and Educational Placements; 20 U.S.C. 1414)**—In providing or arranging for the provision of nonacademic and extracurricular services and activities, including meals, recess periods, and the services and activities set forth in Section 300.306, each public agency shall ensure that each child with a disability participates with nondisabled children in those services and activities to the maximum extent appropriate to the needs of that child.

• **Section 300.555, Technical Assistance and Training Activities**—Each SEA [Special Education Agency] shall carry out activities to ensure that teachers and administrators in all public agencies—(a) Are fully informed about their responsibilities for implementing Section 300.550; and (b) Are provided with technical assistance and training necessary to assist them in this effort.

• **Section 300.556, Monitoring Activities**—(a) The SEA shall carry out activities to ensure that Section 300.550 is implemented by each public agency; (b) If there is evidence that a public agency makes placements that are inconsistent with Section 300.550, the SEA shall—(1) Review the public agency's justification for its actions; and (2) Assist in planning and implementing any necessary corrective action.

34 CFR PART 303: EARLY INTERVENTION PROGRAM FOR INFANTS AND TODDLERS WITH DISABILITIES
(Part C of the Individuals with Disabilities Education Act)

• **Section 303.12, Early Intervention Services (Section 632, Definitions; 20 U.S.C. 1401, 1432)**—(b) Natural environments. To the maximum extent appropriate to the needs of the child, early intervention services must be provided in natural environments, including the home and community settings in which children without disabilities participate.

• **Section 303.18, Natural Environments (20 U.S.C. 1435, 1436)**— … natural environments means settings that are natural or normal for the child's age peers who have no disabilities.

• **Section 303.167, Individualized Family Service Plans (Section 635, Requirements for State System; 20 U.S.C. 1435, 1436)**—(c) Policies and procedures to ensure that—(1) To the maximum extent appropriate, early intervention services are provided in natural environments; and (2) The provision of early intervention services for any infant or toddler occurs in a setting other than a natural environment only if early intervention cannot be achieved satisfactorily for the infant or toddler in a natural environment.

• **Section 303.344, Content of an IFSP (Section 636, Individualized Family Service Plan; 20 U.S.C. 1436)**—(d) Early intervention services. (1) The IFSP must include a statement of the specific early intervention services necessary to meet the unique needs of the child and the family to achieve the outcomes identified in paragraph (c) of this section, including— (ii) The natural environments, as described in Sec. 303.12(b), and Sec. 303.18 in which early intervention services will be provided, and a justification of the extent, if any, to which the services will not be provided in a natural environment.

REFERENCES

Allen, K. E., & Schwartz, I. S. (2001). *The exceptional child: Inclusion in early childhood education.* Albany, NY: Delmar.

Aponte, J. F., & Clifford, J. (1995). Education and training issues for intervention in ethnic groups. In J. F. Aponte, R. Y. Rivers, & J. Wohl (Eds.), *Psychological interventions and diversity* (pp. 283–300). Boston: Allyn & Bacon.

Bailey, D. B. (1991). Building positive relationships between professionals and families. In M. J. McGonigel, R. K. Kaufman, & B. H. Johnson (Eds.), *Guidelines and recommended practices for the individualized family service plan* (pp. 29–38). Chapel Hill, NC: National Early Childhood Technical Assistance System.

Bailey, D. B., Bruer, J. T., Symons, F. J., & Lichtman, J. W. (2001). *Critical thinking about critical periods.* Baltimore: Brookes.

Bailey, D. B., Palsha, S. A., & Simeonsson, R. J. (1991). Professional skills, concerns, and perceived importance of work with families in early intervention. *Exceptional Children, 57,* 156–165.

Bailey, D. B., & Wolery, M. (1992). *Teaching infants and preschoolers with disabilities.* Englewood Cliffs, NJ: Prentice Hall.

Bandura, A. (1977). Self-efficacy: Toward a unifying theory of behavioral change. *Psychological Review, 84*(2), 191–215.

Bandura, A. (1982). The self-efficacy mechanism in human agency. *American Psychologist, 37*(2), 122–147.

Bardon, J. I. (1983). Viewpoints on multidisciplinary teams in schools. *School Psychology Review, 12,* 186–189.

Barrera, I., & Kramer, L. (1997). From monologues to skilled dialogues: Teaching the process of crafting culturally competent early childhood environments. In P. J. Winton, J. McCollum, & C. Catlett (Eds.), *Reforming personnel preparation in early intervention: Issues, models, and practical strategies* (pp. 217–251). Baltimore: Brookes.

Beckoff, A. G., & Bender, W. N. (1989). Programming for mainstream kindergarten success in preschool: Teacher's perceptions of necessary requisite skills. *Journal of Early Intervention, 13*(3), 269–280.

Bender, W. N., & Ukeje, I. C. (1989). Instructional strategies in mainstream classrooms: Prediction of the strategies teachers select. *Remedial and Special Education, 10,* 23–30.

Boe, E. E., Cook, L. H., Bobbitt, S. A., & Terbanian, G. (1998). The shortage of fully certified teachers in special and general education. *Teacher Education and Special Education, 21*(1), 1–21.

Bray, N., Coleman, J., & Bracken, M. (1981). Critical events in parenting handicapped children. *Journal of the Division for Early Childhood, 3*(1), 26–33.

Bredekamp, S., & Copple, C. (Eds.). (1997). *Developmentally appropriate practices in early childhood programs* (rev. ed.). Washington, DC: National Association for the Education of Young Children.

Brewer, G. D., & Kakalik, J. S. (1975). Serving handicapped children: The road ahead. *Child Welfare, 54*(4), 257–267.

Bronfenbrenner, U. (1979). *The ecology of human development.* Cambridge, MA: Harvard University Press.

Brown, G. F. (1995). *Factors that facilitate or inhibit interprofessional collaboration.* Paper presented at the 17th Annual Interdisciplinary Health Care Team Conference, Pittsburgh, PA.

Bryant, D., & Maxwell, K. (1997). The effectiveness of early intervention for disadvantaged children. In M. J. Guralnick (Ed.), *The effectiveness of early intervention* (pp. 23–46). Baltimore: Brookes.

Buysse, V., Wesley, P., Keyes, L., & Bailey, D. B. (1996). Assessing the comfort zone of child care teachers serving young children with disabilities. *Journal of Early Intervention, 29*(3), 189–203.

Campbell, D., & Fyfe, B. (1995, February). *Reforming teacher education: The challenge of inclusive education.* Annual Meeting of Independent Liberal Arts Colleges for Teacher Education, Washington, DC.

Chow, P., & Winzer, M. M. (1992). Reliability and validity of a scale measuring attitudes toward mainstreaming. *Education and Psychological Measurement, 52,* 223–228.

Christenson, S. L. (1999). Families and schools: Rights, responsibilities, resources, and relationships. In R. C. Pianta & M. J. Cox (Eds.), *The transition to kindergarten* (pp. 143–177). Baltimore: Brookes.

DePoy, E., & Miller, M. (1996). Preparation of social workers serving individuals with developmental disabilities: A brief report. *Mental Retardation, 34,* 54–57.

Diamond, K. E., Spiegel-McGill, P., & Hanrahan, P. (1988). Planning for school transition: An ecological developmental approach. *Journal of the Division for Early Childhood, 12,* 245–252.

Dozier, T., & Berlotti, C. (2000). *Teacher quality initiative: Eliminating barriers to improving teaching.* Washington, DC: U.S. Department of Education.

Drew, C. J., & Hardman, M. L. (2000). *Mental retardation: A life cycle approach* (7th ed.). Upper Saddle River, NJ: Prentice Hall.

Dunst, C., Trivette, C., & Deal, A. (1988). *Enabling and empowering families: Principles and guidelines for practice.* Cambridge, MA: Brookline Books.

Early Childhood Research Institute on Inclusion. (1998). *Teaching all children: Challenges to providing early intervention services in inclusive settings* [ECRII Brief #8]. Retrieved August 13, 2003, from http://www.fpg.unc.edu/~ecrii/ECRII_Resources_for_You_to_Use/ECRII_Briefs/brief08.pdf

Early, D., Pianta, R., & Cox, M. (1999). Kindergarten teachers and classrooms: A transition context. *Early Education and Development, 10*(1), 24–46.

Farran, D. C. (2000). Another decade of intervention for children who are low income or disabled: What do we know now? In J. P. Shonkoff & S. J. Meisels (Eds.), *Handbook of early childhood intervention* (2nd ed., pp. 510–548). Cambridge, UK: Cambridge University Press.

Farran, D. C. (2001). Critical periods and early intervention. In D. B. Bailey, J. T. Bruer, F. J. Symons, & J. W. Lichtman (Eds.), *Critical thinking about critical periods* (pp. 233–266). Baltimore: Brookes.

Fenton, K. S., Yoshida, R. K., Maxwell, J. P., & Kaufman, M. J. (1979). Recognition of team goals: An essential step toward rational decision-making. *Exceptional Children, 45,* 638–644.

Fewell, R. R. (1986). A handicapped child in the family. In R. R. Fewell & P. F. Vadasy (Eds.), *Families of handicapped children* (pp. 3–34). Austin, TX: PRO-ED.

Fleming, D. C., & Fleming, E. R. (1983). Problems in implementation of the team approach: A practitioner's perspective. *School Psychology Review, 12,* 144–149.

Fowler, S. A., Chandler, L. K., Johnson, T. E., & Stella, M. E. (1988). Individualizing family involvement in school transitions: Gathering information and choosing the next program. *Journal of the Division for Early Childhood, 12*(3), 208–216.

Gallagher, P. A., Malone, D. M., Cleghorne, M., & Nelson, K. (1997). The identification of training needs by practitioners in the field of early intervention. *Exceptional Children, 64*(1), 19–30.

Garcia Coll, C., & Magnuson, K. (2000). Cultural differences as sources of developmental vulnerabilities and resources. In J. P. Shonkoff & S. J. Meisels (Eds.), *Handbook of early childhood intervention* (2nd ed., pp. 94–114). Cambridge, UK: Cambridge University Press.

Giangreco, M. F., Dennis, R., Cloninger, C., Edelman, S., & Schattman, R. (1993). "I've counted Jon": Transformational experiences of teachers educating students with disabilities. *Exceptional Children, 59*(4), 359–371.

Glasser, W. (1996). *Reality therapy: A new approach to psychiatry.* New York: Harper & Row.

Graue, E. (1999). Diverse perspectives on kindergarten contexts and practices. In R. C. Pianta & M. J. Cox (Eds.), *The transition to kindergarten* (pp. 109–142). Baltimore: Brookes.

Guralnick, M. J. (Ed.). (1997a). *The effectiveness of early intervention.* Baltimore: Brookes.

Guralnick, M. J. (1997b). Second generation research in the field of early intervention. In M. J. Guralnick (Ed.), *The effectiveness of early intervention* (pp. 3–22). Baltimore: Brookes.

Guralnick, M. J. (Ed.). (2001). *Early childhood inclusion: Focus on change.* Baltimore: Brookes.

Guskey, T. R. (1986). Staff development and the process of teacher change. *Educational Researcher, 15,* 5–12.

Guskey, T. R. (1988). Teacher efficacy, self concept, and attitudes toward the implementation of instructional innovation. *Teaching and Teacher Education, 4,* 63–69.

Hains, A. H. (1992). Strategies for preparing preschool children with special needs for the kindergarten mainstream. *Journal of Early Intervention, 16*(4), 320–333.

Hains, A. H., Fowler, S. A., & Chandler, L. K. (1988). Planning school transitions: Family and professional collaboration. *Journal of the Division for Early Childhood, 12*(2), 108–115.

Hanline, M. F. (1988). Making the transition to preschool: Identification of parent needs. *Journal of the Division for Early Childhood, 12*(2), 98–107.

Hannah, M. E., & Pliner, S. (1983). Teacher attitudes toward handicapped children: A review and synthesis. *School Psychology Review, 12*(1), 12–25.

Harbin, G. L., & McNulty, B. A. (1990). Policy implementation: Perspectives on service coordination and interagency cooperation. In S. J. Meisels & J. P. Shonkoff (Eds.), *Handbook of early childhood intervention* (pp. 700–722). New York: Cambridge University Press.

Hebbeler, K. (1994). *Shortages in professions working with young children with disabilities and their families.* Chapel Hill: University of North Carolina, Frank Porter Graham Child Development Center.

Hoffman, T. (2001). *Family-centered service delivery in early intervention: Home-based versus center-based.* Unpublished doctoral dissertation, University of Cincinnati, Cincinnati, OH.

Huebner, E. S., & Gould, K. (1991). Multidisciplinary teams revisited: Current perceptions of school psychologists regarding team functioning. *School Psychology Review, 20,* 428–434.

Individuals with Disabilities Education Act of 1990, 20 USC § 1400 *et seq.*

Johnson, L. J., & Pugach, M. C. (1996). The emerging third wave of collaboration: Beyond problem solving. In W. Stainback & S. Stainback (Eds.), *Controversial issues confronting special education: Divergent perspectives* (2nd ed., pp. 197–204). Needham Heights, MA: Allyn & Bacon.

Kennedy, M. (1992). The problem of improving teacher quality while balancing supply and demand. In E. E. Boe & D. M. Gelford (Eds.), *Teacher supply, demand, and quality: Policy issues, models, and data bases* (pp. 63–122). Washington, DC: National Academy Press.

Kilgo, J. L., & Bruder, M. B. (1997). Creating new visions in institutions of higher education. In P. J. Winton, J. McCollum, & C. Catlett (Eds.), *Reforming personnel preparation in early intervention: Issues, models, and practical strategies* (pp. 81–102). Baltimore: Brookes.

Klaas, C. S. (1996). *Home visiting: Promoting healthy parent and child development.* Baltimore: Brookes.

LaMontagne, M. J., Russell, G. W., & Janson, M. (1998). Transitions. In L. J. Johnson, M. J. La Montagne, P. M. Elgas, & A. M. Bauer (Eds.), *Early childhood education: Blending theory, blending practice* (pp. 233–255). Baltimore: Brookes.

Larrivee, B., & Cook, L. (1979). Mainstreaming: A study of the variables affecting teacher attitude. *Journal of Special Education, 3*(3), 315–324.

LeAger, C., & Shapiro, E. (1995). Template matching as a strategy for assessment of and intervention for preschool students with disabilities. *Topics in Early Childhood Special Education, 15*(2), 187–218.

Lewis, R. B., & Doorlag, D. H. (1999). *Teaching special students in general education classrooms* (5th ed.). Columbus, OH: Merrill-Prentice Hall.

Lieber, J., Schwartz, I., Sandall, S., Horn, E., & Wolery, R. A. (1999). Curricular considerations for young children in inclusive settings. In C. Seefeldt (Ed.), *The early childhood curriculum: A review of current research.* New York: Teachers College Press.

Lipsky, D. K., & Gartner, A. (2001). Education reform and early childhood inclusion. In M. J. Guralnick (Ed.), *Early childhood inclusion: Focus on change* (pp. 39–48). Baltimore: Brookes.

Logan, K. R. (1996). *The research instructional lead teacher (RILT) model: A school system–university collaboration* [Funded by the U.S. Department of Education]. Lawrenceville, GA: Gwinnett County Public Schools.

Lyman, H. B. (1998). *Test scores and what they mean* (6th ed.). Boston: Allyn & Bacon.

Malone, D. M., Gallagher, P. A., & Long, S. R. (2001). General educators' attitudes and perceptions of teamwork supporting children with developmental concerns. *Early Education and Development, 12*(4), 577–592.

Malone, D. M., & Koblewski, P. (1999). A survey of professionals' attitudes and perceptions of teamwork supporting people with disabilities. *Journal of Developmental and Physical Disabilities, 11*(2), 77–89.

Malone, D. M., & Manders, J. (1995, June). *A rationale for family therapy specialization in early intervention.* 119th Annual Meeting of the American Association on Mental Retardation, San Francisco, CA.

Malone, D. M., McKinsey, P. D., Thyer, B. A., & Straka, E. (2000). Social work early intervention for young children with developmental concerns. *Health and Social Work: Journal of the National Association of Social Workers, 25*(3), 169–180.

Malone, D. M., & Orthner, D. K. (1988). Infant Care as a parent education resource: Recent trends in care issues. *Family Relations, 37*, 367–372.

Malone, D. M., & Troup, K. S. (2000). *Transitioning preschool children with developmental concerns to kindergarten: Social context and classroom ecology* [A Final Report Submitted to the Hamilton County Educational Service Center, Technical Report No. UC-ECE-00-01]. Cincinnati, OH: University of Cincinnati, Early Childhood Education Program.

Malone, D. M., & Troup, K. S. (2002). *Contextual factors supporting the transition of preschool children with developmental concerns into inclusive kindergarten programs.* Manuscript submitted for publication.

Malouf, D. B., & Schiller, E. P. (1995). Practice and research in special education. *Exceptional Children, 61*, 414–421.

McCall, R. B., & Plemons, B. W. (2001). The concept of critical periods and their implications for early childhood services. In D. B. Bailey, J. T. Bruer, F. J. Symons, & J. W. Lichtman (Eds.), *Critical thinking about critical periods* (pp. 267–288). Baltimore: Brookes.

McGonigel, M. J., Kaufmann, R. K., & Johnson, B. H. (1991). *Guidelines and recommended practices for the individualized family service plan* (2nd ed.). Chapel Hill, NC: National Early Childhood Technical Assistance System.

McLeskey, J., Henry, D., & Hodges, D. (1999). Inclusion: What progress is being made across disability categories? *Teaching Exceptional Children, 31*(3), 60–65.

McPherson, J. R., & Malone, D. M. (2002). *A comparison of community and medical early intervention team members' attitudes and perceptions of teamwork.* Manuscript submitted for publication.

McWilliam, R. A. (2000). Recommended practices in interdisciplinary models. In S. Sandall, M. McLean, & B. Smith (Eds.), *DEC recommended practices in early intervention/early childhood special education* (pp. 47–54). Longmont, CO: Sopris West.

Melton, G. B., Limber, S. P., & Teague, T. L. (1999). Changing schools for changing families. In R. C. Pianta & M. J. Cox (Eds.), *The transition to kindergarten* (pp. 179–213). Baltimore: Brookes.

National Association for the Education of Young Children. (1996). *Guidelines for preparation of early childhood professionals.* Washington, DC: Author.

National Association for the Education of Young Children. (1997). *Code of ethical conduct and statement of commitment.* Washington, DC: Author.

Pajares, M. F. (1992). Teacher's beliefs and educational research: Cleaning up a messy construct. *Review of Educational Research, 62*, 307–332.

Pfeiffer, S. I. (1980). The school-based interprofessional team: Recurring problems and some possible solutions. *Journal of School Psychology, 18,* 388–393.

Pfeiffer, S. I. (1981). The problems facing multidisciplinary teams: As perceived by team members. *Psychology in the Schools, 18,* 330–333.

Pfeiffer, S. I., & Heffernan, L. (1984). Improving multidisciplinary team functions. In C. A. Maher, R. Illback, & J. Zins (Eds.), *Organizational psychology in the school: A handbook for professionals* (pp. 283–301). Springfield, IL: Charles C. Thomas.

Pianta, R. C., & Cox, M. J. (Eds.). (1999). *The transition to kindergarten.* Baltimore: Brookes.

Pianta, R. C., & Walsh, D. J. (1996). *High-risk children in schools: Constructing sustaining relationships.* New York: Routledge.

Repetto, J. B., & Correa, V. I. (1996). Expanding views on transition. *Exceptional Children, 62*(6), 551–563.

Riley, R. W. (1999, January). *Teacher quality: A report on teacher preparation and qualifications.* Remarks prepared for the National Center for Education Statistics Press Conference (from the 6th Annual State of American Education Address), Washington, DC.

Rogers, J. (1993, May). The inclusion revolution. Research Bulletin No. 11, *Phi Delta Kappa,* pp. 4–9.

Rosenkoetter, S. E., Hains, A. H., & Fowler, S. A. (1994). *Bridging early services for children with special needs and their families: A practical guide for transition planning.* Baltimore: Brookes.

Rosin, P. (1996). The diverse American family. In P. Rosin, A. Whitehead, L. Tuchman, G. Jeisen, A. L. Begun, & L. Irwin (Eds.), *Partnerships in family-centered care: A guide to collaborative early intervention* (pp. 3–28). Baltimore: Brookes.

Rous, B., & Hallam, R. A. (1998). Easing the transition to kindergarten: Assessment of social, behavioral, and functional skills in young children with disabilities. *Young Exceptional Children, 1*(4), 17–26.

Rule, S., Fiechtl, B. J., & Innocenti, M. S. (1990). Preparation for transition to mainstreamed postpreschool environments: Development of a survival skills curriculum. *Topics in Early Childhood Special Education, 9,* 78–90.

Sainato, D. M., & Lyon, S. R. (1989). Promoting successful mainstreaming transitions for handicapped preschool children. *Journal of Early Intervention, 13*(4), 305–314.

Sameroff, A. J., & Chandler, M. J. (1975). Reproductive risk and the continuum of caretaking causality. In D. F. Horowitz, M. Hetherington, S. Scarr-Stepanik, & G. Seigel (Eds.), *Review of child development research* (Vol. 4, pp. 187–244). Chicago: University of Chicago Press.

Sandall, S., McLean, M., & Smith, B. (Eds.). (2000). *DEC recommended practices in early intervention/early childhood special education.* Longmont, CO: Sopris West.

Schwolwinski, E. J., Barsalou, A. B., & Wehner, T. M. (1999). *The special education guide for Texas school administrators.* San Antonio, TX: OMNI Publishers.

Scruggs, T. E., & Mastropieri, M. A. (1996). Teacher perceptions of mainstreaming/inclusion, 1958–1995: A research synthesis. *Exceptional Children, 63*(1), 59–74.

Shonkoff, J. P., & Meisels, S. J. (Eds.). (2000). *Handbook of early childhood intervention* (2nd ed.). Cambridge, UK: Cambridge University Press.

Spencer, P. E., & Coye, R. W. (1988). Project BRIDGE: A team approach to decision-making for early services. *Infants and Young Children, 1,* 82–92.

State Superintendent's Task Force for Preparing Special Education Personnel. (2001). *Report on the 1999–2000 special education personnel supply and demand survey.* Columbus, OH: Author.

Stein, M. K., & Wang, M. C. (1988). Teacher development and school improvement: The process of teacher change. *Teaching and Teacher Education, 4,* 171–187.

Thomas, C. C., Correa, V., & Morsink, C. (1995). *Interactive teaming: Enhancing programs for students with special needs* (2nd ed.). Upper Saddle River, NJ: Prentice Hall.

Trivette, C. M., & Dunst, C. J. (2000). Recommended practices in family-based practices. In S. Sandall, M. McLean, & B. Smith (Eds.), *DEC recommended practices in early intervention/early childhood special education* (pp. 39–46). Longmont, CO: Sopris West.

Turnbull, A. P., Summer, J. A., & Brotherson, M. J. (1984). *Working with families with disabled members: A family systems approach.* Lawrence: Kansas University Affiliated Facility, University of Kansas.

Turnbull, A. P., & Turnbull, R. H. (1997). *Families, professionals, and exceptionality: A special partnership.* Upper Saddle River, NJ: Prentice Hall.

U.S. Department of Education. (1996). *To assure the free appropriate public education of all children with disabilities: Eighteenth annual report to Congress on the implementation of the Individuals with Disabilities Education Act.* Washington, DC: Author.

U.S. Department of Education. (1998). *To assure the free appropriate public education of all children with disabilities: Twentieth annual report to Congress on the implementation of the Individuals with Disabilities Education Act.* Washington, DC: Author.

U.S. Department of Education. (2000). *To assure the free appropriate public education of all children with disabilities: Twenty-second annual report to Congress on the implementation of the Individuals with Disabilities Education Act.* Washington, DC: Author.

U.S. Department of Education. (2001). *To assure the free appropriate public education of all children with disabilities: Twenty-third annual report to Congress on the implementation of the Individuals with Disabilities Education Act.* Washington, DC: Author.

Wagner, C. (2001). *Study of personnel needs in special education.* Retrieved November 9, 2001, from www.spense.org

Whitehouse, F. A. (1951). Teamwork: A democracy of professions. *Exceptional Children, 18,* 45–52.

Winton, P. J., & McCollum, J. A. (1997). Ecological perspectives on personnel preparation: Rationale, framework, and guidelines for change. In P. J. Winton, J. McCollum, & C. Catlett (Eds.), *Reforming personnel preparation in early intervention: Issues, models, and practical strategies* (pp. 3–26). Baltimore: Brookes.

Wolery, M. (1989). Transitions in early childhood special education: Issues and procedures. *Focus on Exceptional Children, 22*(2), 1–16.

Wolery, M., Werts, M. G., Caldwell, N. K., Snyder, E. D., & Lisowski, L. (1995). Experienced teachers' perceptions of the resources and supports for inclusion. *Education and Training in Mental Retardation and Developmental Disabilities, 30*(1), 15–26.

Wood, J. W. (2002). *Adapting instruction to accommodate students in inclusive settings* (4th ed.). Columbus, OH: Merrill–Prentice Hall.

Yates, T., & Higgins-Hains, A. (1997). State perspectives on meeting personnel challenges: Closing the gap between vision and reality. In P. J. Winton, J. McCollum, & C. Catlett (Eds.), *Reforming personnel preparation in early intervention: Issues, models, and practical strategies* (pp. 27–52). Baltimore: Brookes.

Ysseldyke, J. E., Algozzine, B., & Mitchell, J. (1982). Special education team decision-making: Analysis of current practice. *The Personnel and Guidance Journal, 60,* 308–313.

Ysseldyke, J. E., Algozzine, B., Rostollan, D., & Shinn, M. (1981). A content analysis of the data presented at special education placement team meetings. *Journal of Clinical Psychology, 37,* 655–662.

Zill, N. (1999). Promoting educational equity and excellence in kindergarten. In R. C. Pianta & M. J. Cox (Eds.), *The transition to kindergarten* (pp. 67–105). Baltimore: Brookes.

CHAPTER 3

Going to School

Colleen A. Thoma and Paul Sale

LEARNING GOALS

Upon completion of this chapter, the reader will be able to

- list and describe the key elements of the Individuals with Disabilities Education Act Amendments of 1997 (IDEA)
- describe the No Child Left Behind legislation and its impact on the education of students with disabilities
- describe the use of a universal-design-for-learning approach to education and its impact on educating students with disabilities as well as their inclusion in the general education classroom
- describe the Individualized Education Program (IEP) and the process for development and implementation

n this chapter, we focus on how to select and deliver the most appropriate special education supports and services for students with developmental disabilities. Special educators must understand the legal requirements for providing special education as well as the most effective instructional techniques and strategies. Many strategies will be covered in detail in other chapters of this text, so our focus will be on the legal requirements for education and the use of a universal-design-for-learning approach to providing an individualized education based on the general education curriculum. Before examining the legal requirements, we introduce Jonathan, whose education will be discussed in relation to various points throughout this chapter.

 ## CASE EXAMPLE: JONATHAN

Jonathan is a 9-year-old boy who has cerebral palsy, which results in muscle tightness (spasticity) that prevents him from speaking, walking, and standing on his own. He uses a manual wheelchair for mobility because he does not have enough muscle control to use an electric one. Jonathan has limited ability to move his head, arms, and torso but tires easily from the effort. He receives special education at the neighborhood elementary school, having qualified under the criteria for both intellectual disability (severe) and physical disabilities. His special education teacher believes that Jonathan knows much more than he is able to communicate and that his true abilities are much greater than his assessment and evaluation results indicate. Jonathan appears to be aware of everything that is happening around him. He laughs appropriately at jokes, even those that are subtle. He watches what others are doing, even when he should be doing his own work. His speech–language therapist recommended that he be evaluated for medication to control his distractibility, but his teacher believes that he is merely bored with the eye-gaze board.

Jonathan spends the majority of his day in a classroom for students with cognitive disabilities who have extensive support needs. His goals primarily focus on functional skills such as communication (using an eye-gaze board to answer yes or no questions), attending to tasks, increasing his fine-motor skills, and recognizing functional sight words such as *exit, stop,* and *boy's restroom.* For math, his goal is to recognize coins. He spends less time with peers without disabilities than others in this class because he has a difficult time participating in classes such as music, art, and physical education, given his physical disabilities. He has not been taught to use a computer or a more high-tech communication device because he has not mastered the eye-gaze board.

Jonathan's story is not very different from those of students with developmental disabilities in schools across the country. There are many challenges to providing him with an appropriate education that includes access to the general education curriculum and meeting his unique needs. Does the education that Jonathan is receiving meet the legal requirements, and is it in keeping with the recommendations for educating students with disabilities that exist in the research literature? The answer to both of those questions is no. Although Jonathan's educational experience may have minimally met the legal requirements of an earlier version of the special education law, it does not meet the requirements of the IDEA amendments passed in 1997. After we examine the legal requirements, we provide a revised educational scenario for Jonathan that meets the letter of the law and subsequent court decisions.

LEGAL ASPECTS OF SPECIAL EDUCATION

Since passage of P.L. 94-142, the Education for All Handicapped Children Act of 1975 (EHA), different laws have guided the education of students with and without disabilities. That changed with the passage of the No Child Left Behind Act of 2001 (NCLB). The provisions of this law have a direct impact on the education of all students, with and without disabilities. Some of the major provisions of NCLB are outlined in Table 3.1, but the most significant ones for special education include the requirements that all students must take state-developed tests in the areas of reading and math and that they must pass all requirements for graduation by the age of 18.

Clearly, Jonathan's goals related to reading and math are not in line with what students without disabilities are learning. In fact, it could be argued that Jonathan's teachers are failing in their attempts to teach him reading and math. The issue has more to do with his inability to communicate his true abilities than a lack of ability or potential to learn to read or complete mathematical computations. By failing to make progress in that area, he is unlikely to pass graduation tests in the areas of reading and math by the age of 18.

The requirements of NCLB legislation are added to (and at times contradict) the requirements for special education that are part of P.L. 105-17, the Individuals with Disabilities Act Amendments of 1997. It is important to note that this law is an amendment to EHA and its subsequent amendments. EHA guaranteed that all students with disabilities had the right to a free and appropriate public education in the least restrictive environment possible based on an Individualized Education Program. Subsequent amendments to that original law added such provisions as early intervention services for infants (P.L. 99-457, 1986), services to prepare students for the transition from school to adult life (P.L. 101-476, 1990), and access to the general education curriculum (P.L. 105-17). Table 3.2 describes the major components of each of these reauthorizations to EHA.

Although the IDEA Amendments of 1997 required students with disabilities to have access to the general education curriculum and an opportunity to be involved in all state-mandated tests, the No Child Left Behind law added more emphasis to this requirement. This law requires that schools include the standardized test scores of students with disabilities with the report cards of schools, districts, and states. The conflict between traditional special education supports and services and the newer provisions of NCLB and the 1997 reauthorization of IDEA is the conflict between an education that is designed specifically for an individual student and one that is more closely aligned with the education for all students. At this time, both must receive equal consideration by a student's

TABLE 3.1

Major Provisions of the No Child Left Behind Act of 2001

Component	Stronger Accountability for Results	Flexibility	Concentrating Resources on Proven Methods	More Choices for Parents
State	State report cards. States are responsible for having strong academic standards for what every child should know and learn in reading, math, and science for elementary, middle, and high schools. Beginning in the 2002–03 school year, all schools must administer tests in each of three grade spans: 3–5, 6–9, and 10–12. Beginning in the 2005–06 school year, tests must be administered every year in Grades 3 through 8. Beginning in the 2007–08 school year, science achievement must also be tested.	States will have more freedom to direct more of their federal education money. That means local people will have more say about which programs they think will help their students the most.	In 2002, $900 million was distributed to states for the president's Reading First plan. Federal dollars were tied to programs that use scientifically proven ways of teaching children to read.	
District	District report cards. Districts must decrease the achievement gap between students of various groups.		Communities will benefit from a federally funded program called Early Reading First. This program will help develop language and reading skills in preschool children, especially those from low-income families.	In 2002, approximately $200 million in federal funds were made available to state and local communities to help establish and fund charter schools.

(continues)

TABLE 3.1 *Continued.*
Major Provisions of the No Child Left Behind Act of 2001

Component	Stronger Accountability for Results	Flexibility	Concentrating Resources on Proven Methods	More Choices for Parents
School	School report cards. Schools must develop a plan to improve the academic performance of all students.	No Child Left Behind attempted to combine and simplify programs, so that schools do not have to cut through as much red tape to get and use federal funding.	Schools and teachers get a boost from the more than $4 billion in 2002 that allows schools to promote teacher quality through training and recruitment.	For the first time, parents with children in a school identified as in need of improvement will be able to use federal education funds for what are called "supplemental education services." Those services include tutoring, after-school services, and summer school programs.
Student	All students must perform at a proficient level under state standards.			Parents with a child enrolled in a school identified as in need of improvement will be able to transfer their child to a better-performing public school or public charter school.

educational planning team. This team must include the special educator, a general education teacher, an administrator, the student's parents, and the student if the plan includes a focus on the transition from school to adult life.

Although laws such as the IDEA Amendments of 1997 provide a basic framework, educators and administrators also rely on the courts to make decisions about discrepancies or gray areas. Such decisions have further reinforced the components of IDEA and have for the most part reinforced the rights of students with disabilities to receive an appropriate education in classrooms with their peers without disabilities whenever possible. Table 3.3 outlines some of the most important court cases and their rulings (see also Culatta, Tompkins, & Werts, 2003; Kirk, Gallagher, & Anastasiow, 2003; Heward, 2000; Meyen, 1996; Oakstone Legal and Business Publishing, 1999; Turnbull & Turnbull, 2000).

TABLE 3.2

Changes in Special Education Based on Reauthorization Amendments

Education for All Handicapped Children Act of 1975 (P.L. 94-142)	Education of the Handicapped Act Amendments of 1986 (P.L. 99-457)	Individuals with Disabilities Education Act of 1990 (IDEA, P.L. 101-476)	Individuals with Disabilities Education Act Amendments of 1997 (P.L. 105-17)
Eligibility			
Stated that students (ages 3 to 21) are eligible for special education services if they have a disability that substantially interferes with their learning and education. Disability categories include learning disabilities, emotional disturbance, mental retardation, physical disabilities, vision impairments, hearing impairments, deaf-blindness, communication and language disorders, multiple disabilities, other health impairments.	Added early intervention services for infants (0–3 years old).	Added autism and traumatic brain injury as disability categories.	Required that all students with disabilities have "access to the general education curriculum." This meant that students with disabilities were to have an Individualized Education Program with specific goals and objectives based on what others were learning in the same age or grade level. Any changes from the general education curriculum were to be described and explained.
Services			
Stated that a continuum of services must be available to respond to individual needs of students.	Required services to be provided in the setting that is most typical (often the family's home).	Added a requirement for transition planning and services for students ages 14 and older. Plans must be based on student preferences and interests for an adult lifestyle.	Required students to be involved in state- or district-wide standardized assessments (or an alternative test to measure progress).

(continues)

Despite the introduction of the NCLB legislation, the provisions of the IDEA Amendments of 1997 provide more extensive guidelines to consider when providing special education for students with disabilities. This law is divided into sections, or "parts," that focus on a specific segment of the law. Part A describes the rationale and guiding principles behind the law. Part B focuses on the education of students between the ages of 3 and 21, whereas Part C pertains to

TABLE 3.2 *Continued.*
Changes in Special Education Based on Reauthorization Amendments

Education for All Handicapped Children Act of 1975 (P.L. 94-142)	Education of the Handicapped Act Amendments of 1986 (P.L. 99-457)	Individuals with Disabilities Education Act of 1990 (IDEA, P.L. 101-476)	Individuals with Disabilities Education Act Amendments of 1997 (P.L. 105-17)
Parent Involvement			
Provided for parents to be involved in planning educational goals and services, and gave them the right to due process.	Required an Individualized Family Services Plan (IFSP) in place of an Individualized Education Program (IEP).	Added assistive technology as a service, and required that it must be considered during IEP development.	Required students to have a manifest determination review to determine whether behavior problems existed due to their disability. If so, they could not be suspended or subject to other disciplinary actions, but would need to have a behavioral intervention plan.
Students with Challenging Behavior			
Required that nondiscriminatory assessment be used to establish eligibility and develop educational plans.		Provided for students to "stay put" during due process hearings.	Required that students who engaged in challenging behaviors have a functional assessment of the behavior and a behavioral intervention plan developed based on that assessment.

the education of children with disabilities between birth and age 2. Part D outlines provisions for supporting research, training, and model demonstration projects to further improve the education of children with disabilities.

GUIDING PRINCIPLES

The IDEA Amendments of 1997 have six guiding principles that govern special education, outlined in Part A of the law. The first of these principles, *zero reject*, refers to the requirement that all students with disabilities are entitled to receive an education, regardless of the severity of their disability or the significance of their need for supports. For Jonathan, that means that his parents could not be told that he could not attend public school because he has cerebral palsy and

(*text continues on page 102*)

TABLE 3.3

Major Court Decisions Impacting Special Education

Case	Year	Ruling
Brown v. Board of Education	1954	The concept of separate but equal schools is unconstitutional; all children must have equal opportunity for education.
Diana v. Board of Education	1970	(California) schools could not place students in special education on the basis of culturally biased tests or tests given in a student's non-primary language.
Pennsylvania Association for Retarded Children v. Commonwealth of Pennsylvania	1972	A child with mental retardation could not be excluded from school in the state of Pennsylvania.
Mills v. Board of Education	1972	All students with disabilities are entitled to a public education in the District of Columbia; a lack of funding is not an excuse for failing to provide educational services to exceptional children.
Wyatt v. Stickney	1972	Children with disabilities who are committed to state institutions must be provided with a meaningful education in that setting, or their incarceration is considered unlawful detention.
Larry P. v. Riles	1979	Children should not be labeled as having a disability or placed into special education without adequate diagnosis that takes into account different cultural and linguistic backgrounds.
Jos P. v. Ambach	1979	Bilingual exceptional children need identification, evaluation, and educational procedures that reflect and respect their dual-language background.
Frederick L. v. Thomas	1980	An individual with learning disabilities has a right to services whatever his or her age.
Board of Education v. Rowley	1982	A child with disabilities is entitled to an appropriate, not optimum, education.
Abrahamson v. Hershman	1983	Residential placement in a private school is necessary for a child with multiple disabilities who needs around-the-clock training; the school district is required to pay for the private placement.
Irving Independent School District v. Tatro	1984	Medical procedures that could be performed by a nonphysician qualify as related services, not medical services, and must be provided by the school district so that a child can attend school and benefit from special education.

(continues)

TABLE 3.3 *Continued.*
Major Court Decisions Impacting Special Education

Case	Year	Ruling
Department of Education v. Katerine D.	1984	A homebound instructional program for a child with multiple health impairments does not meet the least-restrictive-environment standard; the child must be placed in a class with children without disabilities and provided with related medical services.
Smith v. Robinson	1984	The state must pay for the placement of a child with severe disabilities in a residential program; the school district must reimburse the parents' attorney fees.
Polk v. Central Susquehanna Intermediate Unit 16	1988	Educational services, although not optimum, must be adequate to ensure that the student can benefit from his or her education.
Honig v. Doe	1988	A student receiving special education services cannot be excluded from school indefinitely (expelled), particularly if the student's behavior is related to a disability.
Timothy W. v. Rochester School District	1989	All children with disabilities are entitled to a free appropriate public education (FAPE), unconditionally and without exception. This over-turned the decision of a district court judge that the local school district was not obligated to educate a 13-year-old boy with multiple and severe disabilities because he could not benefit from special education.
Barnett v. Fairfax County Board of Education	1991	A child with a hearing disability could attend a school several miles from home instead of a neighborhood school because the centralized program at the special school better met the child's needs.
Greer v. Rome City School District	1991	A child with Down syndrome could be placed in a general education classroom rather than in a special education class because of a pre-sumed priority of inclusion in IDEA.
Holland v. Board of Education, Sacramento City Unified School District	1992	School district must accept an 11-year-old girl with an IQ of 44 in a general education classroom. In accessing the inclusion placement, the court considered benefits derived from full-time placement in general classrooms, nonacademic benefits, the impact of the exceptional stu-dent's presence on other students, and the costs of placement.
Community Consolidated School District No. 21 v. Illinois State Board of Education	1991	Compensatory education may be awarded to an individual with a disability after age 21 if an appropriate education was denied during tenure in public education.
Teado v. Strongsville City School District	1991	Compensatory education may be awarded to an individual with a disability after age 21 if an appropriate education was denied during tenure in public education.

(continues)

TABLE 3.3 *Continued.*
Major Court Decisions Impacting Special Education

Case	Year	Ruling
Oberti v. Board of Education of the Borough of Clementon School District	1992	Inclusion is a right, not a privilege; to learn to function effectively, all children with disabilities need integration experiences.
Clyde & Shela K. v. Puyallup School District	1994	A child with a serious attention deficit and acting-out behavior should be placed in a special school rather than in the general education classroom.
Mary P. v. Illinois State Board of Education	1996	Academic achievement may be a component of an eligibility decision but might not form the sole basis for the determination.
Frank S. v. School Committee of Dennis–Yarmouth Regional School District	1998	After graduation, the student was no longer eligible for FAPE because the school had discharged its duties in fulfilling the IEP.
Walczak v. Florida Union Free School District	1998	Although IDEA does not establish any level of academic achievement for an IEP, the courts may look at passing grades and test scores to determine appropriateness.
Cedar Rapids v. Garret F.	1999	Local school district must pay for the one-on-one nursing care for a medically fragile student who required continuous monitoring of his ventilator and other health-maintenance routines.

requires technology to support his education. Jonathan's education clearly meets this principle of IDEA.

The second principle is that of *nondiscriminatory evaluation,* the requirement that any evaluation used to determine whether someone has a disability must be conducted in the individual's native language and use testing instruments that have been determined to be free from racial, cultural, and ethnic biases. If Jonathan and his family spoke Spanish instead of English, his evaluation would need to be conducted in Spanish. Jonathan does need to use an alternative form of communication, and it should be used throughout the evaluation process. The use of augmentative or alternative communication systems has not been adequately addressed in relation to the principle of nondiscriminatory evaluation, so Jonathan's education meets this principle of IDEA as it is currently stated.

The third principle, *appropriate education,* refers to the individualization of education, to providing educational supports and services that meet a student's needs as determined by a team. Although the law requires that this education be based on the general education curriculum, the specific needs of an individual student must also be addressed. Students like Jonathan who have a cognitive or intellectual disability need to receive support in learning adaptive skills in addition to academics, because the disability impacts both cognitive and adaptive abilities. Jonathan's education does address his functional needs as understood from the results of his nondiscriminatory evaluation. However, it does not provide ample opportunities for Jonathan to access the general education curriculum, either in an inclusive or a separate setting. Nor does it provide an adequate communication focus. Therefore, it could be reasonably argued that Jonathan's education fails to meet the principle of appropriate education.

The fourth principle, *least restrictive environment* (LRE), requires that educational supports and services be provided in typical settings, unless the student requires more intensive supports. More and more students with disabilities are being educated in general education classrooms, alongside students without disabilities. Performance data related to students with disabilities released by the Office of Special Education Programs included the settings in which they receive their education. During the 1998–1999 school year, settings varied across disability categories. Students with speech or language impairments and specific learning disabilities continued to be served predominantly in the regular classroom for most of the school day. Students with emotional disturbance, cognitive disabilities, and multiple disabilities were more likely to receive services outside the regular classroom for more than 60% of the school day (U.S. Department of Education, 2003). This principle presumes that inclusive options will be provided, and that supplementary aids and services will be used to support an inclusive education. Only when a student's educational needs cannot be met despite the use of appropriate supplementary aids and services should more segregated options be considered (R. Turnbull, Turnbull, Shank, Smith, & Leal, 2002).

Jonathan spent the majority of the day in a self-contained classroom for students with disabilities—not all options for supplementary aids and services had been considered. The communication system would not provide him either with access to the general education curriculum or with the communication ability necessary to succeed in a general education classroom. Too often, special education starts from the restrictive setting and attempts to move to a less restrictive one. The principle of LRE, however, requires the opposite strategy, that the student start in the least restrictive setting, with appropriate supports, and move to a more restrictive setting if and only if the student is not receiving educational benefit. Jonathan's education does not meet the principle of least restrictive environment.

The fifth principle is *procedural due process*. Due process refers to the procedures put in place to ensure fair dealing and accountability. There are specific procedures to ensure that parents agree with school personnel regarding the individualized education for their son or daughter, and that parents have the opportunity to mediate disagreements. Of course, parents must be made aware of the due process procedure as well as other options that could affect the education of their son or daughter. In Jonathan's case, the current members of his educational planning team do not have other choices for his educational goals, educational placement, or supplementary aids and services (especially his need for an alternative communication system).

TABLE 3.4

Steps of the Referral and Assessment Process

Step	Explanation	Teacher Interventions
Assessment: Before prereferral	This is done by the general education classroom teacher, who collects information about all students and their progress in learning the curriculum as well as inter- actions between the students and their environment(s).	A general education teacher often makes adjustments to the environment, to teaching methods, and to teaching materials when students are not successfully meeting the educational or environmental demands of the classroom. Changes are targeted for all, not for a specific child.
Assessment: Prereferral	If a student continues to have difficulty after changes are implemented, a closer look is taken at the individual child, generally by the general education teacher in consultation with a prereferral team.	Changes in instructional strategies and methods, behavior management strategies, and environmental changes may be rec- ommended by the preferral team and implemented by the teacher. Information is then collected about student progress after implementation of these changes.
Assessment: Referral	When prereferral strategies are insufficient, a referral can be initiated by the classroom teacher based on documentation of the prereferral process and student response to the implementation of these strategies.	Information is presented based on the prereferral process. Information about student concerns (if any) from parents is included. A special education referral team screens all referrals and decides on the next stage of the process.
Assessment: Formal assessment	A determination of a student's disability is made, as well as the degree to which the disability impacts the student's ability to learn and participate in the educational environment.	A multidisciplinary team works together to conduct the formal assessment. The team, including the parents, decides what assessments need to be conducted and who should administer them.
Eligibility determination	A multidisciplinary team, including the par- ents, reviews the assessment data and deter- mines (a) whether thestudent qualifies as having a disability and (b) whether the stu- ent requires specialized education to learn.	Both a general education and a special education teacher can be members of this multidisciplinary team.

(continues)

The final principle is that of *parent participation.* This principle refers to a process of shared decision making, which parents are an integral part of, from initial referral for testing to the assessment and evaluation process and through the process of developing the Individualized Education Program. Table 3.4 out- lines the steps of the referral and assessment process. Parents must be informed of and give consent for each step of the process.

TABLE 3.4 *Continued.*
Steps of the Referral and Assessment Process

Step	Explanation	Teacher Interventions
Development of the IEP	A multidisciplinary team meets annually to determine educational goals for the student, based on assessment data, the general education curriculum, and parent concerns. Assistive technology must be considered for all students with disabilities. Students who engage in challenging behavior must have a functional assessment prior to a behavior plan. When their transition plan is discussed, the students themselves must be members of the multidisciplinary team.	The general education teacher provides information about the general education curriculum, the environmental demands of the general education classroom, and other components of the school. This helps with making decisions about participating in the general education classroom with peers and the degree to which the student may need additional supports or modifications. The special education teacher provides information about assistive technology, adapting curriculum, instructional strategies, and behavior support plans.
Ongoing evaluation	Information is gathered about student progress on annual IEP goals and the general education curriculum (including participation in standardized tests).	The general education teacher collects information about student progress on curricular goals and annual goals that are implemented in the general education classrooms. The special educator collects additional information about student progress on goals.

Both of Jonathan's parents were informed about his evaluation for services, the development of his IEP, and the annual review and update of the plan. This principle was met. When Jonathan reaches the age of majority (typically the age of 18), he will assume this responsibility should he need to continue his education through the age of 21.

Part B is the section of the IDEA Amendments of 1997 that outlines guidelines for providing education to students with disabilities between the ages of 6 and 21. Not only does the law identify categories of disabilities that qualify students to receive special education services, it also outlines procedures for determining which students with disabilities qualify for services, the types of services and supports that can be included, and the process for developing an IEP for a student with disabilities.

ELIGIBILITY FOR SERVICES

Students who qualify for special education must meet two requirements. First, they must meet the qualifications for a specific disability category, as described in the definition. Disability categories include the following: specific learning disabilities, emotional disturbance, intellectual disability, autism, other health impairments, orthopedic impairments, traumatic brain injury, speech or language impairments, hearing impairments, and visual impairments. Second, students must need specific educational services as a result of that disability. If the disability does not impact their ability to learn the general education curriculum in a general education classroom, they do not qualify for special education. For instance, many students with visual impairments are able to wear glasses or contact lenses to correct their vision. Their visual impairment does not require any additional educational or related services for them to benefit from their education.

How many children and youth are now receiving special education services? This is important information for planning by the states and for funding local school programs. According to the Office of Special Education Programs (U.S. Department of Education, 2003), 5,683,707 students with disabilities were served in the United States during the school year of 1999–2000. Approximately 11% were identified with intellectual disability and 51% with a specific learning disability. Table 3.5 presents the total numbers of students and the change in numbers from the 1990–1991 school year within the 13 categories that the U.S. Department of Education uses to track students. Many of these disability categories are fully or at least partially discussed in this volume under the broader category of developmental disability.

Diversity is an important issue to discuss related to the number of students receiving special education. It can be argued that students from diverse cultural and linguistic backgrounds are more likely to be identified as having a disability that requires special education services. The data from the Office of Special Education and Rehabilitative Services demonstrate that for some diverse groups this is the case, and for others it is not. Asian–Pacific Islander students were underrepresented among the students served under IDEA. Hispanic students and, to a lesser extent, White (non-Hispanic) students overall also were underrepresented compared to their relative representation in the estimated resident population. African American students, however, were overrepresented in special education across all disability categories. In addition, the representation of American Indian and Alaska Native students with disabilities slightly exceeded their representation in the resident population in most disability categories. Table 3.6 describes the data on students with various disabilities and their ethnic and racial backgrounds.

What does this mean for special education services? It calls for an examination into the reasons these over- and underrepresentations occur, and the first consideration is whether the evaluation process is discriminatory. In the court case, *Larry P. v. Riles* (1972), a federal judge in California ruled that standardized IQ tests could not be used to determine eligibility for special education. This ruling was made because the standardized tests of the day were validated on White students and therefore discriminated against students from other backgrounds. Changes to these standardized IQ tests have been made to eliminate the racial bias, but the overrepresentation of students from African American backgrounds has continued. Research is being conducted to answer the lingering questions,

TABLE 3.5

Number of Students Ages 6 Through 21 Served Under IDEA
by Disability Category, 1990–1991 and 1999–2000

Disability Category	1990–1991	1999–2000	Difference	Change (%)
Specific learning disabilities	2,144,017	2,871,966	727,949	34.0
Speech or language impairments	987,778	1,089,964	102,186	10.3
Mental retardation	551,457	614,433	62,976	11.4
Emotional disturbance	390,764	470,111	79,347	20.3
Multiple disabilities	97,629	112,993	15,364	15.7
Hearing impairments	59,211	71,671	12,460	21.0
Orthopedic impairments	49,340	71,422	22,082	44.8
Other health impairments	56,349	254,110	197,761	351.0
Visual impairments	23,682	26,590	2,908	12.3
Autism[a]	—	65,424	—	—
Deaf–blindness	1,524	1,845	321	21.1
Traumatic brain injury[a]	—	13,874	—	—
Developmental delay[b]	—	19,304	—	—
All disabilities	4,361,751	5,683,707	1,321,956	30.3

Note. From the U.S. Department of Education, Office of Special Education Programs,
Data Analysis System (DANS), 2002.

[a]Reporting on autism and traumatic brain injury was first required in 1992–1993.

[b]Optional reporting on developmental delay for students ages 3 through 7 was first allowed
in the 1997–1998 school year.

but the question of bias must be addressed whenever students are evaluated for
special education.

TYPES OF SERVICES THAT CAN BE PROVIDED

Prior to the reauthorization of IDEA in 1997, the special education services provided for students with disabilities were based on the assessment data of an individual student. For many students with disabilities, these services were provided
without much connection to what students without disabilities of the same age
were learning. This disconnection between general and special education occurred so that services could be tailored to meet the needs of students with disabilities. However, the improved outcomes that were anticipated by taking this
individualized approach did not occur. Instead, the National Longitudinal Study
(Wagner, D'Amico, Marder, Newman, & Blackorby, 1992) demonstrated that

TABLE 3.6

Percentage of Students Ages 6 Through 21 Served, by Disability Category
and Race or Ethnicity, 1999–2000 School Year

Disability	American Indian and Alaska Native	Asian–Pacific Islander	Black (non-Hispanic)	Hispanic	White (non-Hispanic)
Specific learning disabilities	1.4	1.6	18.4	16.6	62.1
Speech or language impairments	1.2	2.4	16.1	12.7	67.6
Mental retardation	1.1	1.8	34.2	9.1	53.8
Emotional disturbance	1.1	1.2	27.3	8.9	61.5
Multiple disabilities	1.5	2.3	20.0	11.5	64.8
Hearing impairments	1.3	4.6	16.4	17.9	59.8
Orthopedic impairments	0.8	3.0	14.7	14.8	66.8
Other health impairments	1.1	1.4	14.9	8.0	74.7
Visual impairments	1.1	3.5	18.6	14.0	62.9
Autism	0.7	4.8	20.5	9.2	64.9
Deaf–blindness	2.0	7.5	24.7	11.2	54.6
Traumatic brain injury	1.6	2.4	16.9	10.5	68.5
Developmental delay	0.9	0.8	30.5	4.1	63.7
All disabilities	1.3	1.8	20.3	13.7	62.9
Resident population	1.0	3.8	14.5	16.2	64.5

Note. Due to rounding, rows may not sum to 100%. Race and ethnicity distributions exclude outlying areas because current population estimates by race and ethnicity were not available for those areas. Population counts are July 1999 estimates from the U.S. Census Bureau.

students with disabilities were dropping out of high school at higher numbers than their peers without disabilities, were not going on for postsecondary educational opportunities, and were not being employed in sufficient numbers to justify this different approach to education.

As a result of these findings, the IDEA Amendments of 1997 required that the education of students with disabilities be based on the general education curriculum. This requirement

> assures that what is taught to students with disabilities during the school day is directly related or tied to what their peers without disabilities are required to learn. This change mandated that not only were students with disabilities to learn what all students learn, they were to participate in the same district-wide or state-wide assessments as students without disabilities. (Thoma, Ligon, & Wittig, 2004, p. 95)

In addition, this access to the general education curriculum is presumed to include the informal aspects of the general education experience, including participating in extracurricular activities (Wehmeyer, 2002), although the majority of the focus is on the formal, state-mandated general education curriculum.

The Center for Applied Special Technology, or CAST (Rose & Meyer, 2002), outlines three essential features of universal design for learning:

- multiple means of representing content or material
- multiple means of expression to allow students to respond with their preferred method
- multiple means of engagement to spark interest and increase motivation

Although the focus at this point is typically on academic curriculum, it is easy to see that functional activities can be infused to benefit all students. Many students find their educational experiences unfulfilling because they cannot understand why they have to learn a particular subject. When instruction is tied to real life, students are often more motivated to learn. In particular, when instruction is tied to job skills, all students report increased motivation and are less likely to drop out (the ultimate disengagement from school) (e.g., Saddler, Thoma, & Whiston, 2002). For many students with disabilities, such changes to curriculum, instruction, and assessment may be all that is required to ensure access to the general education curriculum.

Access to the general education curriculum does not necessarily mean that the team cannot make many of the same decisions for a student's education program that it made before the change. Students can still have functional goals in their educational program, they can still receive their education in the most appropriate environment, and they can still receive any necessary therapy they require to benefit from their education. It does mean that decisions are based on helping students with disabilities participate in the same educational experiences as students without disabilities, not merely in the same settings.

THE INDIVIDUALIZED EDUCATION PROGRAM

All students identified as having a disability and needing educational supports must have an Individualized Education Program developed annually. This is a requirement of the IDEA Amendments of 1997. The IEP must be a written statement, developed by a team that consists of the following members:

- a representative of the local education agency or of an intermediate education unit who is qualified to provide, or supervise the production of, specifically designed instruction to meet the student's unique needs
- the teacher
- the student's parents or guardians
- whenever appropriate, the student

While the IEP is meant to individualize the education provided to a student with a disability, the IDEA Amendments of 1997 do outline some basic requirements for it. These requirements include the following:

- A statement of the child's present levels of performance, including how the child's disability affects involvement and progress in the general curriculum.
- A statement of measurable annual goals, including benchmarks or short-term objectives related to meeting the child's needs that result from the disability. The annual goals should enable the child to be involved and make progress in the general curriculum and meet each of the child's other educational needs that result from the disability.
- A statement of the special education and related services and supplementary aids or services to be provided to, or on behalf of, the child. The statement must include (a) any program modifications or supports for school personnel that will be provided for the child to advance appropriately toward attaining the annual goals, (b) how the child will be involved and progress in the general curriculum and participate in extracurricular and other nonacademic activities, (c) how the child will be educated and participate with other children with disabilities as well as nondisabled children, and (d) an explanation of the extent, if any, to which the child will not participate with nondisabled children in the regular (general education) class and in the activities listed above.
- A statement of any individual modifications in the administration of state- or district-wide assessments of student achievement that are needed in order for the child to participate in such assessment. If the IEP team determines that the child will not participate in a particular state- or district-wide assessment of student achievement (or part of such an assessment), there must be a statement of why that assessment is not appropriate for the child and how the child will be assessed.
- The projected date for the beginning of services and modifications, and the anticipated frequency, location, and duration of those services and modifications.
- A statement of how the child's progress toward the annual goals will be measured and how the child's parents will be regularly informed (by means such as periodic report cards), at least as often as parents are informed of their nondisabled children's progress, of their child's progress toward the annual goals. The statement should include the extent to which that progress is sufficient to enable the child to achieve the goals by the end of the year. (IDEA 1997, P.L. 105-17, Section 614[d])

RELATED SERVICES

The Individuals with Disabilities Education Act Amendments (1997) require that professionals provide related services in coordination with special education services. Related services are defined as follows:

Related services include transportation and such developmental, corrective, and other supportive services as are required to assist a child with a disability to benefit from special education, and includes speech pathology and audiology, and psychological services, physical and occupational therapy, recreation, early identification and assessment of disabilities in children, medical and counseling services, including rehabilitation counseling, except that such medical services should be for diagnostic and evaluation purposes only. The term also includes school health services, social work services in schools, and parent counseling and training. (Section 300.16)

Related services, like special education services in general, work best when the services are integrated across a student's academic day rather than provided in isolation (e.g., Rainforth & York-Barr, 1997). A student like Jonathan, who has limited communication skills, needs to learn to communicate in all environments and with multiple partners. Therefore, the special education teacher, teaching assistants, and other general education teachers and staff who interact with Jonathan on a regular or infrequent basis must be able to understand his messages and know that he has understood their messages as well. It does not help Jonathan to benefit from his education if the only person who can do that is the speech–language therapist who works with him for an hour at a time, 2 days a week.

ASSISTIVE TECHNOLOGY

The IDEA Amendments of 1997 included a statement that the IEP team must "consider whether [a] child needs assistive technology devices and services" (Section 614[d]). This requirement for every child receiving special education was a departure from past requirements that IEP teams determine which students required assistive technology devices or services. Assistive technology was defined by IDEA (1990) as "any item, piece of equipment or product system, whether acquired or commercially off the shelf, modified or customized, that is used to increase, maintain, or improve the functional capabilities of children with disabilities" (20 U.S.C. 1401 [25], Section 300.5). Assistive technology services refer to any services that "directly assist a child with a disability in the selection, acquisition or use of an assistive technology device" (20 U.S.C. 1401 [25], Section 300.6). This can include training on the use of the device for teacher, student, and parent; programming of high-technology devices; maintenance and service of devices; assessment; and efforts to find or coordinate funding (Flippo, Inge, & Barcus, 1995).

Assistive technology can have a variety of applications in the classroom and can meet a variety of needs. Students with disabilities may require assistive technology for mobility in order to benefit from their education (moving from classroom to classroom); others may require assistive technology for communication so that they can "tell" others what they have learned. There are many ways to describe assistive technology, but most describe it by the degree of complexity as well as by its primary use. "Low tech" refers to devices that are passive or simple, with few moving parts (Mann & Lane, 1991). Examples include picture communication boards, pointers, and switches. "High tech" refers to devices that are complex and typically have electronic components (Inge & Shepherd, 1995). Examples include voice output communication aides (VOCAs), electric wheelchairs, universal remote controls, and computers. Typically, the complexity of assistive technology devices can be conceptualized as a continuum from low or "no tech" to high tech.

There are many different kinds of assistive technology available that can be considered for use in educational environments. Computers and software are two commercially available products that can significantly support the education of a student with disabilities and, in particular, his or her access to the general education curriculum. Alternative input and output devices such as alternative keyboards, voice input devices, screen readers, touch windows, and joysticks can help a student with physical or cognitive disabilities use a computer for education, for communication, and even to interact with his or her environment. For instance, a laptop computer that has voice output could be used as a communication system in the classroom as well as other settings. A laptop computer equipped with an infrared system can be used as a remote control with electronics, appliances, and even household alarms. Table 3.7 lists typical uses for assistive technology and examples of low-tech and high-tech items that can be used.

TABLE 3.7
Assistive Technology Uses and Examples

Use	Low-Technology Examples	High-Technology Examples
Positioning and mobility	Foam pillows	Global positioning system
Educational	Wide-ruled paper	Cowriter (word prediction) software
Daily living	Picture recipe	Quicken (computerized budget and bill-paying) software
Communication	Tape recorder	Dynavox
Aural	Sign language interpreter	Braille printer
Visual	Glasses	JAWS (screen-reader) software
Work	Calendar	Pocket PC (or PDA) with voice output to keep track of schedule
Transportation	Enlarged bus schedule	Van with motorized lift
Personal care	Toothbrush with a built-up handle	Pocket PC with voice output that provides reminders for tasks such as shaving
Recreation	Playing-card holder	E-mail program that allows the use of pictures instead of names for "buddies"

For Jonathan, a laptop computer that has voice output, a switch to replace the keyboard, and an infrared system to allow him to interact with his environment could provide enough support to allow a better evaluation of his abilities and potential as well as provide a means for him to access the general education curriculum. The assistive technology services that could be provided include training for his teachers and parents and a plan for assessing his abilities using those devices. This approach, starting with a technology that can truly provide him with a means of accessing the general education curriculum and participating in required reading and math tests, matches the requirements of the IDEA Amendments of 1997 as well as the No Child Left Behind legislation.

INSTRUCTIONAL PLANNING AND PLACEMENT

Once the student's needs have been identified and the services and supports a student needs to benefit from his or her education have been described, decisions must be made about instructional planning and placement. Instructional planning involves the selection of components and systems for teaching a student. Placement involves the identification of a student for delivering instruction.

The requirements that focus on access to the general curriculum and participation in state- and district-wide assessments are significantly different from what was required previously and necessitate a change in the strategies used to teach the general curriculum and in the process of instructional planning. Prior to these changes, students with disabilities were assured of an opportunity for a free and appropriate education, with "appropriate" being defined by a team. Annual goals were determined based on information obtained from a series of assessments of student strengths and needs (the present level of performance), and frequently focused on remediating or eliminating those "needs." Typically, there was little, if any, focus on relating those individualized educational goals and objectives to what students without disabilities were learning in the general education curriculum.

Including students with these individual goals in general education classrooms was difficult at best, and students whose Individualized Education Programs included primarily functional goals were most difficult to accommodate. Special educators found that including students with disabilities in general education classrooms was very difficult with this approach (e.g., Gersten, Walker, & Darch, 1988).

Instead of using this approach to instructional planning, teams must now start from the general education curriculum. Access to the general education curriculum does not necessarily mean that the team cannot make many of the same decisions for a student's educational program that it made before this change occurred. Students can still have functional goals in their educational program, they can still receive their education in the most appropriate environment, and they can still receive any necessary therapy or related services they require to benefit from their education. Such access requires that decisions are based on helping students with disabilities participate in the same educational experiences as students without disabilities and not merely be physically present in the same classroom.

Research on including students with disabilities in general education classrooms clearly demonstrates that mere physical presence does not guarantee an optimal learning experience (e.g., Klinger & Vaughn, 1999; McGregor & Vogelsberg, 1998). An optimal learning experience requires teaching that follows the principles of universal design for learning. That is, educational strategies are multimodal with experiences that meet the majority of learning differences. For those who need further accommodations to participate in the educational environment, appropriate accommodations including assistive technology need to be considered.

PRESENT PERFORMANCE LEVELS

"Present levels of performance" refers to a description of a student's educational performance at a given time. It should describe student progress on current educational goals, scores on any standardized district- or statewide assessment, and supports provided for that educational performance. Included in this description should be information about how the student's disability affects his or her involvement in the general education classroom.

It is important that information included in present levels of performance be collected using a variety of assessment tools and instruments. This is particularly important for students with more extensive support needs for whom the problem of reliably and validly assessing their abilities has been widely considered (e.g., see Kaufman, 1990; Luftig, 1989). Although formal assessment instruments are typically used for this task, alternative assessments such as performance-based assessments, portfolios, and demonstrations of mastery can provide more complete information about student abilities, strengths, and needs (Thoma & Held, 2002).

For Jonathan, the process of assessing present levels of performance was very difficult. A psychologist evaluated him within the framework of the *Vineland Adaptive Behavior Scales* (Sparrow, Balla, & Cicchetti, 1984) and other developmental scales. Given the results, he classified Jonathan as severely intellectually disabled, even though he did not measure his intellectual potential. Instead, he obtained further measures of Jonathan's cerebral palsy, his speech and language impairments, and their combined effect on Jonathan's experience and his ability to perform the items in the developmental scales.

A tragic error was nearly made here. Once a student is labeled, people tend to treat him or her according to that label, and the student becomes the condition named in the label. The error was prevented by Jonathan's teacher, who disputed the findings of the formal evaluation. He had curriculum-based data as well as notes of observations of Jonathan's alertness and great sense of humor. The teacher had noticed that Jonathan kept up with the activities in his surroundings. When funny things happened, he laughed; he showed humor appropriate to the situation. Students with intellectual disabilities in the severe range seldom show such characteristics.

Additional evaluations were conducted, this time using diagnostic–prescriptive teaching methods. The diagnostic–prescriptive model involves the sequence of selecting an instructional objective, teaching it intensively, and observing how and how much the student learns. With successive approximations, the teacher can determine the appropriate levels and procedures for teaching the students. Then the teacher sees how far and how fast the student can progress.

As a result of the new information, the diagnosis of severe intellectual disability was rejected and eliminated from Jonathan's records. Subsequently, teachers and therapists acted accordingly.

DEVELOPING INSTRUCTIONAL PROGRAMS

Instructional programs include multiple components:

• *Instructional objectives* are statements about what the student should be able to do if he or she learns through instruction. Objectives are based on the goals for the student. They guide the selection of the instructional procedures and the evaluation procedures.

• *Instructional sequences* are arrangements of instructional objectives in the order they are to be taught. Most sets of objectives for a given topic are arranged from simple to complex. That is, the objectives with no prerequisites are learned first. In turn, they become prerequisites for learning more complex skills.

• *Instructional rates* are based on the timing for presenting the objectives, that is, how fast they are presented or how much time is spent on each objective. Instructional schedules are based on instructional rates.

• A *curriculum* is a set of instructional objectives. A scope and sequence chart for a curriculum includes the instructional objectives and the order in which they are organized.

• *Instructional procedures* are the methods, media, and equipment used to help students reach their objectives.

• *Instructional methods* are recurrent patterns of teacher behavior. They include teacher presentation (lectures, demonstrations), student problem solving (inquiry training, experimenting), group work (discussion, debate), individual work, direct experience (consultants, field trips), and behavioral techniques.

• *Instructional media* are materials and machines. They include print media (textbooks, workbooks); audio, visual, and audiovisual media (photographs, audiotapes, videotapes, three-dimensional models); prototypes (games and simulations); and programs (programmed text, computer-assisted instruction).

• *Special equipment* comprises devices to compensate for particular disabilities, such as computers and braille writers.

• *Instructional settings* are the ways personnel and space are arranged for delivering instruction to particular students or groups.

- *Personnel allocation* refers to how students, teachers, and teacher aids are organized. Common patterns are tutoring, independent study, solitary activity, small groups, and large groups.
- *Space allocation* is how facilities are arranged for instruction. Frequently used patterns are common areas, carrels, special centers, and depositories.
- *Instructional systems* are sets of activities put together to teach a particular topic.

The process of developing instructional programs for students with developmental disabilities is one of making wise decisions about program elements based on a student's present performance levels. In the interests of normalization and better long-term outcomes, one should select as many elements as possible from the programs for students without disabilities. At the same time, as necessitated by the student's present performance levels, one could make different selections than one would make for students without disabilities. Again, the requirements are that students with disabilities have access to the general education curriculum, and that they have an opportunity to participate as much as possible in educational experiences alongside their peers without disabilities.

Jonathan's instructional activities are focused on life-management activities such as consumer economics and academics (e.g., language-related tasks, including listening to and reading literature and written composition; mathematics; social studies; and the sciences). In addition, his instructional program heavily emphasizes expressive communication through oral means and electronic assistive devices. In these latter activities, his teacher works closely with the speech, language, physical, and occupational therapists. Jonathan's teachers use some of the same instructional procedures they use with other students. The difference is that they devote more time to individual work. In addition, they adjust Jonathan's instructional schedule to allow him more time for all of his work. See Bos and Vaughn (1991), Langone (1990), McDonnell, Wilcox, and Hardman (1991), and Widerstrom, Mowder, and Sandall (1991) for more information about instructional activities for students with developmental disabilities.

PLACEMENT FOR INSTRUCTION

Although the IDEA Amendments of 1997 require that students have access to the general education curriculum and have opportunities to learn alongside their peers without disabilities to the maximum extent possible, the law provides for a range of possible "placements" for students with disabilities. The research results, however, consistently demonstrate that students with disabilities benefit when their education is provided in general education classrooms following the practices described as "inclusion" (Peterson & Hittie, 2003). In fact, Peterson and Hittie's review of the literature showed that research on inclusive education revealed positive results for students with and without disabilities (or at worse, neutral results). No research reviewed showed negative or detrimental results for either group of students, yet the law requires that other options be available. The range of placement options is discussed below.

There are a number of options for placing students with developmental disabilities for their special education services. Selecting among these options is governed by the principle of the least restrictive environment, based, in turn, on the goal of normalization. The following list includes the frequently used options for special education placement of students with developmental disabilities, arranged from least restrictive to most restrictive:

- regular class
- regular class with consultation assistance to the teacher
- regular class with assistance by itinerant specialist
- regular class plus resource-room help
- regular class with part-time special classes
- full-time special class
- full-time residential school
- hospital
- home

When one is selecting a placement option for a student with a developmental disability, the goal is to find the least restrictive environment. That is, on the basis of the present levels of performance, the student's Individualized Education Program planning team makes a determination of the environment(s) in which the student will receive an education and work on the goals in the plan. This is based, in part, on the student's ability to get along with others, the types of supports required, and the possibility of behavior problems that could result in injury to the student or to others. Students with disabilities, according to the law, must not be excluded from the regular education classroom environment unless, because of a disability, they cannot be successfully educated there even after the school provides necessary supplementary aids and services (20 U.S.C., Section 1412(a)(5) and Section 1413 (a)(1)).

INCLUSIVE EDUCATION

Quality inclusive education for students with disabilities refers to more than just an educational placement. As stated earlier, educational benefit is a result of quality services, not merely physical proximity to peers without disabilities. Basic tenets of the inclusion concept are provided by Stainback, Stainback, and Jackson (1992):

- All children must be included in both the educational and social life of their schools and classrooms.

- The basic goal is to not leave anyone out of school and classroom communities from the very beginning (thus, integration can be abandoned since no one has to return to the mainstream).
- The focus is on the support needs of all students and personnel.

In a benchmark report, the National Association of State Boards of Education (NASBE; 1992) issued a call for inclusive schools. In its report, NASBE recommended the creation of new belief systems that result in the setting of unified goals for special education and regular education students. They also recommended that the link between funding, placement, and the disabling label be severed. Inclusive schools rely on heterogeneous grouping and flexible learning goals and objectives for all students, including those in special education. The strongest advocates of full inclusion believe that no services should be provided to special education students outside of the regular classroom activities. Thus, full inclusion implemented completely would negate the continuum of services models (where students may be placed in segregated settings for all or part of the day) currently in place in most school districts. Recent litigation supports the idea of full inclusion. In *Sacramento City Unified School District v. Holland* (1992), the court supported the right of an 11-year-old girl to participate 100% of the day in a regular education classroom. The court weighed four factors when deciding the case: (a) the student's educational benefits from full-time placement in a regular education classroom, (b) the nonacademic benefits of a regular classroom placement, (c) the effect of the child with a disability on the other class members, and (d) the cost of a regular education placement with proper supplementary aids and services (Holland, 1994).

A national study of inclusive practices conducted by the National Center on Educational Restructuring and Inclusion (Lipsky, 1994) found six common factors necessary for successful inclusion to take place:

- Visionary leadership. This factor includes a positive view of the value of education to students with disabilities, an optimistic view of the capacities of teachers and schools to change, and confidence that practices evolve and that everyone benefits from inclusion.
- Collaboration. This factor derives from the recognition that no one teacher can be expected to possess all of the knowledge and expertise needed for serving all students and thus must necessarily draw upon the knowledge and expertise of others.
- Increased use of authentic assessment techniques. This factor means changing from the use of assessments as screening devices to the refusal of assessment foci to an appraisal of individual student abilities and needs.
- Supports for staff and students. This factor includes providing systematic staff development, allowing planning time for special and general education staff to collaborate, and providing supplementary aides and supports to students.
- Funding. This factor means moving away from funding formulas that encourage separate special education programs.

- Parent involvement. With this factor, parent participation is encouraged through family support services.

INDIVIDUAL DISPUTES

The IDEA Amendments of 1997 include requirements and procedures for dealing with disputes about actions with respect to an individual student. A parent or advocate who disagrees with a decision may request an administrative hearing at the local school district level. Either party may appeal the decision of the local hearing officer to the state education agency level. In turn, appeals may be made to the federal level, either to the Office of Special Education and Rehabilitation Services (OSERS) or to the Office of Civil Rights (OCR).

A case may be moved to the federal courts once administrative remedies are exhausted, or, in some specified cases, before administrative remedies are exhausted. Within the federal court system, the route is the district courts, the circuit courts of appeal, and the Supreme Court. The use of attorneys' services is allowed in all of these actions. Prevailing plaintiffs in court disputes may claim reimbursement for attorneys' fees and other litigation expenses.

The courts also may award prevailing plaintiffs reimbursement for expenses, such as the cost of private placement while a dispute about placement is being resolved. This may occur if it is reasonable to expect that so much time will be required to resolve the dispute that the student will be harmed by remaining in his or her current situation until a final decision is made. The courts also may award funds for compensatory education. That is, if it is determined that programs either were not provided as stated in the student's IEP or were provided incorrectly, the school district would be required to pay for or provide supplemental programs or services to make up for those losses of educational opportunities.

The complexity of the limitations of students with developmental disabilities may lead to ambiguity about the nature of the best decisions or to decisions that are costly to implement. Consequently, disputes arise frequently. The procedures for resolving disputes through administrative hearings and the federal courts are extremely important for students with developmental disabilities. The provisions in the Handicapped Children's Protection Act for awarding costs to the prevailing plaintiffs makes these avenues more widely available to parties who have legitimate complaints.

A CHANGE IN JONATHAN'S EDUCATIONAL SUPPORTS AND SERVICES

Jonathan's educational plan was developed by a group of educational professionals who had received adequate training in curriculum, universal design, the requirements of both the No Child Left Behind legislation and the IDEA

Amendments of 1997. In collecting information about his present levels of performance, the members of his multidisciplinary team focused on his communication abilities and brought in an assistive technology expert who spent time with him in the classroom and at home, trying various devices and strategies. It was decided that a laptop computer equipped with voice output software programs would meet more of Jonathan's educational and communication needs than a dedicated device (communication only). Jonathan's teachers and parents received training along with Jonathan on the use of the laptop computer and software packages. Jonathan's regular fourth-grade teacher began finding universally designed materials to use for reading and math lessons, areas where Jonathan has particular difficulty. With the universal design approach and the software on his computer, Jonathan was able to work on his reading, social studies, and science goals. He was not able to work at the level of the other fourth graders in math using these strategies, but the special educator worked with him and found that when manipulatives were used, he could learn the math lessons. A peer tutor who could work with him when word problems were the focus was another accommodation that was added to his IEP.

By the end of the school year, Jonathan's classmates found that he enjoyed going to baseball games and they began to invite him to go with them to high school baseball games. He learned to use the computer at home for surfing the Internet and communicated with his friends using instant messaging that he accessed with an alternative keyboard. It was a great way to demonstrate his sense of humor, and he quickly became a favorite friend as he demonstrated how to build simple Web pages and how to find information about Harry Potter on the Internet.

FINAL THOUGHTS

Decisions about educational supports and services must be based on both individual needs and the general education curriculum. Strategies and approaches such as inclusion, collaboration, assistive technology devices and services, and universal design for learning all have helped general and special educators make sure that students with disabilities not only have access to the general education curriculum, but also have opportunities to learn alongside their peers without disabilities. Although the information given here about the legal requirements for providing special education supports and services is based on current law, the one thing constant about special education is that the law will change and court decisions will further define ambiguous components. These changes will reflect both the current research and the values of the times, just as each amendment of IDEA has in the past. Instead of passively waiting to see where the law will go, we hope that special educators help set the direction for the future so that more students can have the kind of educational experience recently depicted for Jonathan.

REFERENCES

Bos, C., & Vaughn, S. (1991). *Strategies for teaching students with learning and behavior disorders.* Boston: Allyn & Bacon.

Culatta, R. A., Tompkins, J. R., & Werts, M. G. (2003). *Fundamentals of special education: What every teacher needs to know* (2nd ed.). Upper Saddle River, NJ: Merrill/Prentice Hall.

Education for All Handicapped Children Act of 1975, 20 U.S.C. § 1400 *et seq.*

Flippo, K. F., Inge, K. J., & Barcus, J. M. (1995). *Assistive technology: A resource for school, work, and community.* Baltimore: Brookes.

Gersten, R., Walker, H., & Darch, C. (1988). Relationship between teachers' effectiveness and their tolerance for handicapped students. *Exceptional Children, 57,* 226–236.

Heward, W. L. (2000). *Exceptional children: An introduction to special education* (6th ed.). Upper Saddle River, NJ: Merrill/Prentice Hall.

Holland, R. (1994, March). Ninth circuit upholds regular classroom placement. *Inclusive Education Programs, 2,* 1.

Individuals with Disabilities Education Act of 1990, 20 U.S.C. § 1400 *et seq.*

Individuals with Disabilities Education Act Amendments of 1997, 20 U.S.C. § 1400–1485.

Inge, K. J., & Shepherd, J. (1995). Assistive technology applications and strategies for school system personnel. In K. F. Flippo, K. J. Inge, & J. M. Barcus (Eds.), *Assistive technology: A resource for school, work and community* (pp. 133–166) Baltimore: Brookes.

Kaufman, A. S. (1990). *Assessing adolescent and adult intelligence.* Boston: Allyn & Bacon.

Kirk, S. A., Gallagher, J. J., & Anastasiow, N. J. (2003). *Educating exceptional children* (10th ed.). Boston: Houghton Mifflin.

Klinger, J. K., & Vaughn, S. (1999). Students' perceptions of instruction in inclusive classrooms: Implications for students with learning disabilities. *Exceptional Children, 66*(1), 23–37.

Langone, J. (1990). *Teaching students with mild and moderate learning problems.* Boston: Allyn & Bacon.

Larry P. v. Riles, 343 F. Supp. 1306 (N.D. Cal. 1972), aff'd, 502 F2d 963 (9th Cir. 1974).

Lipsky, D. (1994). National survey gives insight into inclusive movement. *Inclusive Education Programs, 1*(3), 4–7.

Luftig, R. L. (1989). *Assessment of learners with special needs.* Boston: Allyn & Bacon.

Mann, W. C., & Lane, J. P. (1991). *Assistive technology for persons with disabilities: The role of occupational therapy.* Rockville, MD: American Occupational Therapy Association.

McDonnell, J., Wilcox, B., & Hardman, M. (1991). *Secondary programs for students with developmental disabilities.* Boston: Allyn & Bacon.

McGregor, G., & Vogelsberg, T. (1998). *Inclusive schooling practices: Pedagogical and research foundations: A synthesis of the literature that informs best practices about inclusive schooling.* Baltimore: Brookes.

Meyen, E. L. (1996). *Exceptional children in today's schools* (3rd ed.). Denver, CO: Love.

National Association of State Boards of Education. (1992). *Winners all: A call for inclusive schools.* Alexandria, VA: Author.

Oakstone Legal and Business Publishing. (1999). *Students with disabilities and special education.* Burnsville, MN: Author.

Peterson, J. M., & Hittie, M. M. (2003). *Inclusive education.* Upper Saddle River, NJ: Merrill/Prentice Hall.

Rainforth, B., & York-Barr, J. (1997). *Collaborative teams for students with severe disabilities: Integrating therapy and educational services* (2nd ed.). Baltimore: Brookes.

Rose, D. H., & Meyer, A. (2002). *Teaching every student in the digital age: Universal design for learning.* Alexandria, VA: Association for Supervision and Curriculum Development.

Sacramento City Unified School District v. Holland, 786 F. Supp. 874 (E.D. Cal. 1992), aff'd, No. 92-15608, slip op. (9th Cir. March 1992).

Saddler, S., Thoma, C. A., & Whiston, S. (2002). School-to-career services and experiences: Are they linked with lower dropout rates for high school students in Nevada? *Workforce Education Forum, 29*(1), 41–50.

Sparrow, S. S., Balla, D. A., & Cicchetti, D. V. (1984). *Vineland Adaptive Behavior Scales.* Circle Pines, MN: American Guidance Service.

Stainback, S., Stainback, W., & Jackson, H. J. (1992). Toward inclusive classrooms. In S. Stainback & W. Stainback (Eds.), *Curriculum considerations in inclusive classrooms: Facilitating learning for all students* (pp. 3–17). Baltimore: Brookes.

Thoma, C. A., & Held, M. A. (2002). Measuring what's important: Using alternative assessments in transition planning. In C. L. Sax & C. A. Thoma (Eds.), *Transition assessment: Wise practices for quality lives* (pp. 71–86). Baltimore: Brookes.

Thoma, C. A., Ligon, K., & Wittig, K. (2004). Accessing the general curriculum within a functional curriculum framework. In J. Kregel & P. Wehman (Eds.), *Functional curriculum* (2nd. ed., pp. 95–111). Austin, TX: PRO-ED.

Turnbull, H. R., & Turnbull, A. P. (2000). *Free appropriate public education: The law and children with disabilities* (6th ed.). Denver, CO: Love.

Turnbull, R., Turnbull, A., Shank, M., Smith, S., & Leal, D. (2002). *Exceptional lives: Special education in today's schools* (3rd ed.). Upper Saddle River, NJ: Merrill/Prentice Hall.

U.S. Department of Education, Office of Special Education Programs. (2002). *Data Analysis System (DANS).*

U.S. Department of Education. (2003). *Executive summary: Twenty-second annual report to Congress on the implementation of the Individuals with Disabilities Education Act.* Washington, DC: Author.

Wagner, M., D'Amico, R., Marder, C., Newman, L., & Blackorby, J. (1992, December). *What happens next? Trends in postschool outcomes of youth with disabilities.* Menlo Park, CA: SRI International.

Wehmeyer, M. L. (2002). *Providing access to the general education curriculum: Teaching students with mental retardation.* Baltimore: Brookes.

Widerstrom, A. H., Mowder, B., & Sandall, S. R. (1991). *At-risk and handicapped newborns and infants: Development, assessment, and intervention.* Boston: Allyn & Bacon.

CHAPTER 4

Transition from School to Adulthood

Sharon H. deFur

LEARNING GOALS

Upon completion of this chapter, the reader will be able to

- identify the continuum of unique transition needs of youths and young adults with intellectual disabilities and their families
- discuss promising practices in the development of transition plans for youths and young adults with intellectual disabilities
- develop a transition course of study that incorporates systematic plans to achieve postschool goals for youths with intellectual disabilities
- follow a quality transition planning process that is person-centered and includes the critical partners necessary for effective postschool programming for youths and young adults with intellectual disabilities

Think about the last time you met a new person and the conversation that followed. It probably included one or more of these questions: Where are you from? What is your profession? Where did you go to school? What do you do for fun? Do you have a family? Are you involved in your community? These questions (and the implications that underlie them) are about how you have transitioned into adulthood. Few people make these transitions in a completely straight path, and many need support to navigate the various life transitions. Nonetheless, exit from high school serves as a societal marker for coming of age and represents a "rite of passage" for entry into adulthood.

This transition time presents challenges for most young adults and their families, but having an intellectual disability compounds the challenges. The presence of intellectual disability, by virtue of its defining characteristics (significantly below-average intellectual ability and aptitude for learning, in combination with below-average adaptive skills in two or more areas) creates a demand for a unique system of supports that will enable young adults with intellectual disabilities to participate in social conversations about their lives that are not appreciably different from those of young adults without a disability.

Disability labeling does not serve as a clear guide for education or rehabilitation programs or services. In fact, labels are often criticized for contributing to the lower expectations commonly held for students with disabilities, especially for students with intellectual disabilities. While being intellectually disabled does not define an individual's potential for experiencing positive interdependence as an adult within the community, it does imply that the individual will need some level of support in one or more aspects of adult living. Transition planning and services for youths and young adults with intellectual disability is about creating an environment and offering experiences that foster increased personal independence and decreased need for supports as appropriate for each individual in his or her career development. Career development paths differ, regardless of race, ethnicity, gender, ability, or temperament. Thus, authentic planning for the secondary transition needs of students with intellectual disability demands that Individualized Education Program (IEP) teams consider the individual and his or her contextual experiences and need for supports (Collet-Klingenberg, Hanley-Maxwell, & Stuart, 2000). Read the following three case studies of students who need varying levels of support to explore applying these concepts.

CASE EXAMPLE: JAN

Jan, age 14, receives most of her education in a self-contained special education setting where the focus has been on functional academics. She can read basic vocabulary and complete simple computations, but she cannot recall her phone number or address. She makes her needs known through two-word verbalizations and can follow simple two-step directions. She seldom initiates conversation but smiles and laughs frequently; she is social and tends to hug everyone she meets, even strangers. She helps choose her own clothing each day and needs no assistance in basic self-care skills. She does depend on her mother and sister to prepare meals, wash clothes, and clean up. She has no household responsibilities and has had no vocational assessment or preparation. She enjoys watching basketball and soccer games and gets very excited when the team is winning, but unsupervised she tends to remain isolated and engage in stereotypical behaviors. She does not travel alone beyond her own yard. She has asthma and must be careful to avoid allergens; she is given medication daily to prevent asthma attacks. Jan, her family, and her teachers are unsure about how to guide Jan vocationally. Her family hopes that she will eventually live in a group home and engage in meaningful work.

Imagine that you are on Jan's IEP team. Using the worksheet from Figure 4.1, answer as many of these questions as you can: How would you describe Jan's current level of functioning within each of the adaptive domains identified by the American Association on Mental Retardation (AAMR)? What level of support does she now depend on? Given the information that you have, what might be reasonable long-term goals for her? What curricula and experiences does she need to make progress toward these goals? Who needs to be involved? What supports might she need? What school and community resources will be needed? What other information do you need to be able to complete the transition planning worksheet?

 ## CASE EXAMPLE: ROBERT

Robert is a 17-year-old student who has functional reading, math, and writing skills. He receives most of his education within the regular classroom and in the career–technical education department, where he is seeking a vocational certificate as a carpenter's assistant (consistent with the recommendations from his vocational assessment). He worked last summer in construction and experienced success initially but then lost his job due to tardiness and absences. He used his earnings to buy clothes and to buy the other teens sodas and ice cream when they asked him to. After school, he hangs around with a group of other young men, some of whom have been involved in drugs and gang activities. Robert does not have enough credits to graduate with a diploma but is considering leaving school at the end of this year. He might be willing to stay in a vocational program, but most of his friends will be graduating. He would like to learn to drive but has not been able to pass the written test. Robert lives with his family and is the youngest of five children; his parents have told him that he can live with them as long as he wants. He is not given any household responsibilities and relies on his mother to wake him and prepare his meals. Although his language skills are below what is expected for his age, he can make his needs known verbally and can understand multiple-step directions. He enjoys building and repairing things and often helps his elderly neighbor do basic home maintenance. He often stays out late at night, hanging out on the street with his friends.

Imagine that you are on Robert's IEP team. Using the worksheet in Figure 4.1, answer as many of these questions as you can: How would you describe Robert's current level of functioning within each of the adaptive domains identified by the AAMR? What level of support does he now depend on? Given the information that you have, what might be reasonable long-term goals for him? What curricula and experiences does he need to have to make progress toward these goals? Who needs to be involved? What supports might he need? What school and community resources will be needed? What other information do you need to be able to complete the transition planning worksheet?

CASE EXAMPLE: ALFREDO

Alfredo, age 18, depends on his teaching assistant for all basic self-care needs. He seldom initiates conversation but responds excitedly when spoken to. He especially enjoys music and likes to

Transition Planning Worksheet

Present Level of Performance and Support	Work	Home Living	Recreation/Leisure	Health/Safety	Community	Education/Training
Intermittent (Independence/Interdependence)						
Limited						
Extensive	Long-term goal:	Long-term goal:	Long-term goal:	Long-term goal:	Long-term goal:	Long-term goal:
Pervasive (Dependence)						

1. What transition curricula or activities will provide this student with the skills that support progress toward the long-term goal or facilitate movement to a more independent level of support? Who will provide the curricula or activities?

2. What transition services will provide this student with the level of support needed at this time to access the specified curricula? Who will provide the services?

FIGURE 4.1. Transition Planning Worksheet for students with intellectual disability.

wear earphones. His vocabulary consists of few understandable words and includes *momma, no, go, drink, song, uh-oh, night-night, dada, bed,* and *car.* He seldom follows directions without assistance. His gross- and fine-motor skills, although delayed, should not prohibit independence in self-care and feeding. He does have health concerns and periodically experiences seizures, for which he has been given medication. When given support, Alfredo can sustain task attention for 15 minutes and engage in simple matching and manipulative tasks. He lives with his grandmother, whose health is failing and who is concerned that Alfredo has no other family to care for him should she no longer be able to fulfill that role; his grandmother also is concerned that she has a limited income to support Alfredo now and in the future. They seldom do anything in the community, as she has no vehicle, cannot afford public transportation, and is not aware of affordable alternatives.

Imagine that you are on Alfredo's IEP team. Using the worksheet in Figure 4.1, answer as many of these questions as you can: How would you describe Alfredo's current level of functioning within each of the adaptive domains identified by the AAMR? What level of support does he now depend on? Given the information that you have, what might be reasonable long-term goals for him? What curricula and experiences does he need to have to make progress toward these goals? Who needs to be involved? What supports might he need? What school and community resources will be needed? What other information do you need to be able to complete the transition planning worksheet?

In 1992, Luckasson et al. authored a report for the American Association on Mental Retardation outlining levels of support that individuals with intellectual disabilities may require in one or more areas of living. These supports can be viewed as occurring along a continuum, from supports that occur intermittently to supports that are pervasive and occur continuously. At the same time, support needs are situational and contextual. One young adult with intellectual disability may need only intermittent supports to be successful on a job but require more extensive supports to live and participate in the community. Another young adult may need pervasive supports in all activities of life. Transition planning and services should consider the level of support needed in all areas of adaptive skills, but then develop transition services that lead to skill acquisition or improvement and, when feasible, progress to a decreased level of external support. Table 4.1 provides examples of possible transition outcomes paired with needed level of support.

THE EVOLUTION OF TRANSITION SERVICES

Transition services for students with disabilities first appeared as a mandate in special education law in 1990, but transition services for students with intellectual disabilities have a much longer history. Although these earlier services are not necessarily consistent with the current values of least restrictive environment, full participation in the community, or being student and family centered, professionals who work with individuals with intellectual disabilities have long

TABLE 4.1

Anticipated Transition Outcomes Compared with Needed Level of Support

Level of Support	Employment	Education and Training	Living Arrangements	Community Participation
Intermittent	Competitive employment with job follow-along and assistance as needed	Linkages provided for postsecondary education and training opportunities	Living independently	Participating in all aspects of the community using natural supports
Limited	Supported employment for job transitions with periodic monitoring for job keeping and advancement	Identification and provision of on-going education and training	Supported living environment with monitoring for needed supports, including natural supports	Participating in the community with monitoring for needed direct supports, including natural supports
Extensive	Long-term supported employment and case management	Direct instruction provided as needed	Supported living environment with daily supervision	Participating in the community with supervision
Pervasive	Ongoing supported employment and case management	Direct instruction provided daily	Supported living with constant supervision	Participating in the community with constant supervision

recognized the need to assist youths and young adults in their adult employment and living arrangements. For example, prior to the passage of the Education for All Handicapped Children Act (EHA) of 1975 (P.L. 94-142), most existing special education programs were primarily for children and youth who were believed to have intellectual disability. Vocational rehabilitation counselors often provided community work experience programs in partnerships with the local schools. Sheltered workshops, day activity programs, and institutional living settings represented alternatives to staying at home without income or personal relationships. An unintended outcome of the passage of EHA was a temporary shift in rehabilitation policy focus away from involvement in the schools, based on the assumption that secondary special education would assume the role of providing work experience and vocational development opportunities.

In the early 1980s, policymakers began to examine the impact of the EHA on the educational outcomes of youth and young adults with disabilities, including those with intellectual disability. The findings revealed that young adults with intellectual disability continued to experience significantly lower levels of employment and independence when compared to their peers without disabilities or their peers with other disabilities (Fardig, Algozzine, Schwartz, Hensel, & Westling, 1985; Hasazi, Gordon, & Roe, 1985; Mithaug, Horiuchi, & Fanning, 1985;

Wehman, Kregel, & Seyfarth, 1985). As a result of these research findings, Madeline Will (1984), then director of the Office of Special Education and Rehabilitative Services and parent of a youth with intellectual disability, introduced special education policy inducements encouraging improved secondary and transition special education services. From this evolved what has come to be known as the Will Bridges to Employment model. This model proposed that youth with disabilities, including intellectual disability, had three potential options for support as they transitioned from secondary special education into the world of work. These paths were defined as follows:

1. a path of generic transition services common and available to all youth graduating from high school that theoretically could serve the majority of the transition service needs of most youths with disabilities (these included guidance counseling, vocational education, and extracurricular programs that provide information and support regarding post-school employment)
2. time-limited services (these included services that are provided by adult service agencies on a short-term basis such as those typically provided by vocational rehabilitation and job training agency services; the employment transition service needs for youths with mild to moderate intellectual disability were hypothesized meetable via this path)
3. ongoing services (these included long-term supported employment and were intended for youths with more severe intellectual disability)

During the 1980s, multiple projects and federal initiatives attempted to infuse a practice of interagency coordinated and comprehensive transition planning for all youths and young adults with disabilities. In 1990, with the reauthorization and renaming of EHA, the Individuals with Disabilities Education Act (IDEA) mandated that all IEPs address comprehensive transition services and planning for all youths with disabilities, age 16 and over. The definition of post-school outcomes expanded the goals of transition planning from a singular emphasis on employment to a recognition that full community participation and independent living represented a more complete view of postschool success. For example, the Division on Career Development and Transition of the Council for Exceptional Children holds the position that transition includes concerns for postsecondary education, independent living, community participation, and social and interpersonal relationships, as well as employment (Halpern, 1994).

The reauthorization of IDEA in 1997 (P.L. 105-17) strengthened the federal policy message of the importance of secondary transition and secondary education. For the first time, IDEA 1997 identified preparing students with disabilities for employment and independent living as one of the express purposes of IDEA. IDEA policy that supports this purpose includes defining transition services and requiring that transition needs and comprehensive planning be directly addressed within the IEP of adolescents with disabilities. Table 4.2 provides the IDEA definition of transition services and the implications of the definition for providing transition services to youth and young adults with intellectual disability.

TABLE 4.2
Individuals with Disabilities Education Act of 1997 Definition of Transition Services

Definition of Transition Services	Practical Description
a coordinated set of activities for a student with a disability that is designed within an outcome-oriented process;	There is an expectation that transition services will focus on achieving positive postschool outcomes for youths and young adults with intellectual disability, regardless of the severity of the disability. Furthermore, no single activity defines transition services, and there is an expectation that multiple supporting activities will be coordinated as they are delivered across the transition planning time frame.
they promote movement from school to post-school activities, including postsecondary education, vocational training, integrated employment (including supported employment), continuing and adult education, adult services, independent living, and community participation;	Note that the range of intended outcomes includes not only employment, but also education or training, as well as living, working, and playing inclusively within the community. There is an expectation that IEP transition teams will address the range of postschool outcomes for youths and young adults with intellectual disability.
is based on the individual student's needs, taking into account the student's preferences and interests.	This definition emphasizes the individual and personal contexts of the youth or young adult with intellectual disability and requires that transition planning be student centered, involving the student in the transition plan development and implementation.
They include instruction,	This means defining the special education or specialized instruction and services needed by the youth or young adult with intellectual disability to achieve the postschool outcomes.
related services,	These include those services that enable the youth or young adult with intellectual disability to benefit from special education and achieve transition outcomes (e.g., vocational counseling, assistive technology, and various therapies).
community experiences,	Youths and young adults with intellectual disability benefit from opportunities to learn within real-life settings where they will work, live, and play. IDEA recognizes this and requires that transition plans include services that occur within the community.
the development of employment and other postschool adult living objectives,	Accomplishing long-term goals of employment and independent living requires the setting of objectives or benchmarks that mark progress toward accomplishment of those goals.
and, when appropriate, acquisition of daily living skills and	Many youths and young adults with intellectual disability may require transition plans that outline services to achieve daily living skills that promote independence.
functional vocational evaluation.	Many youths and young adults with intellectual disability will be best assessed vocationally in functional real-life situational settings rather than in paper-and-pencil assessments.

WHEN SHOULD TRANSITION PLANNING BEGIN?

IDEA delineates three specific ages to initiate specific transition planning actions: age 14 (younger when appropriate), age 16, and 1 year before reaching the age of majority (see Table 4.3). In reality, every IEP decision made from the beginning of special education services for a student with intellectual disability potentially impacts that student's transition plan and outcomes. The IEP team would be wise to consider long-term transition outcomes and also initiate efforts to improve adaptive behavior skills as part of the dialogue of services and supports for every IEP for a student identified as having an intellectual disability.

IEP Transition Requirements at Age 14

High school experiences, both academic and social, greatly influence the future options for all students. For adolescents with intellectual disability, those experiences can be pivotal. Yet success for many of these students is too often short-lived and thwarted by insufficient skills or supports. Far too many students with intellectual disabilities drop out of school (particularly students who are considered mildly impaired in cognitive and adaptive skills) when there is a mismatch between their needs, the curriculum offered, and the community supports available. The first year or two of high school can be a time of high incidence of truancy or dropping out of school, and of disciplinary actions such as suspension or expulsion. To combat this pattern, IDEA requires that the IEP team carefully examine the transition service needs for the individual student. By the time a student with intellectual disability reaches age 14, IDEA requires the IEP team to identify the transition service needs for this student. At a minimum, the resulting statement should include a description of the course of study chosen to enable the student to transition successfuly and achieve a successful high school experience.

When the student with an intellectual disability is age 14, by law and consistent with typical guidance planning, the IEP team needs to discuss the planned high school program. This is the time to broaden the discussion of diploma options and graduation requirements. For youths with intellectual disability, IEP teams will need to determine whether an alternate and functional curriculum will be required to augment the general curriculum, including vocational education, available to the student. Conversation should include identifying the student's long-term goals regarding employment, postsecondary education or training, and independent living. Those goals then provide a framework around which to plan the secondary education curricula for that student. For example, if competitive employment with minimal supports is the goal, the IEP team needs to develop a program plan for the high school years that will achieve that goal. Questions such as the following might be posed in the IEP transition dialogue: Can the student's goals be accomplished in the typical 4 years of high school? How will the student attain vocational competence? Will a vocational evaluation be conducted? If so, when and what type? What are the most inclusive environments that offer the most opportunity for attaining vocational skills and for

TABLE 4.3

Integrated IEP Transition Planning Checklist for Age 14 to School Exit

By Age 14 (younger when appropriate)

- The IEP must include a statement of the transition service needs of the student with a focus on the student's course of study for the remainder of his or her secondary education (diploma and state and district assessment options should be identified).
- This course of study is to be updated annually.
- Transition service needs may also refer to extracurricular activities, behavior intervention plans, assistive technology, communication needs, Braille, Limited English Proficiency.
- The student must be invited to participate in the IEP meeting any time transition services are discussed; other steps must be taken to ensure that the student's preferences and interests are considered if the student does not attend.
- Parents must be informed about the purpose of the meeting and who will be participating.

By Age 16 (younger when appropriate)

The IEP must continue to address all of the transition components that began at age 14, plus now it must also include the following:

- A statement of the needed transition services for the student. This includes identifying
  —postschool goals and objectives
  —specialized instruction to meet goals
  —related services to benefit from transition special education
  —community experiences
  —independent living skills instruction, as appropriate
  —functional vocational evaluation, as appropriate
- A statement of interagency responsibilities or any needed linkages to provide transition services.
- A transition plan with services to be provided outlined within the context of the IEP.
- Agencies or organizations that might be paying for or providing transition services are invited to the IEP meeting; if they are unable to participate, other steps must be taken to ensure their participation. Parents are informed about invited agencies. *Note:* Agencies are expected to pay for services that they would otherwise provide.
- Services are provided. If a participating agency fails to provide the agreed-upon service, the IEP team must reconvene to identify an alternative way of providing the needed IEP transition services.
- IEP transition services and plans are reviewed and revised at least annually, consistent with the IEP review process. Progress toward annual transition goals and objectives are monitored and reported to the family along with other aspects of IEP progress reporting.

(continues)

TABLE 4.3 *Continued.*
Integrated IEP Transition Planning Checklist for Age 14 to School Exit

One Year Before Age of Majority

- Educational rights transfer to a young adult upon reaching the age of majority. Youth with disabilities and their families must be informed of this transfer of rights no later than 1 year prior to reaching the age of majority.
- Families, not IEP teams, must take steps to identify their young adult children who are unable to make an informed decision about their educational rights and to present evidence that this is the case. IEP teams should advise families of the alternatives to transfer of rights, such as the following:
  —designating a family member as educational power of attorney
  —state documentation process of the inability to make informed consent
  —guardianship options

Note. All IEP requirements apply including prior notice, team membership, procedural safeguards, annual review, and integration of transition into all aspects of the IEP as appropriate.

gaining increased vocational and community independence? What objectives, activities, or special education supports and services are needed for this year that will contribute to forward progress? This proposed course of study needs to be viewed as a draft that gets revisited as the student progresses through the secondary education program, with the option of revising the course of study as the student's goals change.

In planning the course of study along with special transition education and related services for students with intellectual disabilities, IEP teams should keep current with the research that identifies correlates to positive postschool outcomes (see Figure 4.2 for a graphic organizer of research-based transition practices). To date, research studies confirm that paid work and community-based work experiences while in secondary school correlate highly with positive postschool employment outcomes. Participation in vocational courses and participation in inclusive environments also predict greater postschool success. Interestingly, so do positive secondary recreation and leisure experiences. Exposure to career or vocational guidance programs and competence in functional academic and social skills instruction definitely influence postschool success. Consistently, research studies support the idea that youths with disabilities (including intellectual disabilities) who develop greater skills in self-determination and who participate in their future goal setting fare much better in leading independent adult lives (Benz, Lindstrom, & Yovanoff, 2000; Benz, Yovanoff, & Doren, 1997; Doren & Benz, 1998; Frank & Sitlington, 2000; Heal, Khoju, & Rusch, 1997; Kohler, DeStefano, Wermuth, Grayson, & McGinty, 1994; Patton, Polloway, & Smith, 2000; Patton et al., 1996; Sample, 1998; Wehmeyer & Schwarz, 1997). Vocational assessments help ensure that students with intellectual disabilities can receive job training and placement in fields that are most suited to their needs and interests (Leconte, 1999). Assistive technology offers another promising transition support strategy, expanding many employment and adult living options for

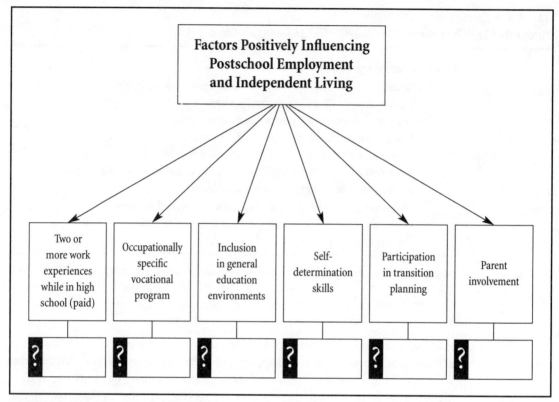

FIGURE 4.2. Experiences and skills linked to postschool success.

youths and young adults with intellectual disabilities (Blackhurst, Lahm, Harrison, & Chandler, 1999; Houchins, 2001; Wehmeyer, 1999). Voice e-mail and Web-based readers offer opportunities for youth and young adults with lower reading and writing skills to interact with others socially and to use the resources available through the Internet. Technologies for job coaching (e.g., Pocket Coach by AbleLink) and video supervision enable supports to be provided without a person being present. IDEA 1997 requires that IEP teams consider whether students need an assistive technology device or services, and that consideration should be made when designing transition education activities and services. Cooperative agreements may be negotiated between school districts and state rehabilitation services to share in the funding of assistive technologies that promote access to and success in employment settings for young adults with intellectual disabilities.

IEP teams should be aware that cultural and gender biases continue to exist and that non-White young adults with intellectual disabilities and female young adults with intellectual disabilities often experience poorer postschool outcomes (Doren & Benz, 1998). Armed with this realization, IEP teams can take intentional steps to combat any explicit or implicit biases and make proactive decisions that provide these youth with the skills and experiences to negate such biases.

The transition from middle to high school challenges many youths, and is a time when IEP teams need to examine at-risk behaviors that students may be exhibiting. These include truancy, a history of suspensions, concerns regarding drug or alcohol abuse, and sexual activity. Many students whose level of intellectual disability may be minimal but real find themselves caught in cycles of learned helplessness and may make poor choices as they attempt to find significance and power in their lives. An IEP team offers an opportunity to create the circle of support that students need to stay in school while developing skills of interpersonal competence and self-determination. This may mean expanding the team beyond the required members to include those school and community resource people who can help coordinate and provide support services to counteract the existing at-risk factors. Participation in extracurricular activities where social skills can develop and engagement in meaningful curricula that match the student's instructional needs, interests, and preferences offer mutually exclusive alternatives to dropping out of school or engaging in inappropriate activities. The transition dialogue at age 14, and younger when appropriate, offers a deliberate time to address these real issues that challenge many youths with intellectual disabilities.

IEP Transition Requirements Beginning at Age 16

By the time a youth is age 16, the IEP team *must* address the comprehensive transition services plan to achieve transition goals and to create a seamless provision of services between school exit and entry into other adult service support systems. Some young adults with intellectual disabilities will complete their high school education along with their age peers; for them, the plans at age 16 must address vocational competence and employability with community work experience and functional skills for living independently. Other young adults with intellectual disability will elect to continue to receive special education services until they have reached the maximum age of eligibility, which is age 21 in most states. For these young adults, in addition to addressing vocational and independent living competencies, transitional teams should explore options of providing transitional special education and related services in settings within the community with more age-appropriate models during the last 2 to 3 years of special education eligibility. By age 16, students with intellectual disabilities should have an adult service case manager, and that person should be attending IEP meetings and participating in making plans and arranging services for the young adult as he or she completes high school education. Too often young adults with intellectual disability exit school to find themselves placed on long waiting lists for supported employment or supported housing; the comprehensive transition process identifies ways to create a seamless transition to employment and independent living, where skills can be maintained and enhanced in adult life. Too often families are surprised that entitlement to special education services end once their young-adult child with intellectual disability exits school. Families frequently feel unprepared to coordinate the necessary supports for their son or daughter to continue to progress developmentally. The transition planning process offers an opportunity to link families directly to adult services and community resources.

By age 16, the IEP transition plan must clearly address long-term goals and objectives related to employment, adult living, and postsecondary education or training. The 10 areas of adaptive skills identified by the AAMR—communication, self-care, home living, social skills, community use, self-direction, health and safety, functional academics, leisure, and work—serve as overarching domains on which to focus for students with intellectual disability. Hagner and Dileo (1993) identified a continuum of job training and employment options for young adults with intellectual disability. The continuum ranges from nonvocational day treatment (daily living skills) to competitive employment. Griffin, Rosenberg, Cheyney, and Greenberg (1996) compared the self-esteem and job satisfaction of adults with mild intellectual disability in sheltered workshops and supported employment. They found that work in any setting enhanced self-esteem, but those working in supported employment settings experienced greater job satisfaction and self-esteem than those working in more restrictive settings. Job satisfaction was also positively related to home living settings, with greater living independence associated with higher job satisfaction. The authors concluded that although more restrictive settings can serve as preparation for competitive employment, such settings should be seen only as a temporary route to an end goal of competitive employment. Youths and young adults should receive their transition services in the least restrictive environment (LRE) possible, with the IEP team making placement decisions for transition education following the same LRE guidelines as any placement in special education.

For each youth with intellectual disability, the IEP team should describe the present level of skills the student exhibits relative to his or her long-term goals, including what level of support the student presently requires to demonstrate the skill (see Figure 4.1). The IEP team then must determine what transition curricula, activities, and services will be necessary to make annual progress toward the student's long-term goals and who on the team will assume responsibility for providing or coordinating the curriculum, activities, or services during the upcoming year. For example, if the student's long-term goal includes being able to use the community transportation system independently, but he or she currently requires constant supervision to use that system, what would be an appropriate and measurable goal for this year? What activities or curriculum or technologies should be used to promote progress? Who will implement the activities or curriculum? When? Where? How will progress be benchmarked, measured, and reported? What supports will the student need to achieve this annual goal?

IEP-identified transition services, supports, and activities must be provided as part of the student's free appropriate public education (FAPE). If an agency other than the local school division offers to provide or coordinate a transition service, support, or activity, but then fails to follow through on that offer, the IEP team must reconvene and identify alternative ways to provide that service or support. Progress toward annual transition-related goals should be reported along with all IEP goals. One way to monitor implementation of agreed-upon activities and services would be to include them in the periodic IEP report.

Clearly, the transition process represents more than a referral to the next service agency; it represents a strategic plan with specific actions that, when implemented, will result in improved postschool outcomes for young adults with intellectual disabilities.

Age of Majority

The Family Education Rights and Privacy Act (FERPA) deems that young adults hold the right to make their own educational decisions once they have reached the age of majority (age 18 in most states). The IDEA Amendments of 1997 clarified that the transfer of educational rights outlined by FERPA also applied to IDEA rights, and added the requirement that families and students be advised of this prior to the actual time of transfer. By 1 year prior to the age of majority in that state, IEP teams must inform students and families about the transfer of educational rights to the young adult with intellectual disability unless the family takes steps to legally maintain those rights. For most young adults with disabilities, there exists little *legal* doubt that they would be deemed able to make an informed decision regarding their education; that is, few would qualify to have those rights removed by the courts. For students with intellectual disability, decisions become less clear and would, in all likelihood, be determined based on the extent to which the student required support in everyday decision making.

States are implementing this IDEA requirement differently, just as states' laws differ regarding guardianship and informed consent. One alternative to transferring the educational rights from the parent to the young adult is for the young adult to give his or her family member or advocate power of attorney over educational decisions. Another alternative is for the family to seek guardianship rights, sometimes a lengthy and costly option. A third alternative is for states to identify ways in which families can have their adult son or daughter with intellectual disability deemed unable to make informed consent. Regardless of the option chosen, families need time to contemplate the decision and to take the necessary steps to implement their decision. One year is the minimum amount of time that should be afforded to families. IEP teams need to have information about the state procedures and share this information with families early on in the transition planning process. Educators should check into the recommended procedures adopted in their state to clarify how best to advise families.

WHO SHOULD BE INVOLVED IN TRANSITION PLANNING?

The IEP transition team has the same membership requirements as the IEP team, as described in the IDEA Amendments of 1997. IDEA also requires the inclusion of the student and adult service providers as team members. The basic roles and responsibilities of the IEP transition team are outlined in Table 4.4.

IDEA has always offered the option to include children with disabilities in their IEP meeting, as appropriate. Transition planning meetings are seen as

(*text continues on page 140*)

TABLE 4.4
IEP Transition Team Members' Potential Roles and Responsibilities

IEP Transition Team Member	Required Member?	Roles and Responsibilities
Student	Yes	Identify personal strengths and needs. Set personal goals and share interests and preferences for employment, adult living, and postsecondary education/training. Assist in identifying transition strategies and activities. Accept responsibility for some IEP transition activities. Provide feedback to the team regarding transition plan implementation. Be active participant in transition IEP meeting.
Parent(s)	Yes	Share strengths and needs of their child and their long-term vision and hopes regarding his or her employment, postsecondary training, and adult living options. Assist team in matching transition services to the needs, interests, and preferences of their child. Accept responsibility for some IEP transition activities. Provide information to the team regarding family natural supports that will be helpful in developing long-term goals. Participate in the implementation of the transition plan and provide feedback to the team regarding transition plan implementation. Be active participant in IEP meeting.
Special educator	Yes	*Prior to the meeting:* Collect student interest information and prepare the student to be an active IEP participant; provide family with inventory or information to help prepare for the meeting; arrange IEP transition meeting with all team members; invite all required participants and inform them of the purpose, time, and location of the meeting and who will be attending. *During the meeting:* Listen to other team members, especially student and family; provide present level of performance information beyond what the student and family share; facilitate participation by all team members; record discussion and final decisions on the IEP. (The IEP transition plan should include long-term goals, annual goals, levels of support needed, transition services, as well as specific linkages needed.) *After the meeting:* Provide follow-up to team members, reminding them of their agreed-upon responsibilities; provide agreed-upon special education services; monitor implementation of the transition and related services, and report progress toward annual transition goals and objectives or benchmarks.
General educator (recommended to include a vocational educator)	Yes	Contribute to observations of the student's participation in the general curriculum and identify ways in which the student can access the general curriculum. Participate in discussion of the appropriate course of study, including preparation for occupational readiness. Provide direct instruction as appropriate to the transition plan. Listen to the other team members, especially student and family.

(continues)

TABLE 4.4 *Continued.*
IEP Transition Team Members' Potential Roles and Responsibilities

IEP Transition Team Member	Required Member?	Roles and Responsibilities
Administrator or designee	Yes	Identify the supports and services available within the school or school district. Make arrangements for supports and services not currently available. Provide supervision to school team members in their implementation of the transition services and activities. Listen to other team members, especially student and family.
Adult service provider (e.g., rehabilitation counselor, mental retardation services case manager, independent living center specialist)	Yes, if paying for or providing a transition service	Participate in the planning process and identify the services and supports available now and in the future through the adult service agency represented. Provide linkages to other adult services and community supports when appropriate. Provide or pay for transition services typically offered by the agency. Communicate with student, parent, and education representative as services and activities are implemented regarding progress toward goals and objectives. Listen to other team members, especially student and family.
Related service provider (e.g., psychologist, speech–language pathologist, occupational therapist, physical therapist, assistive technology specialist, vocational evaluator, school nurse, job coach)	Yes, if providing a related service or interpreting assessment data	Assess student when appropriate and communicate assessment data results. Share observations of the youth's strengths and needs. Participate in the transition planning process, identifying options for practicing and developing transition-related skills. Identify the supports needed based on direct student observation and interactions. Identify and provide direct transition-related services as appropriate to the transition plan. Collaborate, advise, and support team efforts and goals. Consider a consultative role rather than regular therapy when appropriate. Collect data to demonstrate progress. Provide progress reports to the special educator for inclusion in the IEP regular progress reports. Listen to other team members, especially student and family.
Transition coordinator	No	Coordinate interagency linkages and cooperative activities to promote the development of a continuum of transition services within the school division and community. Provide information on transition best practices and effective services. Develop systemic procedures to improve transition curricula, programs, and services for all students. Provide follow-up of students and service providers. Collaborate with employers and other community representatives to develop community-based work experience options. Serve as a resource to the team, providing team members with updated information regarding options within the school division and the community. Listen to IEP transition team members, especially student and family.

(continues)

TABLE 4.4 *Continued.*
IEP Transition Team Members' Potential Roles and Responsibilities

IEP Transition Team Member	Required Member?	Roles and Responsibilities
Guidance counselor	No	Provide the IEP transition team with information regarding course-of-study options, career assessment options, scheduling and class placement options, and counseling support available through the guidance office (including career counseling, truancy and behavior challenges, personal development supports). Provide direct services as appropriate based on student needs. Provide consultation and coordination services within the school setting. Listen to IEP transition team members, especially student and family.

appropriate, and the youth with intellectual disability must be invited to participate in his or her IEP meeting anytime transition plans will be discussed. This will definitely occur at each IEP meeting after the age of 14. If the student chooses not to participate, or for some reason is unable to participate, the special educator or other IEP team member needs to gather input from the student regarding his or her needs, interests, and preferences. Regardless of whether the student attends the IEP meeting, the team uses the IEP preparation opportunity to gather information about the student's interests, goals, and aspirations.

Mere attendance at an IEP meeting does not equal full participation. Adolescents with intellectual disability may find the meeting an awkward place where adults ask many questions and the dialogue includes a lot of jargon. Adults should use this opportunity to examine the clarity of discussion in IEP meetings, which will benefit all attendees.

The IEP meeting does offer a stimulus to teach youths with intellectual disability skills of self-awareness and self-advocacy, a basis for developing self-determination skills (Getzel & deFur, 1997). Preparing the student for the IEP transition meeting through role-playing, videotaping, and other tools that help the student develop social skills and self-understanding can create a meeting that actually serves to empower the student. Practice and opportunities to receive direct instruction enable the youth with intellectual disability to be a more active participant in his or her IEP, while promoting skills in self-determination. Special educators and parents of youths with intellectual disabilities should explore what supports each student will need to more fully participate in each phase of the IEP transition planning process.

Transition planning evolved within a philosophy of student-centeredness; the active inclusion of youth with intellectual disability, regardless of its severity, helps make the intention of being person-centered a reality. Student-centered plans should

- be simple and understandable
- be considered working documents

- be based on a unique vision for the student and those who care most about him or her
- focus on student strengths
- provide for maximum choice and control by the youth
- use a clear outcome orientation (Hagner & Dileo, 1993; Schwartz, Jacobson, & Holburn, 2000)

Representatives of adult service agencies that might provide or pay for upcoming transition services must also be invited to the IEP transition meeting. If a representative cannot attend the meeting, then the special educator or transition coordinator must make other arrangements to provide input into the transition plan. IEP teams cannot obligate adult service agencies to provide transition services without agency participation in the decision. Parents and students should be informed when adult service agency representatives will be attending IEP transition meetings.

Young adults with intellectual disabilities and their families depend on connecting to the adult services available to them in their community. Linkages with these postschool support options must begin early in the transition planning process and continually be refined to facilitate a smooth transfer of services for these young adults as they exit school. Young adults with intellectual disabilities may be able to access services provided under the Rehabilitation Act Amendments of 1998. Individuals served through the Rehabilitation Act have an Individualized Plan for Employment (IPE) developed, which should be coordinated with the student's special education IEP. States and localities operate agencies and boards whose sole mission is to serve individuals with intellectual disabilities, often providing case managers for these young adults. Young adults with intellectual disabilities should also apply for Social Security benefits if they have not been found eligible for those benefits earlier. Medicaid services may be an option for these young adults. Social service agencies and centers for independent living also may be able to provide postschool support for some young adults with intellectual disabilities. In addition to federal, state, and local public agencies, many nonprofit organizations, such as The Arc, offer programs and services that may benefit young adults with intellectual disabilities. Unfortunately, adult service agency participation in transition meetings remains limited. Most follow-up studies find that young adults continue to use the self-family-friend network to find jobs more often than they use adult services, although connections to adult services have improved slightly with the implementation of transition mandates (Doren & Benz, 1998; Frank & Sitlington, 2000; Virginia Department of Education, 1998).

Related service providers and guidance counselors are not required members of the IEP transition team unless they happen to be providing services to the student. However, IDEA specifically notes that related services are to be considered in the identification of comprehensive transition services. Traditionally, related service providers have not been seen as integral to transition services, yet an assistive technology may open doors to independence for students, or a work accommodation identified by an occupational or physical therapist may significantly alter work productivity. Related services for transition planning should focus on accomplishing transition goals and not just therapy clinical benchmarks (deFur & Patton, 1999). Guidance counselors offer unique expertise in career planning as well as being knowledgeable of school course offerings and community resources. IEP transition teams should seek the inclusion of related service providers and guidance counselors as resources to address the in-school transition curricular needs of students with intellectual disabilities.

HOW TO FILL OUT THE FORM

Special education and special educators are sometimes held hostage by a focus on compliance and documentation. Unfailingly, when discussing how to conduct transition planning, someone poses the question, "But how do I fill out the form?" or "What should the transition page look like?" Although these reflect legitimate administrative questions, they reveal a lack of confidence in the robustness of quality programs to respond to compliance requirements. Transition is *not* a page among multiple other pages of the IEP. IEP forms represent one way of framing a dialogue about a student with a disability who requires special education. The form provides an outline that federal, state, and local policy and procedure have dictated, and, theoretically, those policies and procedures emerged from an explicit need. Forms vary from state to state or even district to district. "Completing the form" could be a meaningless fill-in-the-blank activity unless the IEP team engages in thoughtful discussion of the student's and family's hopes and dreams for the future, of the student's strengths and opportunities for growth, of the student's goals for the year and steps to achieve those goals, of the services and supports the student will need to accomplish those goals, and who will be responsible for leading the way for each of the transition goals and activities. Forms, worksheets, and checklists, such as that provided in Figure 4.1, can serve as planning guides and key point reminders for the transition dialogue that must occur, legally and ethically. This documentation is, however, a means to an end, not an end in itself. Comprehensive transition planning and implementation of the plans stand up against any "form" as a factor that promotes postschool success for students with intellectual disability. If the educator engages collaboratively in comprehensive transition planning and implementation, then completing whatever documentation is required will follow easily. Nonetheless, IEPs do need to include—clearly and in writing—the required IDEA transition components and document the special education transition and related services and activities (including duration, location, and provider) that will be provided as part of the student's free appropriate public education.

Examples of transition activities that might evolve from this comprehensive planning include the following:

- assessing student needs, interests, or preferences for future education, employment, or adult living and setting future goals in these areas
- identifying, exploring, and trying out transition placements that match the student's assessment and vision

- instructing the student in the academic, vocational, or adult living skills he or she may need to be successful in achieving transition goals, including skills of self-determination
- identifying and providing accommodations, supports, or related services (including assistive technology) needed to be successful
- coordinating and linking with adult services and organizations and helping families identify resources and natural supports
- providing or planning an opportunity for the student to have appropriate community experiences related to his or her future goals
- providing or planning follow-up or follow-along support once the student either develops independence in a transition activity or graduates

COLLABORATIVE TRANSITION PLANNING

Families and Students as Collaborative Transition Team Members

References to the importance of family and student involvement in transition can be found consistently throughout transition research (deFur, Todd-Allen, & Getzel, 2001; Miller, La Follette, & Green, 1990; Morningstar, Turnbull, & Turnbull, 1995; Repetto & Correa, 1996; Steere, Pancsofar, Wood, & Hecimovic, 1990). Parental involvement is a primary indicator of student success in transition programs. Families (including extended families) serve as informal and formal role models for youths with disabilities. Family support and resources influence making decisions about students' goals for living, community participation, and employment (Morningstar et al., 1995). Family involvement in transition planning for youth and young adults who require more extensive or pervasive supports becomes even more critical, as families may be the one ongoing and consistent source of assistance for these young adults. Unfortunately, during secondary education, parental involvement in IEPs often decreases. In a study of transition services in Virginia, deFur, Getzel, and Kregel (1994) found that family participation in IEP meetings decreased markedly for students who were exiting the secondary-school setting, although student participation remained high. Families need guidance and clear and accurate information from professionals to prepare them for their ongoing role as case managers for a family member with a severe disability (Steere et al., 1990). Keeping families connected to IEP transition planning is a critical consideration for professionals working with youth with intellectual disabilities. Families remain invested when they see the process and the "system" working for their child.

Transition planning offers an opportunity to revitalize the IEP process, making the IEP a dynamic planning document, with families and students as true partners (deFur et al., 2001; Geenen, Powers, & Lopez-Vasquez, 2001). Families and students often report that they feel "talked to" at IEP meetings, without real occasions for input. Collaborative IEP transition planning generates commitment by all team members, including families and students. Try beginning every IEP meeting with the student and family members outlining their vision for the future, and then describing the youth's strengths and challenges; write this information into the IEP. Ask the student and family members about long-term goals for employment, education, and adult living; write down what they say. Use this information to identify annual goals, objectives, accommodations, and needed special education and related transition services. Discuss long-term goals with families during elementary and middle school to prepare them for their potential roles as lifetime case managers. Provide them with needed information about community resources while their child is in public education and about what may be available once the youth has completed school.

Participation on community transition councils can also provide families with information. To empower *all* families and students, community transition councils must make information available through diverse methods. Offering parent workshops, networking coffees, and transition fairs gives family members a structured way to gain information about transition programs and services (particularly if child care can be provided). Published written materials and videos offer other means of information dissemination. Some families cannot attend workshops, and some do not respond positively to written materials. Identifying parents to serve as mentors, or groups of parents to form a support group may offer a less threatening exchange of information for some families. In addition, taking transition information to families on "their territory" such as churches, temples, mosques, community centers, or other community organizations demonstrates trust and commitment, thus empowering families.

Currently, in most communities, there is no standard process that makes it easy for youths with intellectual disability and their families to get needed postschool transition services. In other words, the current "system" of accessing transition services may be fragmented or unclear to families. Changing to a collaborative team effort focusing on improved student outcomes offers an encouraging alternative to the current fragmented system.

Skills for Collaborative Transition Planning

To be collaborative in transition planning, team members need the following:

- an understanding of state and community agencies and community resources (or a willingness to research, learn about, or create these resources)
- skills and a willingness to work with the diversity of people who have an investment in transition services (that is, be able to communicate and cooperate, and to be a team player)
- a willingness to share the knowledge and resources they bring to the process (be open, be generous, no "turfism")
- a willingness to accept responsibility for the decisions made by the collaborative group and for carrying out the agreed-upon plans (keep a focus on achieving outcomes for youths with disabilities; be accountable)

- a broad acquaintance with other agencies' missions, policies, and procedures (deFur & Taymans, 1995)

Defining Transition Team Jargon

Becoming familiar with the vocabulary that may be used in discussions about transition community efforts represents a first step in a collaborative dialogue:

- *Interagency, "between or across agencies," means that a variety of governmental or community entities with differing missions work together.* Multiple agencies or organizations in communities serve or potentially serve youths and young adults with intellectual disabilities. However, the "interagency model" means more than sitting together at a meeting, or exchanging cards or brochures, and more than expecting two agencies such as education or rehabilitation to be the providers of all transition services. Knowing about agencies, community organizations, and other entities that do or might provide transition services is a critical skill for effective transition planning (deFur & Taymans, 1995).
- *Intracommunity, "within the community," illustrates that agencies alone do not offer all the solutions and opportunities.* Intracommunity transition planning offers more creative options for services than can be found in agencies alone. The potential group extends beyond state and local agencies and includes community organizations, faith communities, employers, advocates, therapists, family members, and, first and foremost, the individual.
- *Interdisciplinary approaches, in which people from different frames of references (professions or philosophies) work together, go beyond the sharing of information to a focus on problem solving.* People on teams that use an interdisciplinary approach choose not to be territorial with their information or their ideas; people on these teams remain open to a variety of creative alternatives when faced with challenges.
- *Outcome-driven focus—that is, higher expectations with accountability—sounds like a forceful expectation, but it is a needed one.* Too often, professionals and families spend time together creating plans that never materialize or achieve the stated goals. This leaves families feeling frustrated and mistrusting and professionals feeling misused and ineffectual, but most of all, it fails youths. To make a difference in postschool outcomes for young adults with intellectual disabilities, a focus on outcomes is essential.
- *Collaboration takes families and professionals beyond networking, coordination, and cooperation to a merging of ideas, talents, and solutions.* Collaboration emerges as a powerful way to solve the most complex problems facing youths and young adults with disabilities as they transition to adult life.

FINAL THOUGHTS

The success of young adults with intellectual disabilities who have transitioned from secondary education will serve as one measure of the effectiveness of the special education and transition programs and services those individuals have received. To prepare youths with disabilities for employment and independent lives, special educators and related service providers must reshape programs and services with that end in mind. The past decade represents a time of tremendous change in employment and independent living opportunities and challenges for youths and young adults with intellectual disabilities. Gone are days when un-skilled labor jobs were readily available for young adults who lacked academic or vocational skills. Welfare reform and changes to financial supports such as Social Security supports have reduced the options of dependency on state supports. Demographic changes such as the "graying of America" mean the future promises fewer workers to support economic and social needs. All of this adds to a sense of urgency that IEP transition planning teams work diligently and creatively to ensure that in the future, young adults with intellectual disabilities are prepared for employment and independent living. Therefore, special educators must also serve as transition advocates, ensuring that programs and services, such as in-school vocational training and community-based programs, are made available. At the same time, transition advocates across the community must join together to lobby for an increase in adult service options. These options can continue the transition programming and support that began during secondary education. Young adults with intellectual disabilities continue to experience transitions throughout their lives and many will need ongoing community structures that help them continue to develop their skills of independence and community par-ticipation throughout adulthood (Wehman, 1998).

In summary, youths and young adults with intellectual disabilities represent a wide array of individuals, all of whom require some degree of support (from pervasive to intermittent) to achieve the IDEA purpose of preparing them for employment and independent living. Comprehensive inter- and intra-agency collaborative transition planning that begins early in the student's school career, that includes carefully designed courses of study and specialized instruction that address all adaptive domains, that integrates opportunities for work and com-munity experiences, that structures student programs to achieve increasingly higher levels of independence, and that keeps the student and family in the cen-ter of the dialogue represent known practices to improve postschool outcomes for young adults with intellectual disabilities. IDEA transition requirements serve as a framework under which to carry out this comprehensive approach to advance the education and social development of youths and young adults with intellectual disabilities.

REFERENCES

Benz, M. R., Lindstrom, L., & Yovanoff, P. (2000). Improving graduation and employment out-comes of students with disabilities: Predictive factors and student perspectives. *Exceptional Children, 66*, 509–529.

Benz, M. R., Yovanoff, P., & Doren, B. (1997). School to work components that predict postschool success for students with and without disabilities. *Exceptional Children, 63*, 151–166.

Blackhurst, A. E., Lahm, E. A., Harrison, E. M., & Chandler, W. G. (1999). A framework for align-ing technology with transition competencies. *Career Development for Exceptional Individu-als, 22*, 153–183.

Collet-Klingenberg, L. L., Hanley-Maxwell, C., & Stuart, S. (2000). *The relationship of an ecological model of career development to authentic learning.* University of Wisconsin–Madison, Research Institute on Secondary Education Reform for Youth with Disabilities. Available from www.wcer.wisc.edu/riser

deFur, S., Getzel, E., & Kregel, J. (1994). Individual transition plans: A work in progress. *Journal of Vocational Rehabilitation, 4,* 139–145.

deFur, S. H., & Patton, J. R. (Eds.). (1999). *Transition and school based services.* Austin, TX: PRO-ED.

deFur, S., & Taymans, J. (1995). Competencies needed for transition specialists in vocational rehabilitation, vocational education, and special education. *Exceptional Children, 62,* 38–51.

deFur, S., Todd-Allen, M., & Getzel, E. (2001). Parent participation in the transition planning process. *Career Development for Exceptional Individuals, 24,* 71–88.

Doren, B., & Benz, M. R. (1998). Employment inequality revisited: Predictors of better employment outcomes for young women with disabilities in transition. *Journal of Special Education, 31,* 425–442.

Education for All Handicapped Children Act of 1975, 20 U.S.C. § 1400 *et seq.*

Fardig, D. B., Algozzine, R. F., Schwartz, S. E., Hensel, J. W., & Westling, D. L. (1985). Postsecondary vocational adjustment of rural, mildly handicapped students. *Exceptional Children, 52,* 115–121.

Frank, A. R., & Sitlington, P. L. (2000). Young adults with mental disabilities—Does transition planning make a difference? *Education and Training in Mental Retardation and Developmental Disabilities, 35*(2), 119–134.

Geenen, S., Powers, L., & Lopez-Vasquez, A. (2001). Multicultural aspects of parent involvement in transition planning. *Exceptional Children, 67,* 265–282.

Getzel, E. E., & deFur, S. (1997). Transition planning for students with significant disabilities: Implications for student-centered planning. *Focus on Autism and Other Developmental Disabilities, 12,* 39–48.

Griffin, D. K., Rosenberg, H., Cheyney, W., & Greenberg, B. (1996). A comparison of self-esteem and job satisfaction of adults with mild mental retardation in sheltered workshops and supported employment. *Education and Training in Mental Retardation and Developmental Disabilities, 31,* 142–150.

Hagner, D., & Dileo, D. (1993). *Working together: Workplace culture, supported employment, and persons with disabilities.* Cambridge, MA: Brookline Books.

Halpern, A. (1994). The transition from youth to adult life. A position statement of the Division on Career Development and Transition. *Career Development for Exceptional Individuals, 17,* 115–124.

Hasazi, S. B., Gordon, L. R., & Roe, C. A. (1985). Factors associated with the employment status of handicappped youth exiting high school from 1979–1983. *Exceptional Children, 51,* 455–469.

Heal, L. W., Khoju, M., & Rusch, F. R. (1997). Predicting quality of life of youths after they leave special education high school programs. *Journal of Special Education, 31,* 279–299.

Houchins, D. (2001). Assistive technology barriers and facilitators during secondary and postsecondary transitions. *Career Development for Exceptional Individuals, 24,* 73–88.

Individuals with Disabilities Education Act Amendments of 1997, 20 U.S.C. § 1400.

Kohler, P. D., DeStefano, L., Wermuth, T. R., Grayson, T. E., & McGinty, S. (1994). An analysis of exemplary transition programs: How and why are they selected? *Career Development for Exceptional Individuals, 17,* 187–201.

Leconte, P. (1999). Vocational evaluation. In S. H. deFur & J. R. Patton (Eds.), *Transition and school-based services.* Austin, TX: PRO-ED.

Luckasson, R., Coulter, D. L., Polloway, E. A., Reiss, S., Schalock, R. L., Snell, M. E., Spitalnik, D. M., & Stark, J. A. (1992). *Mental retardation: Definition, classification, and systems of support* (9th ed.). Washington, DC: American Association on Mental Retardation.

Miller, R. J., La Follette, M., & Green, K. (1990). Development and field test of a transition planning procedure, 1985–1988. *Career Development for Exceptional Individuals, 13,* 45–55.

Mithaug, D. E., Horiuchi, C. R., & Fanning, P. R. (1985). A report on the Colorado statewide follow-up survey of special education students. *Exceptional Children, 51,* 397–404.

Morningstar, M., Turnbull, A., & Turnbull, R. (1995). What do students with disabilities tell us about the importance of family involvement in the transition from school to adult life? *Exceptional Children, 62,* 249–260.

Patton, J. R., Polloway, E. A., & Smith, T. E. C. (2000). Educating students with mild mental retardation. In M. L. Wehmeyer & J. R. Patton (Eds.), *Mental retardation in the 21st century* (pp. 71–90). Austin, TX: PRO-ED.

Patton, J. R., Polloway, E. A., Smith, T. E. C., Edgar, E., Clark, G. M., & Lee, S. (1996). Individuals with mild mental retardation: Postsecondary outcomes and implications for educational policy. *Education and Training in Mental Retardation and Developmental Disabilities, 31,* 75–85.

Repetto, J., & Correa, V. (1996). Expanding views on transition. *Exceptional Children, 62,* 551–563.

Sample, P. L. (1998). Postschool outcomes for students with significant emotional disturbance following best-practice transition services. *Behavioral Disorders, 23,* 231–242.

Schwartz, A. A., Jacobson, J. W., & Holburn, S. C. (2000). Defining person centeredness: Results of two consensus methods. *Education and Training in Mental Retardation and Developmental Disabilities, 35,* 235–249.

Steere, D., Pancsofar, E., Wood, R., & Hecimovic, H. (1990). Principles of shared responsibility. *Career Development for Exceptional Individuals, 13,* 143–154.

Virginia Department of Education. (1998). [Project UNITE—Transition services information]. Unpublished data. Richmond, VA: Author.

Wehman, P. (1998). *Developing transition plans.* Austin, TX: PRO-ED.

Wehman, P., Kregel, J., & Seyfarth, J. (1985). Transition from school to work for individuals with severe handicaps: A follow-up study. *Journal of the Association of the Severely Handicapped, 10,* 132–139.

Wehmeyer, M. L. (1999). Assistive technology and students with mental retardation: Utilization and barriers. *Journal of Special Education, 15,* 3–7.

Wehmeyer, M. L., & Schwarz, M. (1997). Self-determination and positive adult outcomes: A follow-up study of youth with mental retardation or learning disabilities. *Exceptional Children, 63,* 245–255.

Will, M. (1984). *OSERS programming for the transition of youth with disabilities: Bridges from school to working life.* Washington, DC: U.S. Department of Education.

CHAPTER 5

Disabilities in Late Life

D. Michael Malone, Nancy P. Kropf, and Lesa Nitcy Hope

LEARNING GOALS

Upon completion of this chapter, the reader will be able to

- discuss the population characteristics of older individuals with lifelong disabilities
- discuss how quality-of-life issues affect older individuals with lifelong disabilities
- identify critical components of the "Bill of Rights" for older individuals with lifelong disabilities
- discuss various health care needs of older individuals with lifelong disabilities
- identify and discuss various residential placement options and the issues that are critical to consider in relocation efforts that affect the lives of older individuals with lifelong disabilities
- identify various types of services and supports and discuss the relative merits of each relative to older individuals with lifelong disabilities

CASE EXAMPLE: NANCY

Nancy is a friendly and outgoing 59-year-old woman who lives with her elderly mother. She has been diagnosed as having mild intellectual disability and experiences seizures. For the last 15 years, she has been employed at a local sheltered workshop, performing a variety of jobs. Although she concentrates on her work, her job performance and earnings are only 40% of the current rate paid to 100% performance workers in the same job. In her free time, Nancy likes to listen to music, watch television, and go shopping. She occasionally so-cializes with friends from the sheltered workshop but considers her mother to be her best friend. Nancy's mother assists her with her finances, transportation, purchases, and acquisition of health-care services. What will be Nancy's future when her mother is no longer able to provide the type of support that Nancy currently receives? Will Nancy be able to continue a similar lifestyle? How will she meet the financial obligations of maintaining the same quality of life she currently enjoys?

 CASE EXAMPLE: DON

Don is a 64-year-old who has been diagnosed as having moderate intellectual disability, has limited communication skills, and demonstrates deficits in daily living skills. He lived at home with his parents until his father passed away, when Don was 45 years old. After his father's death, Don's mother felt she could no longer care for Don by herself and had him admitted to a nearby institution. Prior to his move to the institution, Don was not required to assist in his own care, nor was he engaged in any out-of-the-home work experiences. For the past 5 years, he has been working as a housekeeper in the building where he lives. Lately, he has begun showing resistance when prompted to get ready to go to work. He chooses to lounge on the sofa, watching the television. Numerous prompts by staff are needed to get him to go to work. Staff who know Don believe that he wants to retire. Given that he has made excellent progress in learning new daily living and job-related skills, should he be encouraged to maintain his current working status? To what would he retire? What would his quality of life be if he remains working? If he retires?

To address the issues of best practices that benefit individuals such as Nancy and Don, one must begin with the seemingly simple question, Who are Nancy and Don? Such inquiry must take two forms: the general "who" relative to descriptions of the population to which individuals such as Nancy and Don belong, and the specific "who" relative to individual characteristics and needs. Comprehension of the general "who" provides professionals with information that enables them to understand and address issues related to the specific "who." Indeed, failure to comprehend general population descriptions and trends relative to individuals with developmental disabilities (hereafter referred to as lifelong disabilities) as they enter into late life limits one's ability to develop best practices in service delivery. In this chapter, we attempt to provide material that will contribute to efforts to provide services and supports to individuals with lifelong disabilities as they enter into late life. Specifically, we discuss identification of older individuals who have lifelong disabilities and relevant issues associated with quality of life, health care, service provision, placement and supported living, finance, regulations and legal considerations, and, finally, daily activities and programs.

DEMOGRAPHIC PROFILE

The "graying" of U.S. society has brought about great changes in the national population profile (Dychtwald, 1999; Schaie & Willis, 1986; U.S. Senate Special Committee on Aging, American Association of Retired Persons, Federal Council on the Aging, & U.S. Administration on Aging, 1991). Projections indicate that, in the coming decades, the proportion of U.S. society composed of people who have made the transition into late life will increase substantially. This continued expansion of the elderly population is paralleled by the growth in numbers of individuals with lifelong disabilities who are also aging (Cooper, 1998; Janicki, Dalton, Henderson, & Davidson, 1999; Lubin & Kiely, 1985; Maaskant, 1993; Palley & Van Hollen, 2000; Priestley, 2001). Efforts to estimate the prevalence of individuals with lifelong disabilities who have made the transition from midlife to late life have been limited by several factors. These include estimating only those individuals with diagnoses of mental retardation and excluding other lifelong disability diagnoses, including only older individuals who are connected to formal service systems, and the lack of precision in designating when older age begins for this population (M. Seltzer, 1992).

Although the definition of lifelong disabilities put forth in the Developmental Disabilities Assistance and Bill of Rights Act Amendments of 1993 identifies various conditions that may affect an individual's ability to function independently, most of what is known regarding individuals with lifelong disabilities in the later years is based on individuals with intellectual disabilities. As M. Seltzer (1992) suggested, little is known regarding service provision to those individuals with noncognitive lifelong disabilities. Increases in the numbers of individuals with lifelong disabilities who are elderly may be attributed to a variety of factors, including the shift in the population profile mentioned previously; identification efforts at the state level resulting from increased awareness and attention from federal agencies; and improved health care, which has substantially extended life expectancies of individuals with certain lifelong disabilities (Cotten, Sison, & Starr, 1981; DiGiovanni, 1978; Evashwick, 2001; M. Seltzer & Seltzer, 1985; Thurman, 1986).

To develop services for an aging population, one must determine what constitutes a transition from midlife to late life for this group. The most widely used marker defining late life has been chronological age. The lower limit of "old age" used by professionals has ranged from 30 years of age to 65 years of age (Drew & Hardman, 2000; Segal, 1977; M. Seltzer & Seltzer, 1985; Thurman, 1986; Tymchuk, 1979; Walz, Harper, & Wilson, 1986). Age 60 is considered the point of transition in the Older Americans Act of 1965 (as amended through 1988). Age 55 appears frequently in the literature and is consistent with many federal programs (Segal, 1977). Although chronological age, especially that of 55 years, may be useful as an arbitrary marker for entrance into old age for individuals with extended life expectancies, it proves to be a less than adequate marker for individuals who have limited functional or adaptive skills or whose medical background is associated with a life expectancy below 55 years (Eyman & Borthwick-Duffy, 1994). A more useful approach may be to identify certain life stages or functional abilities that alert one to an individual's transition to late life (Priestley, 2001; M. Seltzer & Krauss, 1987). A number of alternatives to chronological age have been proposed, including Thurman's (1986) suggestion of subtracting 10 years from the average life expectancy of specific groups to determine eligibility for designated elder services, and Eisdorfer's (1983) four life stages identified in Table 5.1.

Finally, other indexes of aging that have been discussed in the literature include biological aging focused on the physical aspects of aging; social aging focused on societal expectations related to productivity and attitudes toward aging in general; and psychological aging focused on intellectual functioning, emotional adjustment, and individual perceptions of aging (Birren, 1959; Cooper, 1998; Lavin & Doka, 1999; M. Seltzer, 1985b; Thurman, 1986). Each of these approaches has its merits in alerting professionals to an individual's transition into late life, but no single measure of the transition period from midlife to late life appears entirely satisfactory. The use of chronological age as a marker is limited due to the variability of life expectancies among subgroups. Dependence on either life-stage or domain-specific aging indexes to determine eligibility for aging services is problematic because both rely on functional limitations in life activities as a diagnostic marker. In light of the apparent limitations of each of the preceding approaches, the reliance on multiple indicators would seem to have the greatest utility to service providers. A definition including chronological age to satisfy agency requirements and qualifiers related to functional aspects of society and aging would be most useful. This definition should include those

TABLE 5.1

Eisdorfer's Life Stages

Stage	Description
1	Early Life: Resources are invested in youth with the expectation that future societal benefits will follow.
2	Midlife: Adult workers contribute goods and services to benefit society.
3	Post Work: Individuals retire healthy and remain functionally independent.
4	Late Life: Less than healthy individuals become functionally dependent on others.

Note. Adapted from "Conceptual Models of Aging: The Challenge of a New Frontier," by C. Eisdorfer, 1983, *American Psychologist, 38,* pp. 197–202. Copyright 1983 by the American Psychological Association. Adapted with permission.

characteristics described in the Older Americans Act Amendments as well as measures of the aging process relative to physical change, change in cognitive ability related to performing daily activities, emotional change, and change in social skills, any of which may impact negatively on the quality of life and longevity of an individual.

For such an approach to be viable, efforts must be made to collect specific demographic and epidemiological data to guide decisions related to services appropriate for a heterogeneous group of individuals with lifelong disabilities as they age. At the present time, little information of this type exists except possibly for individuals with intellectual disabilities, and, even for that group, definitive data are not available. A 1% to 3% prevalence rate is typically applied to figures on the general population to estimate the number of individuals with lifelong disabilities in late life (M. Seltzer & Krauss, 1987; Sison & Cotten, 1989; Tymchuk, 1979; Walz et al., 1986). These prevalence estimates typically refer to individuals with intellectual disabilities and differ dramatically from estimates (e.g., 12% to 13%) made of the total population of individuals with disabilities in various states (J. Jacobson, Sutton, & Janicki, 1985; Walz et al., 1986).

As interest in older individuals with diagnoses other than intellectual disability increases (Gold & Whelan, 1992; Turk & Machemer, 1993), efforts should be made to include these older adults in prevalence estimates. Indeed, the inclusion of all relevant individuals in these efforts would result in a more accurate estimate of the number of elders with lifelong disabilities than that which is currently available only for individuals with intellectual disabilities. Combining prevalence rates used by the United Cerebral Palsy Association (0.3%), the Epilepsy Foundation of America (0.4%), and the National Society for Children and Adults with Autism (0.032%), with the rate suggested by Baroff (1982) of 0.396% for individuals with intellectual disabilities results in a total prevalence rate of about 1%. This 1% prevalence estimate and the population projections reported by Rice and Feldman (1983) result in the estimated number of individuals with lifelong disabilities who are 65 years or older shown in Table 5.2.

Such figures should be viewed with caution because mortality rates for any given subgroup are not considered when prevalence rates are applied to the general population. Research has shown that individuals who do not have significant disabilities (e.g., conditions that significantly, negatively impact one or more areas of development) and who demonstrate adaptive skills related to toileting, eating, and mobility are more likely to live longer than are individuals who experience significant disabilities and have substantial deficits in adaptive skills (Eyman & Borthwick-Duffy, 1994). In addition, it is believed that, as in the general population, the rate of disability accelerates with age after age 50 to 55 (Blake, 1981; Janicki & Jacobson, 1986). Increased disability may be associated with a

TABLE 5.2

Estimated Number of Individuals with Lifelong Disabilities, 65 Years and Older

Year	Prevalence Estimate
1980	258,920
1990	315,580
2000	362,520
2020	526,530
2040	672,560

loss of function and death (Anderson, 1989; Eyman, Call, & White, 1989). Although trends may be discussed, the individual differences in experience, in etiology and functional ability, in gender, and in residential history must not be overlooked.

Although the lack of specific demographic and epidemiological data limits the extent to which professionals can obtain precise figures, reliance on liberal estimates may lead to a service system better prepared to handle the actual population expansion. Error in this direction is preferable to error in a more conservative direction—for example, error resulting from reliance on estimates derived from actual service recipients, because many older individuals are outside or minimally involved with developmental disabilities services (Allen & Mor, 1998; G. C. Smith, Fullmer, & Tobin, 1994). A conservative error could result in the service system's being inadequately prepared to accommodate the increasing numbers of individuals with lifelong disabilities as they reach late life.

QUALITY OF LIFE

The phrase "quality of life," widely used in the field of intellectual disability in the past 2 decades (Bradley, 2000; Landesman, 1986; Turnbull & Turnbull, 2000), seems on the surface to be self-defining. One's quality of life may be viewed as a function of those ingredients in one's life that enhance personal growth, independence, health, and overall happiness. Attainment of optimum quality of life is facilitated through the protection of rights and the receipt of needed services. The definition becomes less clear, however, when service providers working with individuals with lifelong disabilities in later life attempt to specify those elements that contribute to personal growth, independence, health, and happiness and how to guarantee rights and services to this group. Thus, the definition and the understanding of the concept of quality of life have become great challenges in developing best practices for service delivery to individuals such as Nancy and Don.

The concept of quality of life may be defined from three perspectives: social, psychological, and social policy (Schalock, 1996, 2000; Schalock, Keith, Hoffman, & Karan, 1989). From the social perspective, quality of life may be defined in terms of influences external to the individual. Such environmental influences include social welfare, standard of living, formal and informal supports, education, housing, public services, health services, safety, and leisure programming. Edgerton and Gaston's (1991) study of older individuals who had been deinstitutionalized demonstrated how an array of these factors must be present to support older individuals with lifelong disabilities in community settings. Although this list is not exhaustive, it provides direction to addressing quality-of-life issues from a community standpoint.

In contrast to this perspective, the psychological perspective of quality of life represents those things that hold personal relevance to an individual in maintaining or improving life conditions such as independence, productivity, and acceptance. These personal perceptions include satisfaction with the environmental influences discussed previously, as well as general perceived happiness and well-being. An increase in one's satisfaction with personal–social resources seems to be related to increases in life satisfaction, a sense of well-being, and feelings of personal competence.

The final perspective from which the concept of quality of life can be understood is that of social policy (Schalock, 1996, 2000; Schalock et al., 1989). The social policy perspective relates to the documentation of needs that can be used to allocate fiscal resources. As defined by Murrell and Norris (1983), quality of life is a function of the degree to which human and environmental resources complement one another. Best practices in service delivery cannot be developed without an understanding of both the needs of individuals with lifelong disabilities as they enter into late life and the means with which to provide the services to address those stated needs.

How can service providers help elderly individuals with lifelong disabilities continue to grow as individuals and maintain health and happiness in relation to the social, psychological, and social policy perspectives? This challenge can be met in a number of ways. Professionals must be aware of and understand the rights of older individuals as fellow human beings and as recognized by law. A number of these rights, summarized in Table 5.3, have been outlined by Walker (1985), Cotten and Spirrison (1986), Malone (1993), Kaye (1998), and others. Such a bill of rights is applicable to all individuals with lifelong disabilities as they enter into late life.

Acknowledgment and comprehension of these rights, however, are not enough. Service providers must take the appropriate steps to guarantee that individual rights are respected and enforced. Although organizations advocating the rights of individuals with lifelong disabilities exist (e.g., United Cerebral Palsy Association, American Association on Mental Retardation, Epilepsy Foundation of America, National Society for Children and Adults with Autism), a need exists for advocacy groups that focus on issues important to those individuals who are aging (Sison & Cotten, 1989; Tymchuk, 1979; Walz et al., 1986). The basic rights that protect and enhance the quality of life of elderly citizens should be the same for both the general population and for the population of citizens with lifelong disabilities. Professionals must recognize, however, that the latter group may require additional consideration to ensure they have the opportunity to experience life at its fullest. In providing such assurances, service providers must be careful to provide a balance between the role of guardian and respect for autonomy of the individual (Howell, 1988; Kapp, 1996). All too often, professionals fail to ask for input from the individual with a lifelong disability when making decisions that will affect that individual's life. To address this issue, self-advocates and others have strongly supported the idea of self-determination, which they define as having the ability and resources to control one's existence (Nerney & Shumway, 1996; Sands & Wehmeyer, 1996). The importance of consumer direction and self-determination has gained currency with people with lifelong disabilities who are growing older as they make choices around living circumstances, work, retirement, relationships, and other areas of life.

TABLE 5.3
Bill of Rights for Individuals with Lifelong Disabilities

- The right to be considered a person first, not a condition or diagnosis
- The right to be recognized as an individual with likes and dislikes, strengths and weaknesses, and good days and bad days
- The right to an adequate standard of living and economic security
- The right to have the opportunity for self-expression
- The right to individualized and personalized services that promote full personal potential
- The right to an array of services that is generally available to other groups
- The right to live as independently as one wishes in the community of one's choice and in as typical a manner as possible
- The right to participate in and contribute to the community
- The right to supported well-being and to qualified care when required
- The right to be personally involved in setting goals and making decisions affecting one's own life
- The right to occupy one's leisure time in personally satisfying ways
- The right to pursue spiritual satisfaction
- The right to succeed and fail on one's own terms
- The right to a positive future, with appropriate levels of involvement, freedom, and choice, regardless of age
- The right to enjoy typical family relationships, companionship, and romance
- The right to appropriate levels of activity and attention to permit continued integrity of self, individual identity, and purpose
- The right to an interesting environment and lifestyle, with an availability of options to provide a variety of surroundings
- The right to choose to retire, at an appropriate age, and to be able to look forward to postwork life and experiences that are rewarding
- The right to dignity in life and death

The framework of self-determination reflects many approaches to the concept. These run the range of simply having more choice about one's daily life, to having control of resources and funding, designing policy, and implementing or directing programs (Bradley, 2000; National Institute on Consumer-Directed Long-Term Services, 1996; Nerney & Shumway, 1996).

It is important that professionals not abuse the rights and freedoms of those individuals they are intending to help. As noted previously, individuals with lifelong disabilities who reach old age typically experience less significant disabilities and have strengths in skills related to daily living. These individuals have the capacity and deserve the opportunity to have input into decisions that will directly affect the quality of their lives (Charlton, 1998). The acknowledgment of rights such as those identified in this chapter will likely promote and enhance feelings of personal relevance and self-direction within the individual with a lifelong disability and his or her family.

In addition to acknowledging, understanding, and guaranteeing the rights of older individuals with lifelong disabilities, professionals must also be aware of the basic needs of this group. Tibbits (1979) suggested that all older individuals have a need

- to render some socially useful service
- to be considered a part of the community
- to occupy increased leisure time in satisfying ways
- to enjoy normal companionship
- for recognition as an individual
- for opportunity for self-expression
- for health protection and care
- for suitable mental stimulation [and emotional support]
- for living arrangements and family relationships
- for spiritual satisfactions

A primary medium through which rights and needs of older individuals with lifelong disabilities are addressed is the support system, both formal and informal. These issues are discussed later in this chapter. In brief, service providers attuned to the multifaceted nature of quality of life will be better able to develop best practices to benefit individuals with lifelong disabilities who are aging. One must be aware of and work to protect the rights and needs of these individuals (Beaulaurier & Taylor, 2001; Racino, 2000). Issues related to underutilization of services and supports must be addressed. These efforts will do much to enhance the quality of life of individuals with lifelong disabilities as they age.

HEALTH CARE

Individuals with lifelong disabilities who attain late life (by traditional markers) typically experience less significant disabilities, are ambulatory, do not have major physical or behavioral limitations, and have adequate self-care skills (Eyman & Borthwick-Duffy, 1994). Richards (1975) noted that death in this group as it ages may be related more to risk factors particular to a severe disabling condition than to the aging process itself. Although some factors are physiological (e.g., early onset of Alzheimer's disease in individuals who have Down syndrome), other risk factors are a result of social issues such as barriers to adequate medical services, lack of trained health professionals to provide services to older individuals who have lifelong disabilities, and previous negative experiences with health care professionals (Burt et al., 1998; Cooper, 1998; G. Seltzer & Luchterhand, 1994). Even for those individuals who are not affected by such risk factors, health issues play an important role. In general, individuals with lifelong disabilities experience physiological and physical changes associated with aging similar to those experienced by individuals without lifelong disabilities (Hand, 1993; Kapell et al., 1998; Rimmer, 1998). Although there are similarities between individuals with and without lifelong disabilities that are associated with the aging process, age-related health changes may occur earlier in the lives of individuals with lifelong disabilities (Cooper, 1998; Gilson & Netting, 1997; M. Seltzer &

Seltzer, 1985). The most dramatic example of the early onset of an age-related health problem is the diagnosis of Alzheimer's disease in many individuals with Down syndrome when they are 30 to 40 years old (Wisniewski & Hill, 1985). Kapell et al. (1998) also found an increased frequency of thyroid disorders, non-ischemic heart disorders, and sensory impairments. Janicki and Dalton (1998) concurred that sensory disorders were a significant age-associated impairment, occurring with greater prevalence than is seen in the general population.

Care Issues

There do not appear to be any specialized best practices associated with the provision of health services to citizens with lifelong disabilities. There is a general perception, however, that older individuals with lifelong disabilities are underserved in health care and that many health providers have little training in, understanding of, or sensitivity to health issues of this group of older adults (Jablonski, 2000; G. Seltzer & Luchterhand, 1994). Beange and Lennox (1999) developed and identified health indicators for individuals with lifelong disabilities to present to the World Health Organization. An individual who has been relatively independent all his or her life is likely to have used and will continue to use regular health services. Such an individual may require additional assistance from others as he or she ages. Individuals who are less independent (e.g., individuals living in a supervised residential setting) will most likely use generic health services but will require, depending on their needs, a larger array of supports than will individuals with greater degrees of independence. As individuals with less independence age, they may require certain specialized services (e.g., vision screening). Individuals with the least independence, typically individuals with severe disabilities, have historically lived in larger residential care facilities (e.g., intermediate care facilities for individuals with intellectual disabilities [ICFs/ID][1]) that staff medical personnel. Given the availability of health services at the facility, these individuals are the least likely to seek out generic health care services. This pattern may change as the deinstitutionalization process continues and some individuals with the most severe disabilities take advantage of community-based supports.

A national survey of facilities for individuals with lifelong disabilities revealed that individuals ages 63 to 74 years experienced health problems comparable to their cohorts without lifelong disabilities. High blood pressure, arthritis, and heart disease proved to be the most common ailments for both groups (Anderson, 1989; Cooper, 1998). Anderson also found, as did Krauss and Seltzer (1986), that individuals living in institutional settings are perceived to need more medical care than those living in community residences. Community resi-

---

[1]We use "IFCs/ID" to reflect the change in terminology from *mental retardation* to *intellectual disability* unless we are discussing older research, which was published using the earlier terminology (IFCs/MR).

dents were noted to have a greater number of unmet needs by Krauss and Seltzer (1986) and Strauss, Shavell, Baumeister, and Anderson (1998). However, Anderson (1989) speculated that the institutionalized group is not more medically needy, but that service availability is often translated into the concept of need in developmental centers.

Alzheimer's Disease

Dementia is defined as a symptomatologic diagnosis whereby there is a loss of intellectual functioning severe enough to interfere with occupational or social functioning (American Psychiatric Association, 1987). Dementia indicates reduced functional abilities in all aspects of an individual's life. It may follow a rapid, slow, or erratic course. Sometimes the dementia stops temporarily, allowing the individual to enjoy a period of stability. Diagnosis of dementia among individuals without disabilities nominally focuses on four different areas of performance (Wisniewski & Hill, 1985). Intactness of short-term memory, decrease in ability to think abstractly, inflexibility in thinking, and overall slowing of activity manifested in all areas of life are the primary areas of intellectual decline noted. Diagnosis of dementia is particularly difficult with individuals who experience a lifelong disability. The difficulty increases as the severity of disability increases. Apathy, abrupt emotional changes, lack of care in grooming and hygiene, decreased expressive abilities, and the detection of abnormalities during neurological evaluations have been reported in individuals with Down syndrome and Alzheimer's disease.

Although some question has been raised on the issue, current evidence suggests a link between Down syndrome and Alzheimer's disease. Studies have indicated incidence rates that range from 20% to 56% of the groups studied (Janicki & Dalton, 2000). Rasmussen and Sobsey (1994) and Burt et al. (1998) discussed the difficulties in dementia diagnosis in Down syndrome. Complicating factors include a lack of early detection and an imperfect correlation between physiological changes in the brain and corresponding behavioral changes. The problem in estimating prevalence is further complicated by the functional and residential status of participants in many studies, that is, individuals who tend to have severe or profound intellectual disability and who reside in institutional settings (Wisniewski & Hill, 1985). There has also been research to indicate that neuroleptic (medication)-induced dementia is a concern and must be considered when medications are given and people demonstrate symptoms consistent with dementia (Gedye, 1998).

Individuals with Down syndrome ages 30 or older should complete a mental status evaluation yearly. This evaluation can be completed in conjunction with a recommended annual physical examination. A mental status evaluation typically focuses on abilities associated with concentration, orientation, and memory. Intelligence tests should also be administered regularly to examine constancy of intellect. Careful observation by caregivers should reveal any changes in daily living skills. Early signs of dementia require referral to specialists for further diagnosis. Indeed, locating an instrument to assess mental status for individuals with lifelong disabilities can be problematic.

The care of an individual with lifelong disabilities and Alzheimer's disease is essentially the same as that of a person with Alzheimer's disease without a lifelong disability. Reality orientation can provide a routine to help structure the individual's day. The goal is to encourage independence while ensuring safety of the person involved. Respite care is an important part of the intervention plan for the caregivers. Participation in a support group that focuses on the families of patients with Alzheimer's disease is also helpful for many caregivers.

Mental Health

Information-processing problems; associated medical, physical, or sensory disorders; an inability to express one's feelings adequately; and cultural influences are associated with the development of mental health issues in individuals with intellectual disabilities. Although families and service providers may believe that shielding individuals with lifelong disabilities from painful or complicated facts is preferable, providing incorrect or misleading information has the consequence of confusing the recipient or provoking anxiety (see Yanok & Beifus, 1993). Individuals with intellectual disabilities develop severe mental illness or difficult behaviors at a rate almost twice the rate of individuals without intellectual disabilities (Cherry, Matson, & Paclawsky, 1997; Menolascino & Potter, 1989).

In a study of mental illness in individuals with intellectual disabilities, Menolascino and Potter (1989) identified the major types of mental illness encountered. Of 76 elderly individuals with intellectual disability evaluated for 9 months in a psychiatric hospital, almost one third exhibited schizophrenic behaviors. In another study of psychopathology in older adults with severe and profound intellectual disability, Cherry et al. (1997) found that anxiety and impulse control disorders were potentially more problematic for this population. Other diagnoses were dementia (both senile and Alzheimer's type), affective disorders such as depression, adjustment disorders such as brief reactive psychoses, personality disorders including schizoid type, and anxiety disorders (Menolascino & Potter, 1989).

A fundamental requirement in the delivery of services to elderly individuals with intellectual disabilities and mental illness is the provision of an intensive schedule of intervention (Menolascino & Potter, 1989). Thoughtful caregivers who show individuals how to express themselves and who prompt them to learn new coping behaviors are critical to the intervention process. In addition, interventions may involve the use of psychoactive medications. Psychopharmacology in the older population has been controversial for many years because many biological processes important to effective pharmacological intervention (e.g., the absorption, transport, metabolic integration, and excretion of drugs) change with advancing age. As a result, many drugs affect elderly individuals differently than they affect younger cohorts. When psychoactive medications are combined with other medications used to treat physical ailments, the interaction of the drugs can produce unexpected side effects. In addition, psychotropic drugs sometimes produce serious side effects such as heart rhythm changes or involuntary movements as a result of tardive dyskinesia (Rinck & Calkins, 1989). In spite of these considerations, older individuals with lifelong disabilities are prescribed and consume more psychoactive drugs than younger individuals (Anderson & Polister, 1993; Pary, 1993).

Vision

Most people lose some visual function with age (DiStefano & Aston, 1986). Loss of visual acuity (sharpness of image at a distance), loss of ability to focus quickly, inability to see clearly closely, sensitivity to glare, need for increased light, and difficulty seeing well at night are some of the more common difficulties encountered. Each of these occurs as a function of age. The most common causes of visual deterioration are cataracts, senile macular degeneration, diabetes mellitus, and glaucoma (DiStefano & Aston, 1986). Cataracts, which cloud the lens, are the most common cause of reduced vision in elderly individuals. Recommended medical intervention includes the surgical removal of the cataract. Macular degeneration, a second cause of visual deterioration, is the major cause of blindness in elderly individuals. The part of the retina that allows the perception of fine detail and color deteriorates slowly. Blurring and clouding of vision are common complaints. Although laser treatment can be a successful intervention, early diagnosis and prompt treatment of the condition are critical. A third consideration, diabetes, may cause a variety of visual dysfunctions, many of which are caused by uncontrolled blood sugar levels. Prompt medical intervention is a must if any visual irregularities occur, because many of these conditions are treatable. Finally, service providers must consider glaucoma as a causal agent of visual impairment. Although glaucoma is not directly related to the aging process, the slow progression of the disease may result in late identification, after serious damage has occurred. Glaucoma is associated with increased pressure within the eye, which results in nerve damage and permanent loss of peripheral vision. The individual is left with what is commonly called tunnel vision (DiStefano & Aston, 1986).

These vision-related limitations affect the elderly regardless of disability status. However, the person with a lifelong disability may not be able to adequately describe the symptoms and receive appropriate and timely intervention (Flax & Luchterhand, 1998). Unfortunately, assessment of visual impairments has been a neglected area of research and practice for older individuals with lifelong disabilities (G. Seltzer & Luchterhand, 1994). It is imperative for caregivers and others close to the individual with a disability to be attentive to the symptoms of these conditions and to the behavior of the elderly individual with a disability. A person with a lifelong disability may appear to lose some functional daily living skills with no apparent cause. The diminishment of such skills may be associated with visual deterioration and should prompt appropriate screening efforts (Flax & Luchterhand, 1998).

Assistive devices and adjustments to daily routines may allow individuals with visual impairments to capitalize on their remaining vision. Magnifiers can be used for image enlargement; field-expanding devices allow those with tunnel vision to increase their mobility; large-print books are now available; and higher wattage light may be beneficial. Contrasting colors of electrical wall plates, dishes and placemats, combs and brushes, and stairs (by placing contrasting tape on steps) may also assist individuals in leading the life to which they are accustomed. Devices such as the Kurzwell Reading Machine, which translates printed words into synthesized speech via computer and talking books, are available. Finally, mobility training may be warranted (DiStefano & Aston, 1986).

Hearing

Hearing loss is so common in elderly individuals that it is rarely evaluated (Cooper, 1998; Glass, 1986). There is no evidence that older individuals with lifelong disabilities experience symptoms of hearing loss more frequently than the general population of elderly individuals. *Presbycusis* is the term used to describe normal hearing loss due to aging. Inability to hear speech clearly, even though the enunciation and volume are adequate (speech discrimination), an increased sensitivity to certain sounds or pitch that sound especially loud (recruitment), and sounds within one's ears (tinnitus) are characteristic of age-related hearing loss. Any or all of these characteristics may be present in elderly individuals. Ear wax buildup, an inner ear mechanism malfunction, central nervous system changes, trauma due to loud noise, or auditory mechanism damage due to certain drugs are the most common reasons for presbycusis (Glass, 1986).

If an older person with a lifelong disability seems to be unusually preoccupied and inattentive, his or her hearing should be evaluated (Evenhuis, van Zanten, Brocaar, & Roerdinkholder, 1992). Because the individual may not be able to clearly communicate problems that he or she might have experienced prior to or during the evaluation, professionals must be keenly aware of any cues and reactions to environmental stimuli that the individual may provide. Several options are available for individuals with hearing impairments, including hearing aids, cochlear implants, and aural rehabilitation. A variety of techniques are usually used.

Other devices are available to help individuals with hearing impairments function independently and safely. Flashing lights can be attached to the telephone, doorbell, or fire alarm. Personal care dogs may be trained to assist in physical guidance and to alert their human companion to important sounds and environmental situations. Closed-captioned television, amplified telephones, and telecommunication devices for the deaf (TDD) systems that use the telephone lines to send and receive printed messages are available. The TDD system is now used by elderly individuals with hearing impairments as well as by deaf individuals (Glass, 1986).

Nutrition

Physiological changes that occur as a result of the aging process affect the way the body uses nutrients (Huber, 1985). As the body ages, the proportion of lean body mass decreases, resulting in reduced energy, or caloric, needs. If intake is not adjusted, weight is gained. Taste is decreased, dental problems may lessen food intake, nutrients may not be absorbed efficiently, digestive disturbances become commonplace, large-bowel disorders often intensify, and conditions such as osteoporosis and vascular disease may emerge (Huber, 1985). Huber noted that these conditions are common to all elderly individuals. Nutritional status is also affected by medications, disease, and the individual's eating skills. Caregivers and friends should be observant of weight changes and the person's ability to feed him- or herself while maintaining a desirable weight. If physical disability encroaches on an individual's ability to eat independently, investigation into a variety of adaptive utensils and other eating devices should be made.

FINANCIAL AND LEGAL ISSUES

Legislative action has caused aging and developmental disability agencies to begin integrated planning, funding, and delivery of services for the elderly with lifelong disabilities (Janicki, 1994; Scotch, 2001). The Developmental Disabilities Act as amended in 1993 requires more collaborative work between the developmental disability and aging groups. This act also includes fiscal appropriations to support university programs that focus on training personnel to work with individuals who are aging and who have lifelong disabilities.

The Older Americans Act as amended in 1987 called particular attention to the needs of older individuals with lifelong disabilities. In 1992, the Older Americans Act became even more explicit and authorized additional supports for community involvement of older adults and their care providers (Janicki, 1993). The Administration on Aging was directed to develop collaborative relations with the Administration on Developmental Disabilities. This relationship encourages the developmental disability and aging networks at the state and local levels to focus on need rather than category of recipient. The recent amendments specifically targeted providing elderly individuals with lifelong disabilities access to the services offered by the Older Americans Act such as home helpers, legal services, transportation, and congregate meals (Older Americans Act of 1965 as amended through December 1988). Federally funded agencies have been directed to promote research and to sponsor educational opportunities as an incentive to encourage entry into the field as a profession (Special Committee on Aging, 2002). Although more options are becoming available for elderly individuals with lifelong disabilities, the individual and his or her caregivers must move through a maze of legal and financial choices, which may often seem impenetrable, in search of the best fit between individual needs and programs.

There have been sweeping changes over the last decade in the size and type of residential supports available, as well as changes in funding and allocation percentages. In 1990, Braddock, Hemp, Fujiura, Bachelder, and Mitchell found that 85% of all federal funding for residences was spent on congregate living settings (those with 16 or more beds) and intermediate care facilities for people with mental retardation (ICFs/MR). In the next decade, between 1989 and 1998, that percentage dropped to 39% (Fox-Grage, Folkemer, & Lewis, 2001). During those years, the national population of people living in ICF/MR settings decreased by 17.1% (Prouty, Lakin, & Anderson, 2000).

During the same time frame, there was rapid growth in the federal–state Home and Community Based Services (HBCS) Waiver. This program, created by the Omnibus Budget Reconciliation Act of 1981 (P.L. 97-35), is used to enable individuals with lifelong disabilities to avoid institutionalization by providing a residential exception to the Medicaid-funded ICF/MR. From 1989 to 1998, the program increased 27% each year. By 1998, the HBCS Waiver made up 28% of total mental retardation/developmental disabilities (MR/DD) funding nationally. From June 1994 to June 1999, the population receiving services under the HBCS Waiver increased 115.4% (Prouty et al., 2000). Because each state determines which services will be reimbursed under the waiver, a lack of uniformity exists from state to state (Duckett & Guy, 2000).

Services have been transformed from primarily institution-based to community-based services. Braddock, Hemp, Parish, and Westrich (1997) reported that in fiscal year 1996, two thirds of total MR/DD financial resources in the states were allocated to community service activities. Total funding for MR/DD services was $25.6 billion in 1998 (Braddock, Hemp, Parish, & Rizzolo, 2000). The total number of people served in 1999 was 378,530 (Prouty et al., 2000).

The nature and availability of services is changing in part due to the Supreme Court's decision in the case of *Olmstead v. L.C.* (1999). The decision challenges all states to develop a comprehensive array of community supports and services, citing provisions of the Americans with Disabilities Act (ADA). In order to comply, states will need to create and implement plans to place people with disabilities in less restrictive settings within a reasonable period of time (Fox-Grage et al., 2001). Pensions are of interest both to the families who have a member with a lifelong disability and to the individuals themselves. The state of New York (Ross, 1989) has studied the feasibility of several pension options. Ross found that the majority of individuals with lifelong disabilities are supported by Supplemental Security Income (SSI) or Social Security Disability Income (SSDI). Although many individuals work, their jobs are often low paying and part time, and in settings such as sheltered workshops. In such cases, pension benefits are typically not available.

A monthly paycheck is an important symbol of independence. However, because most individuals with lifelong disabilities have likely not paid into a pension program, there are no funds from which they can draw (Ross, 1989). Several options are still possible. For example, one chapter of The ARC in New York pays each retiree with a lifelong disability a bonus of $10 monthly for a maximum of 24 months after retirement. Because the money is not a pension or a fringe benefit, the bonus is not considered income and does not disrupt the SSI support being received.

Sheltered workshops could also charge their customers a nominal surcharge of 1% or 2% to finance their employees' retirement. This method could be undertaken at the local, regional, or state level. A statewide pension program administered by a statewide agency or association of agencies is another option. Although the provision of tax-deferred annuities as pensions is currently being explored, the question arises as to whether this plan might put the worker in an employee status and cause legal difficulties (Ross, 1989). The idea of helping the individual with a lifelong disability open an individual retirement account (IRA) is also under consideration. This option, however, is limited to those individuals with financial resources beyond their job earnings, because SSI recipients cannot maintain over $2,000 worth of assets without jeopardizing their need status. Some proponents believe that the IRA option is the most reasonable. However, existing laws regulating IRAs would have to be modified to accommodate large numbers of individuals who experience lifelong disabilities and who fall into the lower income brackets. If such an instrument were not inheritable by anyone other than the worker or his or her children, there might be an incentive to modify the existing laws.

A final option, one explored by the state of New York, is to use a private insurance company to administer pension plans. Payroll deductions of as little as $10 per month can be deposited into a tax-free annuity account for the individual. One possible limitation to this option is the irregular schedule of earnings often experienced by individuals with lifelong disabilities. A related area of concern is that of permanency planning. As discussed by Howell (1988), such planning has associated practical and ethical considerations. Individuals who experience physical, intellectual, or social–emotional challenges also may experience varying degrees of stability in their service and support networks throughout their lifetimes. The various individual and family transitions that these people experience as they age, although not necessarily significantly different from the transitions that are experienced by people without disabilities, are potentially more complex given (a) the individual's level of functioning and (b) a decreasing array of support options. For instance, there typically is a greater density of individual and family supports geared toward the earlier years than the later years. Further, individuals with disabilities will experience what all of us experience: the death of parents. For people with lifelong disabilities, however, such a loss may represent the end of critical financial and functional support.

Attention is now being directed at how families plan for the future of a member with a disability (Kaufman, Adams, & Campbell, 1991). Unfortunately, many families cope with the stress of future planning by denying the need for preparation or by assuming that other family members (e.g., siblings) will assume care at some future point (Heller & Factor, 1988). Preparation for future care is an especially critical concern of older parents due to anxieties about quality of care or the perception of "uncompleted parenting" that can compromise the planning process (Jennings, 1987; Kelly & Kropf, 1995; Kropf & Greene, 1993; G. C. Smith & Tobin, 1993). An exploratory study of adults with lifelong disabilities who live with their parents showed that the economic status of the family is a major factor in whatever long-term plans are made. In addition, the higher the adaptive functioning level of the child, the greater the likelihood of permanency planning. Permanency planning was also more likely for female children. It was particularly interesting that over 500 of the parents surveyed had not made concrete plans for their child's future (Kaufman, Campbell, & Adams, 1990).

The financial and legal aspects of the life of an individual with a lifelong disability are, for many individuals, vague at best. Permanency planning should be a priority, especially when one considers the likelihood that an individual with a lifelong disability will outlive his or her parents. A host of legal issues arise that warrant consideration when developing permanency systems. Will the individual be able to decide and communicate his or her wishes regarding health, finances (including estates and investments), and life direction? As additional services become available, such as the impetus for supported living and home ownership options (O'Brien, 1994), mechanisms to help older adults and their families with learning options and decision making must be instituted and refined. Research has supported the idea that later-life training programs and planning can help older adults with lifelong disabilities gain knowledge and skills as they age, around work, retirement, health, wellness, and living arrangements (Heller, Miller, Hsieh, & Sterns, 2000).

Another issue involves competency for independent decision making. Can the older individual make competent decisions, or will he or she require assistance due to the inability to conceptualize the situation and its possible outcomes? These are the issues of guardianship. Are competent individuals with lifelong disabilities giving powers of attorney to individuals they trust, so their wishes can be carried out in the future if they are unable to do so themselves? Wishes regarding issues such as refusal of medical intervention, resuscitation orders, advocacy desires, management of financial matters, and life direction might be specified. These are the issues confronted by elderly individuals without disabilities, and elderly individuals with lifelong disabilities should confront the identical issues. An attorney knowledgeable in estates, guardianship, and powers of attorney should be consulted.

SERVICE PROVISION

As previously discussed, formal and informal support systems serve as a primary medium through which rights and needs of older individuals with lifelong disabilities are addressed. The organization and supervision of formal and informal supports leads to increased activity on the part of the person receiving support as that person's needs are met. This outcome is important given that increased activity level is clearly predictive of quality of life in elderly individuals without lifelong disabilities (Osberg, McGinnis, DeJong, & Seward, 1987). Because individuals with lifelong disabilities experience physical or mental impairments that result in life situations that are more constricted than those of individuals without disabilities, the importance of the development of a strong support network becomes apparent.

Formal Supports

Formal supports may be the most easily observed, although not necessarily the most effective, of the two types of supports that we discuss. This support generally includes a variety of services moderated from outside the personal social network. Formal supports may include services related to health, vocational training, transportation, recreation or leisure, counseling, and information and referral (Clements, 1991; Hamilton & Segal, 1975; Keller, 1991; Segal, 1978; Tymchuk, 1979). Unfortunately, such services are often underutilized by those individuals in greatest need. A number of factors may contribute to poor utilization of formal support by individuals with lifelong disabilities in late life (Segal, 1978). First, the level of awareness of service availability among this group is generally low. Efforts must be made to increase this awareness and to ensure positive attitudes toward accessing services once they are made known. Second, inconsistency of services across areas (e.g., city, county, state) may limit access by individuals in need. Such inconsistency can engender confusion and frustration that can lead individuals to "drop out" of the service delivery system. Third, inadequate distribution of services necessarily affects their use by a large number of individuals. Services may be inaccessible because of location, increased caseloads that create waiting lists, and an inadequate system of identifying the population membership. Fourth, personnel who provide services are often not adequately trained to address older individuals' needs (Kropf, 1996). In response to this need for trained personnel, funding has been made available such as that from the Administration on Developmental Disabilities to University Affiliated Programs for training initiatives in the area of aging and lifelong disabilities (see Kropf, Malone, & Welke, 1993).

The intellectual disabilities/developmental disabilities (ID/DD) and aging networks provide a multitude of services. Historically, each has served a specific group, with minimal overlap. As administrative priorities have changed and fiscal resources have diminished, however, the emphasis for program development has shifted to linking these disparate service sectors (Ansello & Eustis, 1992; Factor, 1996). Legislative action in both areas requires more collaboration and information exchange among agencies (G. P. S. Smith, Thyer, Clements, & Kropf, 1997). The ID/DD and aging networks are not insensitive to this pressure. Age discrimination was the impetus for establishing the aging network. Those involved in the aging system focus on creating services that are not specially geared to the elderly but are responsive to the needs of older people in general. The focus has shifted from a specific age, income status, or disability status to the individuals' need for resources (McDowell, 1988). The Older Americans Act is one means of providing services to older individuals. The funding of programs through this act gives state and regional agencies on aging the authority to coordinate and tailor the services they offer according to identified needs (Quirk & Aravanis, 1988).

Much of the current discussion on services for older individuals with lifelong disabilities focuses on the administrative provision of the service rather than on quality, appropriateness, or rationale. Many states have conducted surveys in an attempt to determine the needs of this population of citizens. M. Seltzer and Krauss (1987) have identified three primary means of service provision for elderly individuals with lifelong disabilities: to receive services with other individuals who have lifelong disabilities in an age-integrated group; to receive services with non–age-integrated groups of individuals who are elderly and who experience similar disabilities; or to access aging programs that are designed to serve seniors without lifelong disabilities. The state of Massachusetts conducted a survey of how the state's services were being used. Almost two thirds of the elderly with intellectual disabilities received services in age-integrated, disability-segregated settings; one third received generic senior services; and approximately 5% participated in segregated age and disability programs. The individuals with lifelong disabilities involved were recipients of MR/DD network services (M. Seltzer, 1988). One can only speculate about the number of elderly individuals with lifelong disabilities using generic elder programs. Such information is largely unknown to the ID/DD network. One area of concern for many advocates is the improvement of individual access to aging programs. Referral to aging programs by interdisciplinary teams, with admission contingent on a successful trial period, is discussed as one means of incorporating older individuals with lifelong disabilities in elder programs (Cotten & Spirrison, 1986). Cross-training of service providers is a necessity to ensure effective and comprehensive programs that meet the needs of the older population of individuals with lifelong disabilities (Gibson, 1991). Coordinated interagency projects, including financial sharing, are another critical area (Cotten & Spirrison, 1988; Hawkins & Eklund, 1990). Case management, advocacy, day services, home care, family or natural supports, and respite services are also commonly mentioned as important services (Hawkins & Eklund, 1989, 1990; S. Jacobson, Stoneman, & Kropf, 1994; Leal, 1999).

Caregivers

When services are viewed from the perspective of the caregiver rather than that of the service provider, satisfaction with services seems to be moderated by the caregiver's perception of stress and his or her ability to maintain the caregiver role. High levels of maladaptive behaviors are associated with more intense feelings of stress and burden by the parents. Interestingly, the age of the caregiver does not seem to be related to the perception of burden (Kaufman et al., 1990) or to the assessment of the ability to perform caregiving chores. Caregiver perception of no longer being able to provide appropriate care is the impetus to access formal services (Engelhardt, Brubaker, & Lutzer, 1988).

Attention to the needs of care providers is becoming more prominent, with the recognition that parents of older children now experience extended parenting due to longer life expectancies for both the parents and the offspring. Examples of parent caregivers who are 70 and 80 years of age are not uncommon (Kelly & Kropf, 1995). Jennings (1987) has described these older caregivers as "perpetual parents" due to the extended caregiving responsibilities, which usually begin at the birth of their child with a disability and cease at their own incapacitation or death. The needs of older care providers include both concrete services (e.g., respite care or home maintenance) and psychosocial interventions to address perceptions of uncompleted parenting or excessive worries and fears about the future (Kropf, 1997; Kropf & Greene, 1993; Marshak, Prezant, & Seligman, 1999).

Specialized Services

The most commonly available services are those provided by the Older Americans Act as amended in 1988. Included are congregate meals at nutrition sites, housekeeping services, advocacy, case management, legal assistance, socialization, and leisure activities through senior centers. Less commonly found, but valuable, are adult day-care programs and respite care programs. Although these services are generally thought of as part of the aging network, many are part of the ID/DD network.

Case management, the organization and coordination of activities for another, has long been used by professionals working with individuals with lifelong disabilities to assist each individual in meeting his or her obligations and receiving services as needed. The case manager provides many different functions that can assist both the older individual with a lifelong disability and his or her family. Examples of specific tasks undertaken by case managers include linkage to other programs, advocacy on behalf of the individual, and auxiliary support to the individual or family such as arranging or providing transportation. Case management is essential in the lives of many individuals with lifelong disabilities because this practice approach provides a sense of structure and provides a checks-and-balances system to ensure accountability by other service providers (Greene & Kropf, 1995). A recent trend is private case management, which is reimbursable by insurance.

Informal Supports

Formal support systems should not exist in a vacuum. Ideally, formal support should be balanced by informal, or personal or social, support. Simply defined, informal support is the exchange of emotional, tangible, or instrumental assistance based on the relationships of particular individuals, not on formalized roles. Such support exchanges take place between family members, friends, or neighbors and may include a sharing or coordination of emotional, leisure, and financial resources. In these types of relationships, no formalized agreements are made between the individuals involved (Hooyman, 1983). It is not unusual to find that elderly individuals who have lifelong disabilities have limited informal support systems. Reports by individuals with lifelong disabilities indicate difficulties associated with finding friends, maintaining friendships, and loneliness (Bostwick & Foss, 1981). Understandably, barriers in this area will negatively affect one's self-efficacy and quality of life.

The significance of informal support to older people with lifelong disabilities is underscored by the results of studies conducted (Edgerton, 1988; Harlan-Simmons, Holtz, Todd, & Mooney, 2001). The tremendous success in independent functioning demonstrated by the older participants in the study was attributed in part to the strength of the informal supports enjoyed by the participants. Although small support systems can be high in quality and beneficial to the recipient, the small size of the support network may place the recipient at greater risk when the system eventually breaks down (e.g., from the death of a parent). Because individuals with lifelong disabilities may be unmarried and childless, they are often limited in the breadth of familial support that they can receive (M. Seltzer, 1985a). Although many of these aged individuals are now outliving their parents, who are often their strongest advocates (DiGiovanni, 1978), the strength of sibling relationships must not be ignored.

Although family members serve as the primary informal supports for aging individuals with lifelong disabilities who are living in the family home, the number of such persons who are actually residing with family members is unclear (Krauss & Seltzer, 1986). Across the lifespan, however, families are the nation's "largest 'service provider' for individuals with MR/DD" (Fujiura, Roccoforte, & Braddock, 1994, p. 250). These individuals may receive no support from professionals and have few friends to count on for support. In contrast, individuals living in the community receive support from family, friends, and professionals (Krauss & Erickson, 1988). Not surprisingly, the support networks (formal and informal) for the individuals living in the family home are significantly smaller than for those living in community settings (Hewitt, O'Nell, & Bestgen, 1998; Krauss & Erickson, 1988). Although siblings often provide much support, it is unclear whether they are willing and able to assume the role of primary resource or caregiver when the parent can no longer fill this capacity. Kaufman and colleagues (1990) found that some aged parents have unspoken expectations that their children without disabilities will care for siblings with lifelong disabilities when the parent is no longer able.

Finally, the prevailing social trend of the dissolution of the family network may negatively impact the family support system of individuals with lifelong disabilities. Family members who would otherwise be called upon to accept caregiving responsibilities when the parents are no longer able may not be a stable source on which the individual can rely. Regardless of the reason for potential restriction of informal supports, the threat of losing a critical form of emotional and substantive support is very real to older individuals with lifelong disabilities (M. Seltzer & Seltzer, 1985). The importance of the complementary interaction between types of supports and services becomes evident when one becomes aware of the potentially limited personal support available to older individuals with lifelong disabilities and the potential risks that are faced by the individual should the informal supports that are available erode. When relationships become limited, the importance of community supports is increased. This interaction underscores the importance of the need for an interdependence of supports and services (Carswell & Hartig, 1979; Crane, 2001; Famighetti, 1979; National Council on Disability, 1999; M. Seltzer & Krauss, 1987; Thurman, 1986) that will allow greater flexibility in the provision of services that address the needs of the older individual in the event that restrictions are imposed, by whatever means, upon any part of the system. Such an interdependence of supports would also facilitate more positive transitions and subsequent adjustments than would likely be the case should the older individual remain reliant on any one particular source of support.

Residential Placement Issues

Any discussion of residential placement issues related to individuals with life-long disabilities is likely to elicit a diverse array of responses and viewpoints that reflect a broad continuum of beliefs and values. Without a doubt, the potential placement options for older individuals with lifelong disabilities are varied and range from public residential facilities (i.e., institutions) to private community options in which individuals own their homes. Many self-advocates and their supporters (e.g., family members and friends) have fought for full community inclusion and associated placement considerations. Other advocates have fought equally hard to protect that which they consider their rights—to have a range of placement options available that include public residential facilities (Palley & Van Hollen, 2000). For example, a small but vocal lobbying group, the Voice of the Retarded, has attempted to dismantle the Developmental Disabilities and Assistance Bill of Rights Act because of its support of full community inclusion. Our intent for this section is not to address the philosophical and emotional differences that are evident in the field with regard to placement issues but to highlight important considerations that should be a part of the decision-making process, regardless of philosophical leanings. Interested readers are also referred to Heller (1985), M. Seltzer and Krauss (1987), O'Brien (1994), and Bradley (2000).

The past century has witnessed an increasingly negative social reaction to the short- and long-term placement of individuals with lifelong disabilities in public residential facilities. The mass warehousing of this group of individuals through the first half of the 1900s created such social disdain that the word "institution" now has highly negative connotations. By the year 2000, nearly all states had reduced or closed their state-run institutions. In fact, there were only seven states where more than half of all individuals were served in ICFs/ID. In most states, the majority of individuals are served under the HBCS Waiver program (G. Smith, Prouty, & Lakin, 2001).

This movement to deinstitutionalize individual placement options has been, in part, a result of and, in part, a contributor to the expansion of the continuum of residential options for people with lifelong disabilities. A host of residential options are available for individuals with lifelong disabilities, including public and private residential facilities, nursing homes, group homes, foster homes, family homes, and numerous independent, supported options, such as apartments and owned homes. M. Seltzer and Krauss (1987) have provided an informative resource on residential typologies (see Table 5.4). Such options represent a continuum from most restrictive to least restrictive placements currently available.

Although a variety of residential options for people with lifelong disabilities exist, professionals must be careful to identify program options that are designed to meet the needs of an aging population of individuals. Professionals must not assume that a program that supports younger adults is necessarily equipped to meet the needs of older individuals. Paralleling a growth in national interest and need, the development of community and institutional residential programs that specifically address the needs of elderly individuals occurred on a

TABLE 5.4

Residential Typologies

Author(s)	Typology	Dimensions Used for Classification
Baker, Seltzer, & Seltzer (1977)	1. Small group homes (≤ 10 residents) 2. Medium group homes (11–20 residents) 3. Large group homes (21–40 residents) 4. Mini-institutions (41–80 residents) 5. Mixed-group homes 6. Group homes for older adults 7. Foster family care 8. Sheltered villages 9. Workshop dormitories 10. Community preparatory programs 11. Semi-independent units 12. Comprehensive systems	• Type of administrative structure • Population characteristics • Program philosophy • Program size
Butler & Bajaanes (1977)	1. Custodial 2. Maintaining 3. Therapeutic	• Presence of habilitative programming • Degree of community contact • Level of activity within the residence • Intensity of caregiver involvement

Campbell & Bailey (1984)	1. Family-oriented placements
	  a. Natural family
	  b. Foster family
	  c. Boarding homes
	2. Client-directed placements
	  a. Independent living options
	3. Agency-directed placements
	  a. Group homes
		• Type of program sponsorship

Hill & Lakin (1986)	1. Specialized foster home 2. Small group residence (1–6 or 7–15) 3. Large private group residence (16–63, 64–299, or 300+) 4. Large public group residence (16–63, 64–299, or 300+) 5. Semi-independent 6. Board and supervision 7. Personal care 8. Specialized nursing	• Program model • Program size • Program sponsorship

(continues)

TABLE 5.4 *Continued.*
Residential Typologies

Author(s)	Typology	Dimensions Used for Classification
Scheerenberger (1983)	1. Natural family home 2. Foster family home 3. Group home 4. Private residential facility 5. Semi-independent living 6. Independent living 7. Boarding home 8. Community psychiatric program 9. General medical hospital 10. Public residential facility 11. Hospital for the mentally ill 12. Nursing home 13. Correctional facility 14. School for the blind 15. Intermediate care facility 16. Rest home 17. Work placement	• Discrete service type

M. M. Seltzer & Krauss (1987)	1. Community-based residential programs
	  a. Foster homes
	  b. Group homes
	  c. Group homes with nurses
	  d. ICFs/MR
	  e. Apartment programs
	  f. Mixed residential programs
	2. Institutional residential programs
		• Program setting
		• Program type

Note. Adapted from *Aging and Mental Retardation: Extending the Continuum* (pp. 54–55), by M. M. Seltzer and M. W. Krauss, 1987, Washington, DC: American Association on Mental Retardation. Copyright 1987 by the American Association on Mental Retardation. Adapted with permission.

significant level in the mid-1980s (M. Seltzer & Krauss, 1987). Many of these programs evolved into the position of serving and supporting older individuals with lifelong disabilities as a function of the aging of the program's resident base.

Many individuals with lifelong disabilities, especially those who are elderly, appear to fall victim to the "relocation shuffle." As institutional residential facilities are closed, residents are moved to other residential placements. As individuals age and as other life or agency circumstances change (e.g., the diminishment of functional ability, the loss of informal support systems, change in administrative priorities), individuals are at risk for transferral from one program to another. In spite of the range of residential placement options and the reduction in the numbers of institutional residential programs, there appears to be a disproportionate increase in the rate of admission and readmission of individuals with lifelong disabilities into institutional residential programs as they grow older. Given this trend and other relocation efforts, professionals must address questions about the appropriateness of relocation (i.e., is it truly in the best interests of the individual?) and the impact of the relocation on the individual concerned.

Before any relocation effort is undertaken, one must weigh the potential benefits against the potential risks for the individual, independently of professional beliefs. Although relocation trauma was at one time considered to be a critical factor, it is now known that such risk may be minimal for many individuals (Heller, 1985). Individuals in good health may experience short-term physical, emotional, and behavioral change; however, with such individuals it is believed that the benefits outweigh the potential risks. As suggested by Heller (1985), O'Brien (1994), and M. Seltzer, Krauss, Hong, and Orsmond (2001), quality of residential life and the impact of relocation on any one individual is likely to be influenced by the following factors:

- individual characteristics related to strengths, vulnerabilities, physical and psychological health
- individual perceptions related to familiarity with residence, preparation prior to relocation, control allowed, power in decision making related to residence and relocation
- level of social support, both formal and informal
- characteristics of the program environment related to individual suitability, degree of restrictiveness, parallels with previous residence, physical design, and social climate and orientation
- management of the relocation process, especially preparatory efforts; respect for the individual involved; and overall administration of the change process

Tantamount to these discrete issues is the goodness of fit between them, with an emphasis placed on the individual's needs, desires, and health (physical and psychological) condition. Relocation is most detrimental to individuals in poor health.

An often neglected factor, independent of specific setting characteristics, is the desire of the individual being considered for relocation. Many individuals who have maintained long-term residence in an institutional residential program have developed routines, adjusted to the safety of the program, created a social network, and developed a sense of permanency and stability (Dickerson, Hamilton, Huber, & Segal, 1979; M. Seltzer et al., 2001; M. Seltzer & Seltzer, 1985). The disruption of a life caused by relocation may be severe (DiGiovanni, 1978; Heller & Factor, 1988; Rago, 1985; Strauss et al., 1998; Thurman, 1986) if, in fact, an individual expresses a desire to maintain his or her residence in the program from which he or she is to be moved. In one study, 18 of the 23 individuals interviewed expressed a preference to stay in the institutional residential program (Dickerson et al., 1979). This is not to say that these elderly individuals cannot or will not adjust to other, less restrictive programs or that they will not realize benefits in their overall functioning. Indeed, evidence supports positive outcomes to this effect. However, professionals are faced with a social and philosophical dilemma because, on the one hand, they support personal independence and opinions but, on the other hand, their beliefs about best practice are contradictory to the personal independence and opinion of the individual whose life will be affected. The outcome in such cases is often that the opinion of the individual or his or her primary agents is devalued by assignment of a lesser degree of importance than that assigned to the celebrated cause (whatever it may be) of the people with the true power of decision making. We have put forth this extreme, although not unrealistic, example, not as a statement in favor of institutional residential facilities, but to underscore the dilemmas that professionals may face if they sincerely attempt to put in practice what they espouse. Although this issue of true personal rights and options in decision making may not be reconciled, professionals must be aware of the potential effect of this issue on relocation efforts and must develop means to alleviate the effect on the individual (S. Jacobson & Kropf, 1993).

Activities and Programs

As we have discussed in earlier sections, most money spent on individuals with lifelong disabilities is spent within the ICF/DD setting. Certain criteria must be met for an agency to qualify for this money, whether it is in a large or small community setting. A brief history reveals the background and reasoning for the criteria used for activities conducted in ICF/DD-funded settings.

The ICFs/DD are funded through Title XIX/Medicaid of the Social Security Act (1990). The funding itself is channeled from Medicaid through the Centers for Medicare and Medicaid Services (CMS), formerly known as the Health Care Finance Administration (HCFA). Medicaid, having a medical orientation, takes the perspective that the individuals receiving the funding need medical or rehabilitation intervention (Braddock et al., 1990; Braddock, Hemp, Parish, & Westrich, 1998). The intervention for individuals with lifelong disabilities is to present them with the opportunity to acquire new knowledge and skills. The goal is that all experiences should be quality learning opportunities that are objective and measurable. Thus, the term *active treatment* was born. Active treatment means that each individual must participate in daily activities that will increase or maintain the individual's current level of functional independence.

In recent years, active treatment has been redefined to include more flexible intervention options for older individuals who are ready to retire from work or continuous skill-building activities. The standards focus on the wishes of the individual, his or her quality of life, and maintenance of existing skills. Rather than discuss specific activities in detail in this section, we will briefly discuss the issues associated with activities of elderly individuals with lifelong disabilities. Perhaps at no other time in their lives do individuals with and without lifelong disabilities have more in common. Many individuals of both groups have spent a significant period of their lives working and are looking forward to retirement.

There are those who want to work forever and cannot imagine retirement. There are also those who have never been employed but are aging and feeling the effects of the aging process.

The literature on activity and older individuals with lifelong disabilities does not provide a dominant program model. Both disability-segregated and disability-integrated programs have been used with success (M. Seltzer & Krauss, 1987). Some fear that individuals with lifelong disabilities will be isolated as they age due to the combination of two conditions, aging and disability, both often the basis of discrimination in U.S. society. However, elderly individuals with lifelong disabilities qualify, as do elderly in the general population, for many government-sponsored services, such as those funded by the Older Americans Act.

Although hesitation and resistance may be encountered when elderly individuals with intellectual disabilities begin participating in generic senior centers, M. Seltzer and Krauss (1987) found general acceptance by the seniors without intellectual disabilities and senior center staff to be the norm. Good health and the age of the individual with the lifelong disability were the most important factors that influenced acceptance in the generic senior centers. An important point noted by M. Seltzer and Krauss is that the use of generic senior centers is not desirable for all elderly individuals with lifelong disabilities. An individualized approach to this decision is recommended.

Common elements to many elder services programs are health awareness, physical exercise, independent living skills, reality orientation, counseling, nutrition, and leisure and recreation activities. In addition, some elders with lifelong disabilities may need assistance or prompting in the areas of self-help skills (Catapano, Levy, & Levy, 1985). One suspects that older individuals with lifelong disabilities have the desire for socialization, including romance with others; participation in spiritual or religious activities; age-appropriate activities; intergenerational contact; and meaningful activities in their lives. Little investigation has been conducted with this group to identify and explore their desires. Creative approaches to obstacles will enable sensitive professionals to help them achieve their wishes.

FINAL THOUGHTS

Over the life course of the current cohort of older people with developmental disabilities, numerous medical, social, and political changes have occurred. As with the general aging population, the number of older people with developmental disabilities who live as members of their families and communities is expected to greatly increase in the coming century. Unfortunately, the developmental disabilities, aging, social welfare, and health care service networks have paid limited attention to the unique needs of this segment of our older population. Indeed, with the current political atmosphere—one of program reduction, diminishing fiscal resources, and a shifting of attention away from social service programs—this already neglected population stands at even greater risk for being "lost between the cracks." As people with developmental and other lifelong disabilities (e.g., physical, psychiatric) live longer lives, service providers will need to creatively develop and bridge resources across service networks to provide support and assistance to these older adults.

In addition to changes in formal services, greater attention needs to be given to the informal support systems of older people with lifelong disabilities. Greater emphasis must, and will, be placed on grassroots groups composed of families and other community advocates in order for individual needs to be met. Families often bear sole responsibility for providing care to people with disabilities across the life span. The cumulative stresses of lifelong caregiving can compromise families' coping strategies, economic resources, and the physical and emotional health of the care providers. Macrolevel changes, such as in legislative and financial support for family caregivers, increased flexibility in employment options, and accessible and affordable respite care options, are necessary.

With the coming decades, the older population will become more diverse. Although diversity is usually conceptualized as ethnic and racial plurality, people with lifelong disabilities will also be members of the older generations and bring to late life unique experiences, resources, and needs. Formalized service systems need to include greater numbers of practitioners, administrators, educators, and politicians who are aware and concerned about the older people who have lifelong disabilities.

REFERENCES

Allen, S., & Mor, V. (1998). *Living in the community with disability: Services needs, use and systems.* New York: Springer.

American Psychiatric Association. (1987). *Diagnostic and statistical manual of mental disorders* (3rd ed. rev.). Washington, DC: Author.

Anderson, D. J. (1989). Healthy and institutionalized: Health and related conditions among older persons with developmental disabilities. *Journal of Applied Gerontology, 8,* 228–241.

Anderson, D. J., & Polister, B. (1993). Psychotropic medication use among older adults with mental retardation. In E. Sutton, A. R. Factor, B. A. Hawkins, T. Heller, & G. B. Seltzer (Eds.), *Older adults with developmental disabilities: Optimizing choice and change* (pp. 61–76). Baltimore: Brookes.

Ansello, E. F., & Eustis, N. N. (Eds.). (1992). *Aging and disabilities: Seeking common ground.* Amityville, NY: Baywood.

Baker, B. L., Seltzer, G. B., & Seltzer, M. M. (1977). *As close as possible: Community residences for retarded adults.* Boston: Little, Brown.

Baroff, G. S. (1982). Predicting the prevalence of mental retardation in individual catchment areas. *Mental Retardation, 20,* 133–135.

Beange, H., & Lennox, N. (1999). Health targets for people with an intellectual disability. *Journal of Intellectual and Developmental Disability, 24*(4), 283–298.

Beaulaurier, R., & Taylor, S. (2001). Social work practice with people with disabilities in the era of disability rights. *Social Work in Health Care, 32*(4), 67–92.

Birren, J. E. (1959). Principles of research on aging. In J. E. Birren (Ed.), *Handbook of aging in the individual* (pp. 3–42). Chicago: University of Chicago Press.

Blake, R. (1981). Disabled older persons: A demographic analysis. *Journal of Rehabilitation, 47,* 19–27.

Bostwick, D. H., & Foss, G. (1981). Obtaining consumer input: Two strategies for identifying and ranking the problems of mentally retarded young adults. *Education and Training of the Mentally Retarded, 16,* 207–212.

Braddock, D., Hemp, R., Fujiura, G., Bachelder, L., & Mitchell, D. (1990). *The state of the states in developmental disabilities.* Baltimore: Brookes.

Braddock, D., Hemp, R., Parish, S., & Rizzolo, M. C. (2000). *The state of the states in developmental disabilities.* Washington, DC: American Association on Mental Retardation.

Braddock, D., Hemp, R., Parish, S., & Westrich, J. (1997). Fiscal efforts for community services in the states: Leaders and laggards in 1996. *Mental Retardation, 35*(4), 321.

Braddock, D., Hemp, R., Parish, S., & Westrich, J. (1998). *The state of the states in developmental disabilities* (5th ed.). Washington, DC: American Association on Mental Retardation.

Bradley, V. (2000). Changes in services and supports for people with developmental disabilities: New challenges to established practice. *Health and Social Work, 25*(3), 191–201.

Burt, D., Loveland, K., Primeaux-Hart, S., Chen, Y., Phillips, N., Cleveland, L., Lewis, K., Lesser, J., & Cummings, E. (1998). Dementia in adults with Down syndrome: Diagnostic challenges. *American Journal on Mental Retardation, 103*(2), 130–145.

Butler, E. W., & Bajaanes, A. T. (1977). A typology of community care facilities and differential normalization outcomes. In P. Mittler (Ed.), *Research to practice in mental retardation: Vol. 1. Care and intervention* (pp. 337–347). Baltimore: University Park Press.

Campbell, V. A., & Bailey, C. J. (1984). Comparison of methods for classifying community residential settings for mentally retarded individuals. *American Journal of Mental Deficiency, 89,* 44–49.

Carswell, A. T., & Hartig, S. A. (1979). *Older developmentally disabled persons: A survey of impairments.* Unpublished manuscript.

Catapano, P. M., Levy, J. M., & Levy, P. H. (1985). Day activity and vocational program services. In M. P. Janicki & H. M. Wisniewski (Eds.), *Aging and developmental disabilities: Issues and approaches* (pp. 305–316). Baltimore: Brookes.

Charlton, J. (1998). *Nothing about us without us: Disability oppression and empowerment.* Berkeley: University of California Press.

Cherry, K., Matson, J., & Paclawsky, T. (1997). Psychopathology in older adults with severe and profound mental retardation. *American Journal on Mental Retardation, 101*(5), 445–458.

Clements, C. (1991). *The arts/fitness quality of life project: Creative ideas for working with older adults in group settings.* Baltimore: Health Professions Press.

Cooper, S. (1998). Clinical study of the effects of age on the physical health of adults with mental retardation. *American Journal on Mental Retardation, 102*(6), 582–589.

Cotten, P. D., Sison, G. F. P., & Starr, S. (1981). Comparing elderly mentally retarded and non–mentally retarded individuals: Who are they? What are their needs? *The Gerontologist, 21,* 359–365.

Cotten, P. D., & Spirrison, C. L. (1986). The elderly mentally retarded developmentally disabled population: A challenge for the service delivery system. In S. J. Brody & G. E. Ruff (Eds.), *Aging and rehabilitation* (pp. 159–187). New York: Springer.

Cotten, P. D., & Spirrison, C. L. (1988). Development of services for elderly persons with mental retardation in a rural state. *Mental Retardation, 26,* 187–190.

Crane, L. (2001). *Mental retardation: A community integration approach.* Belmont, CA: Wadsworth/Thomson Learning.

Dickerson, M., Hamilton, J., Huber, R., & Segal, R. (1979). The aged mentally retarded client: A challenge to the community. In D. P. Sweeney & T. Y. Wilson (Eds.), *Double jeopardy: The plight of the aging and aged developmentally disabled persons in mid-America* (pp. 8–35). Ann Arbor: University of Michigan Press.

DiGiovanni, L. (1978). The elderly retarded: A little-known group. *The Gerontologist, 18,* 262–266.

DiStefano, A. F., & Aston, S. J. (1986). Rehabilitation for the blind and visually impaired elderly. In S. J. Brody & G. E. Ruff (Eds.), *Aging and rehabilitation: Advances in the state of the art* (pp. 203–218). New York: Springer.

Drew, C., & Hardman, M. (2000). *Mental retardation: A life cycle approach*. Upper Saddle River, NJ: Merrill.

Ducket, M., & Guy, M. (2000). Home and community-based services waivers. *Health Care Financing Review, 22*(1), 123–126.

Dychtwald, K. (Ed.). (1999). *Healthy aging: Challenges and solutions*. Gaithersburg, MD: Aspen.

Edgerton, R. B. (1988). Aging in the community—A matter of choice. *American Journal of Mental Retardation, 92*, 331–335.

Edgerton, R. B., & Gaston, M. A. (1991). *I've seen it all: Lives of older persons with mental retardation in the community*. Baltimore: Brookes.

Eisdorfer, C. (1983). Conceptual models of aging: The challenge of a new frontier. *American Psychologist, 38*, 197–202.

Engelhardt, J. L., Brubaker, T. H., & Lutzer, V. D. (1988). Older caregivers of adults with mental retardation: Service utilization. *Mental Retardation, 26*, 191–195.

Evashwick, C. (Ed.). (2001). *The continuum of long-term care* (2nd ed.). Albany, NY: Delmar Thomson Learning.

Evenhuis, H. M., van Zanten, G. A., Brocaar, M. P., & Roerdinkholder, W. H. M. (1992). Hearing loss in middle-age persons with Down syndrome. *American Journal on Mental Retardation, 97*, 47–56.

Eyman, R. K., & Borthwick-Duffy, S. (1994). Trends in mortality rates and predictors of mortality. In M. M. Seltzer, J. W. Krauss, & M. P. Janicki (Eds.), *Life course perspectives on adulthood and old age* (pp. 93–108). Washington, DC: American Association on Mental Retardation.

Eyman, R. K., Call, T. L., & White, J. F. (1989). Mortality of elderly mentally retarded persons in California. *Journal of Applied Gerontology, 8*, 203–215.

Factor, A. R. (1996). *Final report: Innovative Internetwork service models serving older adults with developmental disabilities and older caregivers*. Chicago: Institute on Disability and Human Development, Rehabilitation Research and Training Center on Aging with Mental Retardation.

Famighetti, R. A. (Ed.). (1979). *Aging and aged developmentally disabled: An exploration into issues and possibilities*. Union, NJ: Kean College.

Flax, M. E., & Luchterhand, C. (1998). *Aging and developmental disabilities: Changes in vision*. Washington, DC: U.S. Department of Education, Office of Educational Research and Improvement.

Fox-Grage, W., Folkemer, D., & Lewis, J. (2001). The states' response to the *Olmstead* decision. Retrieved June 15, 2004, from the National Conference of State Legislatures Web site: http://www.ncsl.org/programs/health/forum/olmsreport.htm

Fujiura, G. T., Roccoforte, J. A., & Braddock, D. (1994). Costs of family care for adults with mental retardation and related developmental disabilities. *American Journal on Mental Retardation, 99*, 250–261.

Gedye, A. (1998). Neuroleptic-induced dementia documented in four adults with mental retardation. *Mental Retardation, 36*, 182–186.

Gibson, J. W. (1991). Aging and developmental disabilities: Service provider health-care training needs. *Educational Gerontology, 17*, 607–619.

Gilson, S., & Netting, E. (1997). When people with pre-existing disabilities age in place: Implications for social work practice. *Health and Social Work, 22*, 290–299.

Glass, L. E. (1986). Rehabilitation for deaf and hearing-impaired elderly. In S. J. Brody & G. E. Ruff (Eds.), *Aging and rehabilitation: Advances in the state of the art* (pp. 218–239). New York: Springer.

Gold, N., & Whelan, M. (1992). Elderly people with autism: Defining a social work agenda for research and practice. In F. Turner (Ed.), *Mental health and the elderly: A social work perspective* (pp. 102–114). New York: Free Press.

Greene, R. R., & Kropf, N. P. (1995). A case management approach with Level I families. In A. Kilpatrick & T. Holland (Eds.), *Working with families* (pp. 85–104). Needham Heights, MA: Allyn & Bacon.

Hamilton, J. C., & Segal, R. M. (1975). *A consultation-conference on developmental disabilities and gerontology.* Ann Arbor, MI: University Park Press.

Hand, J. E. (1993). Summary of national survey of older people with mental retardation in New Zealand. *Mental Retardation, 6,* 424–428.

Harlan-Simmons, J., Holtz, P., Todd, J., & Mooney, M. (2001). Building social relationships through valued roles: Three older adults and the Community Membership Project. *Mental Retardation, 39*(3), 171–180.

Hawkins, B. A., & Eklund, S. J. (1989). Aging and developmental disabilities: Interagency planning for an emerging population. *Journal of Applied Gerontology, 8,* 168–174.

Hawkins, B. A., & Eklund, S. J. (1990). Planning processes and outcomes for an aging population with developmental disabilities. *Mental Retardation, 28,* 35–40.

Heller, T. (1985). Residential relocation and reactions of elderly mentally retarded persons. In M. P. Janicki & H. M. Wisniewski (Eds.), *Aging and developmental disabilities: Issues and approaches* (pp. 379–389). Baltimore: Brookes.

Heller, T., & Factor, A. (1988). Permanency planning among Black and White family caregivers of older adults with mental retardation. *American Journal on Mental Retardation, 26,* 203–208.

Heller, T., Miller, A., Hsieh, K., & Sterns, H. (2000). Later-life planning: Promoting knowledge of options and choice-making. *Mental Retardation, 38*(5), 395–406.

Hewitt, A., O'Nell, S., & Bestgen, Y. (1998). *With a little help from my friends—A series on contemporary supports to people with mental retardation.* Washington, DC: U.S. Department of Health and Human Services, Administration for Children and Families, President's Committee on Mental Retardation.

Hill, G., & Lakin, K. C. (1986). Residential support systems. *American Journal of Mental Deficiency, 91,* 162–168.

Hooyman, N. (1983). Social support networks in services to the elderly. In J. K. Whittaker, J. Garbarino, & Associates (Eds.), *Social support networks: Informal helping in the human services* (pp. 133–164). New York: Aldine.

Howell, M. C. (1988). Ethical dilemmas encountered in the care of those who are disabled and also old. *Educational Gerontology, 14,* 439–449.

Huber, A. M. (1985). Nutrition, aging, and developmental disabilities. In M. P. Janicki & H. M. Wisniewski (Eds.), *Aging and developmental disabilities: Issues and approaches* (pp. 257–268). Baltimore: Brookes.

Jablonski, R. (2000). Caring for adults with mental retardation. *Nursing, 30*(11), 32–36.

Jacobson, J. W., Sutton, M. S., & Janicki, M. P. (1985). Demography and characteristics of aging and aged mentally retarded persons. In M. P. Janicki & H. M. Wisniewski (Eds.), *Aging and developmental disabilities: Issues and approaches* (pp. 115–142). Baltimore: Brookes.

Jacobson, S., & Kropf, N. P. (1993). Facilitating residential transitions of older adults with developmental disabilities. *Clinical Gerontologist, 14,* 79–94.

Jacobson, S., Stoneman, Z., & Kropf, N. P. (1994). *The consumer discovery process: Aging individuals with developmental disabilities.* Athens, GA: Governor's Council on Developmental Disabilities and University of Georgia.

Janicki, M. P. (1993). *Building the future: Planning and community development in aging and developmental disabilities.* Albany: New York State Office of Mental Retardation and Developmental Disabilities.

Janicki, M. P. (1994). Policies and supports for older persons with mental retardation. In M. M. Seltzer, J. W. Krauss, & M. P. Janicki (Eds.), *Life course perspectives on adulthood and old age* (pp. 143–165). Washington, DC: American Association on Mental Retardation.

Janicki, M. P., & Dalton, A. J. (1998). Sensory impairments among older adults with intellectual disabilities. *Journal of Intellectual & Developmental Disability, 23*(1), 3–12.

Janicki, M. P., & Dalton, A. J. (2000). Prevalence of dementia and impact on intellectual disability services. *Mental Retardation, 38*(3), 276–288.

Janicki, M. P., Dalton, A. J., Henderson, M., & Davidson, P. W. (1999). Mortality and morbidity among older adults with intellectual disabilities: Health services considerations. *Disability and Rehabilitation, 21*, 284–294.

Janicki, M. P., & Jacobson, J. W. (1986). Generational trends in sensory, physical, and behavioral abilities among older mentally retarded persons. *American Journal of Mental Deficiency, 90*, 490–500.

Jennings, J. (1987). Elderly parents as caregivers for their adult dependent children. *Social Work, 32*, 430–433.

Kapell, D., Nightingale, B., Rodriguez, A., Lee, J., Zigman, W., & Schupf, N. (1998). Prevalence of chronic medical conditions in adults with mental retardation: Comparisons with the general population. *Mental Retardation, 36*, 269–279.

Kapp, M. (1996). Enhancing autonomy and choice in selecting and directing long-term care services. *Elder Law Journal, 4*(10), 55–97.

Kaufman, A. V., Adams, J. P., & Campbell, V. A. (1991). Permanency planning by older parents who care for adult children with mental retardation. *Mental Retardation, 29*, 293–300.

Kaufman, A. V., Campbell, V. A., & Adams, J. P. (1990). A lifetime of caring: Older parents who care for adult children with mental retardation. *Community Alternatives: International Journal of Family Care, 2*, 39–54.

Kaye, S. (1998). *Trends in disability prevalence and their causes: Proceedings of the Fourth National Disability Statistics and Policy Forum, May 16, 1997, Washington, DC.* Washington, DC: U.S. Department of Education, Office of Special Education and Rehabilitative Services, National Institute on Disability and Rehabilitation Research.

Keller, M. J. (Ed.). (1991). *Activities with developmentally disabled elderly and older adults.* New York: Haworth.

Kelly, T. B., & Kropf, N. P. (1995). Stigmatized and perpetual parents: Older parents caring for adult children with lifelong disabilities. *Journal of Gerontological Social Work, 24*, 3–16.

Krauss, M. W., & Erickson, M. (1988). Informal support networks among aging persons with mental retardation: A pilot study. *Mental Retardation, 26*, 197–201.

Krauss, M. W., & Seltzer, M. M. (1986). Comparison of elderly and adult mentally retarded persons in community and institutional settings. *American Journal of Mental Deficiency, 91*, 237–243.

Kropf, N. P. (1996). Infusing content on older people with developmental disabilities into the curriculum. *Journal of Social Work Education, 32*(2), 215–226.

Kropf, N. P. (1997). Older parents of adults with developmental disabilities: Practice issues and service needs. *Journal of Family Psychotherapy, 8*(2), 35–52.

Kropf, N. P., & Greene, R. R. (1993). Life review with families who care for developmentally disabled members. *Journal of Gerontological Social Work, 21*(1/2), 25–40.

Kropf, N. P., Malone, D. M., & Welke, D. (1993). Teaching about older people with mental retardation: An educational model. *Educational Gerontology, 19*, 623–634.

Landesman, S. (1986). Quality of life and personal life satisfaction: Definition and measurement issues. *Mental Retardation, 24*, 141–143.

Lavin, C., & Doka, K. (1999). *Older adults with developmental disabilities.* Amityville, NY: Baywood.

Leal, L. (1999). *A family-centered approach to people with mental retardation.* Washington, DC: American Association on Mental Retardation.

Lubin, R. A., & Kiely, M. (1985). Epidemiology of aging in developmental disabilities. In M. P. Janicki & H. M. Wisniewski (Eds.), *Aging and developmental disabilities: Issues and approaches* (pp. 95–113). Baltimore: Brookes.

Maaskant, M. A. (1993). *Mental handicap and aging.* Dwingeloo, The Netherlands: KAVANAH.

Malone, D. M. (1993). *Bill of Rights.* (Available from Interdisciplinary Training Program and Core Curriculum, University Affiliated Program for Persons with Developmental Disabilities, Dawson Hall, University of Georgia, Athens, GA 30602.)

Marshak, L., Prezant, F., & Seligman, M. (1999). *Disability and the family life cycle.* New York: Basic Books.

McDowell, D. (1988). Aging and developmental disability: Personal reflections on policy for persons. *Educational Gerontology, 14,* 465–470.

Menolascino, F. J., & Potter, J. F. (1989). Mental illness in the elderly mentally retarded. *Journal of Applied Gerontology, 8,* 192–202.

Murrell, S. A., & Norris, F. H. (1983). Quality of life as the criterion of need assessment and community psychology. *Journal of Community Psychology, 11,* 88–97.

National Council on Disability (U.S.). (1999). *Lift every voice: Modernizing disability policies and programs to serve a diverse nation.* Washington, DC: National Council on Disability.

National Institute on Consumer-Directed Long-Term Services. (1996). *Principles of consumer-directed home and community based services.* Washington, DC: Author.

Nerney, T., & Shumway, D. (1996). *Beyond managed care: Self-determination for people with disabilities.* Concord, NH: Institute on Disability.

O'Brien, J. (1994). Down stairs that are never your own: Supporting people with developmental disabilities in their own homes. *Mental Retardation, 32,* 1–6.

Older Americans Act Amendments. (1987). [U.S. House of Representatives Committee on Serial Print No. 101-A and U.S. Senate Special Committee on Aging Serial No. 101-B]. Washington, DC: U.S. Government Printing Office.

Older Americans Act Amendments. (1992). [U.S. House of Representatives Committee on Serial Print No. 101-A and U.S. Senate Special Committee on Aging Serial No. 101-B]. Washington, DC: U.S. Government Printing Office.

Older Americans Act of 1965 as amended through December 1988. (1989). [U.S. House of Representatives Committee Print Serial No. 101-A and U.S. Senate Special Committee on Aging Serial No. 101-B]. Washington, DC: U.S. Government Printing Office.

Olmstead v. L. C. (98-536) 527 U.S. 581 (1999). Retrieved August 3, 2004, from http://www.usdoj.gov/osg/briefs/1998/3mer/1ami/98-0536.mer.ami.html

Omnibus Budget Reconciliation Act of 1981, § 2176, United States Statutes at Large, 95, 812–813. Washington, DC: U.S. Government Printing Office.

Osberg, J. S., McGinnis, G. E., DeJong, G., & Seward, M. L. (1987). Life satisfaction and quality of life among disabled elderly adults. *Journal of Gerontology, 42,* 228–230.

Palley, H., & Van Hollen, V. (2000). Long-term care for people with developmental disabilities: A critical analysis. *Health and Social Work, 25*(3), 181–190.

Pary, R. (1993). Psychoactive drugs used with adults and elderly adults who have mental retardation. *American Journal on Mental Retardation, 98,* 121–127.

Priestley, M. (Ed.). (2001). *Disability and the life course: Global perspectives.* New York: Cambridge University Press.

Prouty, R., Lakin, K. C., Anderson, L. (2000). Five-year trends in Medicaid institutional (ICF/MR) populations, home and community based services reflect major changes. *Mental Retardation, 38,* 294–296.

Quirk, D. A., & Aravanis, S. C. (1988). State partnerships to enhance the quality of life of older Americans with lifelong disabilities. *Educational Gerontology, 14,* 431–437.

Racino, J. (2000). *Personnel preparation in disability and community life: Toward universal approaches to support.* Springfield, IL: Charles C. Thomas.

Rago, W. V. (1985). The impact of technology on the delivery of mental retardation services in the year 2000: A research perspective. In C. M. Gaitz, G. Niederehe, & N. L. Wilson (Eds.), *Psychosocial and policy issues* (Vol. 2, pp. 209–218). New York: Springer.

Rasmussen, D. E., & Sobsey, D. (1994). Age, adaptive behavior, and Alzheimer disease in Down syndrome: Cross-sectional and longitudinal analyses. *American Journal on Mental Retardation, 99,* 151–165.

Rice, P. R., & Feldman, J. F. (1983). Living longer in the United States: Demographic changes and health needs of the elderly. *Health and Society, 61,* 362–396.

Richards, B. W. (1975). Mental retardation. In J. G. Howells (Ed.), *Modern perspectives on the psychiatry of old age* (pp. 171–189). New York: Academic Press.

Rimmer, J. (1998). *Aging, mental retardation and physical fitness.* Chicago: Rehabilitation Research and Training Center on Aging with Mental Retardation.

Rinck, C., & Calkins, C. F. (1989). Pattern of psychotropic medication use among older persons with developmental disabilities. *Journal of Applied Gerontology, 8,* 215–227.

Ross, D. M. (1989). *A report to the New York State Developmental Disabilities Planning Council on the feasibility of different pension support systems for New York State residents with a developmental disability.* Unpublished manuscript.

Sands, D., & Wehmeyer, M. (1996). *Self-determination across the lifespan.* Baltimore: Brookes.

Schaie, K. W., & Willis, S. L. (1986). *Adult development and aging* (2nd ed.). Boston: Little, Brown.

Schalock, R. (1996). *Quality of life: Perspectives and issues* (2nd ed.). Washington, DC: American Association on Mental Retardation.

Schalock, R. (2000). Three decades of quality of life. *Focus on Autism and Other Developmental Disabilities, 15*(2), 116–128.

Schalock, R. L., Keith, K. D., Hoffman, K., & Karan, O. C. (1989). Quality of life: Its measurement and use. *Mental Retardation, 27,* 25–31.

Scheerenberger, R. C. (1983). *Public residential services for the mentally retarded, 1982.* Madison, WI: National Association of Superintendents of Public Residential Facilities for the Mentally Retarded.

Scotch, R. (2001). *From good will to civil rights: Transforming federal disability policy.* Philadelphia: Temple University Press.

Segal, R. (1977). Trends in services for the aged mentally retarded. *Mental Retardation, 15,* 25–27.

Segal, R. (1978). Services for the aged developmentally disabled person: A challenge to the community. In M. G. Rose, D. Berstein, & L. Plotnick (Eds.), *Conference proceedings on the aging/developmentally disabled person* (pp. 5–13). College Park: University of Maryland.

Seltzer, G. B., & Luchterhand, C. (1994). Health and well-being of older persons with developmental disabilities: A clinical review. In M. M. Seltzer, J. W. Krauss, & M. P. Janicki (Eds.), *Life course perspectives on adulthood and old age* (pp. 109–142). Washington, DC: American Association on Mental Retardation.

Seltzer, M. M. (1985a). Informal supports for aging mentally retarded persons. *American Journal of Mental Deficiency, 90,* 259–265.

Seltzer, M. M. (1985b). Research in social aspects of aging and developmental disabilities. In M. P. Janicki & H. M. Wisniewski (Eds.), *Aging and developmental disabilities: Issues and approaches* (pp. 161–173). Baltimore: Brookes.

Seltzer, M. M. (1988). Structure and patterns of service utilization by elderly persons with mental retardation. *Mental Retardation, 26,* 181–185.

Seltzer, M. M. (1992). Aging in persons with developmental disabilities. In J. E. Birren, R. B. Sloane, & G. D. Cohen (Eds.), *Handbook on aging and mental health* (2nd ed., pp. 583–599). San Diego, CA: Academic Press.

Seltzer, M. M., & Krauss, M. W. (1987). Aging and mental retardation: Extending the continuum. *Monographs of the American Association on Mental Deficiency, 9,* 3–187.

Seltzer, M., Krauss, M. W., Hong, J., & Orsmond, G. (2001). Continuity or discontinuity of family involvement following residential transitions of adults who have mental retardation. *Mental Retardation, 39,* 181–194.

Seltzer, M. M., & Seltzer, G. B. (1985). The elderly mentally retarded: A group in need of service. In G. Getzel & J. Mellor (Eds.), *Gerontological social work practice in the community* (pp. 99–119). New York: Haworth Press.

Sison, G. F. P., & Cotten, P. D. (1989). The elderly mentally retarded person: Current perspectives and future directions. *Journal of Applied Gerontology, 8,* 151–167.

Smith, G., Prouty, R., & Lakin, K. C. (2001). Medicaid long-term services for people with developmental disabilities—That was then, this is now. *Mental Retardation, 39,* 488–491.

Smith, G. C., Fullmer, E. M., & Tobin, S. S. (1994). Living outside the system: An exploration of older families who do not use day programs. In M. M. Seltzer, J. W. Krauss, & M. P. Janicki (Eds.), *Life course perspectives on adulthood and old age* (pp. 19–38). Washington, DC: American Association on Mental Retardation.

Smith, G. C., & Tobin, S. S. (1993). Practice with older parents of developmentally disabled adults. *Clinical Gerontologist, 14*(1), 59–77.

Smith, G. P. S., Thyer, B. A., Clements, C., & Kropf, N. P. (1997). An evaluation of coalition building training for aging and developmental disability service providers. *Educational Gerontology, 23,* 105–114.

Special Committee on Aging. (2002). *Developments in aging: 1999 and 2000* (Vol. 1) (Rept. 107-158). Washington, DC: U.S. Government Printing Office.

Strauss, D., Shavelle, R., Baumeister, A., & Anderson, T. (1998). Mortality in persons with developmental disabilities after transfer into community care. *American Journal on Mental Retardation, 102*(6), 569–581.

Thurman, E. (1986). Maintaining dignity in later years. In J. A. Summers (Ed.), *The right to grow up: An introduction to adults with developmental disabilities* (pp. 91–115). Baltimore: Brookes.

Tibbits, C. (1979). Can we invalidate negative stereotypes of aging? *The Gerontologist, 19,* 10–20.

Turk, M. A., & Machemer, R. H. (1993). Cerebral palsy in adults who are older. In R. H. Machemer & J. C. Overeynder (Eds.), *Understanding aging and developmental disabilities: An in-service curriculum* (pp. 111–130). Rochester, NY: Strong Center for Developmental Disabilities.

Turnbull, A., & Turnbull, R. (2000). Achieving "rich" lifestyles. *Journal of Positive Behavior Interventions, 2*(3), 190–193.

Tymchuk, A. J. (1979). The mentally retarded in later life. In O. J. Kaplan (Ed.), *Psychopathology of aging* (pp. 197–209). New York: Academic Press.

U.S. Senate Special Committee on Aging, American Association of Retired Persons, Federal Council on the Aging, & U.S. Administration on Aging. (1991). *Aging America: Trends and projections.* Washington, DC: U.S. Senate Special Committee on the Aging.

Walker, B. R. (1985). Presidential address 1985: Inalienable rights of persons with mental retardation. *Mental Retardation, 23,* 219–221.

Walz, T., Harper, D., & Wilson, J. (1986). The aging developmentally disabled person: A review. *The Gerontologist, 26,* 622–629.

Wisniewski, K., & Hill, A. L. (1985). Clinical aspects of dementia in mental retardation and developmental disabilities. In M. P. Janicki & H. M. Wisniewski (Eds.), *Aging and developmental disabilities: Issues and approaches* (pp. 195–210). Baltimore: Brookes.

Yanok, J., & Beifus, J. A. (1993). Communicating about loss and mourning: Death education for individuals with mental retardation. *Mental Retardation, 3,* 144–147.

DEVELOPMENTAL DISABILITIES

PERSONAL PERSPECTIVE

Raising a child with a developmental disability can be overpowering. The complex needs presented by a child with cognitive, medical, and behavioral issues results in continuous pressure to solve problems and obtain resources. To survive, one needs a lot of love, commitment, and long-term endurance. Autism is especially perplexing and requires intuitive as well as analytical problem solving. The body of knowledge focused on understanding autism spectrum disabilities is in its infancy compared to that of other disabilities. Families, educators, and health and human service professionals are generally unprepared to meet the challenges of these children.

Cognitive issues related to autism present in the early years, age 1 or 2, when it becomes apparent your child is not learning to speak. Pediatricians are sometimes reluctant to diagnose the problem as autism and call it a "developmental delay." Our son was diagnosed with a developmental delay at 18 months of age, and by the age of 2½ years, the term *autism* was used by professionals. At that time, he could say only a few words and his fine-motor skills were slow to develop.

As he got older, our fear focused on the realization that he cannot tell us what hurts or bothers him. He communicates through his behavior. At times, he lies on the floor screaming as loud as he can and arching his back as he rages against the world. It seems to be the only way he can make his needs known, or he is chased by some demon invisible to the rest of us. He may be raging, or he may have a pain, an illness, or any other number of indefinable problems. Some of us speculate that his perception is like that of a television that can only get poor sight and sound reception, that it's caught between the channels. His sense of touch, as well, is likely very different from what most of us feel. His periodic raging may go on for an hour, and it's as if he's stuck in the emotional inertia of screaming long beyond the issue that caused it. Later he may be calm and even affectionate.

Obsessive compulsiveness is mixed into this process. He goes around the house touching edges of furniture and those places where tables and other surfaces touch walls. Or he spins once or twice before completing an act. The inability to communicate can give one a feeling that this child is like a being from another world, living only partially and part of the time in our world. He certainly does not appear to understand most body language, and only minimal aspects of words and abstract concepts.

Medical issues are various and complex, such as rashes, colic, infections, and allergies, and can surface at an early age. We must become knowledgeable in medical approaches and constantly research medications. Our son, as well as many other children with autism, has gastrointestinal problems that result in chronic constipation. For other children, it may be chronic diarrhea. Some of these medical issues are approached in part with special diets, like the elimination of wheat, yeast, sugars, and dairy products. We get our son tested for allergies every year because they change. Those tests require five to six people to hold him down while a nurse draws a blood sample.

Gastrointestinal problems result in formidable toileting challenges, since every bowel movement is an emotional event that involves discomfort or pain. Our son has displayed a lot of agitation, screaming, self-injury, and aggression during toileting.

It seems that times of highly charged emotions, whatever those may be for each child, enable the child to develop behaviors such as screaming, self-injury, and hostility to other people and objects. Self-injury involves behaviors such as biting, scratching, hair pulling, and hitting objects like walls or glass with head, hands, and feet. Hostility to others takes the form of biting, scratching, hair pulling, hitting, and head butting. The child might break furniture, appliances, walls, or windows.

This has been true for our son; however, we also see times when he shows incredible insight and adaptation, like how to work the television, stereo, or VCR. He puts silverware in the sink, closes drawers and doors. He can distinguish one tape or DVD from another as if he can read. He likes vibration and movement, like riding in the car or on a porch swing. He can remember and sing all the words in his favorite songs and nursery rhymes. He selects or asks for a favorite movie or music. He has begun using multiple-word sentences, like "Applesauce, please" and "Go in the car?"

We, as parents, first have to learn to separate the behavior from the child. Once we are able to do that, and can get a basic understanding of his world, his behavior begins to make sense. For example, when someone does not understand most body language and spoken words, his world is very confusing and he gets irritated. Is it really a mystery that he starts banging on the table?

Unfortunately, his behavior does make sense to the rest of the world and creates a barrier to his learning. The challenge then becomes learning about behavior management and building a consistent method to apply the strategies. This has been very difficult for us to do because he interacts with a variety of individuals in the family, at school, and from human services. We hire trained individuals or others that we train. Also, we cannot provide the same one-on-one teaching that teachers and life-skills trainers can provide because we need to take care of our other child and daily responsibilities that go with a home and family. We share the ultimate fear with all parents of children with severe disabilities—that our child will have to live in an institution if we fail to help him solve his behavioral problems.

Behavior is also affected by medication. It requires parents to find skilled pediatricians, psychiatrists, and neuropsychiatrists and have them coordinate their services. Many children with autism take antipsychotic medications. It takes a psychiatrist with specialized skills who can mix and match a variety of medications to help reduce the child's anxiety, obsessive compulsiveness, hyperactivity, and irritability. The parents work with the professionals to try to determine the right amount of medication so that the child is not constantly aggressive yet not groggy or tired.

Parents also become skilled, out of necessity, at making home modifications and acquiring assistive technology. We have fixed drywall, put Plexiglas or Lexan on windows, put fences around the back yard, installed cabinet locks and room gates, added childproof electrical outlet covers, and bolted many appliances and bookcases to walls. We lock bedroom and pantry doors. We installed video cameras in various rooms of the house. We use plastic and paper plates and cups while trying to teach him what goes in the trash and what goes in the sink. We use a bike helmet when necessary to protect him from head banging.

Finding the best medical services for an autistic child means a thorough search through local and even national services. Many doctors are not fully prepared for working with children with autism. They also have difficulty diagnosing symptoms that are interwoven with behaviors. Parents seek out the best they can find by talking with professionals and other parents. For example, after years of frustration, such conversations led us to successful gastrointestinal remedies for our son at a hospital in Boston.

School is a complex set of issues that involves evaluation, the best placement, transportation, and other resources. For parents, the hope is that their child will gain some functional living and basic academic skills. It's uncertain if these goals will ever be attained. It is also difficult for schools to find and provide all the resources the child needs, even when the school system is progressive. Some school administrators start with a defensive position because of limited resources. The parents who educate themselves about special education services and how to work the system, and are willing to fight, seem to make the most gains for their children. But protracted and assertive negotiations with school administrators are stressful for everyone.

In many families, both parents have to work full time. Or worse, a single parent is raising the child. This means parents have to build a complex system of care and respite by hiring personal care assistants and life-skills trainers; especially difficult are times when school is closed, such as during breaks and holidays. This also means they must ensure their child is safe and secure with all these services and people. Our experience is probably fairly typical in that we have used a mixture of family members, trained professionals, and other assistants that we have trained ourselves. We have used a mixture of funds, as well, such as the Medicaid Waiver, Social Security, and personal funding, to obtain the needed services.

The family learns to make many sacrifices that focus on the needs of the autistic child. Siblings may not get an equal amount of attention and see that the child with the disability has a different system of rewards and consequences related to behavior. Some people believe that growing up with a brother or sister with a disability can help a child become more tolerant and caring. That is hard to determine because there are many factors. Parents have to ensure first that the siblings are safe, feel secure, and get the attention they need. They also have to be careful not to imply expectations that the siblings are or will be responsible for the care of their brother or sister with a disability. In our family, we watch carefully to ensure that the younger brother does not take on a parental role with his older brother with autism.

Often our relationship is stressed by the lack of time we need to nurture and support each other. We learn ways to build in small amounts of shared time, and try to remain caring and supportive during times of stress. We have to be careful not to get angry with each other when there is a lot of chaos and stress. Autism also has an isolating effect on us and our family. We don't get to see friends as often, go to movies or get-togethers. We don't often get to vent our frustrations or worries to friends or family because we're at home.

One of the troubling aspects of raising a child with autism is weathering the ups and downs of hope and disappointment related to new medical, educational, and behavioral approaches. For example, we learned about classroom integration and fought for it, but after behavior problems increased for our son, he was placed in a more restrictive setting than he was before. We explored the concentrated behavioral learning approach, and he made progress in learning shapes, words, and sentences. Then his aggressive behaviors increased again, we pulled him from the program, and within 2 years he lost over half of what he had learned. Research showed that some cognitive progress for children with autism could be obtained by injecting digestive enzymes such as Secretin. We went through great efforts to obtain injections, but they did not work for our son.

The ultimate challenge for parents is to build goals and lifelong supports for their child with a disability. This requires knowledge and planning for transition from school to community integration and work. It requires securing Social Security benefits and building some sort of financial trust. Many parents hope that their child can live in a group home or assisted living. The question is: Who will continue to provide the care and case management for that individual when the parents are gone?

Fortunately, there are some good informational resources available on many aspects of autism, such as autism resource centers, university technical assistance projects, pilot projects, the Autism Society, and the growing network of other parents facing similar problems and issues. The Defeat Autism Now (DAN) group is an excellent clearinghouse for information on autism and holds an annual conference.

It is very difficult to raise a child with autism. It seems like every week the problems change or compound. We try to keep our balance while dealing with constant chaos. It makes us tougher. At times, it feels as if we are just surviving. At other times, we celebrate the child and all his accomplishments. We become good case managers and advocates. We continue to make sure he gets every opportunity to succeed.

—Ray Graesser[1]

---

[1]The physical loss of Ray Graesser on July 9, 2004, comes as a profound shock to all of us who were fortunate enough to have worked with him and could call him a friend. He leaves his wife Cindi, his son Eren, and his stepson Kendall, along with his sisters, brothers, nieces, and nephews. He was a wonderful, loving professional and a dear person. When I first heard that Ray had passed on, I was convinced it was a mistake. Ray was bigger than life, with a ready smile, always concerned about not hurting other people—a classic rehabilitation expert. He lived with disability, he understood disability as part of the life experience, and above all, he made the lives of thousands of persons with disabilities a lot better. He may be gone physically, but emotionally and spiritually, he is here right now. We must do our part to carry on his legacy of class and professionalism and compassion. He left the world a much better place. He was a friend to all.

—Paul Wehman

CHAPTER 6

Mild Intellectual Disability

Pamela Targett and John Langone

LEARNING GOALS

Upon completion of this chapter, the reader will be able to

- define and discuss the 2002 American Association on Mental Retardation definition of mental retardation
- outline the effects of limited or intermittent support on the perceptions that society may have of people with intellectual disabilities
- discuss the major learning and cognitive characteristics of persons with mild intellectual disabilities
- discuss and give examples of important concepts such as generalization, self-direction, and work ability
- discuss the importance of striving to help adults with intellectual disabilities reach economic self-sufficiency
- describe the need for using task analyses as a technology of teaching
- discuss the importance of teaching independent living skills

FUNCTIONAL DESCRIPTION

A widely used definition of intellectual disability or mental retardation is the one developed for and updated by the American Association on Mental Retardation (AAMR). Since 1908, the AAMR has updated the definition of mental retardation 10 times. Changes in the definition have occurred when there is new information, or there are changes in clinical practice or breakthroughs in scientific research. It should be noted that in this chapter the term *mental retardation* is used interchangeably with *intellectual disabilities,* a description favored by an increasing number of persons with disabilities, families, and some professionals. In August 2003, the President's Committee on Mental Retardation (PCMR) changed its name to the President's Committee on Intellectual Disabilities.

Despite the move toward the name change, the AAMR's most recent revision of the definition includes limited changes from the one published a decade earlier. The 10th edition of *Mental Retardation: Definition, Classification, and Systems of Supports* (Luckasson et al., 2002) contains a comprehensive update to the landmark 1992 system and provides important new information, tools, and strategies for the field. The 2002 manual defines *mental retardation* as "a disability characterized by significant limitations both in intellectual functioning and in adaptive behavior as expressed in conceptual, social, and practical adaptive skills. This disability originates before age 18" (Luckasson et al., 2002, p. 1). Five assumptions that are essential to the application of the definition are also presented:

1. Limitations in present functioning must be considered within the context of community environments typical of the individual's age peers and culture.
2. Valid assessment considers cultural and linguistic diversity as well as differences in communication, sensory, motor, and behavioral factors.
3. Within an individual, limitations often coexist with strengths.
4. An important purpose of describing limitations is to develop a profile of needed supports.
5. With appropriate personalized supports over a sustained period, the life functioning of the person with mental retardation generally will improve. (Luckasson et al., 2002, p. 1)

These critically important assumptions reflect the research of the 1980s and 1990s. They establish the fact that some people with intellectual disabilities may eventually acquire sufficient competence through supports that they may no longer be considered as having a disability.

The 2002 definition retains the three elements of the earlier mental retardation definition: limitations in intellectual functioning, concomitant limitations in adaptive behavior, and occurrence in the developmental period. The definition also retains the focus on mental retardation as a function of the relationship among individual functioning, supports, and contexts. The manual emphasizes five dimensions—intellectual abilities; adaptive behavior; participation, interactions, and social roles; health; and context—that when filtered through a system of supports, impact individual functioning. *Context* is operationalized as the

> interrelated conditions within which people live their everyday lives. Context as used here represents an ecological perspective that involves at least three different levels: (a) the immediate social setting, (b) the neighborhood, community or organizations providing education or habilitation services or supports, and (c) the overarching patterns of culture, society, larger populations, country or sociopolitical influences. (Luckasson et al., 2002, p. 15)

Through the years, the concept of adaptive behavior has been the definitional component that has continually caused the most controversy among professionals. In the 1983 definition, adaptive behavior was defined as an individual's ability to meet the standards of maturation, learning, personal independence, and/or social responsibility one would normally demonstrate at each of life's stages (Grossman, 1983). The 1992 and current definitions, although maintaining this basic premise, provide a considerably more detailed description of the basic components of adaptive functioning. Each of the 10 adaptive skill areas is described in more precise behavioral terminology and thus may provide the basis for more precise measurement strategies.

Accurate measurement of adaptive behavior is important. This fact is especially crucial for those individuals whose intellectual functioning falls in the borderline range of mental retardation. For example, a person whose score falls below approximately 70 on an individually administered intelligence test would not be considered to have mental retardation if he or she did not demonstrate concurrent deficits in adaptive behavior. The importance of an accurate measurement of adaptive behavior is obvious when one considers that the outcome of this evaluation may be all that stands between an individual and the label "mental retardation."

The current definition of mental retardation still includes four important assumptions that must be met before a diagnosis can be established. First, an assessment must consider cultural and linguistic diversities, differences in the forms people use to communicate, and differences in the behaviors they exhibit. For example, assessment strategies should consider whether a person engages in nonverbal communication or requires an augmentative or assistive communication device.

The second and third assumptions address the issue of adaptive behavior. The definition emphasizes the need to assess adaptive behavior in the context of the individual's community. Specific consideration should be given to comparing the adaptive skills of an individual to those of same-aged peers who come from the same cultural or linguistic background (AAMR, 1992). Also the need to compare a person's strengths in adaptive skills to the deficits that have been identified is emphasized. The fourth assumption is that with the appropriate supports over time, an individual with mental retardation will improve.

Beginning in 1992, a positive outlook toward mental retardation was included in the definition, reflecting what has been proven in the literature over the past 20 years and continues today. That optimistic perspective is that over the course of their lives, persons with mental retardation will generally improve in the areas related to life functioning given the appropriate type and intensity of supports.

Prior to the 1992 definition, significantly subaverage intellectual functioning was described by severity levels (mild, moderate, severe, and profound), that is, in terms of how far an individual's measured intelligence deviated from the norm. Supports were an innovative aspect of the 1992 AAMR manual, and they remain critical in the 2002 system. In 2002, however, they have been dramatically expanded and improved to reflect significant progress over the last decade. Supports are defined as the resources and individual strategies necessary to promote the development, education, interests, and personal well-being of a person with mental retardation. These four levels of support included as a part of the overall definition now relate to the intensity of a person's needs. These include intermittent supports that may be episodic or short term and may be needed over a person's life span; limited supports that require more consistency over longer periods of time; extensive supports that involve regular involvement by service providers; and pervasive supports that require constant and intense involvement by service providers and may potentially require life-sustaining assistance.

Although these four intensities of support roughly parallel the historical categories of mild, moderate, severe, and profound, they are fundamentally different in the approach that the AAMR intended toward categorization. Instead of categorizing an individual solely on the basis of an IQ score, this new system in theory allows professionals, in concert with parents, to design programs based on the intensity of any given individual's needs. The 2002 manual extends discussion about supports and their application to people with mental retardation and proposes a model that indicates that the intensity of a person's needed supports is to be determined for each of the nine support areas: human development, teaching and education, home living, community living, protection and advocacy, employment, health and safety, behavioral, and social. According to the model, the support functions may also include teaching, befriending, financial planning, employee assistance, living assistance, community access and use, health assistance, and behavioral support. These supports are offered to enhance personal outcomes such as independence, relationship contributions, school and community participation, and personal well-being.

The latest manual does not make the dramatic changes to understanding mental retardation that occurred in the 9th edition. However, according to Wehmeyer (2003), in the time between the release of the 9th and 10th editions, the context of special education has changed dramatically, as it has attempted to align with standards-based reform and to ensure that students with disabilities are not left behind. Wehmeyer states that this realignment, in the form of access to the general curriculum mandates, provides a compelling reason for special educators to pay more attention to the current edition than they did to the earlier one—particularly since the current definition and classification system could alter the way educators think about mental retardation and challenge them to consider more closely the types and intensities of supports people will need to participate in a variety of environments.

SUPPORTS FOR PEOPLE WITH
MILD INTELLECTUAL DISABILITIES

Over the years the number of persons identified and labeled as needing special education services has decreased considerably (U.S. Department of Education, 1997). This decrease is the result of a number of variables, including a lack of clear evidence that special education has helped these individuals to make significant academic and social gains, along with the identification of inappropriate testing practices that labeled a disproportionate number of students of racial and ethnic minority groups as having mild intellectual disabilities (Bynoe, 1998; Council for Exceptional Children [CEC], 2001).

In any event, the population of individuals identified as having mild cognitive disabilities is smaller. The changes over the years in the AAMR definition have radically altered who is considered mentally retarded (Polloway & Smith, 1983a, 1983b). Polloway and Smith observed that the concept of mild mental retardation, noncategorized programming, and labeling are issues and trends that the nature of the definition of mental retardation will directly influence.

As previously discussed, the definition of mental retardation changed dramatically in 1992 (Luckasson & Spitalnik, 1994) and now has significantly different elements to it. Perhaps the most significant element is that individuals can outgrow their label of mental retardation with appropriate supports. Individualized supports are often needed to assist people with mild intellectual disabilities in achieving their goals and maximizing their independence (Bradley, Agosta, & Kimmich, 2001). Supports are resources and strategies that enhance the lives of individuals with or without disabilities. Individuals with mild intellectual disability differ greatly from one another and will therefore require different levels of support. The possibility exists that some individuals with mild disabilities will require only intermittent supports, whereas others might require limited supports at certain periods of their lives. People with mild intellectual disabilities will succeed in most aspects of their life when supports are available in their homes, communities, and workplaces (Bradley, Ashbaugh, & Blaney, 1994; Kregel & Wehman, 1997). The question remains as to whether school systems have adopted this new classification scheme or continue to place students on the basis of antiquated IQ cutoff scores.

Intermittent Supports

People with mild intellectual deficits demonstrate cognitive abilities and adaptive skills that probably will require intermittent supports as identified in the 1992 and 2002 AAMR definitions. A person's strengths and weaknesses should be described in relation to four dimensions outlined in the AAMR procedures: (a) intellectual functioning and adaptive skills, (b) psychological and emotional well-being, (c) health and physical well-being and etiology, and (d) life activity environments (AAMR, 1992). Prior to 1992, the definition included the four classifications that were based on IQ scores and moved toward a single diagnostic label of mental retardation. However, since 1992, a diagnosis might identify a student with mental retardation with intermittent support needs in the areas of social skills, functional academics, and work. For example, Will was referred for testing by his teacher because of his poor academic achievement and lack of social skills that the teacher deemed appropriate for individuals in his age group. Testing revealed that Will's IQ score fell below 70, and scores on an adaptive behavior scale indicated significant limitations in three areas: functional academics, social skills, and self-direction. His performance indicated that he needed additional assistance in the form of intermittent supports, so the psychologist, referring teachers, and remedial specialists worked together to develop strategies that could be used with Will in the general education class. These strategies included teaching and educational activities related to learning and using determination skills, interacting with others, and using functional academics.

Individuals with mild intellectual disabilities still constitute the greatest number within the category of mental retardation, yet the causes of mild mental retardation are the least understood. Heredity is certainly an important factor in the onset of mild intellectual disabilities; however, medical researchers are currently unable to pinpoint identifiable organic causes for most cases.

Other variables such as environmental pollution (e.g., lead emissions in the air), lack of environmental stimulation, little or no pre- and postnatal health care, and poor nutrition contribute to the intellectual disabilities experienced by some individuals. This complex interaction of heredity and environment (nature *and* nurture) results in a disproportionate number of individuals with mild intellectual disabilities coming from families at the lower socioeconomic level of society.

Children with mild intellectual deficits develop social, motor, and language skills at a slower rate than their peers do. These developmental delays, however, often go unnoticed during the preschool years (Thurman & Widerstrom, 1990). When these children enter school, their disabilities become more pronounced, and a combination of academic and behavioral deficits cause teachers to begin the referral process (Ysseldyke & Algozzine, 1990). The case of Tonya illustrates this pattern.

CASE EXAMPLE: TONYA

Tonya's mom stated that Tonya was always "slower" than her playmates and near-aged siblings. She began walking later than her older brother and younger sister and has always had trouble communicating her needs. Tonya's mother believed that these delays were normal for a child who was "born early" and believed she would "catch up" to other children over time. When Tonya entered kindergarten, her teachers noticed that she exhibited deficits in preacademic readiness skills. For instance, she did not recognize any letters of the alphabet, the numbers 1 to 10, or colors. They also noted a delayed maturity level of about 2 years. After Tonya repeated a second year of kindergarten, during which she made some small gains, the teacher referred her for additional assessment to determine if special education services were needed.

More Extensive Supports

Those children whose intellectual disabilities are more pronounced are usually identified earlier, often at birth, and will probably require limited to extensive supports over the course of their lives. For example, Martin's composite IQ score on the *Stanford–Binet Intelligence Scale, 4th Edition* (Thorndike, Hagen, & Sattler, 1986), was 38, and he demonstrated significant developmental delays (approximately 2 years) in learning to sit, crawl, and walk. He is currently 8 years old and requires assistance with getting dressed, brushing his teeth, and feeding himself more difficult foods such as spaghetti or soup. Martin's language continues to be delayed. He has good receptive language, but his ability to express himself verbally is limited to single words and short phrases.

A variety of clinical syndromes, such as Down syndrome, have observable physical characteristics that are associated with moderate mental impairments. Some individuals with moderate cognitive disabilities also have additional disabling conditions (e.g., cerebral palsy). The disabilities associated with moderate intellectual disabilities are more likely to be linked directly to a genetic or biochemical problem that manifested itself during the prenatal period.

In the past, the common outcome for individuals with more pronounced mental retardation was institutionalization. Fortunately, today, however, society is realizing that the prognosis for community placement of these individuals is excellent. With early and continual support to the person and their families and innovative educational programs, these individuals can become independent and productive citizens.

♠ CASE EXAMPLE: KATE

Kate is an 18-year-old high school student who has Down syndrome. She enjoys attending after-school activities such as volleyball games and occasionally attends movies with a boy she met in her special education class. The special education class emphasizes community-based instruction. Kate spends most of her day out in the community learning how to work, shop, and live as independently as possible. She also attends some regular education classes such as physical education and arts and crafts, with her nondisabled peers. In addition, she participates in an after-school fundraising club and eats lunch in the cafeteria, where she often dines with her neighborhood friends. Kate's long-term goals include living in an apartment with a nondisabled roommate and becoming employed full time at a local retail store. Short-term goals include increasing leisure skills—for example, becoming a member of a local bowling league—and joining a support group for individuals with disabilities to learn more about disability rights.

CURRICULAR AND INSTRUCTIONAL PRACTICES

Individuals with mild to moderate intellectual disabilities who require supports have desires to be independent just like anyone else. As a group, people with these disabilities are more alike than different in terms of the program goals set by parents and professionals and the instructional strategies designed to help them reach those goals.

The main differences among people with intellectual disabilities are not between subgroups (e.g., mild compared with moderate mental retardation), but in the distance between each individual's current level of functioning and his or her life goals. All individuals have differing needs regardless of their disabilities. The common denominator is that all people have the right to live as independently as possible. Professionals must take into account the life goals of each individual when developing programs to teach academic, social, community living, or vocational skills (Snell, 1993; Szymanski & Hershenson, 1998; Wehman & Kregel, 1996).

Developing program options that help individuals with disabilities make successful transitions from school to all aspects of life has received national emphasis over recent years. Previously, only those activities that dealt with movement from school to the world of work were stressed. However, today there is more consideration on instruction needed to assist the person with a successful transition at every important life juncture. Transition plans should be updated whenever a major program change is initiated (Wehman, 2002) to help ensure ongoing progress toward student goals and that little ground is lost when the change is made.

Activities should be taught in the environments in which the individual is expected to use the targeted skills (Patton, Cronin, & Wood, 1999). For example, Jack, a student with a mild intellectual disability who needs limited supports, has problems choosing appropriate foods to prepare for a well-balanced meal and has been taught to purchase good foods at his local grocer. Langford, a student who needs more extensive supports, has been taught to prepare a microwave meal. Both students require assistance in learning self-care skills; they differ only in the distance to their life goals of independently working and living in the community.

Past research has shown that community-based instruction is an important variable for students with intellectual disabilities. Instructional methods that use functional materials in realistic settings will promote the retention and transfer of skills. As more and more students with mild intellectual disabilities are placed in inclusive school settings, teachers will need to find creative ways to include functional or community-based experiences. Special education teachers will most likely be involved in inclusive settings. They should be prepared to show how real-life topics can be integrated into an existing curriculum, as well as to share ways to accommodate the needs of students with disabilities.

A functional curriculum should be longitudinal in design and should focus on ways to prepare young people with mild intellectual disabilities for adulthood. Community-based instruction is essential to enabling students to learn how to lead successful and independent lives to the fullest extent possible. Outcomes should relate to employment, independent living, and leisure time. Functional curricula can also encompass academic subjects such as reading, writing, and arithmetic (Browder & Snell, 2000), as well as other areas of instruction such as history and science. A functional academic curriculum can cover any skill.

Table 6.1 lists traditional academic content areas and examples of functional activities that may be used to convey academic subject matter.

Because functional academics can encompass a wide range of life skills, it is important to identify what activities students need to know to successfully participate in adult life. Some authors have identified major activities or life demands that most adults must be able to perform and have developed curricula to aid educators in teaching those functional skills (Cronin & Patton, 1993; Wehman, 2002).

As previously mentioned, the 2002 definitional framework, specifically the move from levels of severity (i.e., mild, moderate, severe, and profound) to levels of support (i.e., intermittent, limited, extensive, and pervasive), promotes greater access to the general curriculum as the focus shifts from the student with a deficit to the curriculum and its design and implementation. It indicates that the interaction between the person and the environment is what creates disability, rather than the person him- or herself. According to Wehmeyer (2003), the principles of universal design should be applied to curriculum development and instruction to ensure that all students with intellectual disabilities have access to

TABLE 6.1

Traditional Academic Content Areas and Examples of Functional Activities

Reading	Mathematics	Science	History	Writing	Health
Use local bus schedule to determine how to go from home to the mall.	Balance a checkbook.	Grow a vegetable garden.	Tell a story about an ancestor.	Write an employer a thank-you note.	Make an appointment to see a dentist or doctor.
Read directions for preparing a microwave meal.	Calculate mileage and travel time to destination using a map.	Identify household chemicals that should not be combined.	Dress like a famous person from a specific time period.	Send an e-mail to a friend. Take messages for others.	Purchase grocery items to prepare a healthy meal.
Understand warning labels on over-the-counter medications.	Determine what time to remove food from an oven.	Understand what common insects should be exterminated.	Prepare a meal from another country.	Complete a job application.	Exercise 30 minutes a day.
Follow instructions on how to use cleaning products to clean different types of surfaces.	Calculate approximate cost to fill up an automobile with gas.	Know how to safely plug in and unplug household items.	Interview someone from another country to learn more about its history.		Demonstrate how to care for a burn and open wound.

the general curriculum. Universal design allows teachers to design instruction and activities in a way that allows students with a wide range of abilities to learn the curriculum in different ways and for different purposes (Wehmeyer, 2003).

In addition, the use of technology provides teachers with more opportunities to individualize instruction for students with mild intellectual disabilities who are included in general education programs. Also, the emphasis on learning real-life skills that prepare all students for the challenges of adulthood may lead to more community-based educational opportunities.

Mere labels cannot predict what individuals with disabilities need to learn in relation to their life goals. Nevertheless, if individuals have intellectual disabilities, they will need help learning some skills. The level of skills ultimately learned and the intensity of the strategies used to teach them are dependent on each individual's needs and life goals. In the remainder of this chapter, a variety of curricular areas that relate to the needs of all learners with intellectual disabilities are described. Each section includes a general description of characteristics that individuals with these disabilities often exhibit and suggestions for program development and instructional strategies.

Self-Care

The greater one's independence in completing basic tasks of daily living, the less one will have to depend on others for support (Spooner & Test, 1994). For individuals with mild to moderate intellectual disabilities, deficits in ability to complete these tasks are evident. In most cases, however, these individuals can learn to care for their personal needs at least as well as members of the nondisabled population. Because of the heterogeneity of this group, self-care needs and the intensity of training required to help these individuals master the related skills vary tremendously. For example, Regina, a student with mild intellectual disabilities, needs to learn to use appropriate table manners at a local restaurant. Another student, LeAnn, with a moderate intellectual disability, needs to learn how to use eating utensils properly when faced with a variety of foods.

Cleanliness and the ability to toilet, eat, and dress are basic self-care skills. Table 6.2 illustrates typical self-care skills according to the age when they usually develop. The table provides a small sample of self-care skills that might be targeted

TABLE 6.2
Age of Acquisition of Typical Self-Care Skills

Age of Acquisition	Skills
Infant–toddler	Toileting, independent eating
5 to 12 years old	Independent bathing, dressing, toothbrushing
Adolescence	Personal hygiene (e.g., shaving, menstrual care, deodorant use)
Adulthood	Meal preparation, clothing care, medication management, and nutrition

for instruction in an educational program for students with mild to moderate intellectual disabilities. Regardless of the age of the learner, the educator would first determine, by implementing a functional needs assessment, what self-care skills the student has and what skills the student needs in current and future environments (Dymond, 2003). The functional needs assessment is accomplished through interviews with the student, interviews with those who know him or her best, and observations of the person's ability in a variety of real-life settings. The outcome of this thorough approach should provide information on the student's current level of self-care skills.

Again, because of the heterogeneity among people with mild to moderate intellectual disabilities, the range of skills addressed is broad and based on the age of the learner. For example, a 5- or 6-year-old with moderate cognitive delay may not be completely toilet trained or may demonstrate inappropriate toileting skills (e.g., refusal to wipe him- or herself after a bowel movement). In such cases, instructional strategies can be designed to omit the inappropriate responses and to teach appropriate alternative behaviors.

The literature is replete with examples of interventions designed to teach basic self-care skills such as toileting, dressing, and eating to younger individuals who have mild to moderate intellectual disabilities. Strategies include training students to perform skills independently or at various levels of partial participation (Brooke, Inge, Armstrong, & Wehman, 1997; Snell, 1993).

▲ CASE EXAMPLE: JUSTINE

Justine, a high school student with a mild intellectual disability, often comes to school dressed in clothes that are both mismatched and provocative for her age. During the community needs assessment process, the teacher learns that Justine's mother also dresses in this fashion and condones her daughter's appearance. During this process, the teacher gathers information about the types and styles of dress appropriate for future job interviews.

Afterward, the teacher develops an instructional program designed to teach Justine how to choose the appropriate dress when interviewing

for employment. The teacher attempts to do this without attaching a value judgment to Justine's current style. Knowing that Justine's mother also dresses in this fashion helps the teacher avoid alienating the mother or Justine. The goal is to help Justine learn to discriminate among the environments in which specific types of clothing can be worn. The teacher helps by exposing Justine to many appropriate role models in community employment settings and by designating specific outfits that may be worn during her job search.

Receptive and Expressive Language

Speech and language deficiencies occur at a significantly greater frequency among learners with mild intellectual disabilities than might be expected in the general population (Rosenberg & Abbeduto, 1993). This observation appears to be the result of three factors. First, more individuals with moderate mental retardation may have associated physiological problems that adversely affect their ability to produce clear speech. Second, individuals with mild mental retardation who come from lower socioeconomic groups may not be exposed to as many good role models (e.g., their parents may not be able to talk to them as often as parents in higher socioeconomic groups). Finally, cognitive ability and language development are linked, and a decrease in cognitive ability may lead to language deficits (Fazio, Johnston, & Brandl, 1993; Patton, Beirne-Smith, & Payne, 1990).

For many individuals with mild cognitive impairments, speech and language problems can be a secondary disabling condition. Receptive and expressive language difficulties range in severity from problems with articulation of sounds or pronunciation of words to a significant delay in language development (Bedrosian, 1993).

There is some evidence suggesting a relation between speech–language impairment and aberrant behavior in persons with developmental disabilities. Schroeder, Schroeder, Smith, and Dalldorf (1978), for example, found that 63% of persons with severe self-injurious behaviors and 72% of those with mild self-injury were also described as having no expressive language. In contrast, within the same residential facility for 1,150 people with mental retardation, only 20% of those without self-injury lacked expressive language. Chung and his colleagues (Chamberlain, Chung, & Jenner, 1993; Chung, Jenner, Chamberlain, & Corbett, 1995) have collected data showing a similar inverse relation between communication ability and the presence of a number of aberrant behaviors (e.g., self-injury, aggression, property destruction) in adults with developmental disabilities. A recent study by Bott, Farmer, and Rhode (1997) found that those individuals with mental retardation and good speech skills had a lower frequency of aberrant behavior compared to individuals with impaired speech.

These findings support the conclusion that communication deficits place the individual at risk for severe behavior problems (Schroeder, Tessel, Loupe, & Stodgell, 1997). However, the relation between communication development and the emergence of aberrant behavior has not been established.

Speech and language problems in this group can also be attributed to cultural differences (Patton et al., 1990). Researchers and government statistics have demonstrated that a disproportionate number of students identified as mildly retarded come from racial or ethnic minority groups (CEC, 2001; Geenen, Powers, Vasquez, & Bersani, 2003). The cultural differences and language barriers working in tandem with environmental influences possibly contribute to the language delays experienced by many of these individuals.

In addition, individuals with more moderate intellectual disabilities run the risk of having secondary physical impairments that can adversely affect their speech and language development (Thurman & Widerstrom, 1990). Motor development problems and physiological anomalies may decrease the individual's ability to produce intelligible speech. For example, a protruding tongue, a characteristic found in many individuals with Down syndrome, adversely affects the pronunciation of words.

Hearing problems are more common in learners with moderate intellectual disabilities than in the general population of individuals without disabilities (Patton et al., 1990). These problems may be directly linked to language delays and poor speech production (Thurman & Widerstrom, 1990). Regardless of the cause, the presence of deficits or delays in speech and language development is increased for individuals with mild to moderate intellectual disabilities.

As with all other areas of the curriculum, the best place to teach appropriate use of receptive and expressive language is in the settings where these skills will be used. The results of research indicate that those individuals with intellectual disabilities who live in the community engage in more appropriate conversation and can use more sophisticated language than their peers who live in institutions (Brinton & Fujiki, 1993). Over the years, researchers and educators have found that language skills learned in isolated classroom activities do not automatically generalize to other settings.

Younger children require more traditional language training designed to help them master basic verbal behaviors and verbal prerequisites (Bricker, 1983). These children, however, still need assistance with generalizing newly acquired language skills to play groups, family functions, and other community-based activities. The best time to assist children with mild to moderate intellectual disabilities to obtain language skills is during their early years (Thurman & Widerstrom, 1990). Language training by an early-intervention specialist should include both direct service to the child and assistance to the parents that is designed to help them teach and foster these skills in their children. However, as individuals become older, their language skills can continue to improve (Fujiki & Brinton, 1993; Schiefelbusch, 1993); thus, instruction should not cease during the elementary years.

Early instruction involves systematically teaching and reinforcing the learner's ability to imitate and discriminate gestures or vocalizations. The teacher accomplishes these objectives by using both chaining and shaping strategies. Initially, the teacher reinforces all vocalizations, thereby increasing the overall number. Gradually, only those vocalizations that more closely resemble the final objective are reinforced until the learner can reliably produce the sound or word. Eventually, the teacher reinforces only more complex vocalizations such as a statement (e.g., "I want a drink" or "I'm thirsty").

The most important component of a language and communication program and the one most often overlooked is the promotion of the generalization of these skills. As with all skills, a systematic program designed to enhance generalization is necessary because these students do not easily transfer learned skills. As the student initially acquires language and communication skills, the teacher simply increases the number of stimuli the student is exposed to during the course of instruction. For example, when teaching the student to respond to the request "Pick up your cup," the teacher can use a variety of containers of different sizes and weights, such as a drink box, a canned drink, a bottled drink, a glass, and a cup.

Teaching students to generalize more advanced language and communication skills requires increasing their exposure to naturally occurring events. Students with mild to moderate intellectual disabilities appear to learn more advanced communication skills when they are in the setting where the communication demands have real-life value (Bedrosian, 1993; Fujiki & Brinton, 1993). Teaching advanced language skills across community and school environments helps the learner to see that language is a way to control the environment, a realization that motivates them to master these skills. For example, Wendi might be learning to remember and repeat orally four important criteria for renting an apartment. Once she can state the four points, the teacher might ask her, on site in a model apartment, to repeat each point orally for the group and to note its significance. A final activity or evaluation for Wendi would be to call or visit apartment managers and ask them the questions related to the criteria (the location, cost of rent, size, and special features such as a pool or community events). Generalization of Wendi's advanced communication skills continues to improve as she practices these activities overtime in real-life situations. A variety of instructional strategies are used to teach language to learners with mild to moderate intellectual disabilities. In most cases, these individuals can learn to control their environments and to communicate with people using language. The extent to which they advance their skills depends on the types and numbers of innovative social and other community activities developed for them by their teachers and family.

Learning and Cognition

Individuals with mild to moderate intellectual disabilities have pervasive limited cognitive ability (Keogh, 1988). This pervasive limited cognitive ability is not as inconsistent, in terms of intelligence versus achievement, as one might expect from students accurately identified as having learning disabilities or behavior disorders. These students have frequent "peaks and valleys" in their ability to grasp new concepts and to apply new skills. Fortunately, remedial supports can be of major assistance.

All comparisons are relevant. Although students with mild to moderate intellectual disabilities show much less of a discrepancy between measured intelligence and achievement compared with nondisabled students, they differ considerably within their own group (Edgar, 1987; MacMillan, 1982). The major characteristic shared by all categories of learners with mild to moderate intellectual disabilities is that they fall significantly behind their general education peers in tasks that require learning and using academic skills (Rossi, Herting, & Wolman, 1997). Deshler and Schumaker (1986) found that by high school, many learners categorized as having mild disabilities had fallen at least 6 years behind their general education peers in academic achievement. If this finding is indeed true for those students with mild disabilities, the differences for those with moderate intellectual disabilities are great enough that comparisons lose their meaning.

Two basic theories have been used to describe the cognitive development of individuals with mild to moderate intellectual disabilities. The developmental theory, best described by Zigler (1969), postulates that individuals with intellectual disabilities progress through the same developmental levels as those who do not have disabilities, but they do so at a slower rate. Adherents to the developmental approach also postulate that the highest developmental levels reached by individuals with intellectual disabilities are lower than the highest levels reached by their peers without disabilities.

The difference theorists postulate that the mental capabilities of individuals with intellectual disabilities are qualitatively different from those of their nondisabled peers (Zigler, 1969). These theorists contend that differences exist in the ability of people with intellectual disabilities to process learned information.

Research supporting or refuting both theories is equivocal. Regardless of one's theoretical point of view, the results of these studies underscore the fact that individuals with intellectual disabilities are slow to learn new skills, do not grasp concepts well at symbolic or abstract levels, are inefficient learners, and do not readily transfer learned skills to new settings or when different materials are required (Hayes & Taplin, 1993; Langone, 1986). Therefore, more recent research has focused on finding the most effective and efficient instructional strategies to use in helping these individuals overcome the deficits resulting from intellectual disabilities.

Learning Skills

For many reasons, individuals with intellectual disabilities may learn facts and lists by intensive drill, but they fail to master higher-order learning skills. Abstract concepts such as numerical reasoning, time, measurement, and use of money may be difficult skills for them to master (Langone, 1990).

Part of the question that has not been answered adequately is whether the problem is that these learners cannot master advanced learning skills or that professionals have not adequately identified and taught these skills because they overemphasize the drilling of basic facts. The trend toward improving the learning skills of individuals with intellectual disabilities is to teach more advanced skills in environments where these skills have a high probability of being used. For example, high school students with mild mental disabilities may have great trouble learning to use fractions in classroom activities involving a blackboard and paper-and-pencil tasks. These same students, however, may be able to master the use of fractions when they are taught them while performing cooking exercises in a restaurant's kitchen or in building-trade exercises conducted while participating in a home remodeling project.

Having acknowledged that individuals with mild intellectual disabilities have varying deficits in memory, attention, ability to organize materials, ability to model others, and language, researchers have turned their attention to identifying and testing strategies to accommodate for these deficits (Turner, Dofny, & Dutka, 1994; Wright & Schuster, 1994). For example, effective teachers instruct learners how to pay close attention to the relevant parts of any task by color coding the important components of reading, mathematical, or vocational tasks. This approach helps students discriminate between what is important and what is not, thus minimizing their memory problems and improving the quality of their work.

There are many other examples of instructional strategies that can be used to help learners with mild to moderate intellectual disabilities to minimize their weaknesses in cognition. For example, using a memory aid like mnemonics may help some students to learn and remember how to complete a variety of tasks.

In addition, teaching students more socially acceptable behaviors assists them in developing better problem-solving skills (Healey & Masterpasqua, 1992). Finally, the use of computer-based instruction appears to be a promising medium for teaching learners higher-order cognitive skills (Gerber, 1994) and a promising means to enable people with disabilities to become, in essence, their own support (Davies, Stock, & Wehmeyer, 2001; Wehmeyer, 1998).

 ## CASE EXAMPLE: PATRICK

Patrick, a high school–aged student with moderate mental retardation, has been taught to remember the word "code" as a mnemonic when he goes to his community-based job at a local insurance company. By recalling each letter in the word, he can remember the sequence of job duties that he must complete while at work:

C = Clock in
O = Organize files
D = Distribute files
E = Enter data

Patrick has learned a variety of mnemonics that he uses in other situations. The instructor taught Patrick the mnemonics by having him model her saying each letter and statement aloud. Over subsequent trials, he was encouraged and was given reinforcement for repeating the statements in an increasingly softer voice, until he eventually repeated them silently to himself. The teacher judged the use of the mnemonics by the accuracy of Patrick's task completion. At some point, it may become difficult to judge whether Patrick is using the mnemonic device or completing the task because he has learned the chain of steps. However, the mnemonic can always serve as a reminder of what to do if for some reason the sequence of duties or tasks is interrupted and he cannot recall what to do next.

Generalization of Skills

Individuals with mild to moderate intellectual disabilities have trouble generalizing skills they have learned in one setting to other settings that involve different materials, different people, and different time. This problem also exists among people in the general population, but it appears more pronounced among individuals with intellectual disabilities (Hughes, 1992; Turner et al., 1994).

A number of behaviorally oriented strategies have been developed to assist these learners in overcoming most deficits they have in generalizing learned skills. Varying the settings, the time of day, the materials, and the people working with a student appears to facilitate generalization (Alberti & Troutman, 1995; Kregel, 2002). These seem like commonsense suggestions, but unfortunately, many educational programs that provide services to learners with intellectual disabilities do not take such issues into account. Community-based instruction helps learners to minimize their problems with generalization by allowing them to practice a variety of real-life skills in the different environments where they are expected to use them (Alberti & Troutman, 1995; Billingsley, Liberty, & White, 1994; Browder & Snell, 1993; Test & Spooner, 1996; Wehman & Targett, 2003).

⚐ CASE EXAMPLE: MR. RADER

Mr. Rader wants his middle school–aged students, including a few who have mild intellectual disabilities, to apply math skills to everyday problems such as cost-comparison shopping. He has taught this skill in the classroom for a week. On a community-based learning trip to a local grocery store, Mr. Rader was dismayed to discover that several students became confused and were unable to compare prices.

At the time, Mr. Rader did not realize that the root of the problem was those students' inability to generalize. He should have taught and practiced some of the skills in classroom-based activities and concurrently allowed frequent practice applying the skills in a variety of real community retail settings (e.g., grocer, clothes store, bookstore).

Mobility

Mobility for individuals with mild to moderate intellectual disabilities is usually not a crucial issue. The majority of individuals who fall into this category do not have long-term physical problems that impede their ability to move from one place to another. This statement is, however, relative. For example, many children with mild deficits develop motor skills at a slower rate than their peers do (Patton et al., 1990). Similarly, most children with moderate cognitive disabilities develop motor skills (e.g., crawling and walking) at a slower rate than do their peers with mild mental disabilities (Thurman & Widerstrom, 1990).

The same relationship exists across categorical areas for multiple disabling conditions. On the basis of the variety of biomedical conditions associated with moderate mental cognitive impairment, one would expect a higher percentage of these individuals to have physical impairments, compared with their peers with mild cognitive delays. In any case, the number of individuals with mild to moderate intellectual disabilities who have mobility problems as a result of physical impairments is small compared with people who have severe mental impairments. Those students who have mobility problems should work with physical and occupational therapists who can assist parents and educators, too. For example, occupational therapists can guide students, their families, and teachers in choosing appropriate adaptive devices, such as an expanded computer keyboard to enable a student to use a computer in both the classroom and at home.

Self-Determination

Today, educators are making more efforts to teach students with mild intellectual disabilities the skills they need to become self-determined. People who are self-determined act in ways that enable them to achieve desired goals and enhance their quality of life. Fostering self-determination is essential for a successful transition from school to adult life. For example, Field and Hoffman (2001) pointed out that students who were involved in planning, decision making, and implementing their educational program performed better than their peers who were not. Because of this powerful relationship, many researchers suggest that classroom instruction plays a key role in promoting student self-determination skills (Wehman, 1998). Informal means of encouraging self-determination in schools have been inadequate for ensuring that students successfully transition from school to adulthood (Eisenman & Chamberlin, 2001). Instead, according to Field, Martin, Miller, Ward, and Wehmeyer (1998), explicit instruction and opportunities for the generalization of skills are necessary for teaching self-determination skills.

Over the years, numerous self-determination curricula have surfaced. Test, Karvonen, Wood, Browder, and Algozzine (2000) identified 60 curricula and 675 other resources designed for this purpose. However, there is limited research to empirically validate links between self-determination instruction and post-school outcomes (Algozzine, Browder, Karvonen, Test, & Wood, 2001). Evaluation of these curricula revealed mixed findings in terms of their effectiveness in increasing student self-determination skills (e.g., Zhang, 2000, 2001a).

Furthermore, it is believed that this may relate to why many educators are reluctant to implement and include self-determination objectives in Individualized Education Programs (IEPs; Agran, Snow, & Swaner, 1999; Wehmeyer, Agran, & Hughes, 2000; Wehmeyer & Schwartz, 1998; Zhang, 2001b; Zhang & Stecker, 2001). Wehmeyer et al. (2000) surveyed 1,219 teachers about their beliefs and practices regarding self-determination. Although the vast majority of teachers noted that self-determination was an important area of instruction, only 22% indicated that all of their students had IEP goals in the area of self-determination. Furthermore, 31% of the teachers indicated that none of their students had goals in this area.

More effort must be expended on teaching students how to gain control of their lives and how to adapt to changes in their environments (Martin & Huber Marshall, 1995). Agran, Blanchard, and Wehmeyer (2000) used the Self-Determined Learning Model of Instruction to teach 19 adolescent students to set goals, take action, and adjust goals based on the results of their actions. The study found that 17 of the 19 students changed dramatically in their independence skills, exceeding teacher expectations. Of the goals the students set, 89% were attained at or above the expected level. The model was found to be effective for students with a variety of disabling conditions. Wehman, West, and Kregel (1999) have noted that self-determination is the number one need for program development, research, and policy analysis as it relates to employment success of individuals with disabilities. There is an urgent need to focus on and evaluate specific strategies that teachers and parents can use to promote self-determination of students with disabilities (Wehmeyer et al., 2000; Zhang, 2001b; Zhang & Stecker, 2001). Until that is successful, many will remain dependent on other people to make decisions, provide support, and make changes.

CASE EXAMPLE: BETSY

Betsy was born with moderate intellectual disabilities. Soon after her birth, her family began to react in an overprotective manner. In addition, reportedly due to an increase in her family's level of stress and ability to cope, Betsy had few quality interactions with other family members. In short, she was told what to do, how to do it, and when to do it. Over the years, she became highly dependent on others for instruction and reinforcement that she was doing things the right way. This led her to believe that she could never do anything right and certainly not on her own. Since receiving instruction in self-determination skills and having the opportunity to practice those skills in

her daily life, Betsy has become a new person. She has learned a number of new skills, including how to speak out for herself and make her voice heard. She is currently investigating summer job opportunities and places where she can live in her community.

The tendency of individuals with mild to moderate intellectual disabilities to be less self-determined can be minimized if caregivers practice commonsense strategies (Misra, 1992). For example, by gradually fading prompts and cues, teachers can assist students to rely more on their own problem-solving skills. This approach, paired with a systematic and gradual fading of tangible reinforcers, allows learners to become less reliant on external motivations. Asking students if they are proud of themselves when they accurately complete tasks, while showing them you are proud of their efforts (using smiles, pats on the back) helps them to "internalize" reinforcers.

Task analysis involves breaking a task down into smaller steps, which allows learners to deal with more manageable tasks and improves their chances of success. Applying task analysis to the range of academic, vocational, and leisure and recreation skills has become the most successful curricular and instructional tool available to special educators. Breaking tasks (skills) into component parts reduces the student avoidance behavior and anxiety that often accompany the presentation of activities that they perceive as being beyond their abilities.

Finally, self-determination should increase as more students with disabilities move to inclusive classes and regular educators team with special educators to provide quality instruction for all children on their individual levels (Sailor, Gee, & Karasoff, 1993). Children with disabilities have the potential to make positive gains in social, language, and academic skills when placed in close contact with their nondisabled peers and when a well-designed program with the appropriate supports is available.

Capacity for Independent Living

The word *independence* is one that, in daily use, has many different meanings. Most professionals would agree that the major goal of all special education programs is to help people with disabilities become as independent as possible. For individuals with mild to moderate intellectual disabilities, *independence* has been narrowly defined.

People who have cognitive impairments have often been relegated to positions of dependence from which they continually look to others to meet their needs. Most individuals with mild intellectual disabilities are assimilated into society as part of the lower class, at the lowest socioeconomic level. Individuals with moderate cognitive disabilities lead dependent or semidependent lives, with the smallest proportion living in group homes or semi-independent apartments managed by state agencies. Most of these citizens are cared for by their families or are relegated to residential or institutional settings.

In either case, the quality of life for these citizens, in terms of the number of independent living activities they are taught, does not compare to what their peers without disabilities learn. This situation can be traced to the emphasis placed on academic training in school programs. People without disabilities usually learn independent living skills outside of school, in the context of extracurricular clubs and groups, through instruction in their homes, or simply through trial and error by modeling the behaviors of others.

Individuals with intellectual disabilities are included less often in extracurricular activities, come from homes less likely to provide this training, and do not have the same ability to learn through trial and error by modeling the behaviors of others. This lack of continued exposure to out-of-context, academically based activities or, at best, to simulations of independent living skills hinders any successful transition to community living.

During the past decade, educators have been increasingly interested in teaching independent living skills to students with moderate intellectual disabilities in environments where they ultimately would be required to use those skills. Programs have been designed to teach independent shopping skills in community grocery stores, restaurant skills in fast-food establishments, and other leisure skills at a variety of community-based sites (Inge & Dymond, 1994; Sowers & Powers, 1995). After an assessment of what a student already knows and needs to learn is performed, teachers can design functional and community-based activities that will provide him or her with opportunities to learn the skills needed. For example, Table 6.3 illustrates competencies that a student may need to acquire to manage his or her finances as independently as possible.

The importance of teaching independent living skills is obvious when one considers that the major goal of education is to assist learners to become as independent as possible (Erlbaum & Vaughn, 1999; Grumpel, Tappe, & Araki, 2000). Students with mild to moderate intellectual disabilities often have deficits in social skills, and these deficits can severely affect their successful integration into both the community and other school environments. Teaching social skills appears to be most effective when it is done in context with actual daily living activities (Gresham, Sugai, & Horner, 2001; O'Neill et al., 1997). In addition, the broader area of independent living skills (e.g., home management, family care, leisure, consumer skills) can provide realistic opportunities for developing activities that help these students apply a variety of general cognitive, academic, and language skills (Elksnin & Elksnin, 1998).

Economic Self-Sufficiency

A person's worth, both in his or her own perception and in the perception of others, is often judged by the person's ability to earn a living. Status is placed on the type of job one does, and this status may affect the individual's overall qual-

TABLE 6.3

Money Management Curriculum Topics

Sample Competency	Sample Subcompetency
Managing personal finances	Manage a budget Pay bills Keep financial records Use credit responsibly Save for the future
Banking	Open a bank account Make a deposit Keep a record of transactions and finances Organize documents Reconcile bank statements
Filing taxes	Read a paycheck stub Organize documents for filing Use a tax service File taxes
Building a financial portfolio	Identify investment options Make investments Plan for retirement
Using currency	Count money Make change Use automatic teller machine Use a credit card Write checks

ity of life. Because of the status that society places on work, it is important for individuals with mild to moderate intellectual disabilities to enhance and increase their status by finding and maintaining employment.

According to a 1998 Louis Harris & Associates national survey of people with disabilities, more than 71% of working-age adults with disabilities are unemployed, despite the fact that two thirds of these individuals want to work. In addition, an extensive national longitudinal study of students with disabilities who had exited schools found that the employment rates of individuals with disabilities lagged significantly behind those of their peers without disabilities (Wagner, D'Amico, Marder, Newman, & Blackorby, 1992). Individuals with disabilities who *were* employed received lower wages and fewer benefits. Other studies confirm a continuing troublesome trend toward high rates of unemployment or underemployment for former recipients of special education services (Colley & Jamison, 1998; Rogan, 1997). These results suggest that educational and career development approaches still need to be identified and implemented for individuals with disabilities to receive reasonable opportunities to obtain employment and lead satisfying lifestyles. Fortunately, the potential for economic self-sufficiency of individuals with mild to moderate intellectual disabilities is excellent. Research and practice have confirmed many of the curricular interventions and career development activities that result in positive postschool employment outcomes.

Many published research studies, project reports, and program guidelines outline successful vocationally related programs for these individuals (Benz, Lindstrom, & Yovanoff, 2000; Luecking & Fabian, 2000; Wehman, Moon, Everson, Wood, & Barcus, 1988).

The employability potential of learners with mild to moderate intellectual disabilities is dependent on the quality of their entire school program, not just on their educational opportunities in high school. The amount and quality of the time students with disabilities spend participating in paid and unpaid vocational activities appear to influence their eventual success in competitive employment (Benz et al., 2000; Colley & Jamison, 1998; Eisenman, 2000; Kohler, 1993; Luecking & Fabian, 2000; Wagner, Blackorby, Cameto, & Newman, 1993). The importance of restructuring special education curricula with more emphasis on work-related and independent living skills is evident.

The emphasis on appropriate work-related skills begins in elementary school and continues throughout one's life. For example, to minimize or eliminate poor work attitudes, students beginning in elementary school can spend time in the community with their teachers learning work-related skills through job tasks simplified for their needs (Wehman & Targett, 2003). This process allows students to learn about the world of work in actual community settings and allows them to observe community members doing their jobs. Teachers can choose good role models for the students to observe and talk to and generally to help them see the positive side of employment.

As students progress through middle and high school programs, the amount and sophistication of the activities increase. Accompanied by their teachers, students can participate in a variety of job sites that represent a cross-section of their community's employment possibilities. These activities allow the students to learn work-related behaviors (e.g., social and community skills, task behavior, and assertiveness) and allow teachers to teach academic skills related to each job (Brinton, 1994; Brinton & Fujiki, 1993).

Unger, Parent, Gibson, Kane-Johnston, and Kregel (1998) provide a model for identifying and organizing needed supports. They designed this model for use in supported employment planning, but it has direct applicability to planning support needs for students who will be leaving the K through 12 school system. There are seven steps in this model:

1. Determine individual needs and preferences.
2. Brainstorm potential options.
3. Assess job and community supports.
4. Identify individual choices.

5. Develop strategies for accessing supports.
6. Evaluate support effectiveness.
7. Arrange provision for ongoing monitoring. (Unger et al., p. 3)

No matter what supports are identified and used, the determination of appropriateness centers on the effectiveness or success of the supports. Finally, the educator must remember that, as with all other services and programs, natural supports must be individualized. Thus, they will vary from one student and one setting to another (Inge & Tilson, 1997).

A growing emphasis in the education field is on the preparation of students to solve problems, think critically, and work cooperatively—all skills that contribute to employment success. An additional goal is to assist youth to acquire knowledge, skills, and attitudes to pursue career pathways (Lynch & Reimer, 1997). Based on research by Halpern, Benz, and Lindstrom (1992) and Kohler (1993, 1996), some of the key characteristics of effective career development approaches include student-centered planning, self-determination, and family involvement; participation in career exploration and development approaches starting in elementary school and continuing through high school; collaborative partnerships with school and community to identify or create comprehensive resources and supports; real-life work experiences within businesses; a focus on other aspects of adult life; and coordination with adult service providers to ensure a smooth transition from school to the community.

FINAL THOUGHTS

The field has come a long way. Professionals have observed a painfully slow movement away from segregated settings for people who have intellectual disabilities toward environments where they are fully included in daily life activities enjoyed by many citizens. Also, instructional methodologies and assistive technologies have helped people with disabilities become productive citizens and lifelong learners.

Unfortunately, the field still has a long way to go. Although professionals know a great deal about what can be done to improve the quality of life for people with disabilities, they now must work hard to see that these advances become widespread and available to all. Professionals must continue to work together to ensure that students with intellectual disabilities receive access to high-quality, community-based, and inclusive instruction, as well as opportunities for employment, lifelong learning, and self-determination.

To accomplish these goals, professionals must first identify personnel who will excel in education and who demonstrate a strong work ethic. The demands placed on professionals in the future will increase as more students with disabilities participate in the regular classroom. Meeting these demands will require staff that know how to work hard and are not easily distracted from their primary responsibility of providing instruction and assistance to those who have intellectual disabilities and their families.

REFERENCES

Agran, M., Blanchard, C., & Wehmeyer, M. L. (2000). Promoting transition goals and self-determination through student self-directed learning: The Self-Determined Learning Model of Instruction. *Education and Training in Mental Retardation and Developmental Disabilities, 35,* 351–364.

Agran, M., Snow, K., & Swaner, J. (1999). Teacher perceptions of self-determination: Benefits, characteristics, strategies. *Education and Training in Mental Retardation and Developmental Disabilities, 34,* 293–301.

Alberti, P. A., & Troutman, A. C. (1995). *Applied behavior analysis for teachers* (4th ed.). Columbus, OH: Merrill.

Algozzine, R. F., Browder, D. B., Karvonen, M., Test, D. W., & Wood, W. M. (2001). Effects of interventions to promote self-determination for individuals with disabilities. *Review of Educational Research, 71,* 219–277.

American Association on Mental Retardation. (1992). *Mental retardation: Definition, classification, and systems of supports* (9th ed.). Washington, DC: Author.

Bedrosian, J. L. (1993). Making minds meet: Assessment of conversational topics in adults with mild to moderate mental retardation. *Topics in Language Disorders, 13,* 36–46.

Benz, M. R., Lindstrom, L., & Yovanoff, P. (2000). Improving graduation and employment outcomes of students with disabilities: Predictive factors and student perspectives. *Exceptional Children, 66,* 509–529.

Billingsley, F. F., Liberty, K., & White, O. (1994). Instructional technology. In E. Cipani & F. Spooner (Eds.), *Curricular and instructional approaches for persons with severe disabilities* (pp. 81–116). Needham Heights, MA: Allyn & Bacon.

Bott, C., Farmer, R., & Rhode, J. (1997). Behaviour problems associated with lack of speech in people with learning disabilities. *Journal of Intellectual Disability Research, 41,* 3–7.

Bradley, V. J., Agosta, J. M., & Kimmich, M. (2001). Social and community participation: How to enhance supports for people with mild cognitive limitations. In A. J. Tymchuk, K. C. Lakin, & R. Luckasson (Eds.), *The forgotten generation: The status and challenges of adults with mild cognitive limitations* (pp. 169–189). Baltimore: Brookes.

Bradley, V. J., Ashbaugh, J. W., & Blaney, B. C. (Eds.). (1994). *Creating individual supports for people with developmental disabilities: A mandate for change at many levels.* Baltimore: Brookes.

Bricker, D. (1983). Early communication development and training. In M. Snell (Ed.), *Systematic instruction for the moderately and severely handicapped* (pp. 269–288). Columbus, OH: Merrill.

Brinton, B. (1994). Ability of institutionalized and community-based adults with retardation to respond to questions in an interview context. *Journal of Speech and Hearing Research, 37,* 369–377.

Brinton, B., & Fujiki, M. (1993). Communication skills and community integration in adults with mild to moderate retardation. *Topics in Language Disorders, 13,* 9–19.

Brooke, V., Inge, K. J., Armstrong, A. J., & Wehman, P. (1997). *Supported employment handbook: A customer-driven approach for persons with significant disabilities.* Richmond: Virginia Commonwealth University, Rehabilitation Research and Training Center.

Browder, D. M., & Snell, M. E. (1993). Functional academics. In M. E. Snell (Ed.), *Systematic instruction of students with moderate and severe disabilities* (4th ed., pp. 442–479). New York: Merrill.

Browder, D. M., & Snell, M. E. (2000). Teaching functional academics. In M. E. Snell & F. Brown (Eds.), *Instruction of students with severe disabilities* (5th ed., pp. 493–542). Upper Saddle River, NJ: Merrill.

Bynoe, P. (1998). Rethinking and retooling teacher preparation to prevent perpetual failure by our children. *Journal of Special Education, 32,* 37–40.

Chamberlain, L., Chung, M. C., & Jenner, L. (1993). Preliminary findings on communication and challenging behaviour in learning difficulty. *British Journal of Developmental Disabilities, 39,* 118–125.

Chung, M. C., Jenner, L., Chamberlain, L., & Corbett, J. (1995). One year follow-up pilot study on communication skill and challenging behaviour. *European Journal of Psychiatry, 9,* 83–95.

Colley, D. A., & Jamison, D. (1998). Post school results for youth with disabilities: Key indicators and policy implications. *Career Development for Exceptional Individuals, 21,* 145–160.

Council for Exceptional Children. (2001). New study verifies the disproportionate number of students from diverse backgrounds in special education. *CEC Today, 7*(8), 7.

Cronin, M. S., & Patton, J. R. (1993). *Life skills across the curriculum for youth with special needs.* Austin, TX: PRO-ED.

Davies, D. K., Stock, S. E., & Wehmeyer, M. L. (2001). Enhancing independent Internet access for individuals with mental retardation through the use of a specialized Web browser: A pilot study. *Education and Training in Mental Retardation and Developmental Disabilities, 36,* 107–113.

Deshler, D., & Schumaker, J. B. (1986). Learning strategies: An instructional alternative for low-achieving students. *Exceptional Child, 52,* 583–590.

Dymond, S. K. (2003). Community participation. In P. Wehman & J. Kregel (Eds.), *Functional curriculum for elementary, middle, and secondary age students with special needs* (2nd ed., pp. 259–291). Austin, TX: PRO-ED.

Edgar, E. (1987). Secondary programs in special education: Are many of them justifiable? *Exceptional Children, 53,* 555–556.

Eisenman, L. (2000). Characteristics and effects of integrated academic and occupational curricula for students with disabilities: A literature review. *Career Development for Exceptional Individuals, 23,* 105–119.

Eisenman, L. T., & Chamberlin, M. (2001). Implementing self-determination activities: Lessons from the schools. *Remedial and Special Education, 22,* 138–147.

Elksnin, L. K., & Elksnin, N. (1998). Teaching social skills to students with learning and behavior problems. *Intervention in School and Clinic, 33*(3), 131–141.

Erlbaum, B., & Vaughn, S. (1999). Can school-based interventions enhance the self-concept of students with learning disabilities? *Exceptional Parent, 29*(9), 92–94.

Fazio, B. B., Johnston, J. R., & Brandl, L. (1993). Relation between mental age and vocabulary development among children with mild mental retardation. *American Journal on Mental Retardation, 97,* 541–546.

Field, S., & Hoffman, A. (2001). Lessons learned from implementing the Steps to Self-Determination Curriculum. *Remedial and Special Education, 23,* 90–98.

Field, S., Martin, J., Miller, R., Ward, M., & Wehmeyer, M. (1998). *A practical guide for teaching self-determination.* Reston, VA: Council for Exceptional Children.

Fujiki, M., & Brinton, B. (1993). Growing old with retardation: The language of survivors. *Topics in Language Disorders, 13,* 77–89.

Geenen, S., Powers, L., Vasquez, A. L., & Bersani, H. (2003, Spring). Understanding and promoting the transition of minority adolescents. *CDEI, 26,* 1.

Gerber, B. L. (1994). Beyond drill and practice: Using the computer for creative decision making. *Preventing School Failure, 38,* 25–30.

Gresham, F., Sugai, G., & Horner, R. A. (2001). Interpreting outcomes of social skills training for students with high-incidence disabilities. *Exceptional Children, 67*(3), 331–344.

Grossman, H. J. (Ed.). (1983). *Manual on terminology and classification in mental retardation* (Rev. ed.). Washington, DC: American Association on Mental Deficiency [now called American Association on Mental Retardation].

Grumpel, T. P., Tappe, P., & Araki, C. (2000). Comparison of social problem-solving abilities among adults with and without developmental disabilities. *Education and Training in Mental Retardation and Developmental Disabilities, 35*(3), 259–268.

Halpern, A., Benz, M., & Lindstrom, L. (1992). A systems change approach to improving secondary special education and transition programs at the community level. *Career Development for Exceptional Individuals, 12,* 167–177.

Hayes, B. K., & Taplin, J. E. (1993). Development of conceptual knowledge in children with mental retardation. *American Journal on Mental Retardation, 98,* 293–303.

Healey, K. N., & Masterpasqua, F. (1992). Interpersonal cognitive problem-solving among children with mental retardation. *American Journal on Mental Retardation, 96,* 367–372.

Hughes, C. (1992). Teaching self-instruction utilizing multiple exemplars to produce generalized problem solving among individuals with severe mental retardation. *American Journal on Mental Retardation, 97*(3), 302–314.

Inge, K. J., & Dymond, S. (1994). Challenging behaviors in the workplace: Increasing a student's access to community-based vocational instruction. *Journal of Vocational Rehabilitation, 4,* 272–284.

Inge, K., & Tilson, G. (1997). Ensuring support systems that will work: Getting beyond the natural supports vs. job coach controversy. *Journal of Vocational Rehabilitation, 9*(27), 133–142.

Keogh, B. K. (1988). Improving services for problem learners: Rethinking and restructuring. *Journal of Learning Disabilities, 21,* 19–22.

Kohler, P. (1993). Best practices in transition: Substantiated or implied? *Career Development for Exceptional Individuals, 16,* 107–121.

Kohler, P. (1996). Preparing youth with disabilities for future challenges: A taxonomy for transition programming. In P. D. Kohler (Ed.), *Taxonomy for transition programming: Linking research and practice* (pp. 1–62). Champaign-Urbana: University of Illinois Transition Research Institute.

Kregel, J. (2002). Designing instructional programs. In P. Wehman & J. Kregel (Eds.), *Functional curriculum for elementary, middle, and secondary age students with special needs* (2nd ed., pp. 37–66). Austin, TX: PRO-ED.

Kregel, J., & Wehman, P. (1997). Supported employment: A decade of employment outcomes for individuals with significant disabilities. In W. E. Kiernan & R. L. Schalock (Eds.), *Integrated employment: Current status and future directions* (pp. 31–48). Washington, DC: American Association on Mental Retardation.

Langone, J. (1986). *Teaching retarded learners: Curriculum and methods for improving instruction.* Boston: Allyn & Bacon.

Langone, J. (1990). *Teaching students with mild and moderate learning problems.* Boston: Allyn & Bacon.

Louis Harris & Associates. (1998). *The ICD Survey III: Employing disabled Americans.* Washington, DC: National Organization on Disability.

Luckasson, R., Borthwick-Duffy, S., Buntinx, W. H. E., Coulter, D. L., Craig, E. M., Reeve, A., Schalock, R. L., Snell, M. E., Spitalnik, D. M., Spreat, S., & Tasse, M. J. (2002). *Mental retardation: Definition, classification, and systems of supports* (10th ed.). Washington, DC: American Association on Mental Retardation.

Luckasson, R., & Spitalnik, D. M. (1994). Political and programmatic shifts of the 1992 AAMR definition of mental retardation. In V. Bradley, J. W., Ashbaugh, & B. C. Blaney (Eds.), *Creating individual supports for people with developmental disabilities: A mandate for change at many levels* (pp. 81–96). Baltimore: Brookes.

Luecking, R. G., & Fabian, E. S. (2000). Paid internship and employment success for youth in transition. *Career Development for Exceptional Individuals, 23,* 205–219.

Lynch, P., & Reimer, J. (1997). Meeting the needs of special populations in the 21st century: The role of vocational special needs personnel. *Journal for Vocational Special Needs Education, 19*(3), 99–102.

MacMillan, D. L. (1982). *Mental retardation in school and society* (2nd ed.). Boston: Little, Brown.

Martin, J. E., & Huber Marshall, L. H. (1995). ChoiceMaker: A comprehensive self-determination transition program. *Intervention in School and Clinic, 30*(3), 147–156.

Misra, A. (1992). Generalization of social skills through self-monitoring by adults with mild mental retardation. *Exceptional Children, 58,* 495–507.

O'Neill, R. E., Horner, R. H., Albin, R. W., Sprague, J. R., Storey, K., & Newton, J. S. (1997). *Functional assessment and program development for problem behavior.* Pacific Grove, CA: Brookes/Cole.

Patton, J. R., Beirne-Smith, M., & Payne, J. S. (1990). *Mental retardation* (3rd ed.). Columbus, OH: Merrill.

Patton, J. R., Cronin, M. E., & Wood, S. J. (1999). *Infusing real-life topics into existing curricula: Recommended procedures and instructional examples for the elementary, middle, and high school levels.* Austin, TX: PRO-ED.

Polloway, E., & Smith, J. D. (1983a). Changes in mild mental retardation: Population, programs, and perspectives. *Exceptional Children, 50*(2), 149–158.

Polloway, E. A., & Smith, J. D. (1983b). Current status of the mild mental retardation construct: Identification, placement, and program. In M. C. Wang, M. C. Reynolds, & H. J. Walberg (Eds.), *The handbook of special education: Research and practice* (pp. 7–22). Oxford, England: Pergamon Press.

Rogan, P. (1997). *Review and analysis of postschool follow-up results: 1996–1997 Indiana postschool follow-up study.* Indianapolis: Indiana Department of Education, Division of Special Education.

Rosenberg, S., & Abbeduto, L. (1993). *Language and communication in mental retardation: Development, process, and intervention.* Hillsdale, NJ: Erlbaum.

Rossi, R., Herting, J., & Wolman, J. (1997). *Profiles of students with disabilities as identified in NELS: 88.* Washington, DC: American Institutes for Research. (ERIC Document Reproduction Service No. ED409663)

Sailor, W., Gee, K., & Karasoff, P. (1993). Full inclusion and school restructuring. In M. Snell (Ed.), *Instruction of students with severe disabilities* (4th ed., pp. 1–30). New York: Macmillan.

Schiefelbusch, R. L. (1993). Communication in adults with mental retardation. *Topics in Language Disorders, 13,* 1–8.

Schroeder, S. R., Schroeder, C. S., Smith, B., & Dalldorf, J. (1978). Prevalence of self-injurious behavior in a large state facility for the retarded: A three-year follow-up study. *Journal of Autism and Childhood Schizophrenia, 8,* 261–269.

Schroeder, S. R., Tessel, R. E., Loupe, P. S., & Stodgell, C. J. (1997). Severe behavior problems among people with developmental disabilities. In W. E. MacLean, Jr. (Ed.), *Ellis' handbook of mental deficiency, psychological theory, and research* (3rd ed., pp. 439–464). Hillsdale, NJ: Erlbaum.

Snell, M. (Ed.). (1993). *Systematic instruction of persons with severe disabilities* (4th ed.). Columbus, OH: Merrill.

Sowers, J., & Powers, L. (1995). Enhancing the participation and independence of students with severe physical and multiple disabilities in performing community activities. *Mental Retardation, 33,* 209–220.

Spooner, F., & Test, D. W. (1994). Domestic and community living skills. In E. C. Cipani & F. Spooner (Eds.), *Curricular and instructional approaches for persons with severe disabilities* (pp. 149–183). Needham Heights, MA: Allyn & Bacon.

Szymanski, E. M., & Hershenson, D. B. (1998). Career development of people with disabilities: An ecological model. In R. M. Parker & E. M. Szymanski (Eds.), *Rehabilitation counseling: Basics and beyond* (3rd ed., pp. 327–378). Austin, TX: PRO-ED.

Test, D. W., Karvonen, M., Wood, W. M., Browder, D., & Algozzine, B. (2000). Choosing a self-determination curriculum. *Teaching Exceptional Children, 33,* 48–55.

Test, D. W., & Spooner, F. (1996). *Innovations: Community-based training as an instructional support.* Washington, DC: American Association on Mental Retardation.

Thompson, D., & McLaughlin, T. F. (1992). Social skills coaching: The effects of social skills coaching on the social interaction of a mainstreamed TMH student and peers. *British Columbia Journal of Special Education, 16,* 212–222.

Thorndike, R. L., Hagen, E. P., & Sattler, J. M. (1986). *Stanford–Binet Intelligence Scale* (4th ed.). Chicago: Riverside.

Thurman, S. K., & Widerstrom, A. H. (1990). *Infants and children with special needs: A developmental and ecological approach* (2nd ed.). Baltimore: Brookes.

Turner, L. A., Dofny, E. M., & Dutka, S. (1994). Effect of strategy and attribution training on strategy maintenance and transfer. *American Journal on Mental Retardation, 98,* 445–454.

Unger, D., Parent, W., Gibson, K., Kane-Johnston, K., & Kregel, J. (1998). An analysis of the activities of employment specialists in natural support approach to supported employment. *Focus on Autism and Other Developmental Disabilities, 13*(1), 27–38.

U.S. Department of Education. (1997). *Eighteenth annual report to Congress on the implementation of IDEA.* Washington, DC: Author.

Wagner, M., Blackorby, J., Cameto, R., & Newman, L. (1993). *What makes a difference? Influences on postschool outcomes of youth with disabilities.* Menlo Park, CA: SRI International.

Wagner, M., D'Amico, R., Marder, C., Newman, L., & Blackorby, J. (1992). *What happens next? Trends in post school outcomes of youth with disabilities.* Menlo Park, CA: SRI International.

Wehman, P. (1998). Foreword. In M. L. Wehmeyer, M. Agran, & C. Hughes (Eds.), *Teaching self-determination to students with disabilities* (pp. ix–xi). Baltimore: Brookes.

Wehman, P. (2002). *Individual transition plans: The teacher's curriculum guide for helping youth with special needs* (2nd ed.). Austin, TX: PRO-ED.

Wehman, P., & Kregel, J. (1996). *Teaching independent living skills to individuals with special needs: A longitudinal curriculum appeal.* Austin, TX: PRO-ED.

Wehman, P., Moon, M. S., Everson, J. M., Wood, W., & Barcus, J. M. (1988). *Transition from school to work: New challenges for youth with severe disabilities.* Baltimore: Brookes.

Wehman, P., & Targett, P. S. (2003). Principles of curriculum design: Road to transition from school to adulthood. In P. Wehman & J. Kregel (Eds.), *Functional curriculum for elementary, middle, and secondary age students with special needs* (2nd ed., pp. 1–36). Austin, TX: PRO-ED.

Wehman, P., West, M., & Kregel, J. (1999). Supported employment program development and research need: Looking ahead to the year 2000. *Education and Training in Mental Retardation and Development Disabilities, 34*(1), 3–19.

Wehmeyer, M. L. (1998). National survey of the use of assistive technology by adults with mental retardation. *Mental Retardation, 36,* 44–51.

Wehmeyer, M. L. (2003). Defining mental retardation and ensuring access to the general curriculum. *Education and Training in Developmental Disabilities, 38*(3), 271–282.

Wehmeyer, M. L., Agran, M., & Hughes, C.A. (2000). A national survey of teachers' promotion on self-determination and student directed learning. *Journal of Special Education, 34,* 58–68.

Wehmeyer, M. L., & Schwartz, M. (1998). The self-determination focus on transition goals for students with mental retardation. *Career Development for Exceptional Individuals, 21*(1), 75–86.

Wright, C. W., & Schuster, J. W. (1994). Accepting specific versus functional student responses when training chained tasks. *Education and Training in Mental Retardation and Developmental Disabilities, 29,* 43–56.

Ysseldyke, J. E., & Algozzine, B. (1990). *Introduction to special education* (2nd ed.). Boston: Houghton Mifflin.

Zhang, D. (2000). The effect of self-determination instruction on high school students with mild disabilities. *Louisiana Education Research Journal, 25,* 29–54.

Zhang, D. (2001a). The effect of "Next S.T.E.P." instruction on the self-determination skills of high school students with learning disabilities. *Career Development for Exceptional Individuals, 25,* 121–132.

Zhang, D. (2001b). Self-determination and inclusion: Are students with mild mental retardation more self-determined in regular classrooms? *Education and Training in Mental Retardation and Developmental Disabilities, 36,* 357–362.

Zhang, D., & Stecker, P. (2001). Student involvement in transition planning: Are we there yet? *Education and Training in Mental Retardation and Developmental Disabilities, 36,* 293–303.

Zigler, E. (1969). Development versus difference theories of mental retardation and problems of motivation. *American Journal of Mental Deficiency, 73,* 536–556.

CHAPTER 7

Severe Intellectual Disability

William R. Sharpton and Michael D. West

LEARNING GOALS

Upon completion of this chapter, the reader will be able to

- discuss the different teaching and supporting options that can be used when working with people with severe intellectual disability

- discuss how persons with severe intellectual disability function in self-care skills

- identify one good communication goal for a student with severe intellectual disability

- describe the difference between a group home and supported living in terms of the life of a person with severe intellectual disability

- discuss the importance of providing opportunities for making choices in educational and habilitative services for individuals with severe intellectual disability

- describe the theoretical base and program components of supported employment

FUNCTIONAL DESCRIPTION

Reference works on persons with intellectual disability typically describe expectations of their abilities, capacities, and potential for development. For persons with severe and profound intellectual disability, however, what one is more likely to find is a description of inability, incapacity, and little or no expectation for growth and development. Descriptions such as these are common:

- unlikely to achieve any measure of productivity
- unable to enter into relationships
- total dependency on family or support agencies
- potential limited to self-help skills
- require lifelong supervised care

In this chapter, we take a different approach, by illustrating competencies developed by individuals with severe or profound disability. The key to their success has been the manner in which service providers train and support persons with disabilities, which may be summarized in the following framework:

- If a task can be taught, teach it.
- If it cannot be taught, adapt it.
- If it cannot be adapted, support it.

Table 7.1 illustrates this framework, along with decision rules for the use of each option. This service delivery model can be successfully used to assist persons with severe and profound intellectual disability in performing meaningful, rewarding, and socially valued activities in a variety of real-life settings. First, we

TABLE 7.1
Model for Selection of Instructional Options

Instructional Options	Decision Questions
OPTION 1: Teach the task	1. Can the task be divided into smaller steps that are easier to master?
	2. Does the learner have the capacity to complete the task as it is typically performed?
OPTION 2: Adapt the task	1. Will adaptation of the environment facilitate task completion?
	2. Will adaptation of the steps facilitate task completion?
	3. Will adaptations to the learner (prosthetics) facilitate task completion?
OPTION 3: Support the task	1. Have all other options been considered?
	2. Will support be provided in the least intrusive environment?

briefly describe the options available within this framework and introduce some fundamental concepts. Case examples presented throughout this chapter illustrate the use of these options in varying combinations and to varying degrees, based on the individual characteristics, needs, and preferences of the learners.

Option I: Teach the Skill

Students with severe cognitive impairments can be taught to perform tasks in the same manner that a typical learner would perform them using systematic instructional procedures. The key to effective instruction is to provide only the level of assistance needed by the learner to successfully complete the task, a determination that must be supported by collection of training data. Ideally, the learner will be able to complete the task without any assistance other than that provided in the natural setting. For example, in a laundromat there are signs that explain the operation of the machines. This kind of information is called a natural cue. The information is not always written, however. For example, the rubber mat in front of an electric door is the cue for its operation. One of the first steps to teach someone who has difficulty learning new skills is to note the natural cues that are available, which can be emphasized for the learner, and which can be modified or enhanced so that learner can use them. As one example, a learner with severe cognitive deficits may not be able to read a bus map or schedule but can be taught to focus on certain buildings or landmarks to know where to get on and off.

In most cases, learners with severe intellectual impairment need to be provided some instructional assistance if the task is to be performed correctly. This instructional assistance is known as a prompt. Prompts vary in terms of type and intensity, and the prompt selected for successful instruction should offer sufficient information for correct task completion but not so much assistance that the learner is not challenged. Instructional data can be used to assist the trainer in making decisions about what types of prompts to provide.

Detailed descriptions of systematic training procedures are beyond the scope of this chapter. Interested readers are referred to these excellent sources: Browder (2001), Gable and Warren (1992), Snell (1993), and Wehman and Kregel (1997). However, there are some considerations that need to be taken into account before instruction begins. These considerations are especially relevant when teaching in community-based settings.

1. First, what method best ensures the safety of the learner in the particular situation? Some methods of instruction may not be suitable for teaching skills that involve some degree of risk. For example, if a student who has difficulties with impulse control is being taught how to use potentially harmful cleaning supplies, the most appropriate method would likely be one in which the instructor provides the maximum amount of control in the early stages. Maximum prompt or graduated guidance methods meet this criterion best.

2. Second, what method "fits" best in the situation? If a student's instructional goal is to learn to order food or purchase items in a store, the instructor must be cognizant of the potential effect of the teaching method on clerks or other customers. Many

clerks and customers are very patient and willing to be inconvenienced so that the student with severe disabilities can benefit. However, if the teaching method causes excessively long waits in line, some ill feelings may result, particularly among those who do not understand the nature of cognitive disabilities.

3. Finally, what method draws the least negative attention to the learner? Instructional materials and methods should be as unobtrusive as possible and should not call attention to the learning deficits of the learner.

Option 2: Adapt the Task

Adaptations can be designed to make the task easier or to assist an individual in task performance. Most adaptations have to be developed by the trainer, and, therefore, it is very important for trainers to know how to determine whether an adaptation is appropriate for the individual. These are some questions service providers should ask regarding the adaptive devices and techniques they develop to address specific tasks:

1. Is the adaptation effective? That is, does the use of the adaptation result in correct task completion?

2. Does the adaptation maintain the dignity of the individual? It is very important that service providers remember their role as advocates for the people we serve. Therefore, adaptations should be developed so that they are appropriate to the age of the individual and do not draw negative attention to him or her.

3. Is the adaptation durable? Can it be used as it was intended without quickly becoming unusable due to wear and tear? Nothing is more frustrating for the learner than to fail in the performance of a task because an adaptation is not working.

4. Is the adaptation portable? The adaptation should be designed so that it can be easily taken by the learner to the place where it is needed. Adaptations are particularly useful if they can be used in a variety of settings.

Option 3: Support the Task

Service personnel can support the learner by assisting with difficult steps and allowing the learner to perform those that are within his or her abilities. The concept of allowing people with intellectual disability to perform part of a task even though they cannot complete all of the task independently is known as partial participation (Baumgart, 1991; Baumgart et al., 1982). The alternative to partial participation is exclusion from the task until the individual has learned all of the prerequisite skills. This model of instruction often results in the instruction of isolated skills over long periods of time, with learners still waiting to perform tasks or to engage in activities that could very well enrich their lives.

Ideally, the person providing the support or assistance should be a part of the setting in which the task naturally occurs. For example, store clerks are available to provide assistance to all shoppers, including those who have disabilities. Of course, in some cases sufficient support is not available in the natural environment, and instructional programs must be designed to provide support. In these cases, it is important for service providers to develop a plan to transfer support as soon as possible to individuals present in the natural setting or to make external supports as unobtrusive as possible.

The primary focus of this chapter is to provide characteristics of individuals with severe intellectual disability, with a general overview of issues related to teaching, adapting, and supporting age-appropriate, functional skills in a variety of environments. However, it is important to understand that services to this population (or to any disability group) do not occur in isolation; they take place within a "landscape" of legislation, programs, services, supports, and social mores. For example, the Americans with Disabilities Act of 1990 (ADA) has improved prospects for all individuals with disabilities by reducing discrimination in hiring, and requiring businesses to accommodate workers with disabilities. Similarly, recent amendments to the Rehabilitation Act have endorsed ongoing support services for individuals with the most severe disabilities, and greater choice in determining career goals and needed services. In addition, research suggests that businesses are becoming more aware of the accommodations needed by workers with disabilities and are willing and able to provide them (Louis Harris & Associates, 1994). These changes in the landscape can serve to mitigate or nullify the adverse effects of severe disability and limited residual functional skills.

THE IMPORTANCE OF THE OLMSTEAD DECISION

In *Olmstead v. L. C.* (1999), the Supreme Court construed Title II of the ADA to require states to place qualified individuals with mental disabilities in community settings, rather than in institutions, whenever treatment professionals determine that such placement is appropriate, the affected persons do not oppose such placement, and the state can reasonably accommodate the placement, taking into account the resources available to the state and the needs of others with disabilities. The Department of Justice regulations implementing Title II of the ADA require public entities to administer their services, programs, and activities in the most integrated setting appropriate to the needs of qualified individuals with disabilities.

In *Olmstead*, the Supreme Court stated that

> The identification of unjustified segregation as discrimination reflects two evident judgments: Institutional placement of persons who can handle and benefit from community settings perpetuates unwarranted assumptions that persons so isolated are incapable or unworthy of participating in community life ... and institutional confinement severely diminishes individuals' everyday life activities. (*Olmstead v. L. C.*, 1999)

This decision affects not only all persons in institutions and segregated settings, but also people with disabilities who are at risk of institutionalization, including people with disabilities on waiting lists to receive community-based services and supports.

The Court indicated that one way states can show they are meeting their obligations under the ADA and the *Olmstead* decision is to develop a "comprehensive, effectively working plan for placing qualified people with mental disabilities in less restrictive settings" (*Olmstead v. L. C.*, 1999). Based on this, almost all states are in the process of developing, or have already developed, such plans.

In support of these state efforts, President George W. Bush issued Executive Order 13217: Community-Based Alternatives for Individuals with Disabilities (the *Olmstead* Executive Order) on June 18, 2001, in which he extended application of the Supreme Court's decision to all Americans with disabilities and called upon selected federal agencies, including the U.S. Departments of Labor, Health and Human Services, and Education, to help support governors in their implementation of the *Olmstead* decision.

Because individuals with severe intellectual disability are at risk for institutional placement, they are prime beneficiaries of the *Olmstead* decision and of President Bush's Executive Order. As of this writing, significant amounts of federal monies are being proposed to assist the states in making the transitions from segregated services to community-based services. Most states have implemented *Olmstead* task forces or planning groups to begin the process of realigning and refocusing state systems and funding to make community-based, consumer-directed options available to all individuals with severe disabilities, not only in their housing situations but in employment, recreation, transportation, family support, and other areas. The *Olmstead* decision and the responses from federal and state governments are very encouraging for individuals with severe intellectual disability and their families.

DESCRIBING SEVERE INTELLECTUAL DISABILITY

Historically, there has been some disagreement over definitions of mental retardation. The American Association on Mental Retardation (AAMR) has put forth the following definition:

> Mental retardation is a disability characterized by significant limitations both in intellectual functioning and in adaptive behavior as expressed in conceptual, social, and practical adaptive skills. This disability originates before age 18. (AAMR, 2002, p. 1)

This definition recognizes the interplay and occasional incongruity between measured intelligence levels and an individual's ability to function in a relatively unhindered manner within social and cultural environments. Many individuals may score in the range of retardation on intelligence tests but be able to function adequately within the social norms of their own family, school, neighborhood, and other immediate environments. They are not "retarded" because no one suspects that they are, and labeling them mentally retarded would cause tremendous stigma and potential harm.

For individuals with a significant degree of intellectual disability, inconsistency between measured intelligence and social adaptation is rarely an issue. From birth or early childhood, many of these individuals will show outward signs of an organic pathology, such as a genetic syndrome or brain damage, to account for the presence of impairment in mental functioning.

Diagnosis depends on formal assessment of general intellectual capabilities, typically derived from an intelligence quotient (IQ) or mental age level (MA). According to diagnostic standards established by the AAMR (see Grossman, 1973), an individual scoring at least four standard deviations below the mean on a standardized intelligence test with comparable deficits in adaptive behavior would be termed severely retarded, and those scoring at least five standard deviations below the mean would be termed profoundly retarded. Persons with severe or profound mental retardation compose no more than 3% to 4% of all persons with mental retardation (Scheerenberger, 1983).

Since 1992, the AAMR has discouraged classification based on levels of retardation and has instead focused on the types and intensities of supports needed by the individual, either intermittent, limited, extensive, or pervasive (Luckasson et al., 1992). The impetus for these modifications is the changing perceptions of mental retardation and persons who are mentally retarded, a growing social acceptance, and the evolution of the service delivery system (Luckasson & Spitalnik, 1994). Although the elimination of stigmatizing diagnostic labels is welcome, the use of the terms "severe mental retardation" and "profound mental retardation" have been pervasive throughout educational and adult service systems, and will likely continue to be used for many years.

According to Carr (1984), reduced intellectual capacity generally will be manifested in two ways: First, there will be limitations in the range of cognitive skills that the individual can master; second, there will be limitations in the individual's capacity to respond to environmental cues. Persons with severe intellectual impairment will exhibit significant delays or complete interruptions in the development of motor skills, language abilities, problem solving, and other aspects of learning. Their inability to respond to environmental cues may result in lack of affect or the presence of self-stimulatory, repetitious, and socially immature or inappropriate behaviors.

Persons with severe or profound intellectual disability have been found to be more likely to have other disabling conditions as well. For example, the incidence rates for visual and hearing impairments, health problems, cerebral palsy and other physical handicaps, epilepsy, and psychiatric or behavioral impairments have been found to increase with level of intellectual disability (Kelleher & Mulcahy, 1986; Kobe, Mulick, Rash, & Martin, 1994; Tager-Flusberg, 1994; Thompson & Gray, 1994). In large part, these secondary problems likely result from the organicity that also contributed to retardation.

Self-Care

Individuals with severe and profound intellectual disability do not typically develop many self-care skills through the maturational process. However, with intensive training, adaptation, and support, all can participate to some degree in dressing, feeding, toileting, grooming, and other self-care responsibilities (Snell, 1993).

To effectively train and involve their clients, service providers must view self-care not as the sole focus of an instructional program, but as a part of the normal routine of life. Thus, self-care skills should be taught at times they naturally occur and within the natural contexts of preparation for school, work, and bed. Too often, self-care skills are instructed apart from the natural routines during therapeutic encounters, a practice resulting in ineffective, pointless instruction.

CASE EXAMPLE: MARY

Mary is a young woman in her late 20s with severe intellectual disability who currently lives in a group home with three other young adults. Her active treatment plan includes an intensive training program for building self-help skills. When the training program was first designed, the staff decided to provide instruction during the evening hours after dinner because more time could be spent with Mary on an individual basis. Unfortunately, Mary's ability to prepare herself in the morning when she was getting ready to go to work did not seem to improve significantly.

The group-home support staff decided to change the instructional program for Mary. First, they decided that it made more sense to provide instruction on these tasks twice daily: once during the morning when Mary was preparing for work, and once in the evening when she was preparing for bed. Next, they identified all of the tasks involved during her morning and evening routines. For each task, the critical steps were identified, and for each step, the staff decided whether to teach a typical performance, to design an adaptation, or to provide support. Where possible, the tasks that

required the most assistance were grouped so that the staff could provide needed support for one "cluster" of tasks and Mary could complete the remaining tasks more independently. Thus, it was much easier for the staff to schedule their instruction and to provide support to the other residents of the household.

Problems remained with Mary's moving from one self-help task to the next. The staff designed a checklist that included a picture of each critical task in the order in which it should be performed. The checklist was laminated and a grease pen attached so that Mary could mark each task as it was performed. Of course, she did not learn to use this adaptation independently. The support staff used prompts systematically to teach her to perform the critical tasks. Careful collection of instructional data over a 6-week period demonstrated that Mary had significantly improved her ability to prepare herself for work and bed. She still requires support for some steps, but the staff have noticed that it is much easier to provide assistance to Mary.

Receptive and Expressive Language

Because cognition and language development are interrelated, it is not surprising that persons with severe or profound intellectual disability generally have more severe communicative disorders than do persons with lesser degrees of disability (Romski & Sevcik, 2000; Tager-Flusberg, 1994). In fact, Grossman (1983) indicated that these individuals will typically develop only minimal communication skills of any kind even with intensive training. He noted, however, that some members of this group may develop complex verbal skills, grammar, and sight word recognition.

Impaired receptive and expressive language abilities of people with severe or profound intellectual disability originate from a number of sources, including abnormal speech mechanisms, physiological problems, potential hearing loss, poor language-learning environments, and impaired cognitive processes (Dodd & Leahy, 1989). In recent years, however, tremendous advances have been made in providing members of this population functional communication skills (Butler, 1994; Reichle, Piché-Cragoe, Sigafoos, & Doss, 1988). Service providers can help the person obtain these skills by conducting an ecological examination of the functions that communication serves across natural environments and by providing the learner with either training in communication skills or an adaptive communication system that enables him or her to fulfill those functions (Romski & Sevcik, 2000). Adaptive communication systems include the use of pointing, gesturing, and signing; a graphic system, such as symbols, picture cards, or communication boards; an electronic system; or any combination of these methods. In providing speech or language intervention, service providers need to remember that communication is a function of environment. When communication is deficient, environments should be examined and enriched where needed to promote effective communication.

Too often, language and communication are taught during prescribed times in therapeutic environments, with the expectation that the individual will transfer these skills to real-life encounters. To be effective, communication training, as all training activities, should occur at natural times and places and in natural contexts (Halle, 1988).

Service providers should also remember that the goal of communication training is for the learner to gain some control over his or her immediate environment. The possibility of success toward that goal can be reduced in two ways:

• Service providers teach the learner to use a single form of communication with the expectation that it will work in all settings. It is rare that a single communication board, set of picture cards, gestural language, or other communication system can be developed that the learner can master and that will work effectively in all environments in which he or she will be expected to function. To attempt to do so invites frustration and failure.

• Control over communication systems or communication opportunities is maintained by the service provider and not the learner. A classic example of this is the communication board that the student is taught to use during "speech class" but which is locked up or unavailable during other school activities or when the learner is at home.

🌲 CASE EXAMPLE: LAURA

Laura is a 13-year-old who is severely intellectually disabled and attends a middle school near her neighborhood. Because she is nonverbal, her teacher, in cooperation with the speech therapist, has developed a communication board and taught her to use this system to express a variety of concepts. This year, her Individualized Education Program (IEP) has been expanded to include instruction in community settings. In particular, her parents are interested in Laura's learning how to order a meal in a fast-food restaurant, because the family tends to eat in a variety of these establishments.

Initially, her teacher decided to let Laura use her regular communication board to order food at the restaurant. Unfortunately, Laura became confused because of the large number of symbols on the board and because the personnel at the restaurant were not able to understand what she wanted. After carefully analyzing the problems that were occurring, the instructional team decided to create a special communication board just for the fast-food restaurant. The board was organized so that the items of food were presented within "cat-

egories" of food types (e.g., beverages). Laura was taught to identify a choice in each of the three categories and thus order a complete meal.

Through systematic instruction in the use of this adapted strategy for communication, Laura now independently orders her food in three fast-food settings. In fact, for each restaurant she uses a separate board that has been especially designed to reflect the menu of that establishment. Laura's participation in this task has been expanded to include selecting the correct order card before leaving for the restaurant. She is now able to participate much more independently with her family when they eat out.

 ## CASE EXAMPLE: CHARLES

Charles recently entered his first year of high school on a regular campus; however, he had very little experience performing functional tasks in community settings. In fact, instructional personnel have always set fairly low expectations for Charles because of his severe intellectual disability and learning and visual impairments. His new teacher wanted to involve him in functional activities but was concerned that he attempted to communicate only by grunting or reaching out with his arms. Based on his mother's report that Charles likes soft drinks, the instructional team decided to teach him to purchase a drink from a vending machine. The communication specialist used a pop top as an object cue for Charles. At first, he was given the pop top each time he was

taken to the vending machine to purchase a drink. Later, the pop top was placed in a calendar box that was divided into compartments. By following a left-to-right sequence, Charles could understand which activity should be performed by the object the staff had placed in the compartment. The instructional team was particularly excited the day Charles went to the calendar box and, instead of following the sequence in the set order, searched until he found the pop top, which he held out toward the teacher. In essence, he was saying, "I want to buy a drink." In this case, his language had moved from a receptive to an expressive mode.

Learning and Cognition

Impaired learning ability and capacity is the embodiment of intellectual disability. According to Owens (1989), problems with learning and problem solving originate with impairments in these cognitive processes: identifying salient stimuli and attending to them for sufficient periods of time; organizing and encoding incoming sensory information into categorical groupings; storing and retrieving information in both short- and long-term memory; and transferring learning to new tasks or settings. Persons with severe or profound intellectual disability will typically have significant difficulties in each of these cognitive areas.

In times past, these problems were used to point to the need for segregated, lifelong custodial care for these individuals. Now, more and more people who provide assistance to this population recognize that these deficits point to the need for specialized and individualized instruction, adaptation, and support in inclusive settings (Belfiore, 1994; Mount, 1994). A major evolutionary change is occurring in research and application of instructional technology targeted to the needs of persons with severe and profound intellectual disability (Bradley, 1994). Past efforts have demonstrated the ability of all individuals, regardless of their level of disability, to learn isolated tasks through competent instruction. More recently, emphasis is being placed on teaching functional skills that lead to an enhanced lifestyle for these individuals (Horner, 1989).

🧍 CASE EXAMPLE: GERALD

Gerald is a young man with severe intellectual disability who is involved in a high school vocational training program. During an IEP conference, his mother expressed her concern that her son is not very involved in household routines. In fact, he is very dependent on family members for most activities of daily living, such as selection of clothing, grooming, meal preparation, and maintenance of his bedroom. Gerald is able to count to five but has not mastered many academic skills such as color identification, reading, and typical readiness skills.

Recently, Gerald began training at a new work site that requires employees to wear uniforms. Immediately, the instructional staff noticed that Gerald was highly motivated to wear the uniform. In fact, his mother had problems with his wanting to wear his uniform every day, rather than only on Tuesdays and Thursdays, when he reports to the training site. The instructional team worked with the family to incorporate this new motivation in critical home routines. The teacher adapted a calendar by placing large green Xs on all of the Tuesdays and Thursdays and attaching a red marker on a string. Now when Gerald gets up in the morning, he goes to the refrigerator with his mother to look at the calendar. He locates the current day to determine whether it is a uniform day. After making this determination, he takes the marker and places an X on the day so that he will know where to look for the next day (see Figure 7.1). Now he is ready to assist in the selection

of clothing. The instructional team also decided to teach Gerald to participate in washing the uniform. The laundering has now become a Saturday chore in the home. At this time, Gerald is not able to perform all of the steps, but he does load and unload the machine as well as operate the controls, which are adapted with colored tape.

Even though Gerald is still not independent in the performance of household tasks, he is certainly more involved than he was before. Not only are his parents pleased with his progress, but his younger siblings have begun to comment about their older brother's going to work.

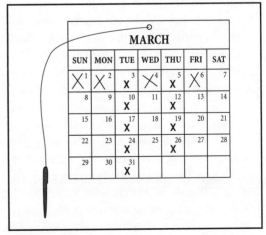

FIGURE 7.1. Gerald's adapted calendar for determining days to wear his uniform.

Mobility

Functional mobility may be assessed along two interrelated parameters: first, as an individual's capacity for physical movement within the specific environments in which he or she functions (e.g., the workplace, the home), and second, as the capacity to move from one environment to the next or through the community at large.

As mentioned previously, persons with severe or profound intellectual disability frequently have physiological or neurological impairments that hinder physical movement. These impairments, along with learning deficits, will result in limited functional mobility both within and among environments.

Mobility is emerging as a critical issue for enhancing the physical integration and participation of people with severe handicaps in work and social activities, particularly as the field has progressed from center- and school-based services to community-based models of instruction and support. Independent ambulation may be instructed or adapted through the use of wheelchairs, walkers, handrails, and other types of aids. Community movement may be facilitated through training and adaptation in order for the person to use a variety of transportation modes, including family vehicle, friends' vehicles, and public transit, and independent movement by foot, bicycle, and so forth. Community movement may also be supported through the use of carpooling and other ride-sharing options.

 CASE EXAMPLE: KESHA

Kesha is 25 years old and had been waiting for an integrated employment opportunity for approximately 6 months. A suitable job became available in a laundry facility within a large urban hospital, but the job coach had concerns about her safety because Kesha is severely intellectually disabled, hearing impaired, and blind. Specifically, concern centered on the fact that Kesha would have to walk down a busy corridor that is used by forklifts to reach the locker rooms and the cafeteria.

Kesha would not need assistance at the folding table because all of the work takes place there. The task is typically structured so that two workers fold clothes at the same station and retrieve clothes from a large bin approximately 20 feet away when all clothes on the table have been folded. The job coach worked with management to alter the task slightly to accommodate Kesha's presenting needs. All of the clothes are retrieved from the bin by her coworker, and Kesha folds a greater number of the smaller items because she does not have to interrupt her work to walk over to the bin.

Through careful planning, the job coach designed a strategy to afford Kesha maximum independence in negotiating the corridor yet ensure her safety. Kesha typically crosses the corridor only three times daily: during her morning and afternoon breaks to get to the bathroom, and during lunch to reach the cafeteria. The job coach decided that support was necessary for Kesha to walk safely down the corridor. The coach also believed that the most important issue besides Kesha's safety was for support to be provided in as natural a way as possible without compromising Kesha's dignity. Two coworkers were identified who would act as sighted guides for Kesha when it was time to go on break or to lunch. They simply walk over to Kesha, sign "break" into her hand, and offer their arm so that she can accept their assistance. Because these workers have the same schedule as Kesha, there is no interruption of the work flow.

CASE EXAMPLE: JEREMY

Jeremy attends a middle school and has been learning to participate in shopping for groceries in a neighborhood supermarket. Because he uses a walker for support, he has been paired with a peer for the shopping activity. Typically, Jeremy identifies the correct item, and the peer is responsible for retrieving it and pushing the cart.

For the past year, the school occupational therapist has become increasingly discouraged with the use of an isolated therapy model. She works with Jeremy in the occupational therapy room twice a week and is concerned that he may or may not use newly learned skills in natural settings. When she expressed these feelings to Jeremy's teacher, they decided to incorporate the occupational therapy objective of transferring to and from the walker with the grocery shopping activity.

The therapist developed a program to teach Jeremy to leave his walker at the front of the store, transfer to the grocery cart, and use the cart for support while he shopped. At first, this task was very difficult for Jeremy, since the cart would roll as he attempted to transfer. Another concern was that Jeremy could not let go of the cart to retrieve an item without losing his balance. Thus, he was taught to move through the aisle selecting items only on the right-hand side. At the end of the aisle, he makes a U-turn so that he can pass down the aisle again to select items on the other side.

Although he still shops occasionally with a peer, Jeremy is especially proud that he can go through the store alone while his teacher waits at the front of the store or his mother completes her own shopping.

Self-Direction

Most people cherish their ability to make decisions and choices regarding the many facets of their lives: where they will live, work, and play, and with whom; the types of social and leisure activities in which they will engage; what to have for dinner; which skills are important to have in one's repertoire; what clothes to wear each day; and so on. These choices and many more are usually made *for* people with intellectual disability, with the likelihood of imposed choices increasing with the severity of the disability. Freedom of choice and decision making have only recently been proposed as viable and essential components in the lives of children, youth, and adults with severe and profound intellectual disability (Belfiore, 1994; Guess, Benson, & Siegel-Causey, 1985; C. Kennedy & Haring, 1993; Parson, McCarn, & Reid, 1993; Shevin & Klein, 1984; Wehmeyer, Agran, & Hughes, 1998).

Persons with significant intellectual disability are highly unlikely to develop sufficient abilities to achieve complete self-direction and autonomy; however, through instruction, opportunity, and encouragement, they can become more self-directed and participate in meaningful decisions about their lives, as opposed to being totally dependent on others (Guess et al., 1985). Therefore, a central theme of each treatment or educational program should be that persons with significant disability are allowed to show preferences, to make choices and decisions, and to exhibit some control over their own day-to-day activities and long-term goals (Belfiore, 1994; Bowen, 1994). Service providers can foster self-direction in several ways:

- Individuals with significant disability can be trained to discover their preferences and to make choices and decisions. In areas where independent choice making is not feasible or safe, choice making can be adapted or supported. Individuals with severe and profound intellectual disability can partially participate in self-direction by exerting control over specific situations or life choices (C. Kennedy & Haring, 1993).
- Opportunities for expressing preferences and making choices and decisions should be available in all areas of service. Learning to make good decisions requires experience with the process of decision making, with alternatives, and with consequences of decisions (M. Kennedy, 1993).
- Service providers should respect the decisions that people with significant intellectual disability make, even if they do not always agree with the result. Service providers should keep in mind that making choices is a means of establishing one's own identity and individuality, not that of the service provider. They should also keep in mind that it is part of the human condition to make bad decisions on occasion and to learn from mistakes.

CASE EXAMPLE: MS. KINDRICKS

Ms. Kindricks decided to incorporate choice making in the shopping activity that her elementary students perform on Wednesdays and Fridays. To assist the children in preparing for the shopping trip to a convenience store, she developed a sequence picture board that paced the children through using the restroom, getting their coats, selecting a dollar bill, and the other tasks associated with "getting ready."

She then added a component to the sequence that assists the children in making a selection of what they want to buy at the store. She de-

signed a "choice board" and hung cards on it to represent the items that the parents reported were their children's favorites. Each item is actually a wrapper affixed to a small piece of laminated cardboard, which is attached to the board with Velcro. When a child decides what he or she wants to purchase, the child takes the choice card off the board and takes it to the store so that he or she will know what to purchase. Ms. Kindricks has made duplicates of each card so that each child can select from the full range of options.

CASE EXAMPLE: JANE

Jane is a young adult with severe intellectual disability who has been working with support for over a year. She does not appear to participate in many leisure activities even though she is now earning money. The support staff in her group home have noticed that she likes certain types of clothing, particularly scarves of bright colors.

The staff decided to teach Jane to shop for clothing items as a leisure activity. At first, she required a great amount of assistance in making a

selection. However, by preselecting stores that have clothing in her price range, teaching her to find the areas of the store with her favorite items, and allowing her multiple opportunities to go shopping, Jane's group home staff have enabled her to select and purchase clothing of her choice. Jane also keeps a catalog at home to get ideas of what she would like to purchase when she goes shopping.

Capacity for Independent Living

There is universal consensus that persons with severe or profound intellectual disability, because of their cognitive impairments, require some form of domestic support. This support will typically include assistance with such activities as meal preparation, shopping, money management, self-care, transportation, and other day-to-day needs. Although most persons with severe or profound disability receive this assistance from their immediate families, this group composes disproportionately large segments of the populations of residential services, especially institutions (Seltzer & Seltzer, 1983).

Recent trends in residential placement for persons with severe and profound intellectual disability have generally mirrored that of the field as a whole: away from large congregate living facilities and toward small group living or individual placement options, such as specialized foster care, adoption, or supported apartment living (Lakin, Blake, Prouty, Mangan, & Bruininks, 1993; Lakin, Hill, & Bruininks, 1988). This trend will in all likelihood continue in the post-*Olmstead* climate. More progressive programs are shifting focus away from funding residential services to supporting individuals with all levels of disability wherever, however, and with whomever they choose to live, thereby promoting a greater degree of independence, integration, and "sense of home" (O'Brien & O'Brien, 1994). In addition, there is growing commitment by service providers and state funding agencies to provide needed and desired supports to families that have a member with severe disability in order to allow the family to remain intact and to prevent or delay out-of-home placement (Cohen, Agosta, Cohen, & Warren, 1989; Farber & Marcel, 1994).

 CASE EXAMPLE: DAVID

After David had lived in a state institution for people with severe intellectual disability, his family decided that they wanted him to live in the community. The caseworker from the Division of Mental Retardation and Developmental Disabilities informed the family that he had two options: a group home for six residents or a supported apartment for David and one other individual.

The family very carefully thought about the two options and the impact of each on David's lifestyle. Their major concern was that David is very outgoing and enjoys being with other people, and they did not want him to be isolated without opportunities for social interactions. After great consideration, they selected the group-home option, even though many professionals had advised them that it is the more restrictive residential option. The family believe that because David is used to living with many people, the group home will require less of an adjustment.

David now lives in the group home, which is located in a suburban neighborhood, with five housemates. He enjoys participating in household tasks and is involved in numerous activities sponsored by a community church. In addition, he is known by many residents throughout the neighborhood because he walks a mile and a half every evening as part of an exercise program.

CASE EXAMPLE: TINA

Tina lived at home throughout her school years and when she first became employed as an office worker. When she reached the age of 24, her parents began to seek an alternative residential option; however, they were not at all pleased with the concept of a group home. They believed that living with a large number of people in one household would be too much of an intrusion on Tina's lifestyle. In fact, they became frustrated with the case worker from the Division of Mental Retardation and Developmental Disabilities because she seemed to believe that Tina did not have sufficient skills to live in a less restrictive setting.

The family was fortunate in that Tina qualified for a new residential initiative for persons with disabilities that allowed for monies to be used more flexibly than in the past. Tina now resides with a nondisabled roommate in an apartment that is convenient to the bus that she takes to work. She pays for her portion of the rent with human services funds and uses part of her salary to contribute to living expenses. Her family has assisted her in decorating the apartment, a leisure activity that Tina enjoys.

Economic Self-Sufficiency

Persons with severe and profound intellectual disability historically have not been economically self-sufficient, relying on financial support from family members, public and private agencies, and income assistance programs such as Supplemental Security Income (SSI) and food stamps. In addition, vocational training and employment programs for increasing economic self-sufficiency historically have excluded members of this population or have placed them in nonremunerative, therapeutic activities from which they were expected to progress to paying jobs when they were "ready."

Research and demonstration projects of the late 1970s and early 1980s established that persons with severe and profound intellectual disability, generally thought to be unemployable outside of the sheltered workshop or activity center, could achieve success in competitive work through a combination of intensive training and postplacement follow-along efforts (Bellamy, Horner, & Inman, 1979; Rusch & Mithaug, 1980; Wehman, 1981; Wehman, Hill, & Koehler, 1979). A central theme to each of these efforts was the abandonment of the "readiness" model of vocational preparation, in which people were endlessly preparing to work, and the adoption of a job-placement methodology of "place first, then train and support." The vocational strategy that emerged from these early efforts, known as supported employment, has since grown in acceptance, funding, and scope and is now a vocational rehabilitation service option for persons with severe disabilities in every state.

Supported employment became a service option by way of the 1986 Amendments to the Rehabilitation Act (P.L. 99-506). The final regulations for the amendments define supported employment as paid work for persons with severe disabilities in integrated settings with ongoing support services, such as job skills reinforcement and continuing monitoring and assessment (*Federal Register,* 1987). More recently, supported employment regulations have defined the target population as those with "the most severe disabilities" (*Federal Regis-*

ter, 1992). Supported employment has dramatically improved the vocational outlook for members of a number of disability groups, including persons with severe and profound intellectual disability (Wehman & Kregel, 1990). This new service delivery option is also affecting the curriculum used in many educational programs at state and local levels. Federal initiatives and funding have made competitive work available to more students and adults with severe disabilities (Wehman, Moon, Everson, Wood, & Barcus, 1988).

Also of significant note is that in January 2001 the Rehabilitation Services Administration (RSA), which regulates the state vocational rehabilitation (VR) agencies, redefined "employment outcome" to include only integrated employment (*Federal Register,* 2001). Before this regulatory change, VR clients could be successfully closed in segregated employment, such as sheltered workshops. In time, this change should provide an impetus for VR systems to expend more service dollars and effort seeking competitive employment for individuals with severe intellectual disability and who are VR clients.

👤 CASE EXAMPLE: MR. CLARKSON

Mr. Clarkson is a vocational rehabilitation counselor who is responsible for identifying individuals in need of supported employment services. Although he would like all persons with severe disabilities to have access to supported employment services, he must often select from among many individuals because a limited number of supported employment opportunities are available at one time. He has been directed to include some individuals who are exiting public school and has just received two descriptions of exiting students in two community school districts.

The first description is approximately one-half page in length and states that the student, Michael, has been involved in 2 years of work-adjustment training. Michael has also participated in an intensive prevocational program that involved assembling, sorting, and packaging a variety of items in a classroom converted into a simulated sheltered workshop. The report describes Michael's fine- and gross-motor skills and his ability to follow one-step, two-step, and multiple-step directions. Finally, the report includes a checklist that describes his ability to count; sort; recite his name, address, and telephone number; and perform other basic skills.

The second report is written in the format of a résumé. Over a 5-year period, the student, Sara, has participated in vocational training in 10 community business sites. Each of the 10 sites represents a different occupational cluster such as food service or office and clerical work. For each cluster, the résumé includes a description of the duties Sara performed and of her work accuracy and speed at the beginning and end of the training period. During her last year of school, Sara has worked part time in a bakery.

A second part of the résumé describes the adaptations and strategies that have been used to assist Sara in completing vocational tasks. In fact, she is able to follow complex sequences through the use of a picture prompting system. The résumé also describes her ability to perform or participate in a variety of essential activities such as shopping, using the telephone, crossing the street, and using the public transit system. Finally, references are provided so that supervisors and coworkers who are familiar with Sara can be contacted.

It is not hard to understand why Mr. Clarkson decided to provide supported employment services to Sara first. Of course, he is charged with the responsibility of providing services to all individuals who meet the eligibility requirements, but the case for serving Sara was stronger because her résumé clearly attested to her employability.

CASE EXAMPLE: JASON

Jason is 26 years old and worked in a sheltered workshop for 5 years prior to taking his new job in a spice factory. Although some adult service personnel wanted to find him an integrated employment opportunity earlier, the fact that he was severely intellectually disabled influenced the decision to allow him to remain in the sheltered workshop. Just this year, his parents felt secure enough about the success of the supported employment program operated by the center to allow Jason to participate.

While in the sheltered workshop, Jason worked approximately 32 hours a week and earned an average of $40 per month. He was not entitled to any benefits such as health care and paid vacation time. Now Jason is working 30 hours a week at his new job and earns $105 a week. He accrues 2 weeks' vacation annually and is eligible for health-care benefits.

Jason has also decided to join the company bowling league. He travels to the bowling alley with a neighbor who is employed at the same company. His parents are beginning to realize the variety of opportunities available to Jason due to his entry into a typical employment setting.

DISCUSSION

When we began this chapter, we wrote that the manner in which service providers operate can help their clients achieve success. This is not intended to discount or detract from the efforts of the learners, for indeed they also have to put forth a great deal of work and enthusiasm for the learning to occur. Our comments here concern the unifying attitudes, beliefs, and practices of the trainers described in the case examples in this chapter.

First, all of the service providers recognized the importance of integrated opportunities for their clients in fostering normative behavior and for setting expectations of families, staff members, students and clients themselves, and other significant individuals with whom they worked, lived, and socialized. These providers began with the belief not only that their clients could participate meaningfully in integrated settings and activities but also that they should participate. The service providers also recognized the value of the individual needs and preferences of their students, clients, and families in selecting activities and settings for the instructional programs, an approach that also contributed to their clients' success.

Second, these service providers achieved success because they perceived that their clients' problems and failures existed either in the task or in the environment, not necessarily in the client. Thus, the focus of training became how to creatively manipulate those obstacles to meet the presenting needs of the learners. This manipulation involved training, adapting, or supporting new behavior and was firmly rooted in (a) a foundation of empirical and theoretical support, (b) a demand that outcomes be meaningful for clients and contribute to a more normal and enriched lifestyle, and (c) respect for the dignity of the learner.

Finally, service providers did not succumb to an "all or nothing" approach to inclusion in normalizing, integrated activities. That is, meaningful activities were not disregarded simply because the learner would not be able to achieve complete independence or to engage in the particular activity in the same manner as persons without disabilities. Participation in normalizing, integrated activities, even if it must be adapted or supported, is more dignified, opens more opportunities, and enhances the dignity and quality of life for persons with significant intellectual disability.

FINAL THOUGHTS

These are exciting times for individuals with severe intellectual disability and their families. No longer do service providers ask questions like these: Can these individuals work at real jobs in the community? Can they go to school with their nondisabled brothers and sisters, friends, and neighbors? Can they participate in making choices and decisions about their lives? After 2 decades of demonstration and legislation in educational and habilitative services, the question now is how to make true community integration and participation the reality for everyone, including those who have severe intellectual disability.

Many of the barriers to full inclusion for people with severe intellectual disability are systemic. For example, many educational systems operate segregated schools into which it is assumed all students with significant disability will be placed. Rehabilitation centers often have "prevocational" or "work activity" programs, which never lead to either real work or a vocation, for their clients with severe intellectual disability. State funding systems often use funding "slots" to predetermine the number of individuals who can enter community-based employment in any year. One of the greatest challenges ahead will be to redesign existing service systems in such ways that will allow individuals with severe intellectual disability and their families to exercise true choice of where and with whom they would like to learn, live, and work. With the recent Supreme Court *Olmstead* decision, the field is closer to meeting that challenge.

REFERENCES

American Association on Mental Retardation. (2002). *Mental retardation: Definition, classification, and systems of support.* Washington, DC: Author.

Americans with Disabilities Act of 1990, 42 U.S.C. § 12101 *et seq.*

Baumgart, D. (1991). Partial participation revisited. *Journal of the Association for Persons with Severe Handicaps, 16,* 218–227.

Baumgart, D., Brown, L., Pumpian, I., Nisbet, J., Ford, A., Sweet, M., Messina, R., & Schroeder, J. (1982). Principle of partial participation in educational programs for severely handicapped students. *Journal of the Association for the Severely Handicapped, 7,* 17–27.

Belfiore, P. J. (1994). *Recognizing choices in community settings for people with significant disabilities.* Washington, DC: American Association on Mental Retardation.

Bellamy, G. T., Horner, R. H., & Inman, D. P. (1979). *Vocational habilitation of severely retarded adults: A direct service technology.* Baltimore: University Park Press.

Bowen, J. N. (1994). The power of self-advocacy: Making thunder. In V. J. Bradley, J. W. Ashbaugh, & B. C. Blaney (Eds.), *Creating individual supports for people with developmental disabilities* (pp. 335–345). Baltimore: Brookes.

Bradley, V. J. (1994). Evolution of a new service paradigm. In V. J. Bradley, J. W. Ashbaugh, & B. C. Blaney (Eds.), *Creating individual supports for people with developmental disabilities* (pp. 11–32). Baltimore: Brookes.

Browder, D. M. (2001). *Curriculum and assessment for students with moderate and severe disabilities.* New York: Guilford Press.

Butler, K. G. (Ed.). (1994). *Severe communication disorders: Intervention strategies.* Gaithersburg, MD: Aspen.

Carr, T. H. (1984). Attention, skill, and intelligence: Some speculations on extreme individual differences in human performance. In P. H. Brooks, R. Sperber, & C. McCauley (Eds.), *Learning and cognition in the mentally retarded* (pp. 189–215). Hillsdale, NJ: Erlbaum.

Cohen, S., Agosta, J., Cohen, J., & Warren, R. (1989). Supporting families of children with severe disabilities. *Journal of the Association for Persons with Severe Handicaps, 14,* 155–162.

Dodd, B., & Leahy, J. (1989). Phonological disorders and mental handicap. In M. Beveridge, G. Conti-Ramsden, & I. Leudar (Eds.), *Language and communication in mentally handicapped people* (pp. 33–56). London: Chapman & Hall.

Farber, A., & Marcel, K. (1994). Parent power: Change through grassroots networking. In V. J. Bradley, J. W. Ashbaugh, & B. C. Blaney (Eds.), *Creating individual supports for people with developmental disabilities* (pp. 373–385). Baltimore: Brookes.

Federal Register. (1987, August 14). 52(157), 30546–30552. 34 C.F.R. 363.

Federal Register. (1992, June 24). 66(14), 28432–28442. 34 C.F.R. 363.

Federal Register. (2001, January 22). 66(14), 7250–7258.

Gable, R. A., & Warren, S. F. (1992). *Strategies for teaching students with mild to severe mental retardation.* Baltimore: Brookes.

Grossman, H. (Ed.). (1973). *Manual on terminology and classification in mental retardation.* Washington, DC: American Association on Mental Deficiency.

Grossman, H. (Ed.). (1983). *Classification in mental retardation.* Washington, DC: American Association on Mental Deficiency.

Guess, D., Benson, H. A., & Siegel-Causey, E. (1985). Concepts and issues related to choice-making and autonomy among persons with severe disabilities. *Journal of the Association for Persons with Severe Handicaps, 10,* 79–86.

Halle, J. (1988). Adopting the natural environment as the context of training. In S. N. Calculator & J. L. Bedrosian (Eds.), *Communication assessment and intervention for adults with mental retardation* (pp. 155–185). Boston: College Hill.

Horner, R. H. (1989). Editorial farewell. *Journal of the Association for Persons with Severe Handicaps, 14,* 253.

Kelleher, A., & Mulcahy, M. (1986). Patterns of disability in the mentally handicapped. In J. M. Berg (Ed.), *Science and service in mental retardation* (pp. 15–22). New York: Methuen.

Kennedy, C. W., & Haring, T. C. (1993). Teaching choice-making during social interactions to students with profound multiple disabilities. *Journal of Applied Behavior Analysis, 26,* 63–76.

Kennedy, M. (1993). Foreword. In P. Wehman (Ed.), *The ADA mandate for social change* (pp. xv–xix). Baltimore: Brookes.

Kobe, F. H., Mulick, J. A., Rash, T. A., & Martin, J. (1994). Nonambulatory persons with profound mental retardation: Physical, developmental, and behavioral characteristics. *Research in Developmental Disabilities, 15,* 413–423.

Lakin, K. C., Blake, E. M., Prouty, R. W., Mangan, T., & Bruininks, R. H. (1993). *Residential services for persons with developmental disabilities: Status and trends through 1991.* Minneapolis: University of Minnesota Center on Residential Services and Community Living, Institute on Community Integration.

Lakin, K. C., Hill, B. K., & Bruininks, R. H. (1988). Trends and issues in the growth of community residential services. In M. P. Janicki, M. W. Krauss, & M. M. Seltzer (Eds.), *Community residences for persons with developmental disabilities: Here to stay* (pp. 25–42). Baltimore: Brookes.

Louis Harris & Associates. (1994). *National organization on disability/Harris survey of Americans with disabilities.* New York: Author.

Luckasson, R., Coulter, D. L., Polloway, E. A., Reiss, S., Schalock, R. L., Snell, M. E., Spitalnik, D. M., & Stark, J. A. (1992). *Mental retardation: Definition, classification, and systems of support* (9th ed.). Washington, DC: American Association on Mental Retardation.

Luckasson, R., & Spitalnik, D. (1994). Political and programmatic shifts of the 1992 AAMR definition of mental retardation. In V. J. Bradley, J. W. Ashbaugh, & B. C. Blaney (Eds.), *Creating individual supports for people with developmental disabilities* (pp. 81–95). Baltimore: Brookes.

Mount, B. (1994). Benefits and limitations of personal futures planning. In V. J. Bradley, J. W. Ashbaugh, & B. C. Blaney (Eds.), *Creating individual supports for people with developmental disabilities* (pp. 97–108). Baltimore: Brookes.

O'Brien, J., & O'Brien, C. L. (1994). More than just a new address: Images of organization for supported living agencies. In V. J. Bradley, J. W. Ashbaugh, & B. C. Blaney (Eds.), *Creating individual supports for people with developmental disabilities* (pp. 109–140). Baltimore: Brookes.

Olmstead v. L. C. (98-536) 527 U.S. 581 (1999).

Owens, R. (1989). Cognition and language in the mentally retarded population. In M. Beveridge, G. Conti-Ramsden, & I. Leudar (Eds.), *Language and communication in mentally handicapped people* (pp. 112–142). London: Chapman & Hall.

Parson, M. B., McCarn, J. E., & Reid, D. H. (1993). Evaluating and increasing meal-related choices throughout a service setting for people with severe disabilities. *Journal of the Association for Persons with Severe Disabilities, 18,* 253–260.

Rehabilitation Act Amendments of 1986, P.L. 99-506, 29 U.S.C. 701 *et seq.*

Reichle, J., Piché-Cragoe, L., Sigafoos, J., & Doss, S. (1988). Optimizing functional communication for persons with severe handicaps. In S. N. Calculator & J. L. Bedrosian (Eds.), *Communication assessment and intervention for adults with mental retardation* (pp. 239–264). Boston: College Hill.

Romski, M. A., & Sevcik, R. A. (2000). Communication, assistive technology, and mental retardation. In M. L. Wehmeyer & J. R. Patton (Eds.), *Mental retardation in the 21st century* (pp. 299–313). Austin, TX: PRO-ED.

Rusch, F. R., & Mithaug, D. E. (1980). *Vocational training for mentally retarded adults: A behavioral analytic approach.* Champaign, IL: Research Press.

Scheerenberger, R. C. (1983). *A history of mental retardation.* Baltimore: Brookes.

Seltzer, M. S., & Seltzer, G. B. (1983). Classification and social status. In J. L. Matson & J. A. Mulick (Eds.), *Handbook of mental retardation* (pp. 185–198). New York: Pergamon Press.

Shevin, M., & Klein, N. K. (1984). The importance of choice-making skills for students with severe disabilities. *Journal of the Association for Persons with Severe Handicaps, 9,* 159–166.

Snell, M. E. (1993). *Instruction of students with severe disabilities* (4th ed.). New York: Merrill.

Tager-Flusberg, H. (Ed.). (1994). *Constraints on language acquisition: Studies of atypical children.* Hillsdale, NJ: Erlbaum.

Thompson, T., & Gray, D. B. (Eds.). (1994). *Destructive behavior in developmental disabilities: Diagnosis and treatment.* Thousand Oaks, CA: Sage.

Wehman, P. (1981). *Competitive employment: New horizons for severely disabled individuals.* Baltimore: Brookes.

Wehman, P., Hill, J. W., & Koehler, F. (1979). Helping severely handicapped persons enter competitive employment. *AAESPH Review, 4,* 274–290.

Wehman, P., & Kregel, J. (1990). Supported employment for persons with severe and profound mental retardation: A critical analysis. *International Journal of Rehabilitation Research, 13,* 93–107.

Wehman, P., & Kregel, J. (1997). *Functional curriculum for elementary, middle, and secondary students with special needs.* Austin, TX: PRO-ED.

Wehman, P., Moon, M. S., Everson, J. M., Wood, W., & Barcus, J. M. (1988). *Transition from school to work: New challenges for youth with severe disabilities.* Baltimore: Brookes.

Wehmeyer, M. L., Agran, M., & Hughes, C. (1998). *Teaching self-determination to students with disabilities: Basic skills for successful transition.* Baltimore: Brookes.

CHAPTER 8

Cerebral Palsy

Katherine Inge

LEARNING GOALS

Upon completion of this chapter, the reader will be able to

- describe the different types of cerebral palsy and the resulting effects on movement and posture

- summarize the techniques for handling and positioning students with cerebral palsy as well as related safety precautions

- discuss the impact of assistive technology and give examples of low- and high-technology devices that can assist people with developmental disabilities

- describe how students with cerebral palsy can participate in functional activities when materials and programs are adapted

- outline the steps in assessing a student's physical abilities for the completion of dressing activities and the implications for developing task analyses to teach dressing skills

- review the effects of proper positioning on oral-motor abilities

- describe a minimum of three oral-motor concerns and their implications for feeding students with cerebral palsy

FUNCTIONAL DESCRIPTION

Cerebral palsy is a developmental disability that is nonprogressive and is caused by injury to the brain prior to birth, during the birth process, or early in childhood (Inge, 1987). Nonprogressive refers to the fact that the actual damage to the individual's brain does not deteriorate over time. However, if proper programming and care are not provided, the individual's ability to move and perform functional activities can decline. The identification of the different types of cerebral palsy is based on the individual's resulting movement difficulties and the portion of the body involved (Bigge, 1989; Copeland & Kimmel, 1989; P. H. Campbell, 1993; Dunn, 1991; Inge, 1987) (see summaries in Tables 8.1 and 8.2). Information about the classification and location of the disability is helpful in program planning. Professionals are cautioned not to limit individuals on the basis of their medical diagnoses, however.

TABLE 8.1

Cerebral Palsy: Classification by Type

Type	Characteristics
Spasticity	• Characterized by increased muscle tone (hypertonicity) • Muscle tone varies in response to movement, stimulation, or effort • Voluntary movement may be slow and difficult • Most common type of motor dysfunction
Athetosis	• Involuntary, uncontrolled movements • Fluctuating muscle tone present during activity and at rest • Movements have a writhing quality
Ataxia	• Movements characterized by poor balance and coordination • More noticeable during movement or purposeful activity than at rest
Rigidity	• Muscle tone is severely rigid ("lead pipe" movement) • Interferes with the individual's purposeful movement as well as movement initiated by the caregiver
Hypotonia	• Floppy or low muscle tone • Difficulty moving against gravity • Joints are hypermobile
Mixed	• Characterized by more than one type, for example, spasticity and athetosis • One type usually is predominant

TABLE 8.2

Cerebral Palsy: Classification by Distribution

Monoplegia	• Only one extremity (limb) involved
	• Usually rare in children with cerebral palsy
Hemiplegia	• One side of the body involved, including the arm and leg on the same side
Triplegia	• Three limbs of the body involved, usually one arm and both legs
Paraplegia	• Only the lower extremities (legs) involved
	• Very rare in cerebral palsy
	• May be person with diplegia who has mild upper extremity involvement
Diplegia	• All limbs involved, but legs more than arms and hands
	• Usually associated with spasticity
Quadriplegia	• Whole-body involvement, including the trunk and four limbs
	• Arms may be more involved than legs

MOBILITY

The foundation for physical movement is postural muscle tone, which allows an individual to have postural stability while moving to complete a motor action (P. H. Campbell & Forsyth, 1993). For example, a person can sit upright with one arm in a stable position while writing with a pen or typing on a keyboard with the other arm. He or she is able to make adjustments in the position—for example, move the hand from left to right across the page—without losing balance in sitting. The individual with cerebral palsy, however, usually has atypical muscle tone that can be excessive (spastic or hypertonic) or insufficient (hypotonic) or that fluctuates between the two (Dunn, 1991).

In addition to problems with atypical muscle tone, the individual with cerebral palsy may have persistent primitive reflexes that would normally disappear as an infant matures (Pellegrino, 2002). For instance, the individual whose movements are affected by the symmetrical tonic neck reflex may have difficulty straightening his or her arm to reach for an object if the head is flexed (bent) forward. Another individual may have difficulty combing his or her hair if movement is affected by the asymmetrical tonic neck reflex. The reflex causes extension of one arm and flexion of the other upon head turning.

It is not the intent of this chapter to describe fully the influences of abnormal muscle tone and reflex movement. The following case studies, however, are provided to describe the different types of cerebral palsy and the resulting effects on movement and posture. The reader should refer to the texts listed in the reference section as well as consult with physical and occupational therapists to obtain additional information. Two individuals with cerebral palsy can have the same classification and body part involvement but have very different abilities. Review and assessment through a team approach can identify each individual's strengths and limitations.

CASE EXAMPLES: BILL AND MARY (PART I)

Bill is physically challenged by spastic cerebral palsy with right hemiplegia. This information reveals that he has increased muscle tone, or hypertonicity, on the right side of his body that includes his arm and leg. His involvement is mild, which means that he can walk with a cane and use his right arm as an assist to the left. For instance, when working on tabletop activities, Bill can hold down a piece of paper while writing with his left hand. He cannot, however, use his right hand to complete fine-motor activities such as buttoning or opening packages.

Mary, Bill's friend, also has spastic cerebral palsy with right hemiplegia. Mary, however, is unable to walk and uses a power chair. Because she had limited programming as a young child, she can no longer straighten her right arm, which is held close to her body with the elbow and wrist flexed (bent). The term used for this immobility is *contracture*. Mary is unable to use her hand or fingers for any functional tasks; however, her left arm has normal muscle tone and movement.

CASE EXAMPLE: SARAH (PART I)

Sarah is a young woman with athetoid cerebral palsy that affects her ability to perform motorically. Movements throughout her body are characterized by flailing, involuntary motions with extensor tone predominating. She is able to sit independently when positioned on the floor and can scoot about on her buttocks. She can bear weight on her legs momentarily when supported by another person, but she is unable to stand independently or walk because of fluctuating muscle tone. She uses an electric wheelchair with a joystick that she pushes with her right fist.

Fine-motor activities are problematic, because Sarah has difficulty stabilizing her arm at the shoulder joint. Involuntary movements are noted at her elbows, wrists, and fingers. Speech is also limited because of athetosis, but she has learned to communicate by typing messages on an augmentative communication device, using a head pointer.

CASE EXAMPLE: KEITH

Keith's ability to move independently is affected by spastic quadriplegia. This information reveals that he has hypertonicity (increased muscle tone) throughout his head, trunk, and limbs. He has difficulty moving any part of his body for purposeful activity. His muscles always appear to be very stiff, and any movement he makes is slow and labored. He uses a manual wheelchair that has knobs on the rims of each wheel. He pushes the knobs with the heels of his hands, because he is unable to adequately grasp the wheel rims. His parents are currently saving funds to purchase an electric wheelchair to improve his mobility skills.

Mobility out of his wheelchair is limited to rolling over from his stomach to his back on a mat and sitting independently once someone has assisted him to that position. He loses his balance easily and falls to one side, unable to return to sitting. The effort to complete any gross-motor task can be seen throughout his body with increased extensor tone.

Fine-motor tasks are also completed slowly with noted spasticity. Keith is able to use his hands for activities such as self-feeding, using a built-up-handled spoon; typing on a computer keyboard, using the index finger of his right hand; and leisure recreation tasks such as playing checkers with his friends. He is able to speak, but his speech is difficult to understand because of spasticity.

HANDLING AND POSITIONING CONSIDERATIONS

Individuals with cerebral palsy often require lifting, handling, and positioning assistance from the many professionals who interact with them on a daily basis. It is critical that these professionals learn to provide this assistance properly to prevent injury to themselves and to the individuals being lifted and positioned (Copeland & Kimmel, 1989; Rainforth & York, 1987). The use of proper "body mechanics" ensures that back strain and injury do not occur when one is moving an individual with cerebral palsy. Table 8.3 provides a list of precautions for lifting and positioning.

The presence of hypertonicity, hypotonicity, or fluctuating muscle tone usually results in atypical movements and postures that limit skill development for individuals with cerebral palsy (P. H. Campbell & Forsyth, 1993; Rainforth & York, 1991). Knowledge of proper positioning and handling techniques can assist the individual in completing an activity that he or she may otherwise be unable to perform. In addition, if an individual is allowed to persist in using abnormal movement patterns and positions, he or she may eventually be unable to move in a more normal fashion.

The goals of proper positioning include normalizing muscle tone, maintaining proper body alignment, stabilizing the body, and promoting participation in activities (Rainforth & York, 1991). For instance, a young child with cerebral palsy who is unable to stand independently may be positioned in a prone stander that stabilizes the hip joint and allows him or her to stand while performing an activity. Some suggested functional activities include making a sandwich on the kitchen counter, drying dishes at the sink, brushing or combing hair in front of the bathroom mirror, or brushing teeth.

Many different positioning devices can be purchased or built, including wedges, side-liers, corner chairs, bolsters, and adaptive wheelchairs. It is critical that each individual's abilities are assessed and that adaptive equipment is selected for optimal functioning. Occupational and physical therapists usually assume these responsibilities in program planning. Table 8.4 provides basic guidelines in this area (see also M. E. Campbell & Kimmel, 1989; Finnie, 1975; Sobsey, 1987).

ASSOCIATED PROBLEMS AND COGNITION

Many individuals with cerebral palsy are not affected by any other disability; however, some may have associated problems. These additional disabilities can

TABLE 8.3
Safety Precautions for Lifting and Handling

- Never try to lift someone by yourself if the person is over one fourth of your total body weight. *If in doubt, seek assistance!*
- Keep the weight you are lifting as close to your body as possible. The farther away the person is, the "heavier" he or she will be.
- Always keep your knees bent and your back straight when lifting. *Never* lift using your back. The leg muscles are much stronger and will allow you to lift the maximum amount of weight.
- Never twist or rotate at the waist when lifting. Move your body as one unit. To change directions, step around and turn your body without twisting at the waist or lower back.
- Never lift an individual with cerebral palsy by taking an arm and leg while someone else takes an arm and leg. This is especially true of an individual with hemiplegia because weight and tone will be different on the two sides of the person's body.
- Always lock the wheelchair brakes prior to moving an individual to and from a wheelchair.
- Make sure all wheelchair seat belts and straps have been unfastened prior to lifting.
- Detach removable arm rests and leg rests from the wheelchair and move them out of the way.
- Clear the environment of all extraneous materials, for example, toys, that you could trip over during lifting.
- If the individual has more involvement on one side of the body than on the other, make the transfer in the direction of the stronger side. For example, if the person has left hemiplegia, transfer him or her to the right whenever possible.
- Always require the individual to assist according to his or her capabilities.
- Movements should be slow and smooth. The individual being lifted should be told what is going to occur and what is expected of him or her.
- If you injure your back, be sure to have it checked by a physician.

include intellectual disability, seizures, visual impairments, hearing loss, speech and language disorders, and learning disabilities (Pellegrino, 2002). However, an individual may have a significant physical disability but normal intelligence. For instance, one may assume that a child with limited mobility who is unable to speak will have limited cognitive abilities, but this assumption may not be true. Professionals are cautioned not to make these assumptions but to assess thoroughly an individual's capabilities. A review of the case studies already presented may be useful in understanding the varying abilities of individuals with cerebral palsy.

Bill, the young man with spastic hemiplegia, also has a learning disability. This disability became evident when he had difficulty learning to read and spell; however, math never seemed to be a problem for him. In fact, he usually earned As and Bs in math. Testing revealed that he had a learning disability but was of normal intelligence. With assistance from a resource teacher, he was able to stay in a regular education classroom throughout his school years and to receive a high school diploma.

TABLE 8.4
Positioning and Handling Guidelines

- Never leave individuals positioned indefinitely in adaptive equipment. Check them frequently and correct body alignment as needed. Remember, many of these individuals cannot move themselves and may develop pressure sores if left in the same position for extended periods of time.
- Select adaptive equipment that assists the individual in completing an activity in as normal a position as possible.
- Identify a "menu" of positioning options and rotate among them during a day's activities.
- Modify the environment to eliminate excessive noise and distractions. Overly stimulating environments can increase muscle tone and facilitate abnormal movement patterns.
- Learn to feel muscle tone changes. *Stop* if you are increasing abnormal patterns.
- Avoid quick movements when positioning and handling individuals with hypertonicity because rapid or jerky movement can stimulate spasticity. Slow, steady movement is important.
- Learn the key points of body control: the head, trunk, shoulders, hips, and pelvis.
- Never pull on a body part that is flexed. This will increase spasticity.
- Never carry the child like an infant because this limits his or her visual field and he or she will never learn head or body control.
- Increase muscle tone in individuals with low tone (hypotonicity) by bouncing or tapping a body part in the direction of the required movement.
- Provide the least amount of assistance and encourage the individual to participate whenever possible. Providing too much support or control does not allow the individual to develop motor control. Assess needs often and change as indicated.

Mary also has a diagnosis of spastic hemiplegia, and she also has severe intellectual disability. Her disability was identified early, because she did not show an interest in people or toys as an infant. Psychological testing revealed that she has an IQ of 27. Her school years have been spent in a program for students with significant disabilities where she receives intensive instruction in domestic, leisure and recreation, vocational, and community skills. Her school days include community-based instruction as well as opportunities to interact with her age-appropriate, nondisabled peers.

Although Sarah has a significant physical disability with athetoid cerebral palsy, she has normal intelligence. As an infant, she was unable to learn to speak, but she was fortunate to have a speech therapist and teacher who quickly recognized her intellectual abilities. She attended regular classes, but, because of her physical limitations, she received personal care assistance and support with her class work. With individualized attention, she was quickly able to learn to read and to type on a computer keyboard using a head pointer. Currently, she is an avid reader of mystery novels and is enrolled in a computer programming course at her local university.

ASSISTIVE TECHNOLOGY

Technology has had great impact on the everyday lives of individuals with cerebral palsy and has allowed them to gain greater control and independence (Inge & Shepherd, 1995). The Individuals with Disabilities Education Act (IDEA) and the 1994 Reauthorization of the Technology-Related Assistance for Individuals Act (Tech Act) define assistive technology device and service as follows:

> The term assistive technology device means any item, piece of equipment, or product system, whether acquired commercially off the shelf, modified, or customized, that is used to increase, maintain, or improve the functional capabilities of a child with disabilities. (20 U.S.C. § 140[25])
> The term assistive technology service means any service that directly assists an individual with a disability in the selection, acquisition, or use of an assistive technology device. (20 U.S.C. § 140[26])

There is a continuum of complexity in technology related to the device itself and the type of materials or manufacturing techniques used to produce the device. Low technology usually includes devices that are passive or simple, with few moving parts (Mann & Lane, 1991). Low-technology devices that individuals with cerebral palsy can use are reachers, weighted or built-up-handled spoons, keyguards, and book stands. Velcro, dycem, and splinting materials are also low-technology materials that aid persons with cerebral palsy to complete tasks. For instance, a placemat made from dycem, a nonslip material, could assist an individual to eat by preventing his or her plate from moving around on the table. In addition, he or she may benefit from a spoon whose handle has been enlarged with splinting materials (Inge & Shepherd, 1995). An individual could become independent in dressing when he or she purchases a pair of shoes with Velcro closures rather than shoelaces.

High technology includes devices that have greater complexity and may have an electronic component (Anson, 1993). Computers, augmentative communication devices, environmental control units, and power wheelchairs are some examples of high-technology devices. Further examples of high- and low-technology devices for individuals with cerebral palsy can be found throughout this chapter.

The cost of assistive technology may be a barrier to access for some individuals with disabilities. This can be related to the high cost of equipment, as well as the unwillingness of funding sources to provide the needed assistive technology (Wallace, 1995). Who should pay for technology may vary based on the age and resources of the person who needs it. For instance, should the school system or the parents pay for a device that the student needs in school?

The Office of Special Education Programs (OSEP) has a policy specifying that schools must consider a student's need for assistive technology on a case-by-case basis in connection with the development of a child's Individualized Education Program (IEP). The IEP is to be developed by a team of individuals, including the parents and school system representatives. If the team determines that a specific device or service is needed for the child to benefit from his or her

IEP, the school system is responsible for the purchase of the equipment. However, equipment purchased by the school system is the property of the district and remains under the district's control as long as the student's IEP goals are being met.

Schools may ask parents to use their funds or insurance to purchase equipment, but the parents are not obligated to do so if the need has been established within the IEP. If parents choose to purchase the assistive technology, then it should not be used by others and is the property of the child. When considering whether they can purchase the device, parents may want to consider if there are any lifetime limits in their private insurance policies and how claims might impact future requests. The reader is referred to Flippo, Inge, and Barcus (1995) for a more detailed description of assistive technology issues and applications.

RECEPTIVE AND EXPRESSIVE LANGUAGE

Individuals with cerebral palsy, as in any area of functioning, may have normal to severe receptive and expressive language difficulties. Abnormal muscle tone can limit not only gross- and fine-motor abilities but also the muscles that control facial and tongue movements. These effects can result in difficulty with articulation, speech production, and breath control (P. H. Campbell, 1993; Copeland & Kimmel, 1989).

Fortunately, major advancements have been made in the area of communication for individuals with severe disabilities (Tanchak & Sawyer, 1995). Many options are available, depending on the abilities of the individual in need of speech and language programming. Speech therapy may be indicated for those individuals who have difficulty with articulation, or an alternative system may be appropriate for individuals unable to develop speech.

Augmentative communication systems can be as simple as a picture or word board or as complicated as a computerized electronic device. Electronic boards are available with synthesized voices or message printouts that can be accessed with a variety of special input devices. Examples include head pointers, light beams, and pressure-sensitive switches that respond with the touch of any body part. The complexity of the system is matched to the individual's intellectual and physical abilities.

The selection and design of an augmentative communication system should include input from the individual with cerebral palsy, speech pathologist, parents, teacher, and occupational and physical therapists. Together, these individuals can determine whether the person will communicate verbally or if an alternative device is needed. If the team determines that speech is not a functional option, physical and occupational therapists can help determine the optimal position and body part to be involved in using a communication system as well as the input device that should be used. The speech pathologist usually is the team member most familiar with the systems available commercially and the level of abilities required to operate the various devices. Parents and teachers can provide information on the individual's communicative intent, which is crucial for matching skill level to an augmentative system.

In any case, language programming should occur in the natural environment during the times of day when the subject would normally use that language. The speech pathologist may accompany a student into the community when he or she is learning how to use a communication board for ordering a meal at the local fast-food restaurant. The following case studies may be useful in understanding the communication needs of individuals with cerebral palsy.

 ## CASE EXAMPLE: MARY (PART 2)

Mary had difficulty developing speech and language due to her combined problems of cerebral palsy and severe intellectual disability. As a young child, she made several sounds that were understood by her parents to indicate that she was happy, uncomfortable, or hungry. When she began school, however, her teacher, speech pathologist, and occupational and physical therapists determined that she would need an alternative communication system.

Because Mary had full use of her left arm, these service providers decided that she could point directly to pictures on a communication board. Initially, only three picture symbols were placed on her board, to indicate eat, drink, and bathroom. Instructional sessions were scheduled during mealtime, snacktime, and toileting time rather than as special sessions for language instruction. Mary's teacher designed a program using a time-delay procedure with a physical prompt to teach her to use the pictures on the board (Halle, Marshall, & Spradlin, 1979; Kaiser, 1993; Snell & Gast, 1981). Initially, 25 trials were implemented at a 0-second delay. For instance, during snack time, the teacher would hold up Mary's cup and say "Mary, what do you want?" At the same time (0-second delay) the teacher asked the question, she physically prompted Mary to point to the picture of drink. Mary was then given the opportunity to drink from the cup.

After the first 25 trials, the teacher gradually began to delay the physical prompt, giving Mary an opportunity to respond independently. The teacher employed this technique systematically by implementing 25 trials with 2-second delays, 25 trials with 4-second delays, and so forth, until Mary met her program objective of pointing to the pictures independently. During the training procedure, the teacher designed an error-correction procedure to use if Mary made more than three consecutive errors during delay levels greater than 0. When that occurred, the teacher dropped back to 5 consecutive trials at 0-second delay before returning to a higher delay level.

 ## CASE EXAMPLE: SARAH (PART 2)

Sarah, the young woman with athetoid cerebral palsy, did not develop speech because of fluctuating muscle tone in her facial muscles and tongue. She was able to make sounds and "talk" in complete sentences, but only people who were familiar with her could understand these vocalizations. Speech therapy was attempted when she was a young child but with little improvement in oral communication.

Initially, a picture communication board was developed, which was replaced with an alphabet board when Sarah learned to read and spell. Because she was unable to use her hands consistently to point to the symbols or letters, she used a head pointer to spell what she wanted to say. She recently received an augmentative communication device that has a synthesized female voice as well as a printout strip. Sarah uses a head pointer to type what she wants to say, and the computerized communication device "talks" for her. This particular device can be programmed to respond to commonly asked questions using codes that

Sarah easily learned how to use. The code system increases her speed, because every word no longer needs to be typed. With the help of this augmentative communication system, Sarah is able to communicate effectively in complete sentences at a good conversational pace.

SELF-CARE

Completion of self-care tasks is often difficult for individuals with cerebral palsy because of the coordinated movements required to perform even simple tasks. Motor responses that most people take for granted, such as sitting or standing without support while dressing, are problematic for the individual whose movements are influenced by spasticity or athetosis. The child with a severe asymmetrical tonic neck reflex may not be able to take a spoon to his or her mouth because turning the head to look at the spoon causes the arm to extend. Another individual may have difficulty with toileting due to a spastic bladder. In frustration, many care providers resort to completing self-care activities for a person with a physical disability, because they assume that it is easier and faster to do it themselves.

This tendency to complete self-care activities for individuals with cerebral palsy can be referred to as the "all or none" philosophy. In other words, if a person cannot complete all of an activity, he or she should not receive instruction on that task. The result is increased dependency and the exclusion of many skills from a training curriculum that an individual could at least partially learn to complete. Baumgart et al. (1982) and Ferguson and Baumgart (1991) have discussed the principle of partial participation and its applications for individuals with severe disabilities. They suggest using material adaptations, adapting the environment, adapting skill sequences, and using personal assistance to allow students access to activities that they otherwise would be excluded from. If caretakers implement these strategies, the individual with a physical disability could participate in age-appropriate, functional activities. Table 8.5 suggests material and environmental modifications to increase participation in self-care activities.

Assistive Technology for Self-Care

Adaptations for individuals with cerebral palsy are usually designed to decrease the physical demands of an activity and range from low to high tech. For instance, Sarah's involuntary movements in her hands, which are related to athetoid cerebral palsy, make it impossible for her to grasp a spoon. She uses a self-feeder designed for individuals with this difficulty. Keith, the young man with spastic cerebral palsy, has trouble grasping small objects. He is successful in self-feeding, using a spoon with an enlarged handle.

These two individuals required an assistive device for the same activity, but two different solutions were identified. Sarah's self-feeder is an example of a high-technology solution, whereas Keith's enlarged spoon handle is an example of low

TABLE 8.5
Using the Principle of Partial Participation for Self-Care Activities

---

Material Adaptations
- Utensils or swivel utensils with built-up handles
- Adaptive hand splints for holding utensils
- High-sided dishes, scoop bowls, and plate guards
- "Nosey" cutout cups
- Cup holders, two-handled drinking cups, adaptive straws
- Suction cups and nonslip mats
- Velcro closures, button hooks, and zipper pulls
- Dressing sticks, reachers, shoehorn aides, and stocking aids
- Weighted toothbrushes with built-up handles
- Dispenser handles on toothpaste pump containers
- Razor holders
- Deodorant and shaving cream dispenser handles to depress nozzles
- Long-handled combs and brushes
- Built-up handles or Velcro-handled combs and brushes
- Bathing mitts and bath brushes
- Soap-holder mitts and sponges
- Hand-held urinals and toileting aids

Environmental Adaptations
- Removing architectural barriers
- Lowering light switches, checking counter heights
- Rearranging furniture
- Adding ramps
- Using doorknob extensions
- Adding grab bars
- Adding bed rails
- Using tub-transfer bench, bath-support chair, shower chair
- Using elevated toilet seat or toilet chair

---

technology. It is important to remember that not all individuals with cerebral palsy can use the same adaptations. When selecting and designing materials, professionals should consider several things. First, an adaptation may not be useful if the person has the ability to learn a task without one. Second, professionals should work in teams that include the individual with cerebral palsy, the teacher, the occupational therapist, and the physical therapist. Together, they can assess the movement required to perform a task and evaluate the individual's abilities. They should then decide what type of assistive device is needed and whether it is available commercially or needs to be customized for the individual.

The final selection should be made on the basis of the least intrusive design that allows the person to be as independent as possible. Keith, for example, is unable to perform fine-motor prehension tasks due to spastic quadriplegia. One activity that he is unable to complete is turning on a lamp switch. At first, his team considered an environmental control unit so that he could perform this task independently. After some thought, they determined that Keith could learn to use a commercially available lamp that turns on when the base is touched. With instruction, he learned to tap the lamp with his forearm and thus turn it on. The adaptation selected was inexpensive and easy to access, and many homes have this type of lamp. If a more complex device were needed, the team could also assist in its selection and in training the user.

Clearly, the use of technology has allowed many individuals with cerebral palsy to partially participate in many functional daily-living activities. Table 8.6 provides suggestions based on the physical ability of the individual. Occupational and physical therapists can provide invaluable input in this area when the service provider is determining which motor response the individual with cerebral palsy can use to activate a device.

Adapting the Task

Often the sequence or manner in which a task is completed can be altered in order for the person with cerebral palsy to be successful. For instance, if a person with limited range of motion of the arms cannot reach under the faucet of a sink, the task of handwashing can be modified by positioning a basin of water, soap, and towel within the individual's reach.

Dressing is another self-care area that can be modified for individuals with significant physical disabilities. To complete dressing and undressing tasks, a person usually needs to be able to maintain a stable base of support; shift body weight when leaning forward, backward, or side to side; reach and grasp clothing; and move arms and legs. Many of these movements are problematic or impossible for the individual with severe cerebral palsy. Modifying the way the task is completed, such as by providing an external base of support in sitting, may make it possible for a person to complete a dressing or undressing task successfully (P. H. Campbell, 1993).

The first step in determining if a task should be altered is to assess the physical capabilities of the individual and the demands of the activity. It is not necessary for a person to be able to stand or sit independently to complete dressing tasks without assistance or at least to participate partially. However, it is important to ensure that abnormal movement patterns are not facilitated when asking a person with cerebral palsy to participate in dressing and undressing activities. It is recommended that the teacher, care providers, and therapists work together as a team when designing self-care programs to determine carefully which movements can be used that do not promote atypical patterns. Table 8.7 provides information that can serve as a guide for conducting an assessment for dressing and undressing activities.

The simplest way to modify a task for a person with a physical disability is to write a task analysis for that skill based on the person's mobility. After completing an assessment of the person's skills and comparing it to the activity

TABLE 8.6

Examples of Motor Responses for Activating Assistive Technology Devices

Head or Face
- Raise or lower eyebrows to activate switch attached to battery-operated toy.
- Nod head to interrupt a light beam to turn on the television.
- Lift head to trigger a mercury switch connected to a tape recorder.
- Bite switch to control an electric wheelchair.
- Lift chin to operate a joystick to play video games.
- Use "sip and puff" switch to move an electric scooter.
- Turn head to touch a pressure-sensitive switch that operates the electric blender (e.g., touch forehead, cheek, or chin to switch).
- Use voice to activate computer system.

Arm or Hand
- Squeeze ball or bulb switch to turn on fan.
- Push joystick to play Nintendo.
- Move arm or hand to touch a pressure-sensitive switch (e.g., touch elbow, palm, forearm, fingers to switch) that operates an environmental control unit.
- Move arm or hand to contact pad switch with skin (no pressure required) to activate a buzzer in parents' bedroom.
- Raise arm with a mercury switch cuff to turn on the radio.
- Extend wrist to use a specialized splint for writing.
- Clap hands to turn Christmas tree lights on or off.
- Move arm to use a ballbearing orthosis for self-feeding.
- Move arm, hand, or finger to interrupt a light-beam switch that operates an augmentative communication device.

Leg or Foot
- Push foot or toes to activate pillow switch to recline electric bed or chair.
- Move toe(s) to activate "splint switch" (molded foot splint with miniature paddle switch mounted near toes) that operates an electric page turner.
- Push joystick with foot or toes to play with an electrical toy train.
- Move leg to touch pressure-sensitive massage cushion.
- Raise leg to activate mercury switch attached to CD player.
- Move foot or leg toward a proximity switch that turns on whirlpool bath (switch is activated when body part is brought within a specific range).

demands, the team is ready to design a task analysis. The following two case studies demonstrate how this analysis can be accomplished.

The process for modifying a task with the use of a team assessment and program-planning strategy can be applied to any instructional activity. This is true for skills in all program domains, including domestic, vocational, leisure and recreation, and community. In fact, it is critical for individuals with cerebral palsy to become as independent as possible.

TABLE 8.7
Assessing Physical Abilities for Dressing Activities

Evaluate the Person's Upper Body Control
Can the person ...
- sit in a straight chair without support?
- lean forward away from the back of the chair without losing balance?
- sit in a chair with arms and pull self forward away from the back of the chair using one hand?
- reach with one or both hands overhead?
- reach with one or both hands to the back of the neck, waist, and feet?
- grasp with one or both hands?
- do "push-ups" using the armrests of the wheelchair to lift the buttocks off the seat?
- lean back in the wheelchair and lift buttocks off the seat? (May be contraindicated for an individual with total-body extension.)

Evaluate the Person's Mobility on the Floor
Can the person ...
- roll from side to side?
- lie on his or her back and independently lift buttocks off mat?
- lift buttocks off the mat by pushing with the feet against a stable surface such as a wall?
- reach with one or both hands overhead?
- place one or both hands on the back of the neck, waist, and feet?
- grasp with one or both hands?
- sit up from supine (back) or prone (stomach position)?
- get to a kneeling position independently?
- use a chair or grab bar to pull to a kneeling position?

Evaluate the Person's Ability To Stand
Can the person ...
- stand momentarily without support?
- use a chair or grab bar to pull to a standing position momentarily?
- reach to his or her neck, waist, knees with one or both hands while standing?
- grasp with one or both hands while standing?

 CASE EXAMPLE: MARY (PART 3)

Mary's mother assumes that her daughter will never learn dressing and undressing tasks because of her cognitive and motor disabilities. The teacher and occupational therapist at her school evaluated Mary's capabilities for dressing and identified the following physical characteristics:

- Mary uses a wheelchair for mobility.
- She can lean forward, away from the back of the chair, for approximately 5 seconds.
- She cannot use her right arm, which is usually flexed tightly at the elbow and hand.

- She can raise her right arm to shoulder height.
- Her left arm and hand have normal motor functioning.

After they discussed the findings, the teacher and therapist decided that putting on a buttoned shirt or cardigan sweater would be a good first objective. They developed a task analysis based on Mary's abilities, as shown in Table 8.8.

An important point to note in this task analysis is that Mary was taught to put her right arm into the sweater sleeve before inserting her left arm. Dressing the arm or leg that is more

---

TABLE 8.8

Task Analysis for Putting on a Buttoned Shirt or Cardigan Sweater (for right-handed person)

1. Lay sweater face up on lap (neck at knees).	9. Lean back in wheelchair.
2. Grasp sweater at armhole using left hand.	10. Grasp neck of sweater.
3. Pull sleeve over right hand.	11. Lean forward in wheelchair.
4. Pull sleeve over right elbow.	12. Shake sweater into position.
5. Pull sweater onto shoulder.	13. Lean back in wheelchair.
6. Grasp neck of sweater.	14. Put left arm into sleeve.
7. Lean forward in wheelchair.	15. Straighten front of sweater.
8. Pull sweater across back.	

---

affected by cerebral palsy first makes the task easier. This is true whether the person is attempting to dress him- or herself or the caregiver is providing assistance.

The other consideration in developing a dressing task analysis for Mary was her ability to lean away from the back of her wheelchair for only 5 seconds. This limitation necessitated several steps in the task analysis that allowed her to lean forward, complete a portion of the activity, rest, and then lean forward again for another step in the task. Time for rest may be a necessary consideration for many individuals with cerebral palsy who have physical limitations that prohibit them from completing a task in a more typical way.

 ## CASE EXAMPLE: DAVID

Mary's classmate David has severe athetoid cerebral palsy and severe intellectual disability. He is dependent on his family for all daily-living activities. No one had worked on dressing tasks with him, because he is not able to sit in his wheelchair without trunk supports and a seat belt. His teacher and occupational therapist decided that David should be able to complete some dressing activities with skill-sequence adaptations and systematic instruction. The assessment of his physical capabilities revealed that David

- rolls from side to side freely when placed on a mat

- can reach his feet when lying on his side and grasp them with both hands
- rolls to his back and lifts his hips off the mat
- cannot sit unsupported

On the basis of these findings, the team selected a pants-off program as David's first dressing goal. Because he had good mobility on the mat, the team believed that David could easily learn to take off a pair of stretch, pull-on pants that did not have fasteners. Undressing was selected because it was an easier initial task to master than dressing.

The next step in the process was to develop a task analysis for use during instruction. The team members decided that each step should be written as a verbal prompt to ensure program consistency from one trainer to another. Regardless of whether the teacher, occupational therapist, physical therapist, or teacher's aide was providing instruction, the verbal prompts would remain the same. This was an important point to consider because of David's severe intellectual disability. Consistency of instruction would be crucial for skill acquisition. The task analysis presented in Table 8.9 was developed.

Once the task analysis was completed, the teacher decided to use a modified version of Azrin's "Rapid Method" of teaching dressing skills to

TABLE 8.9
Task Analysis for Taking Off Pants

Note. The trainer positions the student on the mat for the following instructions:

1. Grasp waistband of pants with both hands.
2. Push pants down to hips.
3. Lift hips off mat.
4. Push pants below hips.
5. Lower hips to mat.
6. Roll onto side.
7. Grasp pants at waistband with both hands.
8. Push pants down onto thighs.
9. Bend leg up to chest.
10. Push pants off leg.
11. Roll onto other side.
12. Bend leg up to chest.
13. Push pants off leg.
14. Straighten out leg.
15. Roll onto back.

individuals with severe and profound intellectual disability (Azrin, Schaeffer, & Wesolowski, 1976; Snell, 1987). The teacher or therapist initially provided a verbal prompt for David to initiate the first step in the task analysis. If no response occurred, the teacher or therapist would point to the part of the garment involved in that step of the task. After several more seconds, the teacher or therapist would mold David's hands around the pants and repeat the verbal instruction. Finally, if no response was initiated, physical guidance was provided to complete the step correctly. A 5-second latency was allowed between prompts to give David time to respond independently. Continuous use of praise and touch for any attempt to complete the task composed the reinforcement strategy. Because his caregivers used a team approach, David began to learn skills for independence.

Personal Assistance for Partial Participation

Personal assistance can be an effective strategy for enabling individuals with severe physical disabilities to perform tasks they could not otherwise manage. A person with cerebral palsy, for instance, may not be able to open a drawer to remove clothing articles; however, if given a choice of two garments to wear, the person can point to the preferred item. Another individual may require assistance in transferring to and from a shower chair for bathing, in washing his or her feet, and in towel-drying the lower part of his or her body. But the remaining bathing activities might be completed independently with the use of adapted bathing mitts, long-handled brushes, soap dispensers, and oversized bath towels. Personal assistance should be the last resort to ensure partial participation in any activity. Modifying the task and supplying assistive technology devices often makes human assistance unnecessary for the individual with a physical disability.

FEEDING CONCERNS

Mealtime is often problematic because abnormal muscle tone results in poor feeding positions; in inadequate oral-motor control that leads to drooling, choking, and gagging; and in lack of motor control for self-feeding. In most cases, the occupational or speech therapist assumes the lead in designing feeding programs. As in all other programmatic areas for individuals with cerebral palsy, however, a team approach is recommended.

Many excellent resources are available for professionals responsible for planning and implementing feeding programs (P. H. Campbell, 2000; Eicher, 2002; Finnie, 1975; Fraser, Hensinger, & Phelps, 1990; Orelove & Sobsey, 1996). Specific program management encompasses many different aspects, including gross-motor and positioning considerations, the presence of primitive postural reflexes, oral-motor reflexes, and abnormalities (Fraser et al., 1990). A brief overview of specific feeding problems and interventions is presented in Table 8.10.

Gross-Motor Concerns and Positioning Considerations

Individuals with cerebral palsy often have abnormal postural reflexes that interfere with gross-motor development and successful feeding (Copeland & Kimmel, 1989; Fraser et al., 1990; Morris & Klein, 1987). The first reflex to consider that has an influence on feeding is the asymmetrical tonic neck reflex. Individuals with this reflex have difficulty in total body reactions as well as in oral-motor functions. For instance, this reflex can be noted when the person turns his or her head to one side. The arm on that side of the body extends while the other arm flexes. Some individuals are so affected by this reflex that voluntary positioning of the head in midline is inhibited. This reflex makes it difficult for the caregiver to get food into the individual's mouth, and it interferes with normal oral-motor control and self-feeding (Sobsey, 1987).

Another reflex that affects feeding is the tonic labyrinthine reflex. This reflex influences the positioning of the individual's head and often results in excessive head extension or flexion. Extreme flexion or extension of the head affects the person's ability to swallow in a controlled manner (Fraser et al., 1990). Neck extension is especially problematic, because it may result in food aspiration, limited respiration, and inhibition of swallowing.

Another problem that may affect gross-motor movement and positioning is muscle tone. Increased muscle tone, or spasticity, can result in head hyperextension and shoulder elevation. As stated previously, this head positioning causes difficulty in swallowing and, in some instances, may be life threatening to the individual who aspirates food.

TABLE 8.10

Feeding Concerns and Treatments

Problem	Description	Intervention
Spasticity	An abnormal increase in muscle tone resulting in a stiffness or lack of mobility that interferes with normal patterns of movement. Jaw thrust may be a problem in individuals influenced by severe extension. A bite reflex is sometimes seen when the person's movements are dominated by flexion.	1. Position person securely so he or she is supported and relaxed. 2. If possible, positioning should be upright or slightly reclined. 3. Head and trunk should be in midline. 4. Hips should be to the back of the chair with protective seat belt. 5. Trunk should be aligned over the pelvis with feet on firm footrest. 6. Check positioning during mealtimes and correct as needed.
Oral-Motor Problems Associated with Spasticity		
Lip retraction	Tone is increased in upper lip so it is drawn over the teeth. The person is unable to relax and pull the lips together.	1. Use manual jaw control. 2. Use firm pressure starting at the bridge of the nose to draw the upper lip over the teeth manually. 3. Use total-body relaxation exercises prior to mealtime. 4. Encourage the person to swallow before offering a bite of food. 5. Do not scrape the spoon on the person's teeth.
Poor jaw gradation	Tone is increased in facial muscles, often resulting in either exaggerated mouth opening or inability to open mouth wide enough for food presentation.	1. Use manual jaw control. 2. Encourage the person to watch the feeder to correctly anticipate when to open the mouth. 3. Use relaxation techniques.
Tongue thrust	Food is pushed out of the mouth by the tongue instead of moving it to the rear of the mouth for swallowing. This is especially aggravated by improper positioning, especially head hyperextension.	1. Minimize problem through positioning. 2. Avoid holding spoonful of food in front of the person. 3. Provide inward and downward pressure on the tongue with spoon. 4. Using manual jaw control, apply firm pressure to the base of tongue.

(continues)

TABLE 8.10 *Continued.*
Feeding Concerns and Treatments

Problem	Description	Intervention
Oral-Motor Problems Associated with Spasticity *Continued.*		
Bite reflex	A touch around or inside the mouth triggers the jaw to clamp down. Aggravated by an increase in flexor tone.	1. Minimize reflex with positioning. 2. Use oral-motor exercises to desensitize oral-cavity. 3. Use rubber-coated spoon. 4. If person clamps on the spoon, allow him or her to relax. Do not pull spoon out of mouth before person relaxes.
Oral hypersensitivity	Adverse response to tactile stimulation that may be seen as anxiety, discomfort, or withdrawal. Can be seen in individuals with hypertonia or hypotonia.	1. Use oral-motor exercises for oral desensitization. 2. Wipe the mouth area by moving toward the mouth with firm pressure.
Hypotonia	An abnormal decrease in muscle tone resulting in decreased posture and movement.	1. Position person securely so that he or she is supported. 2. If possible, positioning should be upright or slightly reclined. 3. Head and trunk alignment should be in midline. 4. Check positioning during mealtimes and correct as needed.
Oral-Motor Problems Associated with Hypotonia		
Lip immobility	Low tone in lips results in inability to remove food from the spoon or make an adequate lip seal.	1. Use manual jaw control. 2. Stimulate lip closure with oral-motor stimulation. Tap around the lips. Stretch upper lip.
Tongue immobility	Low tone in the tongue results in inability to get the food back to the molars where it can be chewed or swallowed.	1. Tap the base of the tongue. Stroke the side of the tongue prior to chewing. 2. Place food on the molars to stimulate chewing and tongue lateralization.
Low tone in facial muscles	Results in reduced ability to chew.	1. Use oral-motor exercises such as tapping facial muscles and stimulating masseter muscle. 2. Work on chewing during feeding.
Hypotonic gag	Absence of gag reflex, often resulting in aspiration of food.	1. Use oral-motor exercises. 2. Feed carefully to prevent aspiration.

A person with hypotonia, or low muscle tone, can also have poor trunk and head control. In this case, the individual may not have the ability to lift his or her head from a flexed position. Excessive head flexion is just as problematic to the feeder as head extension for proper swallowing (Fraser et al., 1990). Finally, the person with athetosis may be difficult to feed because of excessive involuntary movements of the head, neck, and trunk. Athetosis can result in difficulty with mouth closure as well as involuntary tongue movements.

A total-body assessment should be completed to determine the individual's postural strengths and needs. This assessment should include observation of total-body posture, trunk mobility and stability, shoulder position, and head control. None of these can be looked at in isolation, because one body part influences the position of another. For instance, the person who has inadequate trunk control and stability may sit asymmetrically with more weight shifted to one hip than the other. This position results in total-body compensations that make it difficult for the person to eat properly. Another example of posture compensation is seen in the person who does not have adequate foot support in a seated position. This individual may experience an increase of postural muscle tone that is evident even in the oral-motor musculature.

The service provider should also assess hip and pelvis placement during mealtimes when determining feeding problems. Forward or backward tilting of the pelvis can result in problems with head control, breathing, and mouth control (Morris & Klein, 1987). A forward or anterior tilt of the pelvis causes postural compensations throughout the body. The shoulders counterbalance the hips by pulling backward into retraction, which tightens the neck muscles, decreases jaw mobility, and inhibits swallowing. Retraction of the shoulder girdle also causes a tension that can pull the neck into hyperextension.

Fraser et al. (1990) stated that mealtime is not the time to emphasize the development of gross-motor skills such as head and trunk control. Finnie (1975) stressed the need to provide proper positioning control to the "whole" person; if this is not done, the person becomes more spastic or has increased involuntary movements. Appropriate positioning allows the individual to concentrate on eating skills without attempting to maintain the stability and support of other body parts necessary for eating (Fraser et al., 1990). This approach translates into positioning provided manually by the feeder or by external supports until the individual develops better total-body control.

Head support varies based on the abilities of the individual being fed. For instance, individuals like Beth, described in the next case example, may need support from the caregiver, whereas others may benefit from a commercially available headrest on the wheelchair. Still others with severe involvement may find side-lying a functional alternative in a side-lier or on a wedge (Fraser et al., 1990). Morris and Klein (1987) as well as Finnie (1975) have provided excellent diagrams as guidelines for assessment and selection of proper feeding positions.

In any case, positioning should be a team decision made by the teacher and the occupational and physical therapists. Proper positioning helps inhibit abnormal muscle tone and movement and allows for isolated movements of the head, jaw, tongue, and lips. A positioning assessment determines the problems that can be addressed and minimized through adaptive devices or caregiver control.

CASE EXAMPLE: BETH

Beth has severe spastic quadriplegia and requires chest and hip supports to maintain a seated position. Prior to mealtime she is positioned in her wheelchair by use of external support to ensure that her hips are flexed to the back of the chair and that she is upright rather than leaning to one side. Her feet are strapped to the footplates of her chair to provide increased total-body stability.

Beth also has difficulty with head control and usually holds her head in hyperextension. As previously discussed, neck extension leads to aspiration and difficulty in swallowing. Therefore, the person assisting her during mealtime uses manual jaw control to maintain her head slightly flexed 5 to 15 degrees. This assistance reduces extensor hypertonus (Fraser et al., 1990). The caregiver is careful not to flex Beth's head flexion greater than 15 degrees because this can inhibit swallowing.

Oral-Motor Concerns

Tonic Bite

A number of oral-motor problems interfere with successful mealtime experiences for individuals with cerebral palsy. One is the tonic bite pattern, which is an obligatory closure of the jaw upon tactile stimulation of the teeth and gums (Fraser et al., 1990). Several factors stimulate a tonic bite in a person with cerebral palsy: poor positioning with too much hip flexion or extension, posterior pelvic tilt, an overstimulating environment, and oral hypersensitivity (Morris & Klein, 1987).

 ## CASE EXAMPLE: TOM

Tom is a young child with a tonic bite associated with severe spastic cerebral palsy. His treatment team determined that poor positioning with excessive hip extension facilitated Tom's tonic bite reflex. Proper placement of his wheelchair lap strap kept Tom's hips flexed during mealtimes if the feeder checked periodically to make sure that his hips had not moved into extension. If a tonic bite occurred during feeding, the caregiver learned to wait until Tom relaxed to take the spoon out of his mouth. Pulling on the spoon served only to stimulate Tom's tonic bite. Finally, the team designed a program to decrease Tom's oral hypersensitivity. Morris and Klein (1987) provided a detailed description of oral-motor desensitization exercises on the basis of each individual's treatment needs.

Hyperactive Gag Reflex

Individuals who have a hyperactive gag, which is stimulated by input to areas of the mouth other than the posterior tongue or soft palate, have difficulty eating. Several treatment approaches are used to assist the person in dealing with this problem. For example, Mary's mother has been shown how to use applesauce as a "binder food" to assist Mary with forming a bolus of food for swallowing. Her mother alternates a bite of hard, lumpy food with a spoonful of applesauce to bind the remaining loose pieces into a bolus. Mary is then less likely to choke on small pieces of food that she has difficulty swallowing. Her mother has also learned that flexing Mary's head forward when she gags during feeding stops the response.

Also, Mary's occupational therapist designed an oral-motor program to decrease her hypersensitive gag. Firm downward pressure on the tongue was applied with a spoon or tongue depressor and carefully worked to the point of Mary's tolerance. When this program was initiated, she would gag even when the tip of her tongue was stimulated. Over time, the therapist was able to "walk" the spoon farther back into her mouth without stimulating a gag response. This approach may be useful with other individuals who have a hypersensitive gag; however, each individual should have a program designed for his or her specific needs.

Jaw and Tongue Thrust

Jaw thrust is characterized by an abnormally strong downward extension of the lower jaw and is associated with head extension or total-body extension patterns (Fraser et al., 1990). Poor positioning with too much hip extension and posterior pelvic tilt contributes to an increase in jaw thrust. Therefore, program plans that include working on better sitting are indicated. The trunk and pelvis should be in alignment with the shoulder girdle forward and abduction of the scapulae. Manual jaw control during feeding to maintain jaw closure and to promote stability is also indicated. Illustrations can be found in Finnie (1975).

Tongue thrust is an abnormally strong protrusion of the tongue that is characterized by a swallow with anterior rather than posterior movement (Fraser et al., 1990). Tongue thrust makes it difficult to insert a spoon into the individual's mouth and results in expulsion of food. Increased extensor tone, neck hyperextension, and shoulder retraction also create extensor patterns in the mouth. Therefore, assessing the person's positioning during mealtime and making adjustments as needed are critical. Manual jaw control is indicated for some individuals (Finnie, 1975).

It is not uncommon for an individual with cerebral palsy to have difficulty with both jaw and tongue thrust. For instance, Vijay is a youngster who is unable to successfully feed himself because he has severe jaw and tongue thrust. When he attempts to place food in his mouth, the combined force of these two problems causes food to be pushed forward instead of back for swallowing. An assessment of Vijay's physical abilities revealed that he has spastic quadriplegia; however, he is able to walk with a walker and sit in a chair independently. Because he is not dependent on a wheelchair for mobility and support, service providers assumed that positioning was not an issue for feeding. Upon closer observation, however, they noted that he had limited trunk control and that his positioning was influenced by extensor tone and spasticity. He often sat in a cafeteria chair with shoulders slumped forward, pelvis tilted backward, and legs extended at the hips. This position created increased tone in the facial muscles and tongue, resulting in increased tongue and jaw thrust during mealtime. A chair was designed for him to use for meals that ensured that his feet were supported and his hips flexed. Increased support through his lower body decreased the excessive tone, resulting in decreased oral-motor problems. In addition, the caregiver assisted him with manual jaw control to inhibit both tongue and jaw thrust.

Lip Closure

A lack of lip closure often is associated with feeding problems for individuals with cerebral palsy and may be caused by low muscle tone or spasticity. Severe spasticity associated with increased extensor tone can cause lip retraction, which is a pulling back of the lips from the teeth. Poor lip closure causes difficulty in taking food from a spoon and problems with swallowing. Treatment procedures for lack of lip closure are based on whether it is caused by increased or low muscle tone. Tapping around the mouth may be indicated for the individual with low muscle tone but contraindicated for the person with increased tone. Positioning for feeding should be assessed to decrease spasticity and extensor tone as much as possible. In addition, the feeder should use a shallow spoon and be careful not to scrape the food on the individual's teeth. Feeding should be slow, so that the person can use his or her lips to remove the food from the spoon. Manual jaw control may be indicated (Finnie, 1975).

Tongue Lateralization

The final oral-motor problem to be considered is lack of tongue lateralization, which inhibits the development of chewing and is identified by predominating in-and-out movements of the tongue. This problem may be caused by oral hypersensitivity, hypotonicity, or insufficient jaw stability (Morris & Klein, 1987). Positioning to reduce abnormal muscle tone should be the first consideration. Increased sensory input to the tongue should include manual stimulation as well as placement of food directly on the biting surfaces of the teeth. Foods that dissolve easily and are relatively soft, such as graham crackers, pieces of cheese, and cereal, are the items of choice for this activity. One should gradually change the types of food for chewing as the individual's ability to lateralize the tongue improves.

The oral-motor difficulties discussed in this chapter are only a few of those faced by individuals with cerebral palsy. An attempt has been made to provide a representative sample that will serve as an initial guide to assessment and program planning. Table 8.10 provides an overview of feeding concerns and techniques for remediation.

 CASE EXAMPLE: GENNY

Genny has decreased muscle tone, or hypotonia, which is noted throughout her body as well as in the oral musculature. Because she does not use her upper lip to remove food from the spoon during mealtime or attempt to chew, her mother has always fed her baby foods. This practice has only made the problem worse, because Genny has not had any experiences that would stimulate oral-motor development. Because Genny's problems stem from low tone, the occupational thera-

pist designed a program to stimulate muscle tone. Genny's mother and teacher were taught to tap the muscles for lip closure and chewing prior to mealtime. In addition, they were shown how to avoid scraping food on Genny's teeth by stimulating the upper lip to move in response to firm pressure during spoon removal. The next step was to introduce soft foods for chewing, such as oranges, graham crackers, and cheese, by placing the food directly on Genny's molars. Tongue lateralization for this activity was encouraged by stroking the side of her tongue with a spoon or tongue depressor. The texture of Genny's food was gradually changed to replace the baby food with chopped

table food. Her mother is happy to have Genny eating the same food as the other family members.

_____

DRESSING CONCERNS

The principle of partial participation related to dressing skills for individuals with cerebral palsy was discussed earlier in this chapter. However, it may be necessary for caregivers to provide total assistance to some individuals who have severe to profound motor involvement. A number of positioning and handling strategies are available that make assisted dressing easier for the caregiver. Finnie (1975) and Copeland and Kimmel (1989) are excellent sources for this information. Table 8.11 provides some basic ideas for dressing the individual with severe motor limitations.

CAPACITY FOR INDEPENDENT LIVING

One of the most serious barriers to living and working in the community for individuals with cerebral palsy can be the lack of living options and support services. Personal assistance services (PAS) are perhaps one of the most crucial

TABLE 8.11
Positioning and Handling Strategies for Dressing

- Dress and undress a young child or infant with extensor muscle tone while prone (on the stomach) across the lap of the caregiver and diaper him or her while on the stomach rather than on his or her back.
- Bend or flex the individual's hips, knees, and ankles to reduce excessive extensor muscle tone.
- Decrease abnormal movement patterns by side-lying. Roll the individual from side to side while dressing and undressing him or her. This slow rolling movement reduces excessive muscle tone.
- Use side-lying to lessen the individual's tendency to push back into extension, making it easier for the caregiver to bring the head, shoulders, and arms forward for dressing. The individual's feet and legs are also easier to bend.
- Use slow movement with firm pressure when moving an individual for dressing and undressing.
- Put clothes on the arm or leg that is more involved first.
- Straighten the individual's arm prior to putting on clothing. Do not try to pull on the person's hand to get a bent arm through the sleeve.
- Bend the individual's leg before putting on socks and shoes. Extended legs make the ankle and foot stiffer, and the toes are more likely to be flexed.
- Use fuller cut clothing with front openings, elastic waistbands, or Velcro closures when necessary.

needs for the individual with cerebral palsy in order to achieve independent living. PAS can be defined as people or devices that assist a person with a physical, sensory, mental, or cognitive disability with tasks that the person would perform for him- or herself if he or she did not have a disability. This may include assistance with activities of daily living such as dressing, bathing, eating, and toileting. PAS can also include assistance with cognitive tasks such as handling money or facilitating communication with a reader or an interpreter.

Fortunately, there has been a shift away from institutional living toward an understanding of how PAS can facilitate community living for individuals with significant disabilities. Many states now have Medicaid-funded waiver programs that can defray the cost of hiring a personal care assistant. The Medicaid Waiver program has allowed many individuals who would otherwise have to live in an institution or nursing home to live in the community. Generally speaking, access to these services are determined by a state's office of medical assistance services, and there are eligibility criterion that the individual must meet to qualify.

 ## CASE EXAMPLE: CINDY

Consider, for instance, Cindy, who is now 38 years old and has severe spastic cerebral palsy. Twenty years ago, when Cindy turned 18, her parents were elderly and could no longer care for her physical needs. They could not afford to hire an assistant, so their only alternative was to select a nursing home as her living arrangement. Cindy relied on Medicaid to pay her nursing home expenses and to provide her with a $30-a-month allowance.

However, Cindy recently realized a lifelong dream when she moved into her own apartment. She now has a personal care assistant who helps her with her daily living needs as well as upkeep of her apartment. This was made possible by a team of individuals who supported her in her goal to include her case manager and the Medicaid Waiver program in her state. With the assistance of her case manager, Cindy documented the limitations resulting from her disability that required personal assistance services in order for her to live in the community (as compared to the nursing home setting). She also met her state's eligibility criteria and guidelines for use of the Medicaid Waiver. Cindy's apartment is in subsidized housing, and her rent is based on her resources, including income from her 20-hour-a-week supported competitive-employment job. She is now living and working in her community, although in the not so distant past, this was not considered a possibility.

ECONOMIC SELF-SUFFICIENCY

Supported employment has made a difference in the vocational lives of many individuals with severe disabilities. To date, however, limited numbers of individuals with cerebral palsy have achieved employment nationally through the supported-employment initiative (Wehman, Revell, & Kregel, 1995). This may be due to a perceived lack of vocational competence for this group as well as their varied physical abilities and limitations. Employers may have difficulty understanding how a person with limited physical abilities can perform the essential functions of a job. Service providers often focus on the person's disabilities rather than abilities. Focusing on a person's limitations and disabilities can result in an inability to match the person's interests and talents to a potential job in the community. In addition, many professionals lack the skills to identify the physical barriers to employment and to use assistive technology to eliminate the problems (Inge, Strobel, Wehman, Todd, & Targett, 2000). For this group of unserved individuals to be successful in joining the nation's workforce, a number of supports must be implemented.

Workplace supports for individuals with cerebral palsy include the best practices of personal assistance, coworker supports, assistive technology, compensatory strategies, and supported employment (Inge, 2001). Supported employment allows for the needed intervention and support that can be tailored to each consumer. More specifically, a person's abilities and interests are highlighted during the assessment process, allowing the employment specialist to use these identified interests and abilities for career development and job matching. Assistive technology can then enhance the consumer's abilities, while job-site training reinforces and strengthens them. Together a "package of workplace supports" can facilitate employment for a group of individuals who have not achieved success at the rate of their "able-bodied" peers.

Assistive technology for employment may include both high- and low-technology devices, as defined by Congress. For instance, a low-technology device may be blocks to raise the work area of an individual who is seated in a wheelchair. A high-technology device, on the other hand, is usually designed by a rehabilitation engineer or therapist or purchased commercially (e.g., a device for inputting information into a computer). Table 8.12 provides a sample of assistive technology solutions that have been used to facilitate employment for individuals with cerebral palsy. An individual's need for technology should be carefully assessed and the technology provided only if the person cannot function without its use. Professionals also need to assess thoroughly an individual's capabilities and use supported employment strategies to match them to appropriate job types (Sowers & Powers, 1991). Assistive technology cannot provide solutions for all limitations. For instance, it may be unwise to place a person with severe fine-motor limitations in a high-production assembly job, even if devices can be made to assist in task completion. The following case studies demonstrate the use of supported employment and assistive technology in helping individuals with cerebral palsy in the world of work.

♠ CASE EXAMPLE: GINNY

Ginny is a young woman who has spastic cerebral palsy, quadriplegia. She recently began work at a parts store as an office worker. The job was identified for her by a supported-employment program through a process of consumer assessment, job analysis, and job-compatibility analysis. Her employment specialist determined that Ginny had many of the basic skills to complete the job

TABLE 8.12

Sample Assistive Technology Solutions

Environmental Modifications
- Put a portable ramp to the front door.
- Change the height of the elevator buttons to an accessible level.
- Put grab bars in the restroom.
- Change the hinges on a door to swing-away hinges to increase access.
- Add an auditory cue (e.g., doorbell or buzzer to call for assistance).
- Add an automatic door opener.
- Move equipment to an accessible area (e.g., move the copy machine to the first floor).
- Position a divider to reduce the noise level.
- Build accessible shelves for work materials.

Equipment Modifications
- Adjust the height of a chair or table by adding blocks.
- Add arms to a chair.
- Add arm or wrist supports to a computer keyboard.
- Build up a handle.
- Add a handle, knob, or lever.
- Add a switch.
- Use C-clamps, nonslip matting, L-brackets, bungee cords.
- Use a headset or speaker phone.

Technology Purchase
- Use a universal cuff with dowel or pencil.
- Buy a "reacher."
- Add a laptray or knapsack to the wheelchair.
- Buy an electric hole punch or stapler.
- Purchase a mouthstick, headpointer, optical headpointer.
- Obtain a keyguard.
- Use an enlarged keyboard.
- Purchase a trackball.
- Obtain computer software program (e.g., Dragon Dictate, TextHelp, "Sticky Keys").
- Buy a money counter.
- Purchase a scooter or power chair.
- Use an augmentative communication device (e.g., Liberator, Dynovox).

Technology Fabrication
- Make a custom hand splint.
- Fabricate a stamp holder.
- Build a "sticker" dispenser for one-hand operation.
- Motorize a paper guide.
- Customize a work stand to position a computer keyboard.

duties, which included answering the telephone, processing invoices, and filing. She was able to communicate effectively and could read in order to complete the invoice and filing tasks. At first, however, her physical limitations seemed to interfere with the completion of her job duties. She was unable to raise her arms higher than shoulder height, she tired easily from using her hands for activities, and she could not type to meet the production standard of the position. Her electric wheelchair did not fit under a standard desk, and she was unable to access the file cabinets because she could not maneuver her chair close enough to open the bottom and top drawers.

After reviewing the situation, the employment specialist and an occupational therapist determined that a number of low-technology and high-technology devices could be used that would aid Ginny in carrying out her job duties. The office area was rearranged to fit her needs, and a coworker was assigned to provide additional physical assistance as indicated. The following modifications were developed:

- Blocks were used to raise the desk to a comfortable work height.
- A headset was placed on the phone to eliminate the need for picking up the receiver.
- A temporary hanging file was placed next to Ginny's desk for use during a day's worth of filing. A coworker assisted her by placing the files in the office cabinets at the end of the workday.
- An electric stapler was purchased for stapling invoices together.
- A tape recorder was used for taking office messages and orders, eliminating the need for Ginny to write on a notepad.
- The employment specialist worked with the employer to develop a data entry file, and Ginny used voice dictation software to later enter the information from the recorder into the office computer.

♠ CASE EXAMPLE: SUSAN

Susan is currently in a special education program for students with severe intellectual disability and physical disabilities. Because she is 20 years old, her teacher is concerned about transition from school to work and has referred her to a program designed to facilitate employment for students with significant disabilities. Project staff identified a job at the local university library stamping identification numbers on the spines of new books. This job is typically performed daily by graduate assistantship students in a large room of the library (Renzaglia & Hutchins, 1990). An assessment of Susan's physical strengths and limitations identified the following characteristics:

- She uses a wheelchair for mobility and requires personal assistance for movement from one place to another.
- She has limited movements in both arms because of hypertonicity throughout her

head, trunk, and limbs.
- Lateral wheelchair supports and a seat belt are necessary to assist her in sitting upright in her chair. She also requires foot support and straps.
- She can raise her right arm at the shoulder joint so that her forearm is parallel to and 6 inches above her wheelchair lap tray.
- She does not have any functional mobility in her fingers, which are usually tightly fisted into the palms of both hands.
- She is visually attentive and can turn her head from side to side.
- She has severe intellectual disability.

Because of these physical characteristics, Susan needs assistive technology to complete the job of stamping books with the library identification number. Project staff worked closely with a rehabilitation engineer, and a spring-loaded device was designed to assist Susan in completing the task. The first step in the job required personal assistance from a coworker or project staff member to load the equipment with 10 books for stamping. At that point, Susan was responsible for pressing a switch to drop a book into position. She then would touch another plate that held the heat stamp in order to apply heat to the spine of the book. Susan kept this in place for 10 seconds, finally touching another switch to move the book off the work surface. Intensive systematic instruction was provided by a trainer to assist Susan in learning her job.

Susan's community-based work experience highlights a couple of critical issues in the area of vocational programming for individuals with severe disabilities. First, her instruction is taking place outside of the classroom setting. Typically, students with her characteristics have been limited to "classroom-only" programs that have failed to assist students in making the transition from school to work (Moon, Inge, Wehman, Brooke, & Barcus, 1990). Professionals must be creative in providing functional, age-appropriate, vocational experiences for this group of individuals.

Second, Susan is being given an opportunity to interact with nondisabled peers. Integration—that is, physical proximity and the opportunity to interact socially with others—is a primary value of supported employment (Moon et al., 1990). It is a work characteristic that most people take for granted in their everyday lives. For individuals such as Susan, however, work usually translates into sheltered-workshop and activity-center settings, where minimal access to real daily environments is provided. Expectations for individuals with severe disabilities will remain low as long as professionals continue to place them in segregated environments.

Individuals with cerebral palsy can be contributing members of the workforce. For some, it may mean the traditional route from college to employment. Others may require assistive technology and transitional employment services to locate and perform a job. Still others, like Susan, may require job modifications, supported employment, and intensive on-site support to become employed.

FINAL THOUGHTS

An individual with cerebral palsy has the same rights to live and work in the community as do his or her nondisabled peers. Society should no longer consider segregated programs and services as acceptable outcomes, regardless of the severity of the individual's disability. It is the professionals' responsibility to identify and facilitate the needed supports that will promote inclusion in community settings. This chapter has provided information on how this can be achieved given a focus on the person's abilities rather than disabilities.

REFERENCES

Anson, D. (1993). *Rehab 487: Course syllabus.* Seattle: University of Washington, Division of Occupational Therapy, Department of Rehabilitation Medicine.

Baumgart, D., Brown, L., Pumpian, I., Nisbet, J., Ford, A., Sweet, M., Messina, R., & Schroeder, J. (1982). Principle of partial participation and individualized adaptations in educational programs for severely handicapped students. *Journal of the Association for the Severely Handicapped, 1,* 17–27.

Campbell, P. H. (1993). Physical management and handling procedures. In M. Snell (Ed.), *Instruction of students with severe disabilities* (pp. 248–263). New York: Merrill.

Campbell, P. H. (2000). Promoting participation in natural environments by accommodating motor disabilities. In M. E. Snell & F. Brown (Eds.), *Instruction of students with severe disabilities* (5th ed., pp. 291–329). Upper Saddle River, NJ: Prentice Hall.

Campbell, P. H., & Forsyth, S. (1993). Integrated programming and movement disabilities. In M. Snell (Ed.), *Instruction of students with severe disabilities* (pp. 264–289). New York: Merrill.

Copeland, M. E., & Kimmel, J. R. (1989). *Evaluation and management of infants and young children with developmental disabilities.* Baltimore: Brookes.

Dunn, W. (1991). The sensorimotor systems: A framework for assessment and intervention. In F. P. Orelove & D. Sobsey (Eds.), *Educating children with multiple disabilities: A transdisciplinary approach* (pp. 33–78). Baltimore: Brookes.

Eicher, P. S. (2002). Feeding. In M. L. Batshaw (Ed.), *Children with disabilities* (5th ed., pp. 549–566). Baltimore: Brookes.

Ferguson, D. L., & Baumgart, D. (1991). Partial participation revisited. *Journal of the Association for Persons with Severe Handicaps, 16*(4), 218–227.

Finnie, N. R. (1975). *Handling the young cerebral palsied child at home* (2nd ed.). New York: Dutton.

Flippo, K., Inge, K. J., & Barcus, J. M. (Eds.). (1995). *Assistive technology: A resource for school, work, and the community.* Baltimore: Brookes.

Fraser, B. A., Hensinger, R. N., & Phelps, J. A. (1990). *Physical management of multiple handicaps: A professional's guide.* Baltimore: Brookes.

Halle, J. W., Marshall, A. M., & Spradlin, J. E. (1979). Time delay: A technique to increase language use and facilitate generalization in retarded children. *Journal of Applied Behavior Analysis, 121,* 431–439.

Individuals with Disabilities Education Act of 1990, 42 U.S.C. § 12101 *et seq.*

Inge, K. J. (1987). Atypical motor development and cerebral palsy. In F. P. Orelove & D. Sobsey (Eds.), *Educating children with multiple disabilities: A transdisciplinary approach* (pp. 43–65). Baltimore: Brookes.

Inge, K. J. (2001). Supported employment for individuals with physical disabilities. In P. Wehman (Ed.), *Supported employment in business: Expanding the capacity of workers with disabilities* (pp. 153–180). St. Augustine, FL: TRN Publications.

Inge, K. J., & Shepherd, J. (1995). Assistive technology: Application and strategies for school system personnel. In K. Flippo, K. J. Inge, & J. M. Barcus (Eds.), *Assistive technology: A resource for school, work, and the community* (pp. 133–166). Baltimore: Brookes.

Inge, K. J., Strobel, W., Wehman, P., Todd, J., & Targett, P. (2000). Vocational outcomes for persons with severe physical disabilities: Design and implementation of assistive technology and workplace supports. *NeuroRehabilitation, 14,* 1–13.

Kaiser, A. P. (1993). Functional language. In M. Snell (Ed.), *Instruction of students with severe disabilities* (pp. 347–379). New York: Merrill.

Mann, W. C., & Lane, J. P. (1991). *Assistive technology for persons with disabilities: The role of occupational therapy.* Rockville, MD: American Occupational Therapy Association.

Moon, M. S., Inge, K. J., Wehman, P., Brooke, V., & Barcus, J. (1990). *Helping persons with severe mental retardation get and keep employment: Supported employment issues and strategies.* Baltimore: Brookes.

Morris, S. E., & Klein, M. D. (1987). *Pre-feeding skills: A comprehensive resource for therapists.* Tucson, AZ: Therapy Skill Builders.

Orelove, F. P., & Sobsey, D. (1996). *Educating children with multiple disabilities* (3rd ed.). Baltimore: Brookes.

Pellegrino, L. (2002). Cerebral palsy. In M. L. Batshaw (Ed.), *Children with disabilities* (5th ed., pp. 443–466). Baltimore: Brookes.

Rainforth, B., & York, J. (1991). Handling and positioning. In F. P. Orelove & D. Sobsey (Eds.), *Educating children with multiple disabilities: A transdisciplinary approach* (pp. 79–118). Baltimore: Brookes.

Renzaglia, A., & Hutchins, M. (1990, October). *Supported employment for individuals with severe disabilities.* Presentation at the Virginia Commonwealth University, Rehabilitation Research and Training Center Symposium on Supported Employment, Virginia Beach.

Snell, M. E., & Gast, D. L. (1981). Applying delay procedures to the instruction of the severely handicapped. *Journal of the Association of the Severely Handicapped, 5*(4), 3–14.

Sobsey, D. (1987). Mealtime skills. In F. P. Orelove & D. Sobsey (Eds.), *Educating children with multiple disabilities: A transdisciplinary approach* (pp. 219–252). Baltimore: Brookes.

Sowers, J. A., & Powers, L. (1991). *Vocational preparation and employment of students with physical and multiple disabilities.* Baltimore: Brookes.

Tanchak, T., & Sawyer, C. (1995). Augmentative communication. In K. Flippo, K. Inge, & M. Barcus (Eds.), *Assistive technology: A resource for school, work, and the community* (pp. 57–85). Baltimore: Brookes.

Technology-Related Assistance for Individuals with Disabilities Act of 1988, 29 U.S.C. § 2201 *et seq.*

Technology-Related Assistance for Individuals with Disabilities Act of 1994, 29 U.S.C. § 2201 *et seq.*

Wallace, J. F. (1995). Creative financing of assistive technology. In K. F. Flipppo, K. J. Inge, & J. M. Barcus (Eds.), *Assistive technology: A resource for school, work, and community* (pp. 245–268). Baltimore: Brookes.

Wehman, P., Revell, W. G., & Kregel, J. (1995). *Supported employment from 1986 to 1993: A national program that works.* Manuscript submitted for publication, Virginia Commonwealth University, Richmond.

CHAPTER 9

Seizure Disorders

Elizabeth Perry-Varner and Satoko Yasuda

LEARNING GOALS

Upon completion of this chapter, the reader will be able to

- define epilepsy and describe at least five myths about epilepsy
- describe three types of seizures
- identify issues related to the psychosocial and self-esteem implications of seizure disorders
- understand how to provide first aid for people with seizures
- recognize what legal issues are associated with epilepsy

FUNCTIONAL DESCRIPTION

The term *epilepsy* covers many different types of seizure disorders, of which seizures are a symptom. It is the most common chronic neurological disorder. Seizures occur when the brain's electrical system changes or is disrupted, interrupting the normal functions of the brain and the rest of the nervous system. A seizure may be confined to one area of the brain (partial seizure) or take place throughout the brain (generalized seizure).

Epilepsy is often referred to as a "hidden" disability. A person may seem perfectly "normal" between seizures. But even if a person with epilepsy has only one seizure a year, it can have a dramatic effect on his or her day-to-day existence (Schacter, 1993). Embarrassment often accompanies a seizure that occurs in a public place; discrimination is still prevalent among employers, friends, relatives, and others; and laws against people with epilepsy obtaining a driver's license are also commonplace.

Myths concerning people with epilepsy are still somewhat common and are listed in Table 9.1. As pointed out by Driscoll (1988), one reason for these

TABLE 9.1

Myths and Truths About Epilepsy

Myth	Truth
You might catch epilepsy through contact with someone having a seizure.	Epilepsy is not contagious.
Epilepsy is a form of mental illness.	Actually, the majority of persons with epilepsy have normal intelligence; many are highly intelligent. Epilepsy, mental illness, and mental retardation are all distinctly different disabilities.
People with epilepsy look different.	The only difference in appearance occurs during a seizure. Otherwise, there is no physical way to tell that someone has this disability.
A person having a seizure can swallow his or her tongue.	The tongue is attached to the mouth. It may drop to the back of the throat, but swallowing it is impossible.
To have epilepsy is to have convulsions.	Convulsions, formerly known as grand mal seizures, are only one type of seizure.
Epilepsy can be passed on to subsequent generations.	There is a small chance that epilepsy could be passed on. It can also develop in people with no family history of it.
People with epilepsy cannot be employed.	There may be obstacles to acquiring and retaining employment, but persons with epilepsy are employed in many occupations.

myths may be due to our society's expectation for people to be "normal," and people with epilepsy do not fit this mold. For example, when someone has a generalized convulsion, he or she loses consciousness and twitches and thrashes. Someone having a complex partial seizure may pick at his or her clothes. Another society-imposed attitude is that people must at all times maintain self-control, and having a seizure violates this. It has also been hypothesized that a person with epilepsy may be judged for periodically "losing control," unlike a person with an obvious physical disability such as a visual impairment or even cerebral palsy, who never had control to begin with (Driscoll, 1988).

More than 2.3 million people in the United States have been diagnosed with some form of epilepsy (Epilepsy Foundation, 1999; "Epilepsy: Increasing Awareness," 2002; Hauser & Hesdorffer, 1990). An estimated 150,000 to 200,000 people will be diagnosed this year alone (Begley et al., 2000). According to Hauser and Hesdorffer (1990), more than 30% of those with epilepsy are children under 18 years of age. Most of these recently reported cases of seizures are convulsions associated with fever. Men are 1.1 to 1.7 times more likely to have a newly diagnosed seizure or epilepsy than women. It is reported that new cases of epilepsy in children have decreased, while the number has increased for the elderly population.

The cause of seizures is unknown for approximately half of all cases. The causes of the other half include defects in the brain; brain injury during or after birth; infections such as meningitis, measles, mumps, and diphtheria; chemical imbalances; poor nutrition; childhood fevers; brain tumors; vascular diseases affecting the brain's blood vessels; anoxia; and high concentrations of alcohol and drugs. The general incidence of epilepsy is between 1% and 4%, and incidence of epilepsy with a genetic etiology is smaller (1%–2%) (Anderson, 1988). Risk factors include alcohol abuse, hypertension, lower economic status, and depressive illness (Hauser, 1997).

TYPES OF SEIZURES

There still exists a general misconception of exactly what qualifies as a seizure. If the general public were asked to describe their impression of what a seizure is, the response would likely be that the person loses consciousness and convulses. These symptoms occur in only one of many different types of seizures. There is also no consensus as to what defines epilepsy. Despite minor differences, however, most agree that epilepsy is a condition characterized by recurrent episodes of excessive and simultaneous discharge of neurons in one or more areas of the brain, manifested by disturbances of consciousness, sensation, or motor function (Batshaw & Perret, 1992; Lishman, 1987; Vining & Freeman, 1996).

Seizures can be as varied as a brief staring spell or what appears to be picking lint off one's clothes. Some seizures are associated with loss of speech, whereas other types do not affect speech at all. There is a correlation between the area of the brain affected and the type of seizure(s) experiencesd. Some people may have only one type of seizure, whereas others' epilepsy is characterized by two or more types.

Seizures can be classified based on their cause or etiology, the location of the responsible lesion, or the presumed mechanism (Aicardi, 1994). However, seizures are generally categorized according to the 1981 classification proposed by the International League Against Epilepsy (ILAE; www.ilae-epilepsy.org/visitors/center/ctf/index.cfm). The following paragraphs describe the most common types of seizure and their prominent characteristics.

Generalized Tonic–Clonic

Generalized tonic–clonic seizures, fomerly called grand mal seizures, affect the entire brain, hence the term *generalized*. They can be either convulsive or nonconvulsive, and the individual loses consciousness. Tonic–clonic seizures are the most common generalized seizures, occurring in approximately 60% of cases (Yousef, 1985). The person will sometimes cry out and then fall to the floor or ground, unaware of what is going on in the vicinity. Often, the seizure will happen without any warning or aura. (An aura can be an auditory or visual hallucination, a feeling of vertigo, a feeling of unfamiliarity or discomfort, or other unusual sensations.) The person may become incontinent and may bite the tongue or the inside of the cheek. These bites are usually not serious. There will be brief stiffness (tonic phase), then jerking of the arms, legs, or both (clonic phase). The person may experience some difficulty in breathing, due to the tongue's falling to the back of the throat. The seizure may last a minute or two. After the seizure, the person may be sleepy, confused, or both, and may have a headache or other muscle soreness.

 ## CASE EXAMPLE: RICHARD

Richard is 25 years old and has tonic–clonic seizures. He has no warning or aura before one happens. He immediately loses consciousness and convulses. His parents report that he becomes very rigid and that jerking of both his arms and legs immediately follows. The only way they know a seizure is about to happen is the loud cry he lets out just before he loses consciousness. Richard reports that upon regaining consciousness, his tongue is usually bleeding, and sometimes he has been incontinent. He also reports having a severe headache, as well as overall body aches immediately after the seizure, in addition to an overwhelming need to sleep. His speech is affected with the seizure. He has difficulty identifying objects for up to half an hour. Due to the lack of aura, Richard has had to relinquish his driver's license until he is free of seizures for 6 months.

Absence Seizures

Absence seizures, formerly called petit mal seizures, are generalized seizures without convulsions. This type of seizure consists of brief staring spells that usually last only a few seconds. They are usually seen in children between the ages of 6 and 14 years. The person will be briefly unaware of surroundings, then return to full alertness without falling or losing muscle control or consciousness. These seizures are difficult to notice because they are so fleeting. Parents and teachers often think these children are daydreaming or ignoring them. On occasion, there will be rapid eye blinking, mouth chewing movements, turning of the head, or waving of the arms.

 CASE EXAMPLE: ADRIENNE

Adrienne has absence seizures. She is 8 years old and in the third grade. For several months, her teacher was sure that Adrienne was daydreaming because she would stare into space or out the window. When she was called on in class, she sometimes seemed to be ignoring the teacher. Because Adrienne had scored 110 on an IQ test, the teacher knew Adrienne was smart. The teacher thought some further testing for a behavioral disorder might be appropriate. She discussed this idea with the school nurse, who offered to observe Adrienne in class. The nurse concluded that Adrienne was experiencing absence seizures and referred her to a pediatric neurologist.

Simple Partial Seizures

Simple partial seizures, sometimes called Jacksonian, focal, or aura seizures, affect a specific part of the brain. Approximately 60% of people with epilepsy are classified as having partial seizures (Pedley & Hauser, 1988). In simple partial seizures, the epileptic activity remains localized, and, therefore, consciousness is not impaired. During this type of seizure, the person is aware of having the seizure but cannot control the movements because the motor part of the brain is affected. The movements look like "marching," because the seizure involvement moves up the arm or leg. For example, the fingers will twitch or jerk, then the entire hand, then the wrist, and so on up the arm. Depending on what area of the brain is affected, the person may experience a feeling of fear, anger, or excitement.

Complex Partial Seizures

Complex partial seizures, sometimes called psychomotor or temporal lobe seizures, involve more than one symptom, and consciousness is also impaired. During this type of seizure, the person may look as though he or she is in a trance. There may also be repetitive behavior, such as hand rubbing, picking at clothes, or walking around in a daze. The person is not aware of his or her surroundings but may be able to follow simple, one-step commands. This type of seizure may last only a minute or two, but recovery of full awareness of the surroundings may take longer. There may be confusion and irritability after the seizure. This type of seizure is more common in adolescents and adults than in children. Complex partial seizures, as well as simple partial seizures, can become secondarily generalized. That is, as a second phase of the seizure, a generalized convulsion may occur.

 CASE EXAMPLE: WILLIAM

William has complex partial seizures. He might be involved in the middle of a task, such as shaving, making his bed, or working on his computer. He can usually finish the immediate task, often without any memory of having completed it. Further, he usually completes the task as well as when he is not interrupted by a seizure. After finishing what he had begun to do, he usually needs to either sit or lie down until the seizure has run its course. However, sometimes he will attempt to go on to another task, only to discover he has forgotten the steps to complete it, because the seizure activity in his brain has interrupted that thinking process. Because of the extended auras William has, he is able to sit or lie down and to let someone know he is about to have a seizure.

Status Epilepticus

Status epilepticus is a pathologic state in which a person experiences repetitive or prolonged seizures without regaining consciousness. It is a medical emergency, and, if not treated immediately, it can have a stressful effect on the respiratory, cardiovascular, and central nervous systems (Leppik, 1993a).

Sometimes seizures can be precipitated by something in one's environment or immediate surroundings as well as by physical and emotional well-being (Schachter, 1993). Common triggers include flickering lights, fluorescent lights, venetian blinds, stress, missing a dose of medicine, taking medications sporadically or not at a scheduled time every day, exposure to extreme heat, and menstruation.

PSYCHOSOCIAL IMPLICATIONS

Epilepsy can have a significant bearing on one's social interactions. The intermittent occurrence of the seizures can cause some dramatic responses, with withdrawal from social situations being a major one, to avoid embarrassment should a seizure occur.

Compliance with medicines is another significant problem. Persons who are on long-term drug therapy may be considered by society in general, family members, and themselves to have a debilitating illness. Therefore, as a denial tactic, they may discontinue the drug therapy. People often rationalize that if it is not necessary to take medicine, nothing is wrong. Adolescents in particular are extremely influenced by the opinions of their peers and consequently find it embarrassing to take medicine for fear of having to disclose the reason.

In reviewing previous studies, Hermann (1988) suggested that four main factors affect adjustment among individuals with epilepsy: biological, psychosocial, medical, and demographic. Biological factors include age of onset, presence of additional disabilities, and type of seizure activity. Identified psychosocial factors include perceived stigma and limitations, adjustment to seizures, vocational status, financial status, and socialization and recreation. The number and amount of medications one takes can also affect community adjustment. In terms of demographic variables, some older individuals adapt better due to their positive previous life experiences and have an integrated self-concept.

Self-Esteem

Not all people with epilepsy have problems with self-esteem. For those who do, however, diagnosis, environmental enhancement, and self-subscription can be used in a systematic approach to addressing self-esteem issues (Goldin, 1984). Diagnosis determines the areas in which self-esteem is affected. There are many aspects to one's overall image of self, such as intellect, physical attractiveness, sexuality, talents, moral and ethical behavior, and vocational performance. Environmental enhancement can be used to make changes to improve social acceptance. This process helps the person with epilepsy change specific aspects of the way he or she relates to the world. One important tool to develop is coping skills, which can lead to better self-perceptions. Finally, self-subscription is used to identify a person's personal strengths, so that he or she can learn to focus on them. People with any type of disability tend to become focused on what they cannot do. This tool focuses on one's abilities rather than one's disability.

Quality of Life

Quality of life can be negatively impacted by the stigma that a person with epilepsy experiences (Morrell, in press). In addition, perception of quality of life is directly related to level of acceptance of the disability, which in turn affects the level of self-esteem. Santilli (1993) pointed out five important tools to help achieve a "quality" state:

1. *General information about seizures, medication, and lifestyle.* This tool involves adapting one's life around the disability. A young adult who developed epilepsy, for example, would need to be aware of many potential health dangers. Staying up late, consuming alcohol, and experiencing everyday stressors can all cause seizures. Becoming aware of the stressors that produce seizure activity is essential, so that they can be avoided whenever possible. Understanding the importance of taking medicines is also important. Many persons with epilepsy believe that if the seizures are controlled, there is no point in continuing with the prescribed medicines. Another common mistake is doubling doses if a dose was missed. A person should never take a double dose unless directed to do so by a physician.

2. *Ability to recognize potential dangers and determine if immediate medical attention is warranted.* It is essential that a person with epilepsy understand the disability from a holistic perspective. It has not only neurological ramifications but also physical, psychological, emotional, and social ones. Self-awareness and an understanding of how epilepsy affects oneself personally is crucial. Only then can the most appropriate plan(s) of action be taken, medically and otherwise.

3. *Awareness of side effects of medications.* An open relationship with the treating physician and a pharmacist is also crucial. A person with epilepsy needs to report any unusual feelings (e.g., sleepiness, depression, or anxiety) that occur. Education about the particular drug that has been prescribed should be part of the treatment plan.

4. *Awareness of one's own attitudes about epilepsy.* These attitudes can vary widely from one person to another. Some continue to believe the myths for a long time, whereas others are more progressive in their attitudes. Some deny that the epilepsy even exists; others understand the importance of acceptance and understanding it. The attitudes one holds can vary as much as the type of seizures one experiences.

5. *Ability to solve problems.* This ability is imperative to any disability. Avoiding or internalizing problems can only lead to an increase of stress, which increases the likelihood of seizures. Dealing with problems in an inappropriate manner can lead to substance abuse, which is often directly related to seizure activity.

Suicide

Studies have shown that persons with epilepsy can experience psychological distress to the point of committing suicide. According to Stagno (1993), the incidence of suicide is five times greater in this population than in the general population. In a study that investigated the association between the risk of suicide in a person with epilepsy and clinical factors that might increase or have been suggested to increase the risk of suicide in a cohort of 6,880 patients with epilepsy, it was reported that an individual with an early onset of epilepsy but not necessarily severe, psychiatric illness, and perhaps inadequate neurological follow-up were likely to commit suicide (Nilsson, Ahlbom, Farahmand, Asberg, & Tomson, 2002).

Difficult psychosocial situations have been considered the leading cause of the high suicide rate ("Suicide and Epilepsy," 1980). However, psychiatric illness has been identified as the antecedent of suicide and using drugs (Blumer et al., 2002; Mendez, Lanska, Manon-Esaillat, & Burnstine, 1989; Murphy, 1994).

An overdose of antiseizure medication is the most frequent method of committing suicide among people with epilepsy. Phenobarbital in particular has been linked to every stage from suicidal ideations to the actual act of suicide. Repeated attempts have also been shown to be likely. Incidences of suicide appear to be linked to depression.

Some medicines used for seizure control are barbiturates. It has been hypothesized that these medications may induce depression, which thereby increases the possibility of suicide. There is also the question of the existence of mental illness other than depression in those with epilepsy who ultimately commit suicide. Stagno (1993) cited a report in which 61% of those who overdosed received no follow-up treatment prior to the suicide.

Family Dynamics

The psychosocial impact on a family that has a member with epilepsy is significant. The disability upsets the balance of the family, with each member often reacting differently. Moreover, the way the member with epilepsy is treated by his or her spouse, parents, grandparents, children, and siblings has a direct (sometimes drastic) effect on him or her (Whitman & Hermann, 1986).

A family's initial reactions to a diagnosis of epilepsy in one of its members can be similar to reactions to a death. First, there is disbelief or denial, which is a common reaction to an unexpected event. Because the onset of epilepsy usually comes without warnings, this disbelief is based on the difficulty of accepting that a loved one is having seizures. The frightening physical appearance of some types of seizures adds to the disbelief. This emotion can be manifested by the individual's or family's ignoring the fact that a seizure has occurred and not seeking the medical attention that may be necessary.

Anger is the second emotion. The more ramifications the family becomes aware of, the greater the chance of anger. Guilt, depression, and a sense of rejection are all associated with this anger, and therefore the chances are great that many different emotions emerge during this stage.

The third stage is demystification, which occurs when the family seeks information about the epilepsy. Learning more about the disability helps them become more familiar with it. Often, learning about epilepsy means learning more about themselves. The guilt, anger, and depression are now replaced with learning how to cope.

The final stage is conditional acceptance, which happens when there is a sense of having control over the epilepsy. Life with the disability and its ramifications is more tolerable. Control is the key to this phase. Even though the seizures are not necessarily controlled, reactions to them are controlled to a greater degree than before acceptance.

Usually, all family members go through these initial stages, with some exhibiting the characteristics of one phase more than others. However, there can be a vast difference between family members in handling the disability once these stages have been experienced. If the family member with epilepsy is one of the parents, it is extremely important for that parent to talk openly about it with the children. This open discussion allows the children to adjust to the disability and, at the same time, maintain trust in and concern for both parents. Children who are allowed to see the parent have seizures and the treatment for the seizures adapt better to the threat of illness or disability in their own lives. However, there is a fine line between involving the children in seizure care and making them overly responsible for the welfare of the parent with epilepsy.

Siblings of children with epilepsy have an important impact on overall adjustment. It is essential that siblings interact as normally as possible, no matter how much a seizure disrupts a daily routine. Siblings will watch their parents' reactions to a seizure very carefully. If the parents panic, so will the siblings. If parents are overprotective of the child with epilepsy, the siblings will be as well. Brothers and sisters should be allowed to help care for the affected child when a seizure occurs. At the same time, they need to feel free from this responsibility. Many children have special feelings for the sibling with epilepsy.

Also, at times siblings will feel resentful of the attention given to the child with epilepsy. This resentment can cause arguments and fighting. It is important for parents to set rules and to be consistent with enforcement.

Grandparents are often the ones in the family who have the most difficulty adjusting. They tend to encourage the parents to be overprotective and to isolate the grandchild from normal activities. They are also the most affected by the stigma and trauma of epilepsy. They tend to be the most intolerant, perhaps because their opinions about this disability were formed at a time when mainstreaming, seizure control through drugs and surgery, legislative protection, and advocacy were not prevalent. Grandparents, however, can play an important role in the family's adjustment. If their influence is positive, they can provide much reinforcement, whereas if their influence is negative, ways need to be found to neutralize their effect.

The most important area where any family member can help him- or herself is with self-esteem, by either developing or maintaining it. Family members must realize that the affected parent or sibling is still lovable and capable of many things. This realization is an extremely necessary element for high self-esteem, but it takes much courage, energy, and work to succeed.

Providing Medical Assistance for People Having Seizures

Often, some confusion exists as to the proper first-aid procedures to administer to someone who is having a seizure. Table 9.2 provides some of the important basic principles and offers guidance on when a seizure qualifies as an emergency.

LEGAL ISSUES

Driver's License

Receiving a driver's license is often a problem for people with epilepsy. Keeping the license if seizures begin later in life can also be a problem. Many states require a person to be seizure-free for 1 year; other states require a period of 6 months (Krumholz, Fisher, Lesser, & Hauser, 1991). Exceptions are sometimes made for people who have lengthy auras (warnings that the seizure is going to happen) that allow ample time to pull off the road; for people with nocturnal-only seizures; or if the treating physician submits a statement that a change in

TABLE 9.2

First Aid for Seizures

- Stay calm. Help the person lie down. Remove eyeglasses and dentures. Loosen tight clothing.
- Clear the area of any hard, sharp, or hot objects. Place something soft under the head, such as a jacket or a pillow.
- Do not hold down the arms or legs to try to stop the seizure. A seizure cannot be stopped once it has started.
- Never place anything in the mouth. Never attempt to pry the mouth open to insert an object.
- When the seizure ends, roll the person over on his or her side to allow the draining of saliva.
- Wait until the person is fully awake before giving him or her a drink.

Call a doctor or 911 only if
- the person has one seizure after another without regaining consciousness
- the person does not start breathing after the seizure (difficulty breathing during a seizure is normal)
- injuries occur
- this is the first seizure the person has ever had

medication caused a seizure but that, in his or her opinion, the affected person will continue to have good control.

Because there are many different types of seizures, the Epilepsy Foundation of America (EFA) advocates individual evaluations of the ability to drive, rather than general requirements for everyone with epilepsy. Side effects of medicines are an important factor, as are nocturnal seizures and auras.

When a person with epilepsy applies for a driver's license, there needs to be complete honesty about the seizure history. Otherwise, there can be serious liability issues. If a person with epilepsy has an automobile accident and was having a seizure at the time of the accident, the license can be suspended or even revoked, depending on state laws and the result of the accident for any other driver and passengers.

Although the licensing decision lies with the state Department of Motor Vehicles (DMV), some states have a mandatory reporting law, which requires a physician who treats a person with epilepsy to report it to the DMV, along with periodic medical updates, at least for several years (McLin et al., 1997). According to Lehman (1993), the EFA opposes this law for the following reasons:

- Epilepsy is not contagious; therefore, it is not a threat to public health.
- A physician's report of a patient's epilepsy, which is privileged information, to a state's DMV is in direct violation of the doctor–patient privilege, inherent in the relationship.

The EFA would rather see the person with epilepsy self-report, giving him or her responsibility for the disability and ultimately providing a tool for empowerment. Physicians have the right to report people with epilepsy to the DMV if they might be a threat to the public. Such people might include those who have been advised to report themselves or to relinquish their driver's licenses and have not. Some states provide physicians with immunity for reporting such persons.

Employment

Despite the passage of numerous pieces of legislation and the adoption of initiatives such as the Americans with Disabilities Act of 1990 (ADA) in order to alleviate obstacles to employment for individuals with disabilities, the unemployment rate of such people, including those with epilepsy, remains high (Cooper, 1995; Fisher, 2000; Thorbecke & Fraser, 1997; Yagi, 1998). There are numerous factors that influence employment for individuals with epilepsy, such as employers' fears and negative attitudes about people with epilepsy; individuals with epilepsy being concerned about potential discrimination and stigmatization; the type, severity, and frequency of the seizures (Chaplin, Wester, & Tomson, 1998; Gloag, 1985; Heaney, 1999; Yagi, 1998); neuropsychological functions (Clemmoms & Dodrill, 1984; Fraser, Clemmoms, Dodrill, Trejo, & Freelove, 1986); and psychosocial factors such as lack of education, social skills, family support, and social isolation (Devinsky, 1994; Thorbecke & Fraser, 1997). Table 9.3 lists the most frequent barriers that persons with epilepsy encounter when seeking employment.

The perception of an employer who employs people with epilepsy is extremely important to be aware of, as is the reverse. Hiring a person with epilepsy is no different from hiring a person without epilepsy. In fact, research indicates that attendance and performance of employees with epilepsy are equal to or better than that of people without epilepsy (McLellan, 1987). Time lost as a result of seizures is approximately 1 hour for every 1,000 hours worked by individuals with active seizures (Risch, 1968), and Sands (1961) indicated that more accidents in the workplace were caused by sneezing or coughing on the job than by seizures over a 13-year period. However, many employers refuse either to acknowledge or to understand. The ADA states that if an individual is qualified for a position but unable to perform a task due to a disability, the employer is obli-

TABLE 9.3
Employment Barriers

- Obtaining a job
- Disclosing one's epilepsy
- Remaining employed after a seizure occurs
- Underemployment
- Educating coworkers and employers in the proper first-aid procedures as well as in general knowledge about epilepsy

gated to provide reasonable accommodation by making modifications so that the individual can perform the job. Epilepsy should be an issue only if it interferes in some way with job performance or safety.

Having epilepsy, unlike other disabilities, may not be obvious at first and some people become ambivalent about whether to disclose it in the workplace—and if they decide to do so, how to disclose it (Bishop & Allen, 2001). Employees with epilepsy need to learn to advocate effectively for themselves in the interviewing process as well as when their job is threatened because of the discovery of the seizure disorder. Learning how to disclose in a nonthreatening manner the fact that epilepsy exists can be a difficult skill to learn. Table 9.4 provides a comprehensive view of the different ways one can disclose his or her epilepsy and the ramifications of each.

TREATMENTS FOR EPILEPSY

Drug Therapy

The search for effective seizure-preventative medicine started close to 2,000 years ago (Penry, 1993). Clinically speaking, however, it has only been in about the past 20 years that significant advances in both diagnosis and treatment of epilepsy have taken place. Three anticonvulsant drugs have been approved by the U.S. Food and Drug Administration (FDA) in the past few years for use in the United States: Neurontin (gabapentin), Felbatol (felbamate), and Lamictal (lamotrigine). This is very significant because the United States had not approved a major antiepileptic drug (AED) in the preceding 15 years. To this day, antiepileptic drugs are the most common form of treatment for seizure disorders. The efficacy of AEDs in suppressing and preventing seizures in many patients is significant. Numerous studies report 1- and 2-year remission rates in the 5 years following treatment implementation of up to 98% and 78%, respectively (Cockerell, Johnson, Sanders, & Shorvon, 1997; Collaborative Group for the Study of Epilepsy, 1992). However, AEDs are not without problems, specifically in cognitive functioning and psychological effects. Phenytoin (Dilantin), phenobarbital, and carbamazapine (Tegretol) are three well-known AEDs that have been documented to cause problems ranging from loss of memory retention to irritability and drowsiness (Battino, Dukes, & Perucca, 2000; see Table 9.5). Many of these side effects are reported to be dose dependent and are seen in patients who are on multiple-drug therapy (Deckers, Hekster, Keyser, Meinardi, & Renier, 1997). If drug levels in the blood are routinely checked and the lines of communication remain open between physician and patient, the significance of side effects can be dramatically reduced.

Noncompliance in taking one's medications is a major reason for recurring seizures (Leppik, 1993b). One third to one half of persons with epilepsy are noncompliant. The degree of noncompliance may vary widely, but it interferes with appropriate treatment whatever the degree. Noncompliance may also be related to the increase in the cost of health care. Ambulances necessary at times of

TABLE 9.4

Epilepsy Disclosure Chart

Time of Disclosure	Advantages	Disadvantages	Issues
On the job application	Honesty Peace of mind Ease Lets employer decide if epilepsy is an issue	Disqualification No opportunity to present qualifications No recourse Potential discrimination	May have a harder time finding work
During the interview	Honesty Peace of mind Opportunity to respond briefly and positively Discrimination less likely to occur face to face	Too much emphasis on disability may be a potential problem Evaluation may no longer be on abilities	Are you confident in discussing your epilepsy? This is difficult, but you will be a better job candidate and person if you are.
After the interview, when the job is offered, but before beginning work	Honesty Peace of mind If the epilepsy changes the mind of the employer and you are otherwise qualified for the job, this may be violation of the Employment Title of the Americans with Disabilities Act (ADA) Opportunity to discuss any accommodations you may need to enhance your job performance	Employer may believe you should have told him or her before job was offered	Seizures need to be examined in terms of the tasks in the job that you are applying for. Need to be able to explain how the epilepsy will not get in the way of doing job. This includes job safety.
After a seizure on the job	Opportunity to prove yourself on the job before disclosing If the seizures affect your employment status but not your ability to do the job, the employer may be in violation of the ADA	Possible employer accusation of falsifying information Coworkers might not have known seizure first aid Can perpetuate epilepsy's myths and misunderstandings	Any friendships you might have made with coworkers may be hurt if they feel you have not been truthful with them.
Never	Employer cannot react to your epilepsy until you have a seizure	If you have a seizure on the job, you might be hurt by inappropriate first aid Studies show that persons with epilepsy who do not disclose have a higher number of seizures on the job Can perpetuate myths and misunderstandings	If you have not had a seizure in a long time (over 2 years), the issue of disclosure becomes less critical.

Note. From *Issues and Answers: Exploring Your Possibilities. A Guide for Teens and Young Adults with Epilepsy* (p. 77), by the Epilepsy Foundation of America, 1992, Landover, MD: Author. Copyright 1992 by the Epilepsy Foundation of America. Reprinted with permission.

TABLE 9.5

Antiepileptic Drugs (AEDs)

Brand Name	Generic Name	Seizure Types	Side Effects
Dilantin	Phenytoin	• Generalized • Simple partial • Complex partial • Status epilepticus	Rash, gingivitis, drowsiness
Tegretol	Carbamazapine	• Simple partial • Complex partial • Generalized	Sore throat, easy bruising, drowsiness, dizziness
Depakote	Valproic acid	• Absence • Generalized	Liver abnormalities, hair loss, weight gain
Neurontin	Gabapentin	• Simple partial • Complex partial	Dizziness, brain fog, ataxia, visual problems
Phenobarbital	Phenobarbital	• Neonatal • Febrile • Generalized	Drowsiness, sexual dysfunction, paradoxical excitement

transport, the increase in the use of emergency rooms, and the possibility of a physical injury during a seizure all contribute to this increase.

Another important aspect of noncompliance is the danger it poses to others—for example, a driver who has been seizure-free but stops taking his medications or a pregnant woman who does not follow her prescribed regimen.

There are two types of noncompliance: patient controlled and structural (Leppik, 1993b). The former is based on a belief system the person may have—for example, that the seizure is less of a risk than the drugs are. The latter may occur when the seizures are the result of a traumatic brain injury, which resulted in memory problems that make it difficult to remember to take medicine.

Interventions in noncompliance must take place if the management of seizures is to be successful. Education is important to ensure that the person understands what epilepsy is and the importance not only of drug therapy but also of his or her own regimen. The number of visits to the physician's office may need to be increased and a particular staff member designated to monitor progress.

A different concern is the problems that AEDs can cause for pregnant women. Infants born to mothers who receive AED therapy during pregnancy run a greater risk of developing congenital malformations (birth defects) (Canger et al., 1999; Lindhout & Omtzight, 1994), with cleft palates the most common (Yerby, 1993). Although no pattern of malformation is specific for a given drug, there is a greater risk of the infant's developing spina bifida when the mother takes Tegretol or Depakote (Kaneko et al., 1999; Lindhout & Omtzight, 1994).

Nevertheless, close to 90% of women with epilepsy have healthy babies (Canger et al., 1999; Kaneko et al., 1999; Lindhout & Omtzight, 1994).

Despite the significant changes in AED therapy, it is important to remember that this type of therapy greatly depends on the individual. Each person with epilepsy differs from others in terms of the types of drugs that best control seizures. Therefore, there is much trial and error and unpredictability involved in AED therapy to determine the optimum drugs and dosages with the fewest side effects.

Surgery

Since the 1950s, the number of people who choose surgery for treating uncontrollable epilepsy has continued to increase (Dreifuss, 1983). In identifying candidates for epilepsy surgery, the first criterion is determining that other forms of treatment have failed. Usually, the person's quality of life is deteriorating despite the treatment. This deterioration would affect employability, social interactions, academic performance, and level of self-esteem. The next step is extensive neuropsychological testing to identify the region in the brain where the seizure activity is originating, as well as to determine the candidate's psychological stability for undergoing a complicated surgical procedure.

Some changes in cognitive abilities can occur after surgery, including memory, language, and intelligence. These changes can be either positive or negative. Often in cases in which the surgery was performed in the speech hemisphere of the brain, language skills have improved. It is thought that this improvement occurred because the neurological disturbance that was causing the seizures was removed. Some decrease in IQ scores immediately after surgery has been reported, but no long-term losses have been found. Improvement in intellectual abilities has been reported in terms of performance but not in terms of IQ scores.

Ketogenic Diet

Dietary intervention can be used in treating epilepsy in some individuals but should be considered only when other drug treatments are ineffective or have serious side effects. The ketogenic diet was developed in 1921 to be used primarily for children. It accumulates byproducts of fat metabolism in the blood to control seizures (Ekvall & Iannaccone, 1993). As high fat consumption became a dietary issue and better drug therapy became available, ketogenic diets have been used less frequently. In the 1970s, the medium-chain triglyceride (MCT) ketogenic diet was introduced, which reduced some concerns regarding high fat intake.

Advocacy

Physicians, politicians, public officials, attorneys, and human-service workers all act in some capacity as advocates for patients, constituents, or clients. Self-advocacy can also be taught to the patient or client, who can then promote a belief for him- or herself as well as for a group to which he or she belongs. Assistance of a friend or counseling can enhance one's self-esteem, and then a person can define realistic expectation, formulate a life plan, and carry out the plan. Involvement in making desired life changes may make one feel less helpless and more empowered (Dunn, Austin, & Huster, 1999).

Language is often a good starting point when developing advocacy skills. How we refer to people with various disabilities is a direct reflection of our own attitudes and beliefs. Table 9.6 contains the most misused terms when speaking about persons with epilepsy.

There are also other advocacy tools that apply to persons with any disability, such as assertiveness, negotiation skills, letter writing, and other communication skills. The combination of these abilities makes for a very effective advocate.

Ethical Considerations

When clinical ethics comes to mind, one usually thinks of controversial issues such as maintaining persons on life support systems or using aborted fetuses for research. But just as important are everyday, routine aspects of health care. The mundane or frequent component of health care does not eliminate ethical consideration.

Occasionally a life-and-death ethical question concerning a person with epilepsy occurs, but it is not commonplace. For example, such a situation could stem from a "do not resuscitate" order or a severe cerebrovascular accident (stroke) following surgery to correct a seizure disorder and requiring a decision to continue life support. The more common types of ethical considerations are related to informed consent and the relevant responsibilities of the patient, as well as the physician, nurse, counselor, and any other health care provider. Generally defined, informed consent refers to an agreement or permission obtained through a series of meetings involving respect, concurrence, and, sometimes, negotiation.

TABLE 9.6
Terms Misused in Referring to Epilepsy

Disease	Epilepsy is not a disease, which to many implies contagiousness or an ailment. Rather, it is a symptom of a disorder, with the main characteristic being a disruption in the electrical activity in the brain.
Epileptic	A person with any type of disability should never be defined by that disability. The individual is a person first and foremost. Therefore, "person with epilepsy" is more appropriate.
Fit	This is a commonly used term for seizure by the medical profession in England, but people with epilepsy in the United States are very sensitive to it. It implies loss of control. "Seizure" is more appropriate.

Whether or not the circumstances are critical, it is paramount to always remember, as explained by Smith (1993), that the dignity of the person with epilepsy must be emphasized and that the health provider should act as a "moral agent." Often, because of the health care system's attempt to be efficient, patients and clients are treated like numbers or statistics rather than human beings. Consequently, they do not receive adequate explanation for the tests or treatments they are given.

Smith (1993) explained that, just as the provider has a certain area of expertise, so should patients with epilepsy. It is extremely important that they have a firm grasp of what is important to them on a personal level, in terms of values and aspirations. Persons with different types of epilepsy or seizure frequency will opt for different types of treatment. Some may be content with drug therapy, whereas others may opt for surgery.

Patients or clients have a responsibility to themselves, as well as to the professional treating them, to be honest in discussing seizure severity, frequency, substance abuse (or any consumption of a "recreational" drug), and any other vital pieces of information. They also must be willing to cooperate with the course of treatment. If prescribed dosages of medicine are not taken, if the reported number of seizures is deliberately inaccurate, or if a seizure that occurred within the required time frame set by the DMV to retain a driver's license goes unreported, the patient or client is not accepting his or her responsibility.

There are many situations that can hinder the relationship between a patient or client and the service provider. The most significant ones are communication problems, noncompliance, and ulterior motives, such as a desire to continue to receive a financial benefit or entitlement (Smith, 1993). Appropriate measures to educate and empower persons with epilepsy should be initiated when necessary.

FINAL THOUGHTS

It is not difficult to understand why epilepsy has been a misunderstood disability. There is not always an easy explanation for its occurrence. The seizures are sudden and often dramatic. Further, quite a number of psychological, social, and emotional problems accompany the seizures, which substantially compromise one's quality of life. Continued emphasis in this area is essential for change in attitudes, both societal and personal. Dodrill (1993) cited a study of 27 groups of people with epilepsy who were given the Minnesota Multiphasic Personality Inventory (MMPI). Two thirds of these groups showed various abnormalities. This statistic, although based on a relatively small population of people with epilepsy, is nevertheless alarming. The magnitude of its implications should not go unrecognized.

There have been significant changes, however, in diagnosing and treating epilepsy. These include the measuring of levels of drugs in the blood, audiovisual monitoring of seizures, and the FDA's approval of new antiepileptic medications.

Persons with epilepsy need to have choice and control in every aspect of life—education, employment, housing, and personal relationships, to name a few. Without choice and control, myths will continue to prevail. The first step is to develop a personal acceptance of life with this disability and to take the necessary precautions to manage it on a daily basis. This could include everything from changing sleep patterns to substance-abuse recovery. Unless those with epilepsy accept their disability, it would be unreasonable to expect others to do so. Without personal acceptance, obtaining choice and control will be very difficult.

Finally, consumers, working with physicians, counselors, politicians—but, most important, with each other—must advocate for both system and personal changes. President George H. W. Bush said it most succinctly upon signing the Americans with Disabilities Act: "Let the shameful wall of exclusion finally come tumbling down."

REFERENCES

Aicardi, J. (1994). *Epilepsy in children* (2nd ed.). New York: Raven Press.

Americans with Disabilities Act of 1990, 42 U.S.C. § 12101 *et seq.*

Anderson, V. E. (1988). Genetics of the epilepsies. In W. A. Hauser (Ed.), *Current trends in epilepsy: A self-study course for physicians* (Unit 3). Landover, MD: Epilepsy Foundation of America.

Batshaw, M. L., & Perret, Y. M. (1992). *Children with disabilities: A medical primer* (3rd ed.). Baltimore: Brookes.

Battino, D., Dukes, G. M. N., & Perucca, E. (2000). Antiepileptic drugs. In J. K. Aronson & G. M. N. Dukes (Eds.), *Meyler's side effects of drugs.* Amsterdam: Elsevier.

Begley, C. E., Famulari, M., Annegers, J. F., Lairson, D. R., Reynolds, T. F., Coan, S., et al. (2000). The cost of epilepsy in the United States: An estimate from population-based clinical and survey data. *Epilepsia, 41,* 342–351.

Bishop, M. L., & Allen, C. (2001). Employment concerns of people with epilepsy and the question of disclosure: Report of a survey of the Epilepsy Foundation. *Epilepsy & Behavior, 2,* 490–495.

Blumer, D., Montouris, G., Davies, K., Wyler, A., Phillips, B., & Hermann, B. (2002). Suicide in epilepsy: Psychopathology, pathogenesis, and prevention. *Epilepsy & Behavior, 3,* 232–241.

Canger, R., Battino, D., Canevini, M. P., Fumarola, C., Guidolin, L., Vignoli, A., et al. (1999). Malformations in offspring of women with epilepsy: A prospective study. *Epilepsia, 40,* 1231–1236.

Chaplin, J. E., Wester, A., & Tomson, T. (1998). Factors associated with the employment problems of people with established epilepsy. *Seizure, 7,* 299–303.

Clemmoms, D. C., & Dodrill, C. B. (1984). Vocational outcomes of high school students with epilepsy and neuropsychological correlates with later vocational stress. In R. J. Porter, R. H. Mattson, A. Ward, Jr., & M. Dam (Eds.), *Advances in epileptology: XVth Epilepsy International Symposium* (pp. 611–614). New York: Raven Press.

Cockerell, O. C., Johnson, A. L., Sanders, J., & Shorvon, S. D. (1997). Epilepsy in a population of 6000 re-examined: Secular trends in first attendance rates, prevalence, and prognosis. *Journal of Neurosurgery Psychiatry, 58,* 570–576.

Collaborative Group for the Study of Epilepsy. (1992). Prognosis of epilepsy: A review and further analysis of the first nine years of the British National General Practice study of epilepsy, a prospective population-based study. *Epilepsia, 38,* 31–46.

Cooper, M. (1995). Epilepsy and employment: Employer attitudes. *Seizure, 4,* 193–199.

Deckers, C. L. P., Hekster, Y. A., Keyser, A., Meinardi, H., & Renier, W. O. (1997). Reappraisal of polytherapy in epilepsy: A critical review of drug load and adverse effects. *Epilepsia, 38,* 570–575.

Devinsky, O. (1994). *A guide to understanding and living with epilepsy.* Philadelphia: F. A. Davis.

Dodrill, C. (1993). Historical perspectives and future directions. In E. Wyllie (Ed.), *The treatment of epilepsy: Principles and practice* (pp. 1129–1132). Philadelphia: Lea & Febiger.

Dreifuss, F. E. (1983). *Pediatric epileptology.* Boston: John Wright-PSG.

Driscoll, S. (1988). *All you really wanted to know about epilepsy but were afraid to ask.* Richmond: Medical College of Virginia, Virginia Commonwealth University, Department of Neurology.

Dunn, D. W., Austin, J. K., & Huster, G. A. (1999). Symptoms and depression in adolescents with epilepsy. *Journal of American Academic Child Adolescence Psychiatry, 38,* 1132–1138.

Ekvall, S. W., & Iannaccone, S. (1993). Epilepsy. In S. W. Ekvall (Ed.), *Pediatric nutrition in chronic diseases and developmental disorders: Prevention, assessment, and treatment* (pp. 99–102). New York: Oxford University Press.

Epilepsy Foundation of America. (1992). *Issues and answers: Exploring your possibilities. A guide for teens and young adults with epilepsy.* Landover, MD: Author.

Epilepsy Foundation of America. (1999). *Epilepsy: A report to the nation.* Landover, MD: Author.

Epilepsy: Increasing awareness and improving care. (2002, September). Retrieved June 25, 2004, from Centers for Disease Control and Prevention Web site: http://www.cdc.gov/nccdphp/bb_epilepsy/index.htm

Fisher, R. S. (2000). Epilepsy from the patient's perspective: Review of results of a community-based survey. *Epilepsy & Behavior, 1*(Suppl. 1), 9–14.

Fraser, R. T., Clemmoms, D. C., Dodrill, C. B., Trejo, W. R., & Freelove, C. (1986). The difficult-to-employ in epilepsy rehabilitation: Predictions of response to an intensive intervention. *Epilepsia, 27,* 220–224.

Gloag, D. (1985). Epilepsy and employment. *British Medical Journal, 291,* 2–3.

Goldin, G. (1984, July/August). *Building self-esteem in people with epilepsy.* Landover, MD: Epilepsy Foundation of America.

Hauser, W. A. (1997). Incidence and prevalence. In J. Engle & T. A. Bedley (Eds.), *Epilepsy* (pp. 47–58). Philadelphia: Lippincott-Raven.

Hauser, W. A., & Hesdorffer, D. C. (1990). *Epilepsy frequency, causes and consequences.* New York: Demos.

Heaney, D. (1999). Epilepsy at work: Evaluating the cost of epilepsy in the workplace. *Epilepsia, 40* (Suppl. 8), 44–47.

Hermann, B. P. (1988). Interrictal psychotherapy in patients with epilepsy. In W. A. Hermann (Ed.), *Current trends in epilepsy: A self study course for physicians* (Unit 1). Landover, MD: Epilepsy Foundation of America.

Kaneko, S., Battino, D., Andermann, E., Wada, K., Kan, R., Takeda, A., et al. (1999). Congenital malformations due to antiepileptic drugs. *Epilepsy Research, 33,* 145–158.

Krumholz, A., Fisher, R. S., Lesser, R. P., & Hauser, W. A. (1991). Driving and epilepsy: A review and reappraisal. *Journal of the American Medical Association, 265,* 622–626.

Lehman, C. (1993). Legal aspects of epilepsy. In E. Wyllie (Ed.), *The treatment of epilepsy: Principles and practice* (pp. 1168–1177). Philadelphia: Lea & Febiger.

Leppik, I. (1993a). Compliance in the treatment of epilepsy. In E. Wyllie (Ed.), *The treatment of epilepsy: Principles and practice* (pp. 810–816). Philadelphia: Lea & Febiger.

Leppik, I. (1993b). Status epilepticus. In E. Wyllie (Ed.), *The treatment of epilepsy: Principles and practice* (pp. 678–685). Philadelphia: Lea & Febiger.

Lindhout, D., & Omtzight, J. G. (1994). Teratogenic effects of antiepileptic drugs: Implications for management of epilepsy in women of childbearing age. *Epilepsia, 35*(Suppl. 4), 19–28.

Lishman, W. A. (1987). *Organic psychiatry: The psychological consequences of cerebral disorder* (2nd ed.). Oxford: Blackwell Scientific.

McLellan, D. L. (1987). Epilepsy and employment. *Journal of Social and Occupational Medicine, 3,* 94–99.

McLin, W., Beran, R. G., Lehman, C., Falk-Pedersen, J., de Boer, H. M., & Finucane, A. (1997). Legal concerns and effective advocacy strategies. In P. Engels & T. Pedley (Eds.), *Epilepsy: A comprehensive textbook* (pp. 2233–2239). New York: Raven Press.

Mendez, M. F., Lanska, D. J., Manon-Esaillat, R., & Burnstine, T. H. (1989). Causative factors for suicide attempts by overdose in epileptics. *Archives of Neurology, 46,* 1065–1068.

Morrell, M. J. (in press). Stigma and epilepsy. *Epilepsy & Behavior.*

Murphy, G. E. (1994). Suicide and attempted suicide. In G. Winokur & P. J. Clayton (Eds.), *The medical basis of psychiatry* (pp. 529–544). Philadelphia: Saunders.

Nilsson, L., Ahlbom, A., Farahmand, B. Y., Asberg, M., & Tomson, T. (2002). Risk factors for suicide in epilepsy: A case controlled study. *Epilepsia, 43,* 644.

Pedley, T. A., & Hauser, W. A. (1988). Classification and differential diagnosis of seizures and of epilepsy. In W. A. Hauser (Ed.), *Current trends in epilepsy: A self-study course for physicians* (Unit 1). Landover, MD: Epilepsy Foundation of America.

Penry, J. (1993). Historical perspectives and future directions. In E. Wyllie (Ed.), *The treatment of epilepsy: Principles and practice* (pp. 709–711). Philadelphia: Lea & Febiger.

Risch, F. (1968). We lost every game … but. *Rehabilitation Record, 9,* 16–18.

Sands, H. (1961). Report of a study undertaken for the committee on neurological disorders in industry. *Epilepsy News, 7,* 1.

Santilli, N. (1993). Psychosocial aspects of epilepsy: Education and counseling for patients and families. In E. Wyllie (Ed.), *The treatment of epilepsy: Principles and practice* (pp. 1163–1167). Philadelphia: Lea & Febiger.

Schachter, S. (1993). *Brainstorms: Epilepsy in our words.* New York: Raven Press.

Smith, M. (1993). Ethical considerations in the treatment of epilepsy. In E. Wyllie (Ed.), *The treatment of epilepsy: Principles and practice* (pp. 1178–1183). Philadelphia: Lea & Febiger.

Stagno, S. (1993). Psychiatric aspects of epilepsy. In E. Wyllie (Ed.), *The treatment of epilepsy: Principles and practice* (pp. 1149–1162). Philadelphia: Lea & Febiger.

Suicide and epilepsy. (1980). *British Medical Journal, 281,* 530.

Thorbecke, R., & Fraser, R. T. (1997). The range of needs and services in vocational rehabilitation. In J. Engel & T. A. Pedley (Eds.), *Epilepsy: A comprehensive textbook* (pp. 2211–2225). Philadelphia: Lippincott-Raven.

Vining, E. P. G., & Freeman, J. M. (1996). Epilepsy and developmental disabilities. In A. J. Capute & P. J. Accardo (Eds.), *Developmental disabilities in infancy and childhood: Vol 2. The spectrum of developmental disabilities* (2nd ed., pp. 511–520). Baltimore: Brookes.

Whitman, S., & Hermann, B. P. (1986). *Psychopathology in epilepsy: Social dimensions.* New York: Oxford University Press.

Yagi, K. (1998). Epilepsy: Comprehensive care, quality of life, and factors preventing people with epilepsy from being employed. *Clinical Therapy, 20*(Suppl. A), A19–A28.

Yerby, M. (1993). Treatment of epilepsy during pregnancy. In E. Wyllie (Ed.), *The treatment of epilepsy: Principles and practice* (pp. 844–857). Philadelphia: Lea & Febiger.

Yousef, J. M. (1985). Medical and educational aspects of epilepsy: A review. *DPH Journal, 8,* 3–15.

CHAPTER 10

Emotional Disturbance in Children with Intellectual and Developmental Disabilities

Elaine Clark, Daniel E. Olympia,
William R. Jenson, and Thomas J. Kehle

LEARNING GOALS

Upon completion of this chapter, readers will understand

- the nature of emotional problems in children with intellectual and developmental disabilities (ID/DD)
- the problem diagnosing psychiatric illness in an ID/DD population
- the importance of conducting proper assessments that include functional behavior assessments
- the role that self-determination plays in the mental health of individuals with disabilities, and how to facilitate this

C hildren and adolescents with intellectual and developmental disabilities suffer from many of the same types of emotional and behavioral problems as peers with normal intelligence. These include attention-deficit/hyperactivity disorder, stereotypic movement disorder, tic disorders, schizophrenia, eating disorders, major depression, and anxiety (Szymanski & King, 1999). The rate of psychiatric disorders among individuals with disabilities, however, is much higher in the ID/DD population than it is in unaffected groups. According to the American Psychiatric Association (APA), psychiatric disorders are estimated to be three to four times higher in populations with intellectual disabilities (APA, 2000). The exact reason for the increased incidence is unclear, but many suspect that part of the problem has to do with increased stress caused by prolonged disability and limited resources to cope. In some cases, this is quite likely, but not in all. The risk of overattributing emotional problems to intellectual or developmental disability, or what Reiss and Szyszko (1983) refer to as "diagnostic overshadowing," is inadequate, or even inappropriate at times, for treatment. Granted, the diagnosis of comorbid psychiatric disorders is difficult in cases where cognitive impairments and communication problems are so severe that diagnostic criteria cannot be applied (e.g., when using common classification systems such as the *Diagnostic and Statistical Manual of Mental Disorders–Fourth Edition* (*DSM–IV;* APA, 2000); however, even in milder cases of ID/DD, where diagnosis of mental illness is more straightforward, neither this nor the treatment is guaranteed. Einfeld and Tonge (1996), for example, found that in the developmentally disabled population of youth in Australia, 41% had significant psychiatric problems that warranted treatment but only 10% had received related therapy.

Unlike intelligence, which remains fairly stable over time, and relatively impervious to environmental modification (Brody, 1992; Deary, Whalley, Lemmon, Crawford, & Starr, 2000), many of the emotional problems that individuals with ID/DD suffer from respond to treatment. Although some individuals with ID/DD respond differently than their nondisabled peers, for the most part, responses to therapies such as behavior management and drugs are quite similar (e.g., Fleisher, 1999; Stavrakaki, 1999; Szymanski & King, 1999). It is not entirely clear why psychiatric treatment is not offered more often, especially with milder cases of ID/DD that show clearer evidence of emotional difficulties and whose response to treatment can be more easily assessed.

Drug studies have shown that, for the most part, individuals who have disabilities respond similarly to those without disabilities. Drugs that have been shown to be particularly effective with children and adolescents who have ID/DD include selective serontonergic reuptake inhibitors (e.g., Zoloft and Prozac) for depression, anxiety, and obsessional thinking; mood stabilizing drugs (e.g., Lithium and Tegretol); anxiolytic and antiepileptic drugs (i.e., Buspirone and Tegretol) to reduce aggression and self-injury; and antipsychotic drugs (e.g., Resperdol) (Fleisher, 1999). Some individuals with disabilities, however, have particular sensitivities to certain lines of drugs, including sedatives and stimulants. For example, children with Down syndrome have particular difficulty tolerating hypnotics and often become disinhibited. Even the broader ID/DD population, however, has difficulty tolerating the anticholingeric effects of tricyclic antidepressants or the movement effects of stimulants (e.g., stereotypic motor behaviors) (Szymanski & King, 1999). For these reasons, it is critical that drug dosages be started low and increased slowly, and that drug response be monitored over time for effects (and unwanted side effects). Problems with drug therapy in the ID/DD population include poor monitoring for effectiveness, failure to properly justify the need for a particular drug (especially when used for extended periods of time), and a lack of information about the differential effectiveness of nondrug treatments, including treatments such as cognitive-behavioral techniques (e.g., Lewinsohn, 1974).

(UN)COMMON SYMPTOMS, ASSESSMENTS, AND INTERVENTIONS

Common Symptoms of Internalizing Disorders

Common symptoms of anxiety in an ID/DD population include aggression, agitation, sleep disturbance, and obsessive-compulsiveness (e.g., self-injury, rituals, and obsessive fears). According to a study by Stavrakaki (1999), in the majority of cases of anxiety, a stressful life event occurred 3 to 6 months earlier. Frequently reported stressors include loss of caregiver (e.g., parents separating or divorcing), physical or sexual assault, physical illness, involvement in an accident, and relocation of residence. Children and adolescents with depression have been found to have similar stressors, including parent separation and divorce, change in residence, and physical or sexual assault within 1 to 3 months of symptom onset.

The manifestation of depression has been shown to vary widely depending on the severity of intellectual disability. Marston, Perry, and Roy (1997), for example, found that when children and adolescents had only mild ID/DD, depression was manifested by tearfulness, low energy, mood fluctuation, anhedonia, and low self-esteem. Those who had more moderate disability tended to isolate themselves, eat less and lose weight, and engage in self-injurious behaviors. Children and adolescents with severe disability who were thought to be depressed were observed to scream more and act out aggressively, including inflicting injury on themselves. Determining whether a child with ID/DD has a formal thought disorder, or is psychotic, is also problematic; the symptoms are typically delusions and hallucinations. As Clarke (1999) notes, any individual who cannot convey a subjective experience verbally (or even conceptually) can be expected to be difficult to diagnose. In these cases, knowing the family history of psychiatric illness, in addition to behavior observation, becomes critical. Parent and teacher reports of any atypical behaviors that suggest possible psychosis are also important. These reports should mention paranoia or other forms of delusional thinking, hallucinations, affective blunting or inappropriateness, social withdrawal, and anger outbursts. Behaviors that reflect underlying intellectual disability, or underlying pervasive developmental disorder, including unusual preoccupations, vocal repetitions, and stereotypic movements, would by necessity need to be ruled out before diagnosing a psychiatric condition, something that is much easier to do in the case of milder ID/DD. In this case, assessing a child for psychotic thinking may not be that different from the assessment of this condition in a child with normal intelligence. In other words, if an adolescent reports or is observed to be talking to someone who is not present, or reports unusual suspiciousness, ruling out psychosis is important.

Assessment Methods

In addition to the hundreds of measures of emotional and behavioral disturbance that are available today (see Buros's *Mental Measurements Yearbooks* for test reviews), a few checklists have been developed specifically to address psychiatric problems in the ID/DD population. One example is the *Developmental Behavior Checklist* (DBC) by Einfeld and Tonge (1993). The DBC, a 96-item questionnaire to be completed by a parent or caretaker, consists of six factors that are intended to assess disruptive behavior, tendencies to be self-absorbed, language disturbance, anxiety, problems with social relating, and antisocial behaviors (Tonge, Einfeld, & Krupinski, 1996).

Other measures that can be helpful in assessing an ID/DD population for emotional problems include the *Adolescent Behavior Checklist* (Demb, Brier, & Huron, 1989), the *Aberrant Behavior Checklist* (Aman & Singh, 1986), the *Preschool Behavior Questionnaire* (Behar & Stringfield, 1974), the *Emotional Problems Scales: Behavior Rating Scales* (Strohmer & Prout, 1991), the *Conners Rating Scales* (Conners, 1990), and the *Fear Survey for Children With and Without Mental Retardation* (Ramirez & Kratochwill, 1990). All of these scales can provide different pieces of information to assist in the assessment process and have been normed on various groups with ID/DD. Interested readers should refer to the various manuals for specific information about the utility of each test as well as its norms and psychometric properties.

Besides checklists and questionnaires, there are a number of structured interview tools that have been found to be helpful with ID/DD populations who are thought to have psychiatric problems. Examples include the *Schedule for Affective Disorders and Schizophrenia for School-Age Children* (K–SADS; Orvaschel & Puig-Antich, 1987) and the *Diagnostic Interview for Children and Adolescents–Revised* (DICA–R; Reich & Welner, 1989). Both scales are structured interviews that lend themselves nicely to *DSM–IV* diagnoses; however, the K–SADS requires more training for administration than the DICA–R (i.e., the K–SADS is semistructured, whereas the DICA–R has a highly structured format requiring more familiarity and practice in administration). Another standardized measure that can be quite useful for the ID/DD population is the *Autism Diagnostic Observation Schedule* (ADOS) by Lord and colleagues (1989). The ADOS was developed specifically to assess social and communication problems of children with autistic spectrum disorders and has been shown to effectively discriminate children with autism from those who have intellectual disability but without autism. It takes approximately 30 minutes to administer, but the format requires considerable training and experience for interpretation.

Besides administering instruments that provide information about various potential diagnoses, the professional also needs to understand the circumstances that may trigger an individual's emotional and behavioral reactions, and the circumstances that may be maintaining these. Granted, knowing that a child has problems with anxiety and behavioral dyscontrol is important; however, understanding that when the child feels most anxious, he or she acts out behaviorally is also very critical, especially if one expects to design appropriate interventions. If drugs are the only intervention being considered, perhaps this type of information will not be critical. Drugs, however, should not be the only treatment option. To provide adequate treatment for the psychological problems experienced by individuals with ID/DD, professionals need to develop a comprehensive treatment program, and for that, an appropriate assessment of the child's behaviors and circumstances is necessary. Functional behavior assessments can be beneficial by providing critical data to professionals who are trying to better understand the emotional problems of children and adolescence with ID/DD.

Functional Behavior Assessment

When the Individuals with Disabilities Education Act (IDEA) was amended in 1997, the law mandated the use of functional behavior assessment (FBA) for certain circumstances involving special education students, including safe-school violations where determination of manifest disability must be made. Research with FBA has focused on children with severe developmental disabilities who engage in aggressive and self-injurious behaviors (e.g., Iwata, Dorsey, Slifer, Bauman, & Richman, 1994; Repp & Karsh, 1994). FBA, however, not only has the potential to be used to identify low-frequency problems such as sexual acting out and fire setting, it can also be used to assess a number of high-frequency behaviors including noncompliance, arguing, property destruction, and disruptiveness. It can even be used to provide critical information that leads to interventions for children with internalizing problems, including conditions such as anxiety. FBA has its roots in applied behavior analysis. Its purpose is to determine environmental variables that set the occasion for and maintain problem behaviors. Specifically, FBA describes behaviors; identifies events, times, and circumstances associated with occurrences and nonoccurrences of the behaviors; assesses the consequences that maintain the behaviors; provides data to generate hypotheses about the function or purpose of a problem behavior; and allows the collection of data to support (or refute) formulated hypotheses (Johnson & O'Neill, 2001).

Indirect and direct procedures are used for data collection. "Indirect" methods include such assessment devices as interviews, checklists, and rating scales. Two measures that have been used to collect indirect data include the *Motivation Assessment Scale* (Durand & Crimmins, 1988) and the *Functional Analysis Interview* (O'Neill et al., 1997). Direct data collection involves direct observation of behavior and, in some cases, manipulation of antecedent events and consequences. Manipulations, or probes, may not be necessary in all cases, especially when data are collected in the environment where problem behaviors are most likely to occur (Ellingson, Miltenberger, & Long, 1999). Nonetheless, most FBAs are time consuming and may not be practical in time-sensitive environments (e.g., certain classrooms). Johnson and O'Neill (2001) suggest that practitioners who are familiar with the individual consider forgoing the indirect data collection phase—that is, collecting interview and test data from informants—to reduce time involved in the data collection phase. According to Johnson and O'Neill, in this case, the practitioner can proceed directly to the behavioral observations (and probes) to formulate and test hypotheses.

Olympia, Tuesday-Heathfield, Jenson, and Clark (2002) recommend a multifaceted FBA approach to data collection. However, these authors also suggest that practitioners (and researchers) rely more on technology-assisted data collection devices such as palm pilots so that the overall time for assessment can be reduced. This will also help to allow for time to use probes when they are of critical importance to evaluate intervention outcomes (e.g., during the baseline and intervention phases). The researchers also recommend that indirect data be collected, but that time-saving methods be employed (e.g., using the *ABC Assessment Worksheet;* see Olympia et al., 2002, for worksheet format).

Most FBAs are adequate for identifying relationships between behaviors and their antecedents and consequences. However, few directly link assessment information to interventions that can be specifically, and readily, transferred to the classroom. Given the IDEA 1997 mandate, considerable research is expected to be forthcoming to show how best to apply FBA information in a way that is more effective and efficient than it is now. Hopefully, this line of research will also address the internalizing problems of children with ID/DD, not just the externalizing ones that concern practitioners.

Academic Interventions

Not being able to learn—in particular, not being able to read—has been found to be strongly correlated with emotional and behavioral disorders (Wells & Forehand, 1985). This places children with ID/DD at particular risk for problems such as depression, anxiety, and psychotic reactions. Direct behaviorally oriented interventions have been shown to be effective in improving academic performance of children with varying levels of ability, including increases in the amount of work completed and the amount of content mastered (e.g., Elliott & Shapiro, 1990). It is widely known that time on task serves as a good predictor of how much is learned. It is also an accepted fact that being motivated to learn and taking responsibility for one's own work can increase learning. Homework, regardless of the disability, not only provides a means to increase time spent on academic tasks but fosters greater responsibility and independence on the child's part. Unfortunately, researchers have found that much of the homework assigned is not only inconsistent with validated instructional techniques but improperly implemented (Olympia, Jenson, Clark, & Sheridan, 1992).

Regularly scheduled, appropriate homework is an important intervention with children and adolescents with ID/DD. To conform to best teaching practices, homework assignments should (a) be designed to parallel the curriculum and instructional plan, (b) be adequately explained to the student, (c) allow sufficient time for mastery of a given instructional step, and (d) be graded immediately for feedback to the student. Repeated examples and opportunities for practice will also be helpful for the child with ID/DD. *Homework Partners* by Olympia, Andrews, Valum, and Jenson (1994) is intended for students in the fourth to seventh grades but can be adapted for other children. It is a useful tool to enhance homework completion by establishing a partnership between the student, the teacher, and the parent, and it also provides a means by which students can learn to become more responsible for their work and feel more confident and successful.

Academic success for ID/DD students, like normal-intelligence peers, directly impacts self-esteem and contributes to accomplishments in other areas (e.g., other tasks of daily living). It can also set the stage for greater self-advocacy as children mature and become adults. To this end, self-management techniques need to be taught to children and adolescents with ID/DD. Self-monitoring, self-evaluation, and self-reinforcement have all been shown to be effective in improving academic skill (Olympia et al., 1994); however, self-management has the unique feature of increasing independent learning. Self-management uses techniques for contingency control and involves the use of self-instruction (and self-instruction, in and of itself, has been shown to be an effective strategy to enhance learning).

Elliott and Shapiro (1990) believe that one component underlying the various methods that have been effective in improving academic performance is contingent reinforcement. It is, therefore, critical that opportunities for considerable positive reinforcement be made available. When emotional or behavioral problems are found to deter learning, however, the most immediate intervention needs to be aimed at decreasing those emotional and behavioral difficulties. This is especially true in cases where anxiety is preventing the child from participating in the learning environment and engaging with peers. In such cases, doing relaxation exercises, modeling, and using operant procedures that include shaping and positive reinforcement may benefit the child. Further, providing children with greater opportunities to take control of their life circumstances may help reduce anxiety and consequently improve learning.

SELF-DETERMINATION AND QUALITY OF LIFE

According to Kehle's RICH theory, the core features of quality of life include resources, intimacy, competence, and health (Kehle, 1999). Although individuals vary in the degree to which they have the four component traits and the degree to which they value each one, Kehle believes that in a relative sense everyone can acquire all four. Individuals, regardless of disability or ability, need to learn how to allocate resources, make friends, develop skills, and preserve physical and mental health. Explicit and repeated instruction, multiple opportunities for practice, and support will, however, be necessary to help individuals with disabilities acquire these skills and participate more actively in decisions that affect them. Too often, individuals with ID/DD have little or no choice in the decision-making process, and have too little control over what happens to them. Wehmeyer and Schwartz (1998) found that increasing control and power in decision making can significantly improve the quality of life for individuals with disabilities.

Much has been written over the past several years about self-determination, or the ability of a person to be a causal agent in the decision-making process independent of undue external influence or interference (Sands & Doll, 1996; Wehmeyer, Martin, & Sands, 1998). Self-determination basically has to do with personal autonomy and empowerment. According to Wehmeyer (1996), a number of skills are needed for self-determined behavior. These include choice making, decision making, goal setting and attainment, self-management, self-advocacy, leadership, internal locus of control, positive attributions of efficacy and outcome expectancy, self-awareness, and self-knowledge. Wehmeyer, Agran, and Hughes (1998) have provided a curriculum to teach these critical skills. The curriculum includes explicit instruction and recommendations for structured practice. Researchers, however, have found that family involvement is critical to reinforce skills that are learned and provide the reinforcement for self-determination (Field & Hoffman, 1999). Obviously, if parents are concerned that their child is too severely disabled to make certain decisions (e.g., about health care, housing, and finances), it is not likely that choice and independence will be supported. Unfortunately, far too often children and adolescents who have disabilities but are capable of being involved in making decisions and exerting some control over their lives are not given the opportunity. As Sands and Doll (1996) point out, opportunities for this need to be made available early, as does the instruction in autonomous functioning. Further, the entire process needs to begin early, and not only at transition times such as high school graduation.

IDEA requires that students be allowed to participate in the development of educational plans. IDEA also requires that students give input when transition planning is taking place and that their preferences be taken into consideration. The Individualized Education Program (IEP) meeting, however, should not be the first time students are involved in the decision-making process. As noted earlier, students with disabilities should be given instruction and offered opportunities to participate in classroom planning. Involving students with disabilities in educational planning meetings, however, requires careful preparation. Teachers may be most helpful in setting up their classrooms to provide guided opportunities for students to practice being involved in decisions. Even very young children can be taught how to make decisions that reflect their preferences and interests (e.g., what snack to eat and what task to work on), and this can take place at home, in the classroom, and out on the playground, even at a preschool level. Wehmeyer, Martin, and Sands (1998) suggest that children participate in learning activities that teach them to (a) access resources, (b) communicate their preferences, (c) set realistic and attainable goals, (d) plan and manage their time, (e) identify problems and solve them, (f) advocate for themselves certain accommodations (e.g., instructional modifications), and (g) develop an understanding of what their own styles and needs are (e.g., social and learning needs).

Developing autonomy has a direct impact on psychological well-being, and too few individuals with ID/DD have opportunities to make choices and take control. Although IDEA allows for students to participate in IEP meetings and assist in the decision-making process, in reality that rarely happens. When students do attend planning meetings, they are often silent or only peripherally involved. This is unfortunate, because researchers have found that students who are involved in the planning, decision making, and implementing of educational programs have more positive educational outcomes than those who do not participate in this way (Wehmeyer, Martin, & Sands, 1998). It is not difficult to understand that students who participate in the decision-making process are more apt to be invested and motivated to learn. Being involved teaches children and adolescents appropriate ways to express opinions and make requests, and reinforces cooperative learning. Engaging in problem solving and taking responsibility for the outcome is not only intrinsically motivating, but it often leads to greater self-esteem and improved mental health.

The following case examples are intended to illustrate the range of developmental disabilities and the problems that these individuals encounter at home and at school.

CASE EXAMPLE: ELIZABETH

Elizabeth is a 12-year-old with Asperger's disorder. Her cognitive abilities are estimated to be in the mild to borderline range of intellectual impairment. She has spent most of her education in a classroom for serious emotional disturbance but moved at the beginning of the school year to the regular sixth-grade class. Despite special education resource assistance, Elizabeth has not made the expected gains in various academic subjects. She has also regressed in certain behaviors. She has become noncompliant and has been observed to cry often. When the school psychologist met with her for an evaluation, Elizabeth told of how difficult the books were and how much homework she was expected to do. She admitted feeling hopeless and said she had even thought of killing herself. She told the school psychologist that school was no longer fun and that she does not

have enough time to work on art projects and do some of her favorite things (e.g., go to the library to scan the bookshelves). She claims that she liked school better in the preceding year and prefers going back one grade. The school psychologist asked that Elizabeth be a part of the next IEP; in fact, she insisted that Elizabeth be there and express her concerns. Elizabeth agreed and said she would like to "say one word or two words" to everyone at the meeting. The school psychologist also spoke with her teacher about the difficulty level of the work and ways to help Elizabeth get her homework done. The teacher was eager to get the help and also expressed willingness to accommodate Elizabeth's interests and help her gain more independence (and not just academic skills).

CASE EXAMPLE: JONI

Joni is a third-grade student in a classroom for students with severe intellectual disabilities. She has to ride on a bus for more than an hour to get to a special school. She gets very tired and is

often asleep by the time she arrives at school. She does not have verbal communication skills but has learned to sign some and is quite adept in making her needs known. The teacher noticed, however, that Joni has seemed agitated lately and would not participate in the communication training activities she once seemed to enjoy. At a parent–teacher conference, Joni's mother confided that her husband had been physically abusing her, and that, she and the three children had moved into a shelter. The mother did not think that Joni was aware of this abuse, given her intellectual deficits, but acknowledged that she too had noticed that Joni was screaming a lot and did not eat or sleep as much as before. The mother agreed to consult the pediatric psychiatrist who works with Joni to discuss possible changes in her medications, and also agreed that she needed to quickly find a stable home.

 CASE EXAMPLE: JOSHUA

Joshua is a 17-year-old with mild ID/DD who has always been in special education. He has been invited to IEP meetings but finds them boring because he just sits and listens to what his teachers and parents have to say about his progress in school. He does not want to attend the classes that have been set up for him because he does not feel that they will offer him what he really wants, which is the opportunity to meet girls. Joshua has poor self-esteem and experiences frequent bouts of depression. As a result, he often thinks that he would be better off dead. He does not have any plans after graduating from high school and when asked about this, has said, "I've never thought about it." According to his report, his parents have already decided that he will work in his father's auto shop. Joshua confided in the school counselor that he does not want to work in his father's business, as he has no interest in cars and does not get along that well with his father. Joshua has been thinking about dropping out of school but has not as yet because he gets an allowance for attending school. This provides him with the critical funds he needs to meet his friends at the mall after school hours. The family physician commented to Joshua that he might be depressed and might benefit from medication. Joshua claims that he does not want to take anything and is sick of people telling him what he needs.

 CASE EXAMPLE: JENNIFER

Jennifer just turned 20 and is participating in a work program at school for students with disabilities. Her parents decided that she should not graduate with her peers so that she could receive further educational opportunities. Jennifer was extremely angry when her parents made this decision and felt betrayed by them when she was not consulted. She is not happy and would like to quit the program. Her mother insists that she continue in the work program for another 2 years in order to maximize the opportunity for special educational support. Jennifer feels that she is not learning very much since she spends most of the day in a fast-food restaurant cleaning floors. She is more interested in working outside, preferably on a job that involves caring for birds. She has done well in the restaurant but wants some other experiences. She is frustrated with being forced to do jobs that in her words "get me nowhere." She has watched as two older siblings left home and got jobs that they enjoy. Both are also married and have children, something Jennifer wants but claims her parents dissuade her from doing. She told the psychologist that whenever she brings up the issue of marriage or family, her parents lecture her about how bad a parent she will be and how she does not have the intellectual skills to raise a family. Jennifer feels hopeless about her future but does not know where to turn. She has thought about getting an apartment on her own but is frightened that she will not be able to earn enough money to support herself and buy the things she needs and wants. She has always been in special education and has thought of herself as needing this type of help. What she would like, however, is to make more decisions for herself and to make plans for her personal life, including family and work.

FINAL THOUGHTS

Given the challenges that children and adolescents with ID/DD face on a daily basis, it is not surprising to find high rates of emotional disorders. It is also no surprise that so many individuals with disabilities, especially the more severe ones, have psychiatric disorders that go undiagnosed and untreated. Clearly, more effort needs to be made to identify those who suffer from psychiatric illness and to provide adequate treatment. Psychological evaluations that focus solely on intellectual and adaptive functions, however, are not likely to discriminate among children and adolescents who have associated psychiatric conditions. If assessment procedures do not change, it is likely that "diagnostic overshadowing" will continue to plague those who seek to provide services to this population. Measures that specifically address the psychological problems of children and adolescents who have ID/DD should be used. In addition, practitioners are urged to consider using functional behavior assessments to determine if particular environments are triggering and maintaining certain emotional and behavioral responses. Problems adapting to different environments where task demands vary and expectations cannot easily be predicted are often a source of high stress for individuals with ID/DD. Conducting a thorough assessment of environmental and task demands is, therefore, critical so that appropriate modifications can be made. Hopefully, information gained from common, as well as uncommon, assessment sources will help to provide a better idea of what children with disabilities need and what can be done to improve their mental health. This includes reducing the need for polydrug therapies (thus eliminating some of the unwanted side effects from multiple medications) and finding nonpharmacological treatments that address the child's emotional needs.

Practitioners also need to give more serious consideration to implementing activities that will serve to increase personal autonomy so that individuals with disabilities can participate in plans for their future and access important social, economic, and political resources. To help children and adolescents develop skills that will increase their ability for control and choice requires careful planning and considerable support from families and school. Direct instruction in self-determined behaviors needs to be provided, along with ample opportunities for practice. This process needs to begin early—that is, in elementary school, not months before graduation. Providing individuals with disabilities with opportunities to act in self-determined ways is not only "a right" of the individual, it is "*the* right" thing to do for the individual. Self-determination has been found to improve quality of life, which according to Kehle's RICH theory, includes the allocation of resources, the development of friendships, building competencies, and having physical and mental health (Kehle, 1999).

REFERENCES

Aman, M., & Singh, N. (1986). *Manual for the Aberrant Behavior Checklist.* East Aurora, NY: Slosson Educational.

American Psychiatric Association. (2000). *Diagnostic and statistical manual of mental disorders* (4th ed.). Washington, DC: Author.

Behar, L., & Stringfield, S. (1974). A behavior rating scale for the preschool child. *Developmental Psychology, 10,* 601–610.

Brody, N. (1992). *Intelligence* (2nd ed.). New York: Academic Press.

Clarke, D. (1999). Functional psychoses in people with mental retardation. In N. Bouras (Ed.), *Psychiatric and behavioral disorders in developmental disabilities and mental retardation* (pp. 175–187). Cambridge, England: Cambridge University Press.

Conners, C. K. (1990). *Conners Rating Scales Manual.* North Tonawanda, NY: Multi-Health Systems.

Deary, I., Whalley, L., Lemmon, H., Crawford, J., & Starr, J. (2000). The stability of individual differences in mental ability from childhood to old-age: Follow-up of the 1932 Scottish Mental Survey. *Intelligence, 28,* 49–55.

Demb, H., Brier, N., & Huron, R. (1989). *Adolescent Behavior Checklist.* Unpublished manuscript, Rose F. Kennedy Center, Albert Einstein College of Medicine, New York.

Durand, V., & Crimmins, D. (1988). Identifying variables maintaining self-injurious behavior. *Journal of Autism and Developmental Disabilities, 18,* 99–117.

Einfeld, S., & Tonge, B. (1993). *Manual for the Developmental Behavior Checklist.* Melbourne, Australia: Monash University.

Einfeld, S., & Tonge, B. (1996). Population prevalence of psychopathology in children and adolescents with intellectual disability: Epidemiological findings. *Journal of Intellectual Disability Research, 40*(2), 99–109.

Ellingson, S., Miltenberger, R., & Long, E. (1999). A survey of the use of functional assessment procedures in agencies serving individuals with developmental disabilities. *Behavioral Interventions, 14,* 187–198.

Elliott, S., & Shapiro, E. (1990). Intervention techniques and programs for academic performance problems. In T. B. Gutkin & C. R. Reynolds (Eds.), *The handbook of school psychology* (pp. 635–660). New York: Wiley.

Field, S., & Hoffman, A. (1999). The importance of family involvement for promoting self-determination in adolescents with autism and other developmental disabilities. *Focus on Autism and Other Developmental Disabilities, 14*(1), 36–41.

Fleisher, M. (1999). The psychopharmacology of mental illness in developmental disabilities. In N. Bouras (Ed.), *Psychiatric and behavioral disorders in developmental disabilities and mental retardation* (pp. 317–326). Cambridge, England: Cambridge University Press.

Individuals with Disabilities Education Act Amendments of 1997, 20 U.S.C. 1400 *et seq.*

Iwata, B., Dorsey, M., Slifer, K., Bauman, K., & Richman, G. (1994). Toward a functional analysis of self-injury. *Journal of Applied Behavior Analysis, 27,* 197–209.

Johnson, S., & O'Neill, R. (2001). Searching for effectiveness and efficiency in conducting functional assessments: A review and proposed process for teachers and other practitioners. *Focus on Autism and Other Developmental Disabilities, 16*(4), 205–215.

Kehle, T. J. (1999). *RICH-based interventions.* Invited address at the annual meeting of the American Psychological Association, Boston.

Lewinsohn, P. (1974). A behavior approach to depression. In R. Friedman & M. Katz (Eds.), *The psychology of depression: Contemporary theory and research.* Washington, DC: U.S. Government Printing Office.

Lord, K., Rutter, M., Goode, S., Heemsbergen, J., Jordan, H., Mawhood, J., & Schopler, D. (1989). Autism Diagnostic Observation Schedule: A standardized observation of communicative and social behavior. *Journal of Autism and Developmental Disorders, 19,* 185–212.

Marston, G., Perry, D., & Roy, A. (1997). Manifestations of depression in people with intellectual disability. *Journal of Intellectual Disability Research, 41*(6), 476–480.

Olympia, D., Andrews, D., Valum, L., & Jenson, W. R. (1994). *Homework partners.* Longmont, CO: Sopris West.

Olympia, D., Jenson, W. R., Clark, E., & Sheridan, S. (1992). Training parents to facilitate homework completion: A model for home–school collaboration. In S. L. Christenson & J. C. Conoley (Eds.), *Home–school collaboration: Building a fundamental educational resource* (pp. 309–331). Washington, DC: National Association of School Psychologists.

Olympia, D., Tuesday-Heathfield, L., Jenson, W., & Clark, E. (2002). Multifaceted functional behavior assessment for students with externalizing behavior disorders. *Psychology in the Schools, 39*(2), 1–17.

O'Neill, R., Homer, R., Albin, R., Sprague, J., Storey, K., & Newton, J. (1997). *Functional assessment and program development for problem behavior: A practical handbook* (2nd ed.). Belmont, CA: Wadsworth.

Orvaschel, H., & Puig-Antich, J. (1987). *Schedule for Affective Disorders and Schizophrenia for School-Age Children* (4th ed.). Unpublished manuscript, University of Pittsburgh, Western Psychiatric Institute.

Ramirez, S., & Kratochwill, T. (1990). Development of the Fear Survey for Children With and Without Mental Retardation. *Behavioral Assessment, 12,* 457–470.

Reich, W., & Welner, Z. (1989). *Diagnostic Interview for Children and Adolescents–Revised.* St. Louis, MO: Washington University.

Reiss, S., & Szyszko, J. (1983). Diagnostic overshadowing and professional experience with mentally retarded persons. *American Journal of Mental Deficiency, 86,* 567–574.

Repp, A., & Karsh, K. (1994). Hypothesis-based interventions for tantrum behaviors of persons with developmental disabilities in school settings. *Journal of Applied Behavior Analysis, 27,* 21–31.

Sands, D., & Doll, B. (1996). Fostering self-determination is a developmental task. *Journal of Special Education, 30*(1), 58–76.

Stavrakaki, C. (1999). Depression, anxiety and adjustment disorders in people with developmental disabilities. In N. Bouras (Ed.), *Psychiatric and behavioral disorders in developmental disabilities and mental retardation* (pp. 175–187). Cambridge, England: Cambridge University Press.

Strohmer, D., & Prout, H. (1991). *Emotional Problems Scales: Behavior Rating Scales.* Schenectady, NY: Genium.

Szymanski, L., & King, B. (1999). Practice parameters for the assessment and treatment of children, adolescents and adults with mental retardation and comorbid mental disorders. *Journal of the American Academy of Child and Adolescent Psychiatry, 38*(12), 5–31.

Tonge, B., Einfeld, S., & Krupinski, J. (1996). The use of factor analysis for ascertaining patterns of psychopathology in children with intellectual disabilities. *Journal of Intellectual Disability Research, 40*(3), 198–207.

Wehmeyer, A. (1996). Self-determination as an educational outcome: Why is it important to children, youth and adults with disabilities? In D. J. Sands & M. L. Wehmeyer (Eds.), *Self-emotional disturbance determination across the lifespan: independence and choice for people with disabilities* (pp. 17–36). Baltimore: Brookes.

Wehmeyer, M., Agran, M., & Hughes, C. (1998). *Teaching self-determination to students with disabilities: Basic skills for successful transition.* Baltimore: Brookes.

Wehmeyer, M., Martin, J., & Sands, D. (1998). Self-determination for children and youth with developmental disabilities. In A. Hilton & R. Ringlaben (Eds.), *Best and promising practices in developmental disabilities* (pp. 191–204). Austin, TX: PRO-ED.

Wehmeyer, M., & Schwartz, M. (1998). The relationship between self-determination and quality of life for adults with mental retardation. *Education and Training in Mental Retardation and Developmental Disabilities, 33*(1), 3–12.

Wells, D., & Forehand, R. (1985). Conduct and oppositional disorders. In P. H. Bornstein & A. E. Kazdin (Eds.), *Handbook of clinical behavior therapy with children* (pp. 218–265). Homewood, IL: Dorsey Press.

CHAPTER 11

Autism

Marcia D. Smith and Leslie Philippen

LEARNING GOALS

Upon completion of this chapter, the reader will be able to

- describe the characteristics of autism and Asperger's disorder
- list possible genetic, prenatal, and postnatal factors thought to be associated with autism
- describe four types of supports that people with autism might need
- list typical functions that challenging behaviors serve for people with autism
- describe eight types of strategies that can be used singly or in combination to help overcome the challenging behaviors that can be associated with autism

The authors would like to thank Richard W. Crowley, PhD, for his review of the literature on incidence and causes for inclusion in this chapter.

utism is a severe, pervasive developmental disorder that affects communication, social relatedness, and the ability to enjoy the wide range of interests and activities that life has to offer. Autism has implications for all aspects of development and results in the need for supports at home, school, and work to enable the individual to reach maximum potential.

Autism is a controversial term, and diagnosis of the disorder has not been straightforward (Olley & Gutentag, 1999). A variety of definitions have emerged since Kanner (1943) first identified the syndrome. The practitioner who is making a diagnostic determination of autism generally relies on the *Diagnostic and Statistical Manual of Mental Disorders–Fourth Edition* (*DSM–IV*; American Psychiatric Association [APA], 1994). This chapter will review the prominent characteristics, address support and habilitation issues, and provide case studies that demonstrate how three people with autism were helped to overcome some of the more debilitating aspects of the disorder.

INCIDENCE

The number of people with autism varies depending on the diagnostic criteria used. The early epidemiological studies, which applied less inclusive criteria, found that the prevalence of autistic disorder in England (Lotter, 1966) and in the United States (Burd, Fisher, & Kerbeshian, 1987) was approximately 4 cases per 10,000 children. This is similar to the findings of the *DSM–IV* (APA, 1994), which places the rate at 2 to 5 cases per 10,000.

In recent years, however, some researchers have suggested that autism is much more prevalent than previously reported. Recent studies have reported the prevalence for autistic disorder to range from approximately 17 to 40 cases per 10,000 children (Baird et al., 2000; Bertrand et al., 2001; Chakrabarti & Fombonne, 2001). There is considerable debate over whether the higher incidence of autism reported in these recent studies is due to methodological factors between studies or to an actual increase in the number of people with the disorder (Wakefield, 1999). In a review of 23 epidemiological studies conducted between 1966 and 1998, Fombonne (1999) found that higher incidence estimates in most studies could be explained largely by accounting for the use of more accurate diagnostic methods, recent immigration patterns, the recent trend to include persons with both autism and intellectual disabilities, and the identification of increasingly younger children.

CAUSES

Autism, historically thought to result from poor parenting, has long been recognized as a disorder with a physiological basis. Although the exact nature of the physical dysfunction is not known, it is now considered to be a neurological disorder thought to result from abnormalities in the brain structures responsible for receiving information from the senses and processing language (Piven, 2001).

A number of studies comparing identical twins, which have exactly the same genetic makeup, to fraternal twins, who develop from two separate eggs, have firmly established that genetics is a major factor in the development of autism. For example, Folstein and Rutter (1977) observed that in cases where one identical twin suffered from autistic disorder, there was a 60% probability that the other twin would also suffer from the disorder and a greater than 90% chance that the twin would have some of the less severe symptoms within the autistic spectrum. Constantino and Todd (2000) found that in families with autism, the family members without autism were more likely to display some autistic traits, such as impaired social skills, delayed language acquisition, and communication deficiencies.

Although these studies provide compelling evidence implicating a genetic component in the development of autism, no specific gene or genes have been identified (Spence, 2001). Several recent studies suggest that children with autism inherit between 3 and 10 abnormal genes that interfere with normal neurological development (Pickles et al., 1995).

Less than 10% of the cases of autism are thought to be caused by known medical conditions, although none of these conditions occur only with autism (Fombonne, Du Mazaubrun, Cans, & Grandjean, 1997). These include prenatal factors such as an intrauterine infection with rubella and a genetic condition causing brain growths known as tuberous sclerosis (Fombonne et al., 1997). Postnatal factors such as encephalitis caused by herpes simplex virus (Gillberg, 1991) and untreated phenylketonuria are also associated with autism (Miladi, Larnaout, Kaabachi, Helayem, & Ben Hamida, 1992).

CHARACTERISTICS

Impairment in Social Relationships

Autism is characterized by an impaired ability to participate in social relationships (Ritvo, 1983). People with autism often do not have the skills necessary to initiate social relationships or maintain close, reciprocal relationships. When people with autism develop friendships, they are generally with people who are more socially sophisticated than they are, and who provide the leadership in the friendship. For example, Leonard is a young man with autism who has been befriended by Michael, a young man with a learning disability. Michael's social skills are far better than Leonard's, and consequently he takes the primary responsibility for keeping the friendship going.

Individuals with autism often appear incapable of taking on another person's perspective. They may lack empathy for the viewpoint and feelings of others. Sam, a young man with autism, provides a good example of this problem. His maternal grandfather, with whom he was very close, died. About 2 weeks after the funeral, Sam asked his mother when they would be getting a replacement for Grandpa.

Impairment in Communication

Autism can be devastating to language development. Some people with autism develop no spoken language. Others have speech, but it is primarily echolalic and repetitive or is limited to two- and three-word phrases. People with autism who have language might have peculiarities in grammar, volume, rate, rhythm, pitch, or intonation.

Speech might also be devoid of meaningful understanding. This problem is often dramatically evident during periods of behavioral crisis. A person with autism might engage in a tantrum, all the while repeating, "I need to behave like a polite young man." Or a person with autism might strike out while saying "I shouldn't hit people." One young man, upon being caught picking his nose, said, "I didn't do what I just did."

Nonverbal communication can also be affected. Eye contact might be absent or abnormal if present. Facial expressions might lack social convention. For example, an individual with autism might not smile upon initial social contact, or might rarely smile under any circumstances, or might smile perpetually, even under adverse conditions.

Perseveration on Interests and Dependence on Routine

People with autism often have an unusually narrow range of interests. An individual might remain absorbed with one or two topics, such as geography, music, sports, calendars, or modes of transportation, especially trains. The individual might spend inordinate amounts of time researching the topic, talking about the topic, and performing calculations relevant to the topic. The same interest might be maintained over years. Nonverbal, or even verbal individuals might engage repetitively in stereotyped body movements, such as hand flicking, spinning, or rocking.

Related to having narrow ranges of interest, people with autism are often highly dependent on set routines. An individual with autism might insist on certain bedtime routines, mealtime routines, exiting routines, or greeting routines.

Abnormal Responses to Sensory Stimulation

Autism can be associated with disturbances in reactions to sensory stimulation. There might be a fascination with certain types of stimulation, such as spinning objects—round objects and circular motions are often appealing. Many of the repetitive behaviors associated with autism, such as rocking, finger flicking, and twirling, serve the purpose of providing sensory stimulation, at least in part.

Challenging Behaviors

Challenging, sometimes destructive behaviors can be associated with autism. These behaviors include tantrums (accompanied by jumping, arm flapping, and screaming), aggression, self-injury, and property destruction. Behavior problems associated with autism are often secondary to some of the other characteristics discussed above. For example, deficits in communication often lead a person with autism to engage in undesirable behavior problems as a form of communication (Hwang & Hughes, 2000). Deficits in social interaction skills certainly contribute to some of the severe behavior problems associated with autism. Lacking more conventional ways of engaging in social interaction, individuals with autism might come to rely on more disturbing methods.

Special Skills

Some individuals with autism have very specific, amazing skills, often referred to as savant skills. People with autism have demonstrated superior skills in such areas as mathematical calculations, calculations involving the calendar, rote memory, meteorology, navigation, geography, and music. In young children, hyperlexia, the enhanced ability to decode or read words, might be present. These children often can read words much better than expected for their age; however, they often read without comprehension.

Intellectual Disability

Approximately three quarters of people with autism also have some degree of intellectual disability. The remainder of the autistic population has from average to above average intelligence.

ASPERGER'S DISORDER

In 1994, the *DSM–IV* (APA, 1994) introduced Asperger's disorder as a diagnostic subcategory of pervasive developmental disorders. A neurological disorder that falls within the autism spectrum, it manifests in impaired social and motor skills and narrow areas of interest and activities (Volkmar, Klin, Schultz, Rubin, & Bronen, 2000). Individuals with Asperger's disorder are of average or above average intelligence (Connor, 1999). There is less severe impairment of language skills, although comprehension of abstract concepts is deficient.

PROVIDING SUPPORTS

Individuals with autism face additional challenges to adjustment that persons with intellectual disability alone do not face. Faulty social skills, poor judgment, and difficulty with abstract thinking create adjustment issues that supersede those created by intellectual disability. Herman provides a good example. Herman's IQ was 65, which places him in the mild range of intellectual disability. He was referred to a mental health clinic because he was often picked up by the police due to a behavior of entering cars and falling asleep in them. He also would enter office buildings and take candy from people's desks. Individuals with mild intellectual disability typically have good enough judgment to avoid such behavior. However, Herman had autism, and his favorite activity was "taking long walks." He would go on long walks, become tired, and enter an unlocked car for a rest. Similarly, he would become hungry and enter an office building in search of candy. The poor judgment associated with his autism magnified the deficits associated with intellectual disability.

The challenges associated with autism make proper supports critical for the individual to succeed at home, at school, and in the workplace (Gillham, Carter, Volkmar, & Sparrow, 2000). In addition to typical supports that persons with intellectual disability might need, there are supports that can be critical to the success of persons with autism.

Counseling

People with autism can sometimes benefit from counseling. Benefits can be realized by individuals with autism who have some spoken language (Parker, 1996). It is not necessary for language to be fluent. However, the individual should have some verbal language skills in order to be considered for counseling. Counseling strategies that focus on communication skills, social skills, coping skills, and self-management can be effective with persons with autism (Hwang & Hughes, 2000; Thiemann & Goldstein, 2001).

Psychiatry

Having autism does not preclude having psychiatric symptoms that would benefit from medication (Posey & McDougle, 2000; Tsai, 1999). Use of drug therapy, in conjunction with a behavior plan, can be effective in helping reduce destructive behavior, agitation, and anxiety and improving impulse control (Kerbeshian, Burd, & Avery, 2001; King, 2000; Luiselli, Blew, Keane, Thibadeau, & Holzman, 2000).

Medical Services

Providing medical services to people with autism can require patience and expertise that go beyond standard patient care. At times, the medical practitioner's attitude toward autism can hamper the diagnosis of serious illnesses. Arnold is a sad example. Arnold was a middle-aged man with autism. He began to have difficulty walking. Because he was nonverbal, he could not describe other symptoms that might have been occurring concurrently. A physician performed knee surgery, but the problem was not solved. As Arnold's condition deteriorated, and he began to lose muscular functioning of his upper body as well as his lower body, a physician declared that he was not moving because he chose not to move. It was not until 3 weeks before his death that he was finally diagnosed with amyotrophic lateral sclerosis (Lou Gehrig's disease), a fatal neurological condition characterized by a gradual deterioration in the ability to use one's muscles.

Supervision and Job Coaching

The need for supervision of children with autism, like children without autism, is assumed. But growing up is no cure for autism, so as the child with autism becomes an adult with autism, supervision might need to continue (Moxon & Gates, 2001).

Adults with autism can work (Smith, Belcher, & Juhrs, 1995), but in many cases they cannot go to work by themselves. A person with autism might work in a factory, a stockroom, or any of a variety of places. A job coach accompanies the worker to work. At work, the job coach is responsible for teaching the job to the worker with autism. The job coach can also implement strategies recommended by other support personnel, such as a behavioral intervention plan to deal with challenging behavior at work.

A person with autism who does not have serious behavior problems and who has some verbal language and problem-solving skills might be able to work independently, semi-independently, or with natural supports. However, for an individual with severe autism, severe intellectual disability, no verbal skills, and a history of behavior problems, long-term coaching is most likely a necessity.

MEETING BEHAVIORAL CHALLENGES OF AUTISM

Autism can be associated with challenging behaviors that limit success at school and work (Koegel, Koegel, Frea, & Fredeen, 2001). Adults with autism often fail to maintain adult vocational placements, and some still are sent to state institutions for the mentally ill because of behaviors that are too challenging for caregivers. Management of these behavioral challenges requires a consistent approach to problem solving (Eaves & Ho, 1996). This process includes assessing the problem, the individual, and the environment; doing a functional assessment of the behavior; setting goals; and choosing strategies based on the functional assessment (Van Bourgondien & Reichle, 2001).

Behavioral Assessment

Prior to choosing intervention strategies, data collection strategies must be selected. Data should then be kept for a time-limited period in order to collect the necessary information on frequency, severity, and function. Often, interviews with caregivers such as parents and teachers can provide an estimate of baseline levels, so that planning can proceed with haste (Bibby, Eikeseth, Martin, Mudford, & Reeves, 2001).

The functional assessment is a determination of what function the behavior serves for the individual. Individuals with autism who do not have spoken language often use challenging behaviors to serve the following functions: to obtain attention, food, drink, a change of activity, or a change of scene; to avoid a task; or to interact socially. Similarly, individuals with language skills often use undesirable behaviors as a way of establishing social interaction; avoiding tasks; obtaining attention, assistance, or a preferred activity; or changing the activity.

The focus of the functional assessment is often a behavioral excess, or a misbehavior, such as aggression. However, autism often involves behavioral deficiencies—that is, certain desirable behaviors do not occur. An adult with autism, although verbal, may neglect to say hello when a visitor enters. Or an individual who is fully capable of doing a job or task may do it quickly and inadequately or not at all.

Cases in which a desirable behavior is missing also require a functional assessment. For example, a worker with autism might have a job hanging pants in a stockroom. Although the individual gets a paycheck, the paycheck is not motivational because he cannot count and does not understand money. The functional assessment might reveal that in fact pants-hanging serves no good function for the individual. An intervention plan, then, would have to provide a function for the desired behavior.

Selecting Strategies

Once the functional assessment is done, the strategies that the plan will comprise can be selected (Rosenwasser & Axelrod, 2001). An important consideration is that all functions must in some way be addressed by one or more strategies, and each strategy chosen should have some relationship to an identified function. The treatment plan will seek to do one or more of the following:

• *Eliminate antecedents and setting events that evoke misbehavior.* Sometimes it is possible to simply alter antecedents or setting events. For example, if long periods of waiting are an antecedent to aggression, it might be possible to eliminate long waits.

• *Teach the individual a better way to achieve the function.* The individual must learn new ways to fulfill the function of the undesired behavior. For example, an individual who throws tantrums when in need of assistance must learn how to ask for help. Goals can be developed that will specify target behaviors to help the individuals meet their needs in more acceptable ways. Once a functional assessment is done, the original behavior goals might be expanded (McClannahan, MacDuff, & Krantz, 2002). For example, "jumping and screaming" might have been pinpointed, and a more positive set of goals, such as "keeps feet on floor and works quietly," might have been set. The functional assessment might reveal that jumping and screaming occur when the individual is having difficulty with a task. It would then be necessary to teach a new way to ask for assistance. A new goal would be added: "When having difficulty with a task, John will ask for assistance."

- *Give the person more frequent access to what he or she desires so that the undesirable behavior will not be necessary.* For example, an individual who becomes aggressive when denied food might significantly reduce aggressive episodes if put on a liberal snack schedule or allowed free access to food (Adelinis, Piazza, & Goh, 2001).
- *Provide alternate sensory stimuli in cases of self-stimulation and self-injury.* For example, a person who engages in skin picking might benefit from frequent access to lotions to rub into the skin. Lotions would provide an alternate and more acceptable stimulation. A variety of alternate sources of tactile, olfactory, and auditory stimulation can be provided to replace self-stimulation or self-injury (Healey, Ahearn, Graff, & Libby, 2001).
- *Provide motivation so that desired behaviors are more likely to occur.* In cases of task avoidance, provide incentives for the individual to cooperate. Individuals who often throw tantrums or otherwise misbehave in order to avoid tasks may need schedules of positive reinforcement as motivation to engage in the task. Motivation might also be necessary to encourage meeting social goals (Weiss & Harris, 2001).
- *Remove any possible reinforcers that may be maintaining the problem behavior.*
- *Specify how the misbehavior should be handled so as to prevent injury and not inadvertently encourage the behavior.*
- *Provide choices when possible.* Individuals who are given choices in their schedules may be more likely to cooperate. They can help choose activities, chores, leisure events, and reinforcers. Nonverbal individuals can be given choices by being shown one or more pictures.

Combining Strategies

An intervention plan might include one or more treatment strategies. In cases in which the target behavior is not critical to safety or job success, it may be best to choose strategies sparingly and add more elements only if necessary.

For example, an individual who has trouble sharing his work space might only need social skills training (Weiss & Harris, 2001). If that is not sufficient, reinforcement procedures can be added later. However, for behaviors that have serious or dangerous effects, such as aggression or self-injury, or are job threatening, such as screaming, it might be advisable to have a variety of strategies aimed at preventing the dangerous behavior, and promoting and rewarding acceptable alternatives.

Several case studies are provided to illustrate the transition from school to adult services for students with autism. Each case study includes a description of the individual, intervention strategies to achieve behavioral adjustment, and transition strategies to help the individuals move from school to work.

CASE EXAMPLE: LINDA

Linda is a 23-year-old woman with autism and intellectual disability. Her intelligence measures in the mild range of intellectual disability. Her adaptive skills are also consistent with mild intellectual disability. She can perform grooming and hygiene tasks independently and can do household tasks such as washing dishes, laundry, and vacuuming. She needs assistance with meal planning, money management, and arranging for her health care such as arranging and attending doctors' appointments.

Linda has severe deficits in social skills, which are explained by her autism, not her intellectual disability. She greets others, but her greetings are often stilted and appear rote. She has no close friends. She also has a problem with property destruction. When she is upset or frustrated, she is likely to rip her clothing or throw a small object such as a radio, a dish, or a hair dryer.

Linda had been in a special school program for students with autism. During the last 2 years of her schooling, she was rotated through several jobs, always with the assistance of a job coach. Upon aging out of the school system at 22 years of age, she transitioned into a residential and vocational program for adults with autism. She lives in a condominium in a suburb of a large city with one other woman with autism. There is 24-hour supervision by staff, although Linda has independent time both in her home and in the community. She can go out independently for up to 5 hours per day. She uses public transportation, including buses and the subway, once she has been taught the route.

Linda is served by a supported employment program that she entered upon graduation from school. With the help of a job development specialist, she found employment at a manufacturing firm, where she assembles electronic components. She works under the supervision of a job coach. She is easily frustrated at work and has sporadic outbursts of yelling and throwing her tools and work materials.

In order to encourage adjustment to her new job, a plan was developed to manage property destruction and yelling. A functional assessment was done to determine the functions of yelling and property destruction. Review of data and interviews with her job coach revealed several antecedents to yelling and property destruction. It appeared that Linda was most likely to throw something or yell when she was having difficulty with a task. For example, if one of the machines she needed to use became jammed, this would lead to yelling. If she was learning a new task and

had trouble with it, she might throw the tool she was using. An additional antecedent was being corrected or criticized. If she made an error in her work and her job coach or supervisor pointed it out, she was likely to yell or throw her materials. The functional assessment revealed that certain consequences might have been inadvertently encouraging her problematic behaviors. Yelling and property destruction were often followed by her job coach asking her what was wrong, helping her with the problem, offering to take her for a walk, then immediately praising her when she calmed down. It appeared, then, that the functions of her problematic behavior included obtaining help and being allowed to escape from the situation (going for a walk). The praise she received also was likely reinforcing the problem behaviors, since it was given so close in time to the actual outburst.

A plan was developed, based on the functional assessment, to promote more cooperative behavior at work and to help Linda meet her needs in ways other than property destruction and yelling. Social skills training was done to teach her to ask for help when she was having a problem. Sample problems and solutions were rehearsed daily for several weeks, so that she could practice asking for help under a variety of conditions, such as her tool breaking, the machine jamming, or having difficulty learning a new task. She was also given social skills training to learn how to respond to criticism from a supervisor. On a daily basis, she and the job coach practiced responding with, "Okay, I'll take care of it," when given a correction. Also, a reinforcement schedule was established, with a self-management component. Linda was taught to put a check on a calendar at the end of each workday if she handled her materials properly (i.e., no throwing of tools or materials) and maintained an acceptable voice volume (i.e., no yelling). If she received checks for all 5 days of the week, she was taken out to lunch. Finally, the job coach was instructed to remain alert to Linda's having problems or difficulty with her tasks and to provide assistance as soon as possible, to eliminate the need for her to act out in order to get help.

Property destruction and yelling were significantly reduced within the year. Because Linda's behavior became so acceptable at work, and her actual work performance was good, it became possible to phase out the full-time job coach. Coworkers were able to provide assistance when necessary, and a job coach would drop by several times per week to ensure continued good adjustment to work.

 ## CASE EXAMPLE: RAY

Ray is an 18-year-old man, severely disabled by autism, with an IQ that measures in the severe range of intellectual disability. His adaptive skills are consistent with moderate intellectual disability. He needs some assistance with hygiene, grooming, and home-care tasks. He cannot manage money or travel independently. His verbal expression is limited to two- and three-word phrases.

Ray has a history of challenging behavior, most notably severe self-injury, including head banging. In his previous placement, he detached his retina due to head banging. He also fractured his knuckle from banging it.

Ray is enrolled in a community-based residential school for students with autism. He lives in a group home with three other students and residential counselors who assist with the activities of daily living and help keep him safe from his self-injury. He attends a school program during the day. Part of his school program involves job experiences under the supervision of his teaching assistant or teacher.

A treatment plan has been developed to reduce self-injury. Baseline data indicated that self-injury occurred in 95% of the 5-minute time blocks throughout the day—that is, thousands of times. A functional assessment was done based on record review, observations, and interviews with staff. This assessment revealed that self-injurious behavior was usually accompanied by verbal requests for food, which suggested that self-injury served the purpose of obtaining food. Presentation of tasks was an antecedent to self-injury, suggesting that self-injury also served the purpose of escape.

Because some incidents of self-injury were severe, it was often necessary for staff to physically prevent Ray from causing injury to himself. Thus, the possibility was presented that this physical contact was serving as a positive reinforcer. In addition to staff physically preventing harm, consequences to self-injury included staff talking to him, trying to calm him down, telling him to stop, giving him a more preferred activity, and promising him food if he stopped. Review of these consequences provided more evidence that the functions of the self-injury were to obtain food, physical contact, staff attention, and preferred activities, as well as allowing him to escape from less preferred activities.

The intervention plan contained the following elements:

• *Variable interval schedule.* Because the frequency of aggressive behavior was so high—that is, it occurred almost continuously—a variable interval (VI) 3-minute schedule was implemented. Staff were to provide a positive reinforcer approximately every 3 minutes (plus or minus 1 minute) to Ray if he exhibited any of the following target behaviors: hands in lap, hands on work materials, hands on leisure material, hands by side. After his behavior stabilized, at the end of the year, the VI 3-minute schedule was thinned to VI 15 minutes. Positive reinforcers offered were food snacks and physical proximity of staff, including allowing Ray to put his arm around his instructor. Foods that were used were his favorites, such as ice cream, cookies, candy, chicken, popsicles, chips, and pretzels. They were varied to prevent satiation. Also, Ray enjoyed cold contacts, and he was allowed to use an ice pack as a reinforcer.

• *Free access to food on request.* Any time Ray asked for food, staff were instructed to immediately provide him with what he requested. The rationale for this liberal policy was that he would learn that verbal requests worked, and head banging was not necessary.

• *Presentation of tasks.* Short tasks were presented in a one-to-one instructional format. If

Ray worked on the task or activity, positive reinforcement was presented. If he chose not to work on the activity, no attempt was made to force him.

• *Handling of self-abuse.* If Ray became self-abusive, he was verbally redirected to the task at hand. If self-abuse continued, presenting risk of injury, he was physically prevented from harming himself or others. He was redirected to the ongoing activity as soon as he was willing to respond to verbal instructions.

Within 2 months, the percentage of the 5-minute time blocks in which Ray engaged in self-injury decreased from 95% to 10%. After approximately 1 year, the frequency decreased to about 1% to 2%.

Ray was transitioned into a part-time job. He works in a restaurant from 9:00 A.M. to 11:30 A.M. prior to the arrival of the customers. His job is to roll silverware into napkins. He is accompanied to work by a job coach, who assists him with his tasks and implements his intervention plan. He has developed a special relationship with the owner of the restaurant. When he arrives, she offers him a soda, which he keeps with him and drinks throughout the morning as he does his tasks. He is also allowed to keep crackers and occasionally a brownie (again provided by the employer) and to help himself throughout the morning. These treats give Ray control of his access to food and also make the job more enjoyable for him.

CASE EXAMPLE: LEONARD

Leonard is a 25-year-old man with borderline intellectual disability. He also has autism. He had lifelong deficits in the quality of his social relatedness and social interactions. He seems to enjoy social contact and attention, but his interest is at an immature level. Although he can enjoy the company of others, he has not formed friendships or relationships of a reciprocal nature.

Leonard also has impairments in communication. Although he is capable of fluent language, he has deficits in speech production and communication. His speech rhythm is slightly abnormal, a language characteristic that can accompany autism.

Leonard also shows marked impairment in the use of nonverbal behaviors, such as facial expression. He maintains a fixed smile, which appears appropriate at first greeting but does not vary; his facial expressions do not change with the topic of conversation. Even when discussing topics that would presumably be upsetting to him, he maintains the same smiling expression.

Leonard's use and understanding of language is extremely concrete. He can give dates and times of events and activities, but if asked to give explanations or to describe abstract concepts, he falters and resorts to rote recital of what he does know, concrete facts.

Leonard demonstrates severe restrictions in his interests and activities. He has several areas of intense interest: geography (maps), music, and sports. His approach to all three of these interests is characterized by memorizing trivia. He keeps a journal in which he very carefully lists sports scores. He has memorized a great deal of music trivia, including names of artists, dates of release of records, and rankings on the charts. His interest in maps is also intense; he draws detailed maps of cities to which he has traveled or in which he is interested.

Leonard also has an inflexible adherence to routine. He becomes easily upset when his routine is broken; in both written and verbal communications, he has expressed distress that the time he showers has varied.

Leonard exhibits severe aggression, including grabbing, biting, and attempting to choke others. Although he has periods of good adjustment, they are invariably interrupted with severe, violent outbursts.

Leonard spent his adolescence in a residential school for students with intellectual disability. After aging out of the school program, he was tried in several community-based vocational training programs. He was discharged from all of them due to aggression. Several times he was taken to the emergency room of the local hospital because of his violent outbursts. Within a year of leaving school, he was placed in a state mental institution. Due to outbursts of aggression in that setting, including hitting his psychiatrist, he was placed in arm and leg restraints. He remained in that setting for 4 years, often in the arm and leg restraints, until being discharged to a community-based residential and supported employment program for adults with autism.

Providing Leonard with proper supports was critical if his outplacement to the community was to succeed. Due to the nature of his aggression, he was funded with a 1:1 supervision ratio. His past aggression had been violent and against passersby, so close supervision seemed critical to avoid the kinds of incidents that resulted in hospitalization in the past. An intervention plan was developed that provided systematic daily rewards for several behavioral goals, including keeping his hands and feet to himself, remaining with staff, and doing assigned tasks. He was provided with daily and weekly rewards for compliance. He was given choices in his scheduling of tasks and was given wide latitude in the choice of leisure and recreational activities.

Leonard was placed at a job in a store restocking shelves. After about 6 months in his community placement, he had a series of unfortunate incidents, including smashing property, attacking female passersby in a store, and writing threatening letters. A psychiatric consult was sought, and psychotropic medications, which aimed at improving clarity of thought and impulse control and decreasing agitation, were prescribed.

Antecedent conditions were examined and addressed in his revised plan. The revised plan was implemented. He was placed in another job that has less contact with the public. It is a restocking job but in a warehouse, so that customers from the outside are at a minimum. This decreases the likelihood of further assaults against passersby. He remains on a 1:1 supervision ratio. This level of support is necessary because of the severity of his behavioral outbursts, not due to problems with learning or performing his activities of daily living.

Leonard has been out of the hospital for 2 years at this point. He enjoys his job and a variety of community activities, including going to basketball games, shopping malls, restaurants, and the movies. He continues to have sporadic outbreaks of aggression, but he is well managed by his staff and there has been no need for reinstitutionalization.

FINAL THOUGHTS

Although autism remains a debilitating and lifelong condition, there have been vast improvements in understanding its patterns and course. With the evolution of behavioral and pharmacological treatments, many people have graduated from the dark halls of institutions to full integration in their communities, including home, school, and work.

REFERENCES

Adelinis, J. D., Piazza, C. C., & Goh, H. (2001). Treatment of multiply controlled destructive behavior with food reinforcement. *Journal of Applied Behavior Analysis, 34*(4), 97–100.

American Psychiatric Association. (1994). *Diagnostic and statistical manual of mental disorders* (4th ed.). Washington, DC: Author.

Baird, G., Charman, T., Baron-Cohen, S., Cox, A., Swettenham, J., Wheelwright, S., & Drew, A. (2000). A screening instrument for autism at 18 months of age: A 6-year follow-up study. *Journal of the American Academy of Child and Adolescent Psychiatry, 39,* 694–702.

Bertrand, J., Mars, A., Boyle, C., Bove, F., Yeargin-Allsopp, M., & Decoufle, P. (2001). Prevalence of autism in a United States population: The Brick Township investigation, New Jersey. *Pediatrics, 108,* 1155–1161.

Bibby, P., Eikeseth, S., Martin, N. T., Mudford, O. C., & Reeves, D. (2001). Progress and outcomes for children with autism receiving parent-managed intensive interventions. *Research in Developmental Disabilities, 22*(6), 425–447.

Burd, L., Fisher, W., & Kerbeshian, J. (1987). A prevalence study of pervasive developmental disorders in North Dakota. *Journal of the American Academy of Child and Adolescent Psychiatry, 26,* 700–703.

Chakrabarti, S., & Fombonne, E. (2001). Pervasive developmental disorders in preschool children. *Journal of the American Medical Association, 285,* 3093–3099.

Connor, M. (1999). Children on the autism spectrum: Guidelines for mainstream practice. *Support for Learning, 14*(2), 80–86.

Constantino, J. N., & Todd, R. D. (2000). Genetic structure of reciprocal social behavior. *American Journal of Psychiatry, 157,* 2043–2045.

Eaves, L. C., & Ho, H. H. (1996). Brief report: Stability and change in cognitive and behavioral characteristics of autism through childhood. *Journal of Autism and Developmental Disorders, 26*(5), 557–569.

Folstein, S., & Rutter, M. (1977). Genetic influences and infantile autism. *Nature, 265,* 726–728.

Fombonne, E. (1999). The epidemiology of autism: A review. *Psychological Medicine, 29*(4), 769–786.

Fombonne, E., Du Mazaubrun, C., Cans, C., & Grandjean, H. (1997). Autism and associated medical disorders in a French epidemiological survey. *Journal of the American Academy of Child and Adolescent Psychiatry, 36,* 1561–1569.

Gillberg, I. C. (1991). Autistic syndrome with onset at age 31 years: Herpes encephalitis as a possible model for childhood autism. *Developmental Medicine and Child Neurology, 33,* 920–924.

Gillham, J. E., Carter, A. S., Volkmar, F. R., & Sparrow, S. S. (2000). Toward a developmental operational definition of autism. *Journal of Autism and Developmental Disorders, 30*(4), 269–278.

Healey, J. J., Ahearn, W. H., Graff, R. B., & Libby, M. E. (2001). Extended analysis and treatment of self-injurious behavior. *Behavioral Interventions, 16*(3), 181–195.

Hwang, B., & Hughes, C. (2000). The effects of social interactive training on early social communicative skills of children with autism. *Journal of Autism and Developmental Disorders, 30*(5), 331–343.

Kanner, L. (1943). Autistic disturbances of affective content. *Journal of Pediatrics, 25,* 211-217.

Kerbeshian, J., Burd, L., & Avery, K. (2001). Pharmacology of autism. *Journal of Developmental and Physical Disabilities, 13*(3), 199–228.

King, B. H. (2000). Pharmacological treatment of mood disturbances, aggression and self-injury in persons with pervasive developmental disorders. *Journal of Autism and Developmental Disorders, 30*(5), 439–445.

Koegel, L. K., Koegel, R. L., Frea, W. D., & Fredeen, R. M. (2001). Identifying early intervention targets for children with autism in inclusive school settings. *Behavior Modification, 25*(5), 745–761.

Lotter, V. (1966). Epidemiology of autistic conditions in young children, I: Prevalence. *Social Psychiatry, 1,* 124–137.

Luiselli, J. K., Blew, P., Keane, J., Thibadeau, S., & Holzman, T. (2000). Pharmacotherapy for severe aggression in a child with autism: "Open-label" evaluation of multiple medications on response frequency and intensity of behavioral intervention. *Journal of Behavior Therapy and Experimental Psychiatry, 31*(3–4), 219–230.

McClannahan, L. E., MacDuff, G. S., & Krantz, P. J. (2002). Behavior analysis and intervention for adults with autism. *Behavior Modification, 26*(1), 9–26.

Miladi, N., Larnaout, A., Kaabachi, N., Helayem, M., & Ben Hamida, M. (1992). Phenylketonuria: An underlying etiology of autistic syndrome. A case report. *Journal of Child Neurology, 7,* 22–23.

Moxon, L., & Gates, D. (2001). Children with autism: Supporting the transition to adulthood. *Educational and Child Psychology, 18*(2), 28–40.

Olley, J. G., & Gutentag, S. S. (1999). Autism: Historical overview, definition, and characteristics. In D. B. Zager (Ed.), *Autism: Identification, education and treatment* (2nd ed., pp. 3–22). Mahwah, NJ: Erlbaum.

Parker, R. (1996). Incorporating speech–language therapy into an applied behavior analysis program. In C. Maurice & G. Green (Eds.), *Behavioral intervention for young children with autism: A manual for parents and professionals* (pp. 297–306). Austin, TX: PRO-ED.

Pickles, A., Bolton, P., Macdonald, H., Bailey, A., Le Couteur, A., Sim, C. H., & Rutter, M. (1995). Latent-class analysis of recurrence risks for complex phenotypes with selection and measurement error: A twin and family history study of autism. *American Journal of Human Genetics, 57,* 717–726.

Piven, J. (2001). The broad autism phenotype: A complementary strategy for molecular genetic studies of autism. *American Journal of Medical Genetics, 105,* 34–35.

Posey, D. J., & McDougle, C. J. (2000). The pharmacotherapy of target symptoms associated with autistic disorder and other pervasive developmental disorders. *Harvard Review of Psychiatry, 8*(2), 45–63.

Ritvo, E. R. (1983). The syndrome of autism: A medical model. *Integrative Psychiatry, 1*(4), 103–109.

Rosenwasser, B., & Axelrod, S. (2001). The contribution of applied behavior analysis to the education of people with autism. *Behavior Modification, 25*(5), 671–677.

Smith, M. D., Belcher, R., & Juhrs, P. (1995). *A guide to successful employment for individuals with autism.* Baltimore: Brookes.

Spence, M. A. (2001). The genetics of autism. *Current Opinion in Pediatrics, 13,* 561–565.

Thiemann, K. S., & Goldstein, H. (2001). Social stories, written text cues, and video feedback: Effects on social communication of children with autism. *Journal of Applied Behavior Analysis, 34*(4), 425–446.

Tsai, L. Y. (1999). Psychopharmacology in autism. *Psychosomatic Medicine, 61*(5), 651–665.

Van Bourgondien, M. E., & Reichle, N. C. (2001). Evaluating treatment for adolescents and adults with autism in residential settings. In E. Schopler & N. Yirmiya (Eds.), *The research basis for autism intervention* (pp. 187–198). New York: Kluwer Academic/Plenum Publishers.

Volkmar, F. R., Klin, A., Schultz, R. T., Rubin, E., & Bronen, R. (2000). Asperger's disorder. *American Journal of Psychiatry, 157*(2), 262–267.

Wakefield, A. J. (1999). MMR vaccination and autism. *Lance, 354,* 949–950.

Weiss, M. J., & Harris, S. L. (2001). Teaching social skills to people with autism. *Behavior Modification, 25*(5), 785–802.

CHAPTER 12

Learning Disabilities

William N. Bender and Cecil Fore III

LEARNING GOALS

Upon completion of this chapter, the reader will be able to

- discuss the definitional issues associated with learning disabilities
- describe the behavioral skills and deficits that are exhibited by children with learning disabilities
- review the major language, learning, and cognitive challenges for students with learning disabilities and give one example of each
- present the psychological and social–emotional problems faced by many individuals with learning disabilities
- describe the postschool outcomes for students with learning disabilities

A FUNCTIONAL DEFINITION OF LEARNING DISABILITIES

The Learning Disabilities Concept

In a general sense, a learning disability (LD) represents an unexplained inability to master learning-related tasks. Although a number of conditions can create an inability to learn, by definition a learning disability is an *unexplained* inability to learn and therefore cannot be the result of the most widely known and recognized conditions, such as low intelligence, socioeconomic factors, or poor sensory skills (Bender, 2001). In fact, all widely accepted definitions of learning disabilities specifically exclude children with these conditions.

As one may expect, based on such a general definition, the types of learning disabilities manifested in different children are quite different, and diagnosing two individuals as "learning disabled" does not mean that the learning problems of those individuals are the same. In fact, a consistent finding in research on learning disabilities is the amazing heterogeneity of learning problems included under the term (Bender, 2001; Bender & Wall, 1994).

Beyond this general definition, difficulty arises because of the number of different definitions used in the field in recent decades. Definitions differ because of different theoretical perspectives on what a learning disability is, as well as the highly politicized nature of the field. Perhaps more than any other area of special education, the field of learning disabilities has been highly political because of the shear numbers of students identified with this disability, as well as the resulting number of parents advocating for their children with learning disabilities. In a very concrete sense, the definition of a disability will determine who receives services under that disability, so parents have been very active advocates for children with learning disabilities, and the total number of children so identified has grown in recent decades. Today, one in every two students who has an identified disability is identified as learning disabled.

Because of the large number of children identified as having LD, the federal and state governments, as well as professional organizations, have proposed various definitions to delineate this population. In the effort to satisfy everyone in formulating these definitions over the last 3 decades, governmental agencies have satisfied very few. Thus, the use of the definition of a learning disability as a basis for seeking a functional description of learning disabilities is more problematic than for other developmental disabilities.

Terms Used for Learning Disabilities

A number of terms are used to denote learning disabilities, or to describe the people who have them, including *learning disabilities, learning disabled, dyslexia, specific learning disabilities, perceptually impaired,* and *perceptual/communication disordered* (Brachacki, Nicolson, & Fawcett, 1995; Chalfant, 1985). Further, attention-deficit/hyperactivity disorder (ADHD) has been identified as a disability that may often coexist with a learning disability, though few researchers use these terms synonymously. One of the pressing issues within the field of learning disabilities is this overlap of characteristics with ADHD and other disabilities, and this issue is explored in more detail later in the chapter.

For purposes of this chapter, students with learning disabilities will be described and discussed from the more traditional perspective, related to research that focuses on "pure" LD groups—that is, on students with only a diagnosis of LD and no comorbid diagnosis. However, information on students with comorbid ADHD or serious emotional disturbance is provided in the several areas where such information is available. The reader is advised to watch the development of research on ADHD and serious emotional disturbance (most of the comparison research is less than 15 years old) and continually consider how this debate on comorbidity (i.e., overlap of characteristics) may affect the field of learning disabilities in particular and the field of developmental disabilities overall.

The Federal Definition of Learning Disabilities

A variety of terms in various contexts are used to represent learning disabilities. Perhaps the most useful definition for our purposes is the federal definition, which was developed as a result of the passage of the initial federal legislation on special education, the Education for All Handicapped Children Act of 1975. Some variation of this definition is used in all 50 states:

> Specific learning disability means a disorder in one or more of the basic psychological processes involved in understanding or in using language, spoken or written, which may manifest itself in an imperfect ability to listen, think, speak, read, write, spell, or to do mathematical calculations. The term includes such conditions as perceptual handicaps, brain injury, minimal brain disfunction, dyslexia, and development aphasia. The term does not include children who have learning problems which are primarily the result of visual, hearing, or motor handicaps, of mental retardation, of emotional disturbance, or of environmental, cultural, or economic disadvantage.

Even with this federal definition as a basis for most state definitions of LD, there is considerable variety in the various state definitions. However, despite the diversity in terms among states, there are several common aspects to most state definitions of LD. Specifically, most state definitions of learning disabilities include a discrepancy between IQ and achievement, a clause dealing with cognitive processing of information, and an exclusionary clause. Examination of these three components will provide an organizational structure for understanding the current definitions and assessment procedures in the field.

COMPONENTS OF THE DEFINITION OF LD

The Discrepancy Criteria

Ability—Achievement Discrepancies

The most frequently used method of identifying LD is to measure the discrepancy between ability and achievement (Zuriff, 2002). Because of the assumption that students with LD are not performing as well academically as they should, a number of mathematical formulas were developed for identifying students with disabilities, based on this general concept of a difference between a child's ability and his or her achievement. Specifically, these formulas were used to determine the degree of difference between some measure of ability and achievement in various academic subject areas.

At least four major types of ability—achievement discrepancy calculations have been used historically (Chalfant, 1985; Schuerholz et al., 1995). First, practitioners calculated a discrepancy between grade placement (which was, at best, a questionable measure of ability) and achievement, by subtracting the latter from the former. The result of this procedure suggested that a fifth grader who was reading at a second-grade level must have LD. However, this hypothesis was quickly seen to be inadequate because many causes can result in underachievement (e.g., low intelligence, poor study habits). Thus, many of the children who were classified as having LD by that process were merely unmotivated or failed to turn in homework. This particular "discrepancy" concept fell into disuse in the 1970s.

The "formula" calculations were the next to evolve. Because the foregoing procedure did not take into account the child's intelligence level, theorists developed mathematical formulas that did. These formulas usually involved calculation of an "expected achievement" level, based on a child's intelligence score and grade placement, compared to actual achievement. If the observed discrepancy was large enough, the child was considered to have LD. This formula calculation fell into disuse in the late 1980s, because these systems involved inappropriate mathematical comparisons between scores that were not comparable. The formulas were often based on mathematical manipulation of grade-equivalent scores (e.g., a 3.5 in reading). However, when scores from different tests are used, the means and standard deviations of the scores must be the same in order for the scores to be mathematically comparable, and the standard deviations of the different grade-equivalent scores from different tests are often quite different.

Consequently, the concept of a standardized score comparison was developed, whereby the practitioner derives an IQ score and an achievement score based on tests that have the same mean and standard deviation and thus yield scores that are mathematically comparable. Today, standard-score calculation is the most common method of identifying children with LD. However, there is some mathematical error in standard-score comparisons. Repeated tests, resulting in scores that are either very high or very low, tend to yield scores that regress toward (or fall back toward) the mean. This phenomenon is called regression and can create error in simple subtraction of standardized scores.

To address this error, Schuerholz and her coworkers (1995) described an innovation on the standard-score discrepancy concept that takes into account any error associated with the standardized scores. By including the reliability of the scores in the overall calculation, some of the error associated with this standard-score comparison is reduced (Schuerholz et al., 1995). This led to the final discrepancy calculation procedure—the regression-score calculation. Thus, some states use "regression tables," which are basically standard-score comparisons that take this regression phenomenon into account. Today, in almost every state, either a standard-score discrepancy procedure or a "regression" procedure based on standard-score comparisons is used as the primary identification technique for students with LD.

Other Discrepancy Procedures

In addition to the discrepancy between ability and achievement, other types of discrepancies have, on occasion, been used to identify a learning disability. For example, many psychologists believe that different levels of scores on IQ tests, or different patterns of scores on the subtests of IQ tests, indicate a learning disability, since one high score may be a "true" measure of ability, whereas a lower score may measure actual "realized" achievement. It is not uncommon for practitioners to identify children as having LD on the basis of this type of discrepancy. These discrepancy procedures were referred to by various terms, such as *subtest scatter* or *subtest variability*. It is not uncommon, even today, to find eligibility reports for students with LD that attend to the variance in different subtest scores on the same assessment of intelligence as one indication of LD.

Use of Discrepancy Procedures

The continuing use of discrepancy calculations is in question. In 1976, the U.S. Department of Education indicated that a standard-score discrepancy between IQ and achievement that was unexplained by other factors was the only useful indicator of a learning disability. Thus, for the last 2 decades, most states have used one of the two formulations of the standard-score discrepancy in their state definitions.

There is some degree of dissatisfaction, however, with the discrepancy-score process. For example, the Council for Learning Disabilities (1987) recommended that the use of discrepancy formulas be phased out. One should note, however, that the report did not recommend any type of alternative identification procedure, and consequently little change resulted.

A related problem was noted when researchers and parents inquired about identification of learning disabilities during the preschool years. To date, the use of discrepancies has resulted in identification of children with LD only after they enter school. Specifically, if a state's definition of LD stipulates a standard-score discrepancy between IQ and reading achievement of 20 points as indicative of a learning disability (as stipulated in the definition of LD used in Georgia), the identification of children with LD at the age of 4—prior to the availability of scores on school achievement tests—becomes problematic if not impossible.

Consequently, most children with LD are identified after the school years begin. In fact, the available data indicate that most students are identified as learning disabled when they are at the third- and fourth-grade levels. Teachers seem to want to give the students the benefit of the doubt regarding school failure through kindergarten and Grades 1 and 2, but in Grade 3, usually a large number of students are identified with LD.

As noted above, a number of problems with the standard-score and regression-score discrepancies have been noted, and various concerned organizations have suggested that other procedures be developed. However, at present no viable alternatives for identification of LD are widely accepted by the field. Thus, practitioners should continue to use the state-mandated identification procedures, which will typically be based on the standard-score discrepancy concept.

The Psychological Process Criterion

The early assumption inherent in the definition of a learning disability was that some type of disability in perception, language, or cognition prevented an individual from learning. Numerous assessments of copying skills—referred to as visual–motor performance—and motor movement skills have been used over the years, as have various language tests. A more common method for measuring "basic psychological processes" is to use standardized intelligence tests and to examine the discrepancies between various subscale scores on the tests based on visual perception and language skills (see the earlier discussion of subtest variability). Any discussion of these mental or psychological processes includes terms such as *perception; visual learning deficit* and *auditory learning problems; receptive/expressive language* and *memory processes; attention;* and *sensory integration,* or the ability to combine information obtained from several senses, notably hearing and vision. Recent research on two of the psychological processes—attention and memory—is presented later in the chapter.

This psychological process component of the definition has always been problematic because theorists disagree on what processes are basic to learning and how those processes should be measured (Swanson & Ashbaker, 2000; Ysseldyke, 1983). To date, no exhaustive list of these processes has been proposed. Also, the measurement devices used as indicators of different types of perception are not adequate technically (Coles, 1978). For these reasons, the Council for Learning Disabilities (1987) recommended that measurement of such processes be terminated.

Nevertheless, many practitioners still routinely perform assessments of psychological processes in some fashion, and it is not uncommon to find assessments of visual–motor performance, as one example, on many assessment reports today. Because there are no specifics as to what these processes entail, states vary greatly in required assessment practices. The best advice for the practitioner is to adhere to the rules and regulations published by the state department of education for assessment practices in his or her state. These procedures can usually be obtained by interested professionals from the department of education in question.

The Exclusionary Criteria

The last part of the federal definition attempts to state what a learning disability is not rather than what it is. Early definitions of LD included a phrase that suggested that learning disability was not a form of mental retardation and that children with mental retardation should not be considered learning disabled. At that point, during the early and mid-1960s, it was necessary to differentiate LD from mental retardation, not because of major functional dissimilarity of the conditions, but for political reasons: That is to say, the political expedient of securing funding for research and services for children with LD necessitated the separation of this group from students with mental retardation, who had already attracted national attention and funding for research.

Of course, defining a population by what it is not rather than by what it is always results in definitional problems; it is like trying to define the color red by pointing to things that are not red. Such attempts at definition inevitably suggest a real problem in the definition of the term. Again, during that period, securing funding by differentiation of the overall types of disabilities was the driving political force. Also during the 1960s, the exclusionary clause was expanded to include children who are culturally deprived, behaviorally disturbed, or seriously emotionally disturbed. These exclusions also resulted in assessment problems because it is often difficult to tell different types of disabilities apart. For example, a child with learning disabilities and a child with behavioral disorders often behave similarly, and many students with learning disabilities also manifest social–emotional problems (Bender, Rosenkrans, & Crane, 1999). Also, no criteria are provided to make the distinction between LD and serious emotional disturbance.

This problem is further compounded in comparisons between students with learning disabilities and those with attention-deficit/hyperactivity disorders. Bender and Wall (1994) suggested that, minus the discrepancy criteria previously discussed, many students with ADHD may be considered learning disabled, because the attentional problems and organizational skills problems seem to be the root of the problem for both types of children. To date, the exclusionary clause for the definition of learning disabilities does not specify ADHD, and approximately 40% of students with ADHD also demonstrate a learning disability (Barkley, 1992).

A functional perspective that concentrates on the functioning of individuals within schools and society may well lead to differing conclusions concerning what disabilities exist. On a functional level, there are few demonstrable differences between students with learning disabilities, mild intellectual disability, serious emotional disturbance, and ADHD (an issue that is explored in more depth later in the chapter), and from that perspective, the problems associated with the exclusionary clause in the definition of LD are moot. Even in light of these problems, the vast majority of state definitions still include some form of exclusionary clause. In most cases, both students with intellectual disability and students with serious emotional disorders and/or behavioral disorders are excluded.

CHARACTERISTICS OF LD

In view of the heterogeneity among children referred to as learning disabled, the identification of functional characteristics that are universal to this population is difficult. Still, general characteristics that may be found in children with LD can be identified and used to illustrate the types of school problems that are characteristic of this group. Table 12.1 presents the types of behavioral characteristics frequently discussed as indicative of a learning disability. It is, however, merely a list of "potential" characteristics and should not be taken as a checklist for identification purposes. The research evidence clearly demonstrates the profound heterogeneity of LD populations, and no characteristics list can be used as a single criterion for identification.

In addition to these general characteristics, there are several other widely noted facts about students with LD. First, many more male students than female students are identified as learning disabled, as is the case for most mild disabilities (e.g., serious emotional disturbance, mild intellectual disability). In fact, the ratio of male to female individuals identified as learning disabled ranges from 2:1 to 5:1.

Second, students with LD often exhibit language difficulties. Deficits exist among children and adolescents with LD in almost every area of language—semantics, syntax, and pragmatics—in both reception and expression. These difficulties—discussed more specifically below—often result in difficulties in written language, speaking communication, and listening skills. Interventions are generally aimed at providing training in pragmatic language skills with frequent feedback about the adequacy of the spoken or written communication.

Third, the IQ of most students with LD, while in the average range, is usually in the lower average range. The average IQ of populations in public schools identified as learning disabled is approximately 90 to 93, or several points lower than the population norm for nondisabled children, even though the definition of LD stipulates that children identified as learning disabled have average or above average IQs. Fourth, attention deficits are frequently demonstrated by

TABLE 12.1
Behavioral Characteristics of Students with Learning Disabilities

- Excessive distractibility, or inability to concentrate on a learning task for the same length of time as other children
- Awkwardness in use of one's hands for either gross-motor or fine-motor tasks
- Difficulty in reading words on the blackboard, even with corrective lenses
- Excessive hyperactivity, or inability to stay in classroom seat
- Neurological impairment caused by impairment in cranial nerve function, demonstrated by a neurological exam
- Awkwardness of step or gait when walking

students with LD. Research has shown that on-task time among students with LD is consistently lower than that among students without disabilities. Interventions for these attention skills include self-monitoring training of on-task behavior and direct cognitive strategy training in attention to various stimuli. Finally, many students with learning disabilities have problems with short-term memory skills and with working memory skills. Educational interventions for these skills include memory strategies such as memorization of learning-strategy acronyms and use of verbal rehearsal and visual imagery to improve memory of textual material.

With these general characteristics in mind, one of the best ways to understand learning disabilities is to review several case studies, with particular attention to the types of academic, emotional, and social behavior problems that are associated with the condition. Subsequently, the characteristics will be explored further.

 ## CASE EXAMPLE: BOBBY

Bobby has failed several subjects in the fourth grade, and his mother believes that this is related to his low reading skill. Although he passes reading, he was never strong in phonics or detecting letter sounds. He usually passes reading with a grade of D or C. His parents are concerned and have spoken to the fourth-grade teacher. The teacher has indicated that Bobby is in the lowest level reading group, but he still seems to be having problems. She also mentioned several other problem areas, including spelling and handwriting. He does not seem to be "with it" in class and is often staring out the window or moving about the class when he should not be. His homework is rarely turned in, and he seems to be somewhat disorganized in his long-term projects. The teacher also reported that Bobby has difficulty writing a paragraph when one is assigned in class. Despite these problems, he seems to have no difficulty with math, and he usually earns a B for that subject. His parents do not understand this, because they see that he spends at least an hour and a half in his room each night for homework.

 ## CASE EXAMPLE: ALPHONSO

Alphonso is in the 10th grade and has recently transferred into the local high school. The history teacher noted that he has a problem reading the text as well as reading questions on the unit tests. The teacher did an informal reading inventory, which indicated that Alphonso's reading skills were at approximately the fourth-grade level. He has also demonstrated some other problems. For example, his homework, when he does it, is disorganized and indicates problems understanding the material. His written work is barely readable, and his syntax is often confused. He writes in short sentences, and any understanding of paragraph structure seems to be totally lacking. Finally, he seems to realize that he is having significant problems with his work, and his self-concept has suffered. He has begun to demonstrate some anger and defiance in class, which had not occurred prior to his 10th-grade year. Alphonso is a proud teenager and does not like the other students to know that he has problems reading. Consequently, he does not like to share his work with the class, either verbally or in writing. After about a month, during which Alphonso received barely passing grades, the teacher asked for help.

CASE EXAMPLE: THOMAS

Thomas has never read well and has had problems with handwriting since the first grade. When he entered the fourth grade, the teacher decided that he needed help in both of these areas, so she began to work with him during class. When she began, she was sure that the extra work would help, because Thomas seemed to be motivated to improve his reading. As she worked with him, she noted that he would often say one word when he meant another. Also, sometimes his thoughts were confused and he was unable to communicate as clearly as the typical fourth-grade child. It became apparent that the extra work did not help, so in desperation, the teacher approached the special education teacher to discuss having Thomas tested.

CASE EXAMPLE: JESSICA

Jessica earned below-average grades during her first year of school but was passing her work. However, when she entered the second grade, she began to demonstrate additional problems. She could not recognize many words that most of the other students had learned, and she did not understand the stories she read during reading time. She also had trouble when other students or the teacher read the story. Even though she could name the characters in a story, she could not remember the plot well, and if she had to tell the story to someone else, she tended to get the facts confused and could not recall the sequence of events. Despite this problem, Jessica was doing low-average work in math and could complete simple math operations as well as any other student.

In each of the preceding descriptions, there is some indication of relative strengths and weaknesses. Students with LD tend to have some areas in which they do acceptable schoolwork. Most of these students have difficulty with reading, language arts, written expression, or reading-based content subjects, and some students with learning disabilities may be as much as 4 to 6 years behind in academic achievement in the language arts area. However, there are students whose only disability seems to be in math. The types of working memory problems that were evident when Jessica heard a story read are common, as are the organizational problems discussed as a characteristic of both Bobby and Alphonso. Also, the phonics and letter discrimination problems demonstrated by Bobby are quite common.

The characteristics attributed to these students could well be attributed to any child with LD. The attention problems, the lack of organization, and the failure to complete homework are characteristics of many students with LD. Also, in the case study of Bobby, the parents merely assumed that he worked in his room each night, but there was apparently no monitoring to make sure that the time in the room was really spent on homework.

Finally, in older students with LD such as Alphonso, there is often some degree of emotional or personality disturbance, because the older students realize that they are different from their peers, and they do not usually cope well with those differences (Bender et al., 1999). Students with LD are often reported to have poor social skills and lower social acceptance by their peers than nondisabled students (Haager & Vaughn, 1995). This low social acceptance can result in decreased self-concept and lower self-expectations (Bender & Wall, 1994). Also, these social–emotional problems frequently become so severe that students with learning disabilities may be coidentified as seriously emotionally disturbed. Again, the overlap of these categories suggests that perhaps a broader developmental-disabilities perspective may be more appropriate for many students with LD.

ISSUES IN LEARNING DISABILITIES

Comorbid Disabilities and Learning Disabilities

With these characteristics of LD in mind, some researchers have suggested that the existing classification paradigms may not be well founded (Handwerk & Marshall, 1998; Zuriff, 2002). Some researchers argue that the "disability" is practically indistinguishable from several other disabilities or even from low achievement among students with no disabilities (Zuriff, 2002). Other researchers have argued that students with LD are, overall, very similar to students with other mild disabilities (Handwerk & Marshall, 1998; Lilly, 1979; Ysseldyke & Algozzine, 1984). Hallahan and Kauffman (1977) suggested that students with mild intellectual disabilities, mild behavioral disorders, and learning disabilities demonstrated significant overlap in learning characteristics. Of course, the current definitions for various disabilities focus on relatively static indicators (i.e., a score on intelligence or a discrepancy score between IQ score and achievement), and these definitions are specifically constructed to allow for no overlap between various disabilities. However, a more functional approach that focuses on the functional or academic skills of individuals generally indicates a high degree of similarity between students with learning disabilities, serious emotional disturbance, mild mental disabilities, and ADHD. In particular, the overlap between LD and serious emotional disturbance or ADHD is receiving research attention.

Learning Disabilities and Serious Emotional Disturbance

Numerous studies have compared students with LD and serious emotional problems. Handwerk and Marshall (1998), for example, examined the behavioral and emotional problems of children with learning disabilities and serious emotional disturbance, in an effort to tease out the distinguishing characteristics of these groups. This study involved a comparison of three groups: 117 students with learning disabilities, 72 students with serious emotional disturbance, and 68 students with both learning disabilities and serious emotional disturbance. This study examined the academic and social–emotional functioning of these groups of students, using several behavior ratings that were completed by parents and teachers—the *Teacher Report Form* and the *Child Behavior Checklist*. The ages of the students ranged from 6 to 18, and the researchers wanted to determine whether the type and severity of academic and behavioral problems experienced by these groups of students differed. The results indicated that children with LD differed from those with serious emotional disturbance mainly in terms of severity of behavioral problems, and not with respect to the types of functional behaviors.

Other studies likewise have looked at this issue of comorbidity between students with LD and other disabilities. For example, Haager and Vaughn (1995) demonstrated that the social skills of individuals with LD seem to be somewhat impaired, suggesting a similarity to students with severe emotional disturbance and/or other development disabilities. Further, as adults, many students with LD are served by the same social service agencies as those that serve individuals with developmental disabilities. From this perspective, then, perhaps learning disabilities should be conceptualized along the continuum of developmental disabilities, as one of the less severe forms of disability.

Of course, an immediate disclaimer is necessary: By less severe, we do not mean that individuals with LD have fewer problems to contend with or that the burden created by the disability is "lighter." In contrast, the burden associated with a learning disability would seem to be greater, in that the societal expectations for individuals with LD may exceed those for an individual with severe emotional problems or profound intellectual disability. Rather, by less severe, in this context, we intend the reader to focus on the relatively normal prognosis for individuals with LD. These individuals will marry, hold jobs, raise children, and live a relatively normal life in most cases, although the impairment associated with the learning disability will be felt throughout life (Adelman & Vogel, 1993). In this functional sense, then, individuals with LD may be very similar to individuals with mild intellectual disability, serious emotional disabilities, behavioral disorders, and other developmental disabilities.

Comorbidity Between LD and Attention-Deficit/Hyperactivity Disorders

Although students with LD have been discussed as manifesting deficits in attention skills, within the last 15 years another group of students with attention problems has been identified, and some practitioners believe that this group—students with ADHD—may be a subgroup of students with LD. Other researchers suggest that this is a subgroup of students with behavior disorders, and still others consider ADHD as a separate disability. Researchers have attempted to document differences between students with ADHD and those with LD with only limited success (Mayes, Calhoun, & Crowell, 2000; Stanford & Hynd, 1994).

For example, Mayes et al. (2000) investigated learning problems in children with LD and ADHD, to address the potential overlap between these conditions. The authors used IQ and achievement test scores to compare these groups. Clinical and psychoeducational data were analyzed for 119 children, ranging in age from 8 to 16 years. The psychological evaluation included the administration of the *Wechsler Intelligence Scale for Children–III* and the *Wechsler Individual Achievement Test*. The results showed that children with ADHD had a significantly greater frequency of LD than children without ADHD. These results suggest that the learning and attention problems demonstrated by these students may constitute a continuum, and frequently coexist for many children with learning disabilities and ADHD.

Bussing, Zima, Belin, and Forness (1998) reported on special education placement patterns of children with ADHD and explored how ADHD related to placement in programs for students with LD and/or serious emotional disturbance. The authors used data from multiple informants to address this issue of comorbidity. The participants were 722 children in second through fourth grades, including children identified as having LD and serious emotional disturbance in a medium-sized school district. Determination of eligibility for these services was based on federal criteria. Data were gathered on these groups and compared to the criteria for ADHD. The results indicated that 28% of students with LD and serious emotional disturbance fell in the high-risk range for ADHD based on parent questionnaires, and 18% fell into the high-risk range based on teacher ratings.

In other comparison studies, Korkman and Pesonen (1994) demonstrated that students with ADHD were more impulsive than students with LD. Stanford and Hynd (1994) indicated that parents and teachers view these groups as different in several respects, although a great deal of suspicion remains that there may be a strong similarity between LD and ADHD. Barkley (1992) also studied the comorbidity of these disabilities. He indicated that approximately 40% of students with ADHD also met the criteria for learning disabilities. Even using a more rigorous definition of learning disabilities, he estimated that between 19% and 26% of students with ADHD were learning disabled. This high overlap of categories suggests that some reclarification may be necessary. At the very least, the recent research focus on ADHD has fueled the flames in the ever-present definitional problems in the field of learning disabilities. Needless to say, there is, at present, considerable debate about the existence of ADHD as a separate category or placement of these students within the existing categories of LD and serious emotional disturbance (Bussing et al., 1998; Mayes et al., 2000; Reid, Maag, & Vasa, 1994). It is hoped that research may stipulate the relationship between these classifications more accurately in the future.

Regardless of the conceptualization, a learning disability is still a significant developmental insult in a child's or adolescent's life (Bender & Wall, 1994). Also, although the definitional considerations just discussed are crucial for research purposes, a practitioner in the developmental disabilities field is well advised to use the definition of learning disabilities provided by the state in which he or she practices. Although some consistency based on federal legislation has emerged, definitions of learning disabilities do vary from one state to another. Generally, the state's department of education can provide a set of rules and regulations for special education services that include the state definition of learning disability, as well as procedures for assessing and identifying students with learning disabilities.

Self-Care

Self-care as typically defined is not a major problem for most individuals with LD. As indicated previously, most of these students are identified after the school years begin. Most parents report that children with LD seem to learn rudimentary self-care skills as quickly as do their siblings. For example, tying shoes at the age of 3 or 4 years is not a problem (as it usually is for a child with moderate intellectual disability) nor is helping around the home difficult for children with LD.

Subtle differences probably exist, however, because of the lack of organizational abilities on the part of the child with LD. Disorganization is often a problem reported by parents of students diagnosed with LD, and this deficit may result in an inability to follow directions for routine household chores, such as making the bed or separating the white and light-colored clothes for washing.

Self-help skills may be somewhat more important for individuals with very severe learning disabilities, or for individuals whose LD is comorbid with other disabilities, such as ADHD or dyslexia. Individuals with dyslexia, who represent one subgroup of the total LD population—probably less than 10% of the overall population of students with LD—may need additional training in self-care skills throughout life. Many persons who are true dyslexics will never read beyond the second- or third-grade level and will need special training for driving an automobile (because of the need to read road signs, for example) or using a city transportation system (Brachacki et al., 1995). Other self-care adjustments may also be necessary before an individual with dyslexia is truly independent.

Individuals with ADHD may also demonstrate problems throughout life. There are numerous reports of individuals with ADHD who experience extreme difficulties as adults, when managing work schedules or merely arriving at work on time becomes increasingly important. Although few of these problems are severe enough to warrant daily residential care, it is not uncommon to find adults with ADHD whose spouses manage their schedules of daily appointments.

Finally, self-help in the broadest sense may include skills that move beyond mere physical care or personal hygiene. Skills in planning a future for oneself, self-advocacy, and self-understanding may be considered self-help skills from this broader perspective, and research has indicated that students with learning disabilities are much less likely to be active self-advocates. Specifically, Whitney-Thomas and Moloney (2001) interviewed 10 students in a qualitative study and demonstrated that adolescents with disabilities lacked confidence, consistency, and accuracy in describing themselves. Although students with learning disabilities were not specifically identified in this study, the results do represent the lack of self-definition that many students with LD exemplify. These results suggest, once again, that although self-help in the traditional sense is not a high-priority issue among students with learning disabilities, the issues of self-advocacy and self-understanding are more serious problems for students with LD.

Language Disabilities in Students with LD

Phoneme Manipulation

Phonemes represent the basic building blocks of language. A phoneme is the smallest unit of sound with which meaning may be associated, and understanding of early phonics and thus early reading, as well as language skills, is based on how well students can detect and manipulate phonemes. One of the most recent areas of research on the language skills of students with learning disabilities involves the research on phonemes and phoneme manipulation (Moats & Lyon, 1993; Sousa, 2001). Research with infants has suggested that children as young as a few weeks are learning to discriminate between phonemes in their mother's and father's language, and this ability to discriminate between sounds and associate different meanings with different sounds is the basis for all subsequent language, both spoken and written. There are approximately 44 to 46 phonemes in English. (If one were to combine all phonemes from all languages, one would find only about 90 phonemes total [Sousa, 2001].) Thus, in English, all spoken language, writing, and reading skills are built on approximately 44 phonemes, and difficulty in distinguishing between those phonemes represents an extreme difficulty with the "basics" of human language, both spoken and written.

Research has suggested that students with learning disabilities have noted difficulties in phoneme manipulation, which may be the basis for most subsequent language disabilities (Moats & Lyon, 1993). This research has been the fastest growing area in language research, as well as language interventions, for students with learning disabilities. A number of instructional programs that focus on phoneme manipulation have recently been marketed, and the initial research on these programs has been quite promising. Even for students with learning disabilities in the elementary and middle grades, some instruction in phoneme manipulation can be a fruitful intervention, which assists in their overall academic progress. Given the intensity of the growing research on phoneme manipulation as a basis for reading problems, teachers would be well advised to remain abreast of this growing body of intervention research.

Expressive and Receptive Language

As in most children, receptive language is more developed than expressive language in students with LD. One may suspect that there is some language delay among students with LD early in life but not usually enough to determine that a disability exists during the language-learning period characteristic of the second and third years of life. Consequently, the research on early language development in children who are eventually diagnosed as having LD, although quite limited, has not shown any potential for identifying this disability at an earlier stage. From the perspective of parents and siblings, the language development of students who later become diagnosed with LD often appears to be quite ordinary for the first 5 to 6 years of life.

Children with learning disabilities tend to have the more sophisticated types of language problems, generally at a later period (Roth, Spekman, & Fye, 1995). Typically, these children produce recognizable sentences and can participate, though minimally, in conversations from an early age. Whereas the problem in students with moderate to severe intellectual disability may be eliciting rudimentary forms of language, the problems among children with LD concern use of language in academic and social situations. Thus, most of the problems appear only after the child enters the academic environment, which is not only rich in language experiences but also tends to make new and novel demands on the child's language skills.

Syntax and Semantics

The early research on language development among students with LD concentrated on syntax and semantics. Syntax refers to the formal relationships between words in phrases or sentences. Examples of such relationships include the subject–verb relationship and the relationship between the verb and the direct object. Semantics refers to knowledge and comprehension of words. Ability in this area is often measured by receptive vocabulary tests.

Most research on syntax and semantics demonstrated deficits in children with LD (Boucher, 1986; Wiig, Lapointe, & Semel, 1977; Wiig, Semel, & Crouse, 1973). Children with learning disabilities demonstrate deficits in the ability to apply morphologic rules (e.g., formation of plurals, verb tenses, and possessives) and difficulty in both comprehension and expression of syntactic structures such as relationships between words in sentences and phrases (e.g., understanding to whom a pronoun applies and what function is served by a direct object or an indirect object). These deficits are apparent both in the child's understanding of the language of others and in his or her own production of spoken language. Finally, these studies demonstrated that oral language production did not automatically improve with age among students with LD, as it does in most children (Wiig et al., 1977).

Pragmatic Use of Language

Pragmatics involves a more complex use of language in social situations—the use of language in context. In addition to the mechanics of language usage (syntax and semantics), this aspect of language encompasses the social and cultural roles and expectations of the participants in the conversation (Boucher, 1986; Roth et al., 1995). Theorists who study pragmatic language emphasize the ecologically based study of language in real communication situations rather than scores on a test that may not indicate true communicative skill. Researchers in this area tend to measure the actual utterances a child makes when he or she communicates with other children and adults.

An important aspect of pragmatic language is the ability to adjust one's language to the speaker to enhance communication. For example, a person generally uses a more simplistic language with a young child than with an older person. This language adaptation is referred to as *code switching*. Such adaptations may be made in a number of ways, including using more simple sentences or using fewer modifiers in each complete thought. Early research suggested that children with learning disabilities did not code-switch as frequently as children without disabilities (Boucher, 1984; Bryan, Donahue, & Pearl, 1981). Asking questions, responding to inadequate messages, and persuasion were noted as difficult skills to master for children with learning disabilities (Boucher, 1986; Bryan et al., 1981), and the lack of these skills was cited as a possible reason for inadequate social skills among these children (Bryan et al., 1981).

Referential communication, another aspect of pragmatic language, requires that a child communicate specific information to another and/or evaluate the adequacy of communication from another. This form of communication can be quite important in the context of the public school classroom where teachers and students are often giving, receiving, and interpreting instructions for various tasks. Referential communication skills, therefore, include awareness of accurate and inadequate messages as well as of communication choices, such as selection of specific terms, which are based on such communication.

Roth et al. (1995) compared students with learning disabilities to normally achieving students on reference cohesion in oral narratives. *Reference cohesion* refers to the understanding and utilization of pronouns (e.g., *he, she, it*), possessive adjectives (e.g., *mine*), demonstratives (e.g, *this, there, now*), and comparatives (e.g., *same, different*) (Roth et al., 1995). Students with learning disabilities were compared with their age mates at three ages between 8 years and 13 years, because a more sophisticated understanding of reference cohesion is typically developed during those years among children without disabilities. Oral narrative stories were collected and compared. In every age group, students with learning disabilities were less successful at reference cohesion than were peers without disabilities.

Several studies have suggested that children with learning disabilities are deficient in understanding and responding to inadequate communication (Donahue, Pearl, & Bryan, 1980; Feagans, 1983; Wiig, Semel, & Abele, 1981). For example, Spekman (1981) created dyads, or paired groups, some of which included a child with a disability and some of which did not. Each child in each dyad was to communicate information and to act on information received from the partner in the dyad. This research design allowed for comparison of referential communication skills as well as listening competence. The children were told they could ask questions regarding incomplete communications. Although no differences were found in their abilities to follow directions, to complete the task, or to ask appropriate questions, the children with learning disabilities gave less task-relevant information. Consequently, these dyads demonstrated less success in completion of the task than did the dyads that included only normally functioning children.

The implications of this research for the practitioner are relatively straightforward. If a child with a learning disability demonstrates a pragmatic language disability in referential communication skills, that student will be less capable of giving instructions to his or her classmates and playmates. Consequently, this disability will affect the student's performance on group projects that require verbal participation of each group member. Also, the child will have problems responding to instructions given by the teacher or by other members of the group. Clearly, disability in referential communication presents real problems in the typical elementary or secondary school classroom.

A number of educational activities may be used to expand a child's success in pragmatic language skills. Any projects that require a child to communicate information to others utilizing referential communication skills can be a learning experience for these children. In giving directions to others, a child has to plan what the other needs to know, the order in which information should be presented, and the speed with which information should be given. By placing children with learning disabilities in that position and then discussing with them their efforts at communication, a more sophisticated level of pragmatic language may be obtained. However, merely assigning these children to group projects without appropriate postcommunication follow-up will not result in improved communication skill. Alternatively, the communication must be examined and reconstructed so that the child understands the strengths and weaknesses of his or her communication efforts.

Impact of Language Deficits

Deficits in the ability to manipulate phonemes, in grasping semantics and syntax, or in pragmatic language skills will create continuing problems in school achievement in a variety of areas (Moats & Lyon, 1993; Sousa, 2001). For example, such deficits often result in difficulty with written assignments, reading assignments, or group projects. The teacher and other practitioners must be sensitive to these language problems and to the effects of these problems on school tasks, and expectations for schoolwork should be adjusted accordingly.

Adjustments that language deficits require may be simple or extensive. Many students with LD take tests orally rather than in written form. By allowing this form of testing, the teacher can obtain a true picture of the student's comprehension rather than a measure of comprehension that may be unduly influenced by the child's ability to read the test and to write an answer. Other modifications that lessen the impact of language deficits include instruction and practice in referential communication skills, use of alternative texts, use of alternative reading materials that cover the same content but are written at a lower reading level, use of graphic aids during lectures, and frequent checking of notes taken by the student to ensure that the notes are complete. Many of these adaptations are useful for students with other disabilities as well.

Summary of Language Deficits

Although little evidence exists of major delays in expressive or receptive language in children with LD, more sophisticated language problems are well documented (Roth et al., 1995; Sousa, 2001). Students with learning disabilities have deficits in phoneme manipulation resulting in difficulties in both syntax and semantics that negatively affect their school performance. Perhaps a more debilitating disability is the deficit in pragmatic language. Students with learning disabilities do not have the pragmatic language skills to adapt their language to the situation or to use referential communication skills—either receptive or expressive—in a fashion commensurate with their age group. Finally, some evidence suggests that, unlike children without disabilities, children with LD do not overcome these language problems with age. To alleviate these pragmatic language problems, specific instructional techniques, such as frequent use of and feedback on referential communication skills, are necessary.

Learning and Cognition

In addition to language, several major areas of research involve cognition of students with LD. Cognition may include a host of different variables, but most researchers would include, at a minimum, intelligence, attention, and memory as three major cognition areas. The practitioner should be aware of the recent findings in each of these domains.

Intelligence

The definition of LD stipulates that children so diagnosed have average or above average intelligence. However, studies over the years have indicated that the anticipated IQ level for children with learning disabilities, rather than being exactly average, is in reality somewhat lower than average—approximately 90 to 93 (Bender, 1985; Gajar, 1979; Webster & Schenck, 1978). This lower than average range probably reflects several things. First, intelligence, as measured today in Western culture, is heavily dependent on verbal skills, and this dependence may deflate the average IQ levels reported. Because children with LD demonstrate deficits in almost every language measure, as discussed previously, a depressed score on verbal intelligence would be expected, even for children with normal intelligence in other areas.

In addition, these intelligence figures are based on samples of students with LD identified by the public schools. Identification procedures in public schools are not exact, however, and may be quite different from identification procedures used to identify research populations. At present, the average level of intelligence for students with LD remains unclear, though many researchers suspect that the numbers noted above represent a depressed indication of intelligence for this group of students.

Because of the exclusion of students with intellectual disabilities in most state definitions of LD, most states will identify students as having LD only if their intelligence is 70 or above (i.e., the maximum cutoff score for intellectual disabilities). Other states identify students as having LD only if their IQ is 85 or above (i.e., the traditional "normal" IQ range). Thus, it is possible for students to have an identified learning disability in one state but not in another. Needless to say, this can be upsetting for parents who may move from a state where the child was receiving special education services because of a learning disability into a state with different eligibility criteria, to find that the child no longer qualifies for services.

Some students with LD have a level of intelligence in the "gifted" range, and these students are known as "gifted–learning-disabled" students. Some students with IQs above 130, or 2 standard deviations above the mean, also demonstrate an ability–achievement discrepancy, as discussed previously. Although these students may be at or above grade level academically, if there is a large discrepancy between their IQ and their achievement, they may be classified as learning disabled or as gifted–learning disabled.

For example, a child scoring 134 on an IQ test may score only 102 on a comparable reading test, and that 32-point standard-score discrepancy would demonstrate that the child is not meeting his or her potential. Research studies that examine the characteristics of this group are recent and relatively rare. As a result, little is known about this group of students.

Attention

The construct of attention is more complex than it seems and involves at least three different types of skills. On-task behavior indicates the persistence or length of time a student can remain concentrated on a task. This attention variable is usually measured by observation of the student's eye contact during an assigned task and results in a measure of the percentage of on-task behavior. Next, focus of attention indicates the student's ability to inhibit distracting stimuli. This variable is typically measured by a teacher rating of a child's tendency to distractibility (to be drawn off task by competing stimuli in the educational environment). Finally, selective attention is a cognitively based process that involves choosing which aspects of a stimulus to attend to. This variable is typically not measured on the standard assessment battery. However, various research tasks that compare a student's recall of important versus unimportant details about a particular stimulus have been used to measure this attention variable.

Research in each of these areas has indicated that students with LD suffer deficits compared with their age mates (Bender, 1991; Bender & Wall, 1994; McKinney & Feagans, 1983). For example, whereas the average on-task rates for children without disabilities range between 80% and 90%, the average rates of on-task behavior typically reported in the literature indicate that children with LD are on task between 35% and 65% of the time (Bender, 1985, 1991). It is interesting to note that this level of on-task behavior is also characteristic of students identified as having ADHD (Barkley, 1992). This deficit in on-task behavior, quite obviously, has a negative affect on academic achievement. If a student cannot attend to his or her work, there is little likelihood of academic success for that student. This is one reason that attention has received a research focus for the last several decades.

Research has indicated that many children with LD can be trained to stay on task for longer periods of time. This training, usually referred to as self-monitoring, was developed by Hallahan, Lloyd, and Stoller (1982) at the University of Virginia. The training involves a simple procedure that forces the child to ask him- or herself the question, "Am I paying attention?" on a periodic basis during a learning task. When such a procedure is used each day for a period of weeks, the child apparently forms the habit of monitoring his or her on-task skills. This training is relatively simple, and parents of children with disabilities have actually conducted this type of self-monitoring training with their own children during nightly homework sessions. Instructions are available in several sources (Bender, 2001; Hallahan et al., 1982; Mathes & Bender, 1997). Also, this self-monitoring procedure has been successfully employed with students with ADHD (Fowler, 1992; Mathes & Bender, 1997).

Typically, behavioral ratings are used to indicate the levels of distractibility behaviors for students with LD (McKinney, Montague, & Hocutt, 1993). Other diagnostic procedures that are used for measuring distractibility include anecdotal reports from teachers and classroom observations of behavior, conducted by either school psychologists or teachers. Research on the distractibility of students with LD is somewhat equivocal. In studies that used teacher perceptions of distractibility, the data typically reveal that students with LD are highly distractible, thus indicating a general inability to focus on a task (Bender, 1985, 2001; McKinney & Feagans, 1983). However, in experimental studies in which the distracting stimulus is presented in a controlled fashion, such as distracting light shown on the page that the child is reading, students with LD seem to be no more highly distractible than nondisabled students (Zentall, 1986; Zentall,

Zentall, & Booth, 1978). More research, using both of these methods, is necessary before conclusions can be drawn regarding distractibility of students with LD.

Selective attention involves a conscious choice of particular aspects of the stimuli that deserve attention, and research results indicate that children with LD are not able to make consistently correct choices about the importance of competing stimuli (Bender, 2001). Typically, students with LD answer questions more impulsively than other students, and do not make an effort to attend selectively to the discriminative aspects of the stimuli that are used to answer the question. Research, at present, indicates that this deficit in selective attention is not due to a lack of desire to complete the problem correctly but rather to a lack of knowledge about the cognitive steps necessary for good selective attention, that is, concentration on what to attend to and what to ignore (Bender, 2001).

Selective attention skills may be developed for educational tasks by teachers who assist the child in the thought process. When a child gives an answer that indicates incorrect thinking, the teacher should take a moment and verbally reconstruct the child's selective attention process with the child. Many times the teacher can accomplish this by merely asking the child why that answer seems to be correct. The teacher may then be in a position to indicate to the child certain errors in attending to unimportant aspects of the problem or ignoring vital information in the formulation of the answer. This type of teaching requires small classes and a teacher who is highly responsive to the thought processes of the child. Also, it is rarely (if ever) advisable to embarrass a child by such questions in front of peers. Still, this questioning technique can illuminate how children reach the conclusions they reach, and that information can assist a sensitive teacher in making appropriate educational suggestions for the child.

Memory

The research on memory abilities also has indicated various problems among students with LD (Sousa, 2001; Torgesen, 1984). Researchers only a decade ago discussed memory in terms of short-term memory (e.g., holding a stimulus in one's memory for a few seconds) and long-term memory (e.g., holding a stimulus anywhere from a few minutes to many years). These two memory systems were seen as relatively independent (Sousa, 2001), and at that point, the general consensus was that students with LD demonstrated problems in short-term memory rather than long-term memory (Ross, 1976; Torgesen, 1984). However, more recent research has challenged these early conclusions in various ways. First, some research has suggested that students with LD demonstrate problems in long-term memory as well as short-term memory (Swanson, 1999). Moreover, researchers have recently begun to use the phrase "working memory" rather than "short-term memory" to represent the conscious efforts involved in studying or memorizing (Sousa, 2001; Swanson, 1999, 2000). In fact, recent models of memory include several levels of memory beyond merely the short-term and long-term differentiation from several years ago. Although short-term memory is still in the general models (Sousa, 2001), it is now defined as an unconscious memory process, whereas working memory and long-term memory are defined as the higher-order conscious memory processes (Sousa, 2001).

Perhaps a brief description is in order. To transfer a piece of information from working memory into long-term memory, most individuals develop some type of memory strategy, and thus, the individual must work with the fact to be memorized in some conscious fashion—hence, the term *working memory.* For example, many persons use verbal rehearsal to memorize names of individuals. As another common example, when nondisabled children are required to memorize pictures of various stimuli, they typically develop a classification system, place the pictures in the different classes or groups, and memorize the pictures in each group. In that sense, working memory involves the number of items or facts that can be mentally manipulated at one time, and emphasizes the intentionality or conscious effort to manipulate those facts.

Research involving students with LD has consistently shown that students with LD are much less likely than nondisabled children to intentionally manipulate facts by using these common memory strategies (Swanson, 1999, 2000; Torgesen, 1984), and therein lies the deficits shown by students with LD on memory tasks. This makes teaching students with LD quite demanding because they require much more practice and instruction in specific memory techniques to memorize facts, whereas other children generally generate these memory techniques themselves.

Memory research on students with LD is optimistic, however, because it indicates that once a child with LD has been trained in an age-appropriate memory strategy, the child can usually use that strategy and improve his or her memory performance. A number of instructional strategies, generally referred to as "cognitive strategy training" or "learning strategies" instruction, are being used to enhance the performance of children with LD on a wide range of memory tasks. These learning strategies generally include an acronym in which each letter represents a step for the student to perform. For example, the "RAP" strategy enables a child to memorize the major points from a paragraph of written text. The letters stand for Read the material, Ask questions concerning the material, and Paraphrase the material. When students with LD are trained to complete these steps, their ability to memorize important details from written material increases. Research of this nature has led to a large body of information on teaching strategies for students with LD. Sometimes this body of literature is referred to as learning strategies research or metacognitive research. This is one of the more influential areas of research in the learning disabilities field today, and teachers should regularly review the professional journals seeking instructional ideas that use learning strategies of this nature to enhance memory skills of students with LD.

Summary of Cognition

Research has shown that, in almost every aspect of cognition, students with LD demonstrate some deficits, as summarized in Table 12.2. The intelligence of these children seems to be lower than the norm. Deficits are consistently demonstrated in both on-task attention measures and selective attention, and memory research has consistently indicated problems in memory transfer and an inability to develop memory strategies. With these deficits in cognitive skills that are intimately related to academic performance, it is not surprising that the cognitive deficits negatively affect the schoolwork of children with LD.

TABLE 12.2
Cognitive Characteristics of Students with Learning Disabilities (LD)

Characteristic	Description
IQ	Many students with LD demonstrate lower than normal IQs, perhaps because IQ is heavily dependent on language skills.
Memory	Working memory problems seem to be the basis of much learning difficulty for students with LD. These problems are apparent in memory strategies for academic tasks. In contrast to earlier research, some recent research has suggested that long-term memory may also be a problem.
Focusing	Students with LD are on task less than others. Typical on-task averages for LD groups range from 35% to 65%.
Distractibility	Whereas teachers rate students with LD as more distractible in class, laboratory studies have failed to demonstrate higher distractibility.
Selective attention	Students with LD manifest problems attending to the appropriate aspect of the stimuli. However, once selective attention strategies are taught to students with LD, their selective attention improves dramatically.

These summary statements, however, are based on research on groups of children, and no automatic assumptions should be made regarding the cognition of a particular child with LD. For example, some children may have a disability based on memory deficit and still be able to perform educational tasks in a fashion similar to that of nondisabled children. Before making assumptions concerning the particular disability of a child, teachers and practitioners should conduct a thorough assessment to identify the type of disability that is present in the individual case.

Capacity for Independent Living

Among students with LD, the capacity for independent living is not usually in question. These students typically live independently after completing school, and many have families, hold jobs, and lead relatively normal lives. Several factors that result from the disability, including academic and social–emotional outcomes from the schooling process, may impair their capacity to function independently during their adult lives.

Academic and Cognitive Outcomes

There is some evidence that the academic and cognitive difficulties that students with LD experience during school persist after the school years (Adelman & Vogel, 1993; Gregory, Shanahan, & Walberg, 1986; C. Johnson, 1984). In a summary of postschool outcomes for students with LD, Adelman and Vogel indicated that many young adults with LD were limited to low-paying or entry-level positions. Approximately 58% of students with LD were working during the 2 years after graduation from high school, and this approaches the employment rate for individuals without disabilities (i.e., 61%; D'Amico, 1991). However, there are significant gender differences that indicate that women with LD have much higher unemployment rates than do men with LD (Adelman & Vogel, 1993).

In an earlier comprehensive study, Gregory and colleagues (1986) conducted a retrospective study in which they compared outcome measures for high school seniors with and without learning disabilities. The authors used a data set designed to predict outcomes for all high school seniors in the secondary schools in the United States. Over 26,000 students completed a survey with information about themselves, and 439 of these students identified themselves as having LD. This group was compared to a group without disabilities on various academic variables, and the results demonstrated that the academic deficits of students with LD in reading, math, and language arts are apparent as late as the last year in school.

Research on reading and academic skills has demonstrated that many students with LD finish school with academic performance around the fifth-grade level. The reading level of adolescents with LD seems to peak at around the fifth- or sixth-grade level and to improve little thereafter. Also, research indicates that the IQ–achievement discrepancy is still relatively large for most of these students. C. Johnson (1984) identified deficits in reading comprehension, written work, and verbal language problems that continue to plague adults with LD after the postschool transition period. These levels of achievement performance present problems in both further schooling and entrance into the workforce.

Because years of remedial schooling have failed to alleviate these academic problems, more schooling for individuals with LD will probably not help. At this point, it is most beneficial for practitioners to assist youth with LD to identify coping strategies that make normal independent-living skills possible. Use of a functional-skills curriculum during the later years of schooling seems to offer the best remedy for recurring academic problems. In a functional-skills curriculum, daily-living skills, such as completion of tax return forms, job applications, and medical insurance forms, compose the curriculum. With the student's practice in those types of skills, the problems of living independently after school are alleviated somewhat.

Social and Emotional Outcomes

Another set of variables that may impair independent-living skills of students with LD includes social and emotional variables such as self-concept, peer relationships, social skill, and social interactions. Research has shown deficits among children with LD in each of these areas (Bender et al., 1999; Gresham, Sugai, & Horner, 2001). First, several studies of self-concept support this deficit in self-concept among older students and adults with LD (Bender & Wall, 1994; Gregory et al., 1986; Horn, O'Donnell, & Vitulano, 1983; Pihl & McLarnon, 1984). However, not all of the research is consistent on this point. Lewandowski and Arcangelo (1994) compared the self-concept of 40 young adults who had received services for LD in the public schools to that of 40 adults who did not receive any special education services. That study demonstrated no differences in the self-concept of these two groups. Further, the groups compared favorably on overall social adjustment. Clearly, these results are much more optimistic than those of the earlier studies.

Several studies have investigated the locus of control of students with learning disabilities (Gregory et al., 1986; Pintrich, Anderman, & Klobucar, 1994). Locus of control involves the perception of control that one has over one's environment. A high level on "internal" control typically indicates that one feels fairly secure that one's actions can result in positive occurrences in one's environment, whereas a high level of "external" locus of control indicates that one feels rather helpless to effect change in one's own life circumstances. These studies indicated that youth with LD demonstrate higher levels of external locus of control than would be desirable and that level of external control may have negative repercussions for independent-living skills.

Finally, a number of emotional and social variables, including emotional adjustment, legal troubles, depression, and suicide, have been studied among the young adult LD population but not in younger groups. This research indicates that students with LD do not compare favorably with nondisabled students in these areas (Bender et al., 1999; Gregory et al., 1986; Huntington & Bender, 1993). For example, Bender et al. (1999) indicated that youths with LD were more at risk for depression and possibly suicide than nondisabled youths. The study by Gregory et al. (1986) measured several other social and emotional variables, including overall adjustment, self-ratings of personal attractiveness, satisfaction with peer group, trouble with the law, parental interests in the student's activities, adequacy of home-study facilities, and mother's absence from the home. On each variable, school seniors with LD demonstrated less positive outcomes than did the comparison group of nondisabled seniors.

Although some research on social relationships during the school years has been conducted, little is known about how to increase social skills to facilitate independent living during the postschool period. Researchers have focused on the efficacy of social skills training programs that were intended to positively impact social skills of students with disabilities. Gresham et al. (2001) compiled a synthesis of this social skills training literature and demonstrated that only moderate effects of training were observed in most of the literature.

Clearly, these results, summarized in Table 12.3, do not demonstrate positive outcomes of special education interventions during the adolescent years. Further, they indicate potential problems that young adults with LD may find in independent living. For example, trouble with the law, in the form of a simple parking ticket, requires reading. It includes instructions on when and where to pay the fine, and some effort is necessary on the part of the person, or mistakes will be made in that process. Students with limited reading ability or inappropriate understanding of language may be more apt to get into trouble of this type or to respond inappropriately when they do get into such trouble.

TABLE 12.3

Emotional and Social Outcomes During Adolescent Years

Variable	Research Findings
Self-concept	Many students with LD have lower self-concepts than do nondisabled students.
Locus of control	Students with LD generally have higher external locus of control and do not attribute success in their endeavors to their own efforts.
Depression	Research has suggested that some students with LD manifest higher levels of depression and may possibly be at higher risk for suicide than other students.
Social success	Some research indicates that adolescents with LD engage in fewer social outings and enjoy less satisfaction with peer relationships.
Legal problems	Some students with LD have more minor legal problems than do other students, a finding that may indicate less than satisfactory social adjustment.

Economic Self-Sufficiency

College for Students with LD

Economic self-sufficiency depends to a large extent on successful postsecondary schooling in either a vocational program or a higher education program, and adults with LD frequently do attend college or vocational training programs after high school. In one study, D. Johnson and Blalock (1987) reported that 23 of 93 adults with LD attended college, and 19 obtained degrees.

Yost, Shaw, Cullen, and Bigaj (1994) investigated the types of programs that colleges offer for students with disabilities. They surveyed higher education service providers in 2-year, 4-year, and graduate institutions to determine the basic outlines of service that are provided for young adults with LD who attend postsecondary schools. Although most of the responding institutions indicated that services were available, there was no underlying philosophical basis for services, and services often seemed to be uncoordinated. However, a wide variety of services were offered in varying degrees at different institutions, including tutoring, reading assistance, note-taking training, and waivers for particular classes.

More recently, Mull, Sitlington, and Alper (2001) analyzed published research from 1985–2000 reporting on postsecondary education services for students with learning disabilities. Articles included in this review met the following criteria: (a) the focus pertained to postsecondary institutions; (b) the focus pertained to students diagnosed with learning disabilities, as well as dyslexia, attention-deficit/hyperactivity disorder, and attention-deficit disorder; and (c) the article recommended what services should be available at a specific postsecondary institution. Findings generally suggested some inconsistency in higher education programs for students with LD. For example, the only agreement in the literature regarding the definition of LD was that there seem to be a variety of definitions available, and this article pointed out that there is no universally accepted definition of LD. Also, only about one third of these articles emphasized the students' social skills deficits as affecting college performance. Clearly, researchers and practitioners in the field of learning disabilities need to deal with the issue of documentation and characteristics of a learning disability among older students. Further, researchers need to stipulate more accurately the specific areas in which students with LD demonstrate problems (i.e., academic, social, or both).

One may well anticipate that the number of students with LD attending college will increase as most colleges establish programs for them. To date, however, few studies have been conducted on postcollege employment of students with LD. Despite this lack of data, one may tentatively conclude that completing college indicates some degree of economic self-sufficiency for a sizable minority of adults with LD.

Vocational Outcomes

Some data do exist on the overall vocational outlook for adults with LD. Schalock and coworkers (1986) showed, in a 5-year follow-up study of postsecondary schools, that 72% of the students with LD were employed after school, and as mentioned previously, other research has shown employment rates that are similar to those of individuals without disabilities (D'Amico, 1991). However, most of the available data indicate that students with LD, although employed, may be trapped in lower paying jobs and may receive fewer advancement opportunities than other workers (Adelman & Vogel, 1993). Also, a sizable minority of persons with LD are, apparently, not employed even 5 years after school. Thus, the economic picture is not entirely positive for these students. These data are supported by several other studies of children with disabilities (see Bender, 2001, for a review).

Still, based on these data, the prognosis for economic self-sufficiency for most adults with LD appears to be somewhat positive. These data do represent fairly good news for students with LD, and practitioners should let parents and the individuals with disabilities themselves know this. Further, practitioners should endeavor to make vocational educational opportunities available for most students with LD during the secondary school years and thereafter. The content of such programs should focus on job-related skills, as well as on work-related skills (e.g., getting to work on time, punching the time clock) and interpersonal skills needed on the job (e.g., getting along with other workers, supporting newer employees, requesting assistance as necessary). Only by providing a complete vocational training program such as this can the practitioner hope to improve the outlook for economic self-sufficiency for his or her clients.

FINAL THOUGHTS

In view of the characteristics presented in this chapter, one major factor in any discussion of characteristics of an intervention program for children and youth with LD is the heterogeneity of each population. For example, whereas most students with LD may have problems in pragmatic language, not all students with this disability do. Most of these students have problems in selective and sustained attention, but not all of them do. Many students with LD may also demonstrate characteristics of ADHD, but not all do. As shown throughout this chapter, children with LD are quite heterogeneous. Consequently, understanding students with LD is founded on the realization of the amazing diversity of characteristics that are demonstrated by these children. When prepared to investigate this group as a highly diverse group, the practitioner will likewise be prepared to address the unique and individual needs of each and every student with a learning disability, and thus offer each student with these learning challenges the best education available.

REFERENCES

Adelman, P. B., & Vogel, S. A. (1993). Issues in the employment of adults with learning disabilities. *Learning Disability Quarterly, 16,* 219–232.

Barkley, R. A. (1992). *Attention-deficit hyperactive disorder: A handbook for diagnosis and treatment.* New York: Guilford Press.

Bender, W. N. (1985). Differential diagnosis based on the task-related behavior of learning-disabled and low-achieving adolescents. *Learning Disability Quarterly, 8,* 261–268.

Bender, W. N. (1991). *Introduction to learning disabilities: Identification, assessment, and teaching strategies.* Needham Heights, MA: Allyn & Bacon.

Bender, W. N. (2001). *Introduction to learning disabilities: Identification, assessment, and teaching strategies* (4th ed.). Needham Heights, MA: Allyn & Bacon.

Bender, W. N., Rosenkrans, C. B., & Crane, M. K. (1999). Stress, depression, and suicide among students with learning disabilities: Assessing the risk. *Learning Disability Quarterly, 22,* 143–156.

Bender, W. N., & Wall, M. E. (1994). Social–emotional development of students with learning disabilities. *Learning Disability Quarterly, 17,* 323–341.

Boucher, C. R. (1984). Pragmatics: The verbal language of learning disabled and nondisabled boys. *Learning Disability Quarterly, 7,* 271–286.

Boucher, C. R. (1986). Pragmatics: The meaning of verbal language in learning disabled and nondisabled boys. *Learning Disability Quarterly, 9,* 285–295.

Brachacki, G. W. Z., Nicolson, R. I., & Fawcett, A. J. (1995). Impaired recognition of traffic signs in adults with dyslexia. *Journal of Learning Disabilities, 28*(5), 297–301.

Bryan, T., Donahue, M., & Pearl, R. (1981). Learning disabled children's peer interactions during a small-group problem solving task. *Learning Disability Quarterly, 4,* 13–22.

Bussing, R., Zima, B. T., Belin, T. R., & Forness, S. T. (1998). Children who qualify for SED programs: Do they differ in level of ADHD symptoms and comorbid psychiatric conditions? *Behavioral Disorders, 23*(2), 85–97.

Chalfant, J. C. (1985). Identifying learning disabled students: A summary of the national task force report. *Learning Disabilities Focus, 1*(1), 9–20.

Coles, G. S. (1978). The learning disability test battery: Empirical and social issues. *Harvard Educational Review, 48,* 313–340.

Council for Learning Disabilities. (1987). The CLD position statement. *Journal of Learning Disabilities, 20,* 349–350.

D'Amico, R. (1991). The working world awaits: Employment experiences during and shortly after secondary school. In M. Wagner, L. Newman, R. D'Amico, E. D. Jay, P. Butler-Nalin, C. Marder, & R. Cox (Eds.), *Youth with disabilities: How are they doing? The first comprehensive report from the national longitudinal transition study of special education students* (pp. 8–55). Menlo Park, CA: SRI International.

Donahue, M., Pearl, R., & Bryan, T. (1980). Learning disabled children's conversational competence: Responses to inadequate messages. *Journal of Applied Psycholinguistics, 1,* 387–403.

Feagans, L. (1983). Discourse processes in learning disabled children. In J. D. McKinney & L. Feagans (Eds.), *Current topics in learning disabilities* (Vol. 1, pp. 87–115). Norwood, NJ: Ablex.

Fowler, M. (1992). *C.A.D.D. educator's manual: An in-depth look at attention deficit disorders from an educational perspective.* Fairfax, VA: CASET Associates.

Gajar, A. (1979). Educable mentally retarded, learning disabled, emotionally disturbed: Similarities and differences. *Exceptional Child, 45,* 470–472.

Gregory, J. F., Shanahan, T., & Walberg, H. (1986). A profile of learning disabled twelfth-graders in regular classes. *Learning Disability Quarterly, 9,* 33–42.

Gresham, F. M., Sugai, G., & Horner, R. H. (2001). Interpreting outcomes of social skills training for students with high-incidence disabilities. *Exceptional Children, 67,* 331–344.

Haager, D., & Vaughn, S. (1995). Parent, teacher, peer and self-reports of the social competence of students with learning disabilities. *Journal of Learning Disabilities, 28,* 205–215.

Hallahan, D. P., & Kauffman, J. M. (1977). Labels, categories, behaviors: ED, LD, and EMR reconsidered. *Journal of Special Education, 11,* 129–149.

Hallahan, D. P., Lloyd, J. W., & Stoller, L. (1982). *Improving attention with self-monitoring: A manual for teachers.* Charlottesville: University of Virginia.

Handwerk, M. L., & Marshall, R. M. (1998). Behavioral and emotional problems of students with learning disabilities, serious emotional disturbance, or both conditions. *Journal of Learning Disabilities, 31*(4), 327–338.

Horn, W. F., O'Donnell, J. P., & Vitulano, L. A. (1983). Long-term follow-up studies of learning disabled persons. *Journal of Learning Disabilities, 9,* 542–554.

Johnson, C. L. (1984). The learning disabled adolescent and young adult: An overview and critique of current practices. *Journal of Learning Disabilities, 7,* 386–391.

Johnson, D. J., & Blalock, J. W. (1987). *Adults with learning disabilities: Clinical studies.* Orlando, FL: Grune & Stratton.

Korkman, M., & Pesonen, A. E. (1994). A comparison of neuropsychological test profiles of children with attention deficit-hyperactivity disorder and/or learning disabilities. *Journal of Learning Disabilities, 27,* 383–392.

Lewandowski, L., & Arcangelo, K. (1994). The social adjustment and self-concept of adults with learning disabilities. *Journal of Learning Disabilities, 27,* 598–605.

Lilly, M. S. (Ed.). (1979). *Children with exceptional needs.* New York: Holt.

Mathes, M. Y., & Bender, W. N. (1997). The effects of self-monitoring on children with attention-deficit/hyperactivity disorder who are receiving pharmacological interventions. *Remedial and Special Education, 18*(2), 121–128.

Mayes, S. D., Calhoun, L., & Crowell, W. (2000). Learning disabilities and ADHD: Overlapping spectrum disorders. *Journal of Learning Disabilities, 33*(5), 17–24.

McKinney, J. D., & Feagans, L. (1983). Adaptive classroom behavior of learning disabled students. *Journal of Learning Disabilities, 16,* 360–367.

McKinney, J. D., Montague, M., & Hocutt, A. M. (1993). *A synthesis of research literature on the assessment and identification of attention deficit disorder.* Miami, FL: Miami Center for Synthesis of Research on Attention Deficit Disorder.

Moats, L. C., & Lyon, G. R. (1993). Learning disabilities in the United States: Advocacy, science, and the future of the field. *Journal of Learning Disabilities, 26,* 282–294.

Mull, C., Sitlington, P., & Alper, S. (2001). Postsecondary education for students with learning disabilities: A synthesis of the literature. *Exceptional Children, 68*(1), 97–118.

Pihl, R. O., & McLarnon, L. D. (1984). Learning disabled children as adolescents. *Journal of Learning Disabilities, 17,* 96–100.

Pintrich, P. R., Anderman, E. M., & Klobucar, C. (1994). Intraindividual differences in motivation and cognition in students with and without learning disabilities. *Journal of Learning Disabilities, 27,* 360–370.

Reid, R., Maag, J. W., & Vasa, S. F. (1994). Attention deficit hyperactivity disorder as a disability category: A critique. *Exceptional Children, 60,* 198–214.

Ross, A. O. (1976). *Psychological aspects of learning disabilities and reading disorders.* New York: McGraw-Hill.

Roth, F. P., Spekman, N. J., & Fye, E. C. (1995). Reference cohesion in the oral narratives of students with learning disabilities and normally achieving students. *Learning Disability Quarterly, 18*(1), 25–40.

Schalock, R. L., Wolzen, B., Ross, I., Elliot, B., Werbel, G., & Peterson, K. (1986). Post-secondary community placement of handicapped students: A five-year follow-up. *Learning Disability Quarterly, 9,* 295–303.

Schuerholz, L. J., Harris, E. L., Baumgardner, T. L., Reiss, A. L., Freund, L. S., Church, R. P., Mohr, J., & Denckla, M. B. (1995). An analysis of two discrepancy-based models and a processing-deficit approach in identifying learning disabilities. *Journal of Learning Disabilities, 28,* 18–29.

Sousa, D. A. (2001). *How the special needs brain learns.* Thousand Oaks, CA.: Corwin Press.

Spekman, N. (1981). Dyadic verbal communication abilities of learning disabled and normally achieving fourth and fifth grade boys. *Learning Disability Quarterly, 4,* 193–201.

Stanford, L. D., & Hynd, G. W. (1994). Congruence of behavioral symptomatology in children with ADD/H, ADD/WO, and learning disabilities. *Journal of Learning Disabilities, 27,* 343–353.

Swanson, H. L. (1999). Reading comprehension and working memory in learning disabled readers. *Journal of Exceptional Child Psychology, 72*(1), 1–31.

Swanson, H. L. (2000). Are working memory deficits in readers with learning disabilities hard to change? *Journal of Learning Disabilities, 32,* 551–566.

Swanson, H. L., & Ashbaker, M. H. (2000). Working memory, short-term memory, speech rate, word recognition and reading comprehension in learning disabled readers: Does the executive system have a role? *Intelligence, 28*(1), 1–30.

Torgesen, J. K. (1984). Memory processes in reading disabled children. *Journal of Learning Disabilities, 18,* 350–357.

Webster, R. E., & Schenck, S. (1978). Diagnostic test pattern differences among LD, ED, EMH, and multihandicapped students. *Journal of Educational Research, 72,* 75–80.

Whitney-Thomas, J., & Moloney, R. (2001). "Who I Am and What I Want": Adolescents' self-definition and struggles. *Exceptional Children, 67,* 375–389.

Wiig, E. H., Lapointe, C., & Semel, E. M. (1977). Relationships among language processing and production abilities of learning disabled adolescents. *Journal of Learning Disabilities, 9,* 292–299.

Wiig, E. H., Semel, E. M., & Abele, E. (1981). Perception and interpretation of ambiguous sentences by learning disabled twelve-year-olds. *Learning Disability Quarterly, 4,* 3–12.

Wiig, E. H., Semel, E. M., & Crouse, M. A. B. (1973). The use of English morphology by high-risk and learning disabled children. *Journal of Learning Disabilities, 6,* 457–464.

Yost, D. S., Shaw, S. F., Cullen, J. P., & Bigaj, S. J. (1994). Practices and attitudes of postsecondary LD service providers in North America. *Journal of Learning Disabilities, 27,* 631–640.

Ysseldyke, J. E. (1983). Current practices in making psychoeducational decisions about learning disabled students. *Journal of Learning Disabilities, 16,* 226–233.

Ysseldyke, J. E., & Algozzine, B. (1984). *Introduction to special education.* Boston: Houghton Mifflin.

Zentall, S. S. (1986). Effects of color stimulation on performance and activity of hyperactive and nonhyperactive children. *Journal of Educational Psychology, 78,* 159–165.

Zentall, S. S., Zentall, T. R., & Booth, M. E. (1978). Within task stimulation: Effects on activity and spelling performance in hyperactive and normal children. *Journal of Educational Research, 71,* 223–230.

Zuriff, G. E. (2002). The myths of learning disabilities: The social construction of a disorder. In M. Byrnes (Ed.), *Taking sides: Clashing views on controversial issues in special education.* Guillford, CT: McGraw-Hill.

SERVICES AND PROGRAMS

PERSONAL PERSPECTIVE

Acquiring needed services has always been and remains a challenge for people with developmental disabilities (DD) and intellectual disabilities (ID). Those of us with DD are perceived to be incapable of understanding what services we need to live and work in the community. Things have improved over the past 2 decades due to laws being passed that give people with DD and ID the right to choose services. Despite legislation and the developing independent living and self-determination movements, significant barriers remain that make it difficult to obtain needed services.

Many service providers and some parents say they believe in self-determination, but there is still great hesitation when it comes to allowing customers to put it into actual practice. Providers and many parents are fearful of letting their customers or adult children try new things because they may fail or be hurt. Because of these attitudes, individuals who do learn to successfully navigate the service delivery system do so because they have become skilled at using self-advocacy. In many cases, these successful self-advocates have been encouraged by loving parents to practice self-determination.

This was certainly true in my case and is something I have used to draw strength from throughout my life. Although my disability impaired my mobility, coordination, and speech, my parents encouraged me to participate in many of the same activities as those people without disabilities. I participated in Sunday school pageants, became a member of my local Boy Scout troop, and engaged in neighborhood activities with my nondisabled peers. Being encouraged to do these things really gave me a sense of belonging in my community. In participating in such activities, I learned the meaning of being accommodated long before the word became a part of disability rights legislation. For example, if my Boy Scout troop hiked to a campground, I was given permission to ride there in my dad's pickup truck. If my Sunday school class was putting on a program at church, I would be given a singing part with the group instead of having to recite lines in front of the congregation. I do not mean to suggest that my early life was without problems or barriers, but my parents taught me to learn how to work around the difficulties I faced. In essence, at an early stage of my life, I was learning to be a self-advocate to gain my place in my community. I believe this early training from my parents set the stage for my becoming an advocate for myself and others.

Personal experiences and serving others with DD has taught me that self-advocacy is the lubricant that makes any service delivery system more flexible. This flexibility is very necessary to meet the unique needs of the individuals who are seeking the services. Service providers need to understand that although people have similar disabilities, their needs may be different. Providers who do not understand this very important concept tend to deliver services based on disability stereotypes. Delivery of services in this manner does a serious injustice to the customers. In the following pages, I outline how my own personal experiences help me to formulate my philosophy of how services should be delivered to people who have DD and ID. I also describe how the disability rights movement played a role in my becoming a system advocate, trying to make a very rigid service delivery system more customer friendly.

HOW I BECAME AN EFFECTIVE SELF-ADVOCATE

My first experience using self-advocacy to force a needed change came early in my life. My friend Bobby, a classmate, and I joined forces to solve a dilemma when we were beginning our freshman year of high school. When we returned to school that fall with another classmate, we found three stacks of textbooks in the room but no teacher. After we wrote to the Chesapeake school superintendent explaining our situation, a teacher was found almost immediately. In another situation, shortly after we graduated from high school, we were told by rehabilitation professionals that we were unemployable due to our disabilities. This opinion was based on a very short—one day to be exact—vocational evaluation that consisted of working

with outdated typewriters and business machines. Due to our slow production rate, we were advised to return home and seek training in a sheltered workshop or possibly sell pencils on a street corner. As self-advocates who believe we have other abilities and qualifications, we rejected that idea and decided to pursue more meaningful career paths. Our decision eventually led us to jobs with the school system that were more compatible with our skills and abilities. Ironically, once we got the jobs ourselves, the rehabilitation system paid for our college classes and books to enable us to be employed as library assistants. These two valuable experiences taught Bobby and me a valuable lesson, which was that nothing positive would happen for us unless we made it happen through self-advocacy. This lesson not only had an impact on me personally, but has enabled me to become a role model for others whom I have provided services to. In the late 1970s, I moved from the library assistant position to working directly with students with DD. Bobby and I were teaching the students independent living skills, self-advocacy techniques, and some academic subjects. Despite only working 2 days a week for a very meager wage, I considered myself pretty lucky to be working at all and, so, was relatively content with my life. The late 1970s and early 1980s were times of great change for me personally. Also, those eventful years saw the disability rights movement come to life here in Virginia. On a personal level, it was a time of self-examination for me, as I decided where I wanted to go.

During that time, as I entered my mid-30s, all of a sudden I heard Dad planning his retirement and talking about trips he wanted to take with Mom. They were also considering moving farther out in the country. Bobby was hearing his parents talk about the same stuff. We began wondering how this would impact our school jobs and our personal friendship. Well, Bobby and I huddled and made two decisions. First, we would get involved with the new paratransit service we were reading about in the newspaper, and we believed that would get us to and from our part-time jobs independent of our parents. Second, we decided to enroll in a new driver's education class for people with disabilities being offered at Norfolk State University. We hoped that these two moves would help us achieve a little more independence and make us less dependent on our parents. Although Bobby and I did not get our driver's licenses, the class did bring us into contact with the two people who have since become our life partners.

Our experience with the local para-transit system was not exactly as successful as we had hoped. Dealing with the system alone, as self-advocates, was very frustrating, and many nights we had to resort to calling our parents to come and rescue us from school. This experience brought me to the realization that every problem could not be resolved by one or two individuals alone. Making a para-transit system work as it was intended to was definitely a systems advocacy issue. Therefore, Bobby and I decided to unite with others having similar problems with transportation, which led us to join a local advocacy organization called Mobility on Wheels (MOW). Becoming members of MOW set in motion a chain of events that would take Bobby and me in separate directions. I became a disability rights activist, whereas Bobby was content to pursue a career in special education and a romantic interest.

My membership in MOW taught me the importance of coalescing around difficult advocacy issues to bring about systems change. This made me see the difference between using self-advocacy to make a change in my own life and uniting with other advocates to make changes that would benefit all people with disabilities. Understanding this difference excited me and put me on a path that would lead me to different careers. My newfound interest in systems advocacy led me to become a MOW board member and to hold several other leadership positions in Vir-

ginia's emerging disability rights movement. These leadership positions gave me forums where I could speak on the need to make service systems more accessible to people with all types of disabilities. This soon became the driving passion in my life.

FROM SELF-ADVOCATE TO SYSTEMS ADVOCATE

My passion was ignited the first time Bobby and I attended a MOW meeting. The guest speaker was a guy with a disability named John Chappell. At that time, he was president of Handicaps Unlimited of Virginia (HUVA), a statewide cross-disability organization, and he spoke about the importance of implementing Section 504 of the Rehabilitation Act here in Virginia. He also told the membership that HUVA had applied for a federal grant to establish a consumer-controlled center for independent living (CIL) that would be based in Norfolk. I did not fully grasp the significance of all his words, yet I was excited by them. He spoke about CILs being system change agencies that were governed by boards made up of consumers with all types of disabilities. These agencies also had staff, who were primarily people who had disabilities and who served as role models for others. The words of this charismatic speaker captivated my imagination, and I wanted to know more.

After his talk, I briefly chatted with him about disability rights issues and how I could get more involved. I also wanted to know more about the independent living movement and how it might help Bobby and me have more independent lives to relieve the stress on our parents. John patiently answered all my questions and invited Bobby and me to attend the HUVA annual meeting, which was to be held in our capital, Richmond. I did not have the foggiest idea of how I was going to get there, but I instinctively knew I had to be there. About a month later, I boarded a Greyhound bus in Norfolk heading toward Richmond. This trip would have an impact on my life beyond my wildest dreams. At the meeting, I listened to speakers like John explain the importance of united advocacy efforts. I began to understand how it all fit together like pieces of a puzzle to make needed system-wide changes designed to improve the lives of people with disabilities. As HUVA adjourned, I was energized, and John had another disciple and believer.

When I returned home from Richmond, things really began to change in my life. I was asked to sit on a consumer advisory committee that oversaw the establishment of the state's first consumer-controlled CIL. While serving on that committee, John Chappell and others encouraged me to apply to become a part-time peer counselor with the new Norfolk CIL. That I did, and for 18 months I tried to maintain my teacher's aide position while also working at the CIL. When a full-time position became available, I applied and became a full-time CIL employee; being full-time, I gave up my part-time teacher's aide position. This was a significant change for five reasons: First, it severed my working relationship with my lifelong friend, Bobby. Second, I had a real salaried job with benefits. Third, I had to find creative ways to manage a full caseload of CIL participants and file case notes on those participants. I did this with the assistance of volunteers, one of whom has since become my workplace personal assistant at my current job. Fourth, it made me become very familiar with the DD service delivery system in Virginia, because many of my participants were seeking services through that system. And finally, it gave me opportunities to pursue my advocacy leadership role on the state level. Soon I found myself in meetings with state officials, sharing my concerns about barriers to services encountered by people I was serving at the CIL. Being in this position gave me a better understanding of the service systems that my participants were dealing with as they went for services. This was an advantage in preparing my participants to advocate for services, and I took full advantage of it.

PROVIDING CUSTOMER-DIRECTED SERVICES

As a peer counselor and case manager, my job was to provide the services that were selected by my participants. The purpose of those services was to assist them in achieving goals identified in their independent living plans. Following the independent living philosophy, those plans were to be developed jointly by the participants I served and myself. So the idea of customer-driven services and working in partnership with my participants was a value that was ingrained in me the whole time I worked at the CIL. At the CIL, I provided four major services, which included peer counseling, case management, information and referral, and advocacy. Perhaps the most important of these services was advocacy because it helped participants acquire services needed to successfully live in the community. Providing advocacy support was often necessary because participants were encountering difficulty in getting the services they needed.

In the early to mid-1980s, services were not very flexible or customer friendly. This was especially true of services needed by my participants with DD or ID, a population that constituted over 50% of my caseload. Those who administered the services for this underserved group still had a very narrow view of what people with DD or ID could and could not do. On top of that, many professionals who worked in that system were very paternalistic, had low expectations of their clients, and did not respect their clients' right to fail. Being an advocate with DD who was assisting a participant with DD to navigate that system, I encountered some interesting resistance. In some instances, the provider got confused and thought I was a client, and I would have to spend time clarifying exactly what my role was. These encounters proved to be challenging and frustrating at times, but in the end I usually won the respect of the provider. These encounters also caused me to use creative ways to deal with the barriers that both my participants and I encountered as we advocated for the services in that system.

Developing a tough skin and maintaining a strong belief in the abilities of my participants were the tools I used to break down the door to services. Believing in people's abilities and their right to choose services, careers, and where they live has made me a relentless advocate in helping people navigate the ID/DD system. Over the 8 years I served on the CIL staff, I developed some guiding values and some effective strategies in assisting people with DD to acquire services and make choices about their lives. These values and strategies not only guided the way I provided services to my participants but have assisted me in training participants how to advocate for services in other systems.

VALUES

As a teacher's aide, an independent living provider, and a self-advocacy trainer, I have practiced four guiding values in my work: developing partnerships with customers, clarifying roles with customers, understanding my customers' "bottom line," and practicing simple do's and don'ts (listed later in this chapter) in dealing with my customers. These values encourage the customers that I have worked with to direct and choose their own services. They also let customers have a major role in advocating for their own services. Practicing such values allows customers to be the decision makers when choosing the level of service they need. Finally, by using some simple do's and don'ts when interacting with customers, professionals can empower them instead of controlling them. In my view, empowering customers by using such values should be the ultimate goal when serving cus-

tomers with DD or ID. In the paragraphs below, I describe how I have practiced these values in the many roles I have had serving this population.

Working in Partnership with Customers To Establish Goals

As a provider of independent living services, I always considered my participants as my customers. As a peer counselor, it was not my role to tell my customers how to live more independent lives but rather to listen to what they wanted to do. After they told me what they wanted to do, it was my job to assist them to figure out ways to get it done. This not only relieved me of the responsibility of trying to tell people how to live their lives, it also caused participants to take ownership of what they wanted to accomplish. And it was a great incentive for them to make the effort needed to reach their goals. This approach to delivery of services always worked great for me, no matter how high or how low an individual's IQ was. The higher functioning person bought into the process quicker. Many were able to accomplish many goals by themselves with only encouragement from me. For the lower functioning individual, it was a matter of explaining what had to be done in simple but age-appropriate terms and providing the right level of support. With both types of individuals, it was simply a matter of making sure that participants developed their own goals and working with them in partnership to reach their goals. This value, simply put, is that everyone feels more confident when they know that working toward a goal will be a team effort.

Clarify Roles Before Beginning To Advocate for Services

Before starting to assist my participants to advocate for services, I made certain that everyone understood each other's role in the process. It was my job to gather information about the service and find out how to contact the agency providing the service and who the contact person was that we needed to talk to. It was my participants' role to explain why they needed the service, why they were eligible for the service, and how the service could make them more independent. My participants being able to explain these things to service providers for themselves always made a bigger impression than if I attempted to speak for them. Of course, I went over the key points that needed to be made in counseling sessions prior to their appointment. My primary role in the advocacy process was to make certain each person had enough information to feel comfortable being his or her own spokesperson. In the case of higher functioning participants, I simply explained what agency provided the service and who they needed to contact. They did the rest. Some of my lower functioning participants needed some pretty intense training to understand their role in advocating for services. Some actually needed me to accompany them to their appointment with the service provider. Even in those situations, I encouraged the participant to speak up; I was there only to provide clarifying information if needed. Giving the participants this role and responsibility was important because it encouraged the provider to interact directly with the person who was seeking the service. It also gave the participant a great opportunity to practice the self-advocacy skills that were discussed in preparation for the appointment. It was a great confidence builder, which participants could use the next time they went to ask for services. I always tried to make sure my participants were well prepared for their appointments. This allowed me to keep a low profile in the actual meeting, so the provider would focus on the person seeking service and not me.

Understanding the Customer's "Bottom Line" Before Beginning the Advocacy Process

As an advocate for a person seeking services, I always wanted to know exactly what my customer's bottom line was. This not only pre-

vented me from taking on a decision-making role, it also helped me to encourage the person to hold out for what he or she really wanted. This strategy was very effective when I was working with customers who had ID or DD. Typically, this type of customer is very passive and will tend to accept anything being offered. I always tried to teach them to be assertive, and we would reach an agreement on what they needed prior to their meeting with the service provider. Once that was done, I could better support and encourage them. Sometimes, I even encouraged them to ask for more than they needed. This strategy gave them room to negotiate down to what they actually needed.

Do's and Don'ts To Follow When Serving People with DD or ID

When working with people with DD or ID, the provider should do things that will empower them and try to avoid doing things that will intimidate and control them. Empowering the customer is very important when providing customer-driven services. It is also a factor in developing a partnership between the provider of services and the ones who receive the services. Empowering those you serve diminishes your perceived role as an authority figure and makes you a real partner in assisting people to accomplish their goals. The process of empowering the people you serve is not an easy task. There are many barriers that must be overcome, but in the end your efforts can create a win-win situation for all concerned. Some of the barriers include understanding the needs of a person with a speech impairment or making sure a person with a cognitive disability understands his or her role in the advocacy process. It takes a lot of time, patience, and respect to empower customers who have these types of disabilities, but it is well worth the effort when you see what can be achieved.

Over the years, as a provider of services, I have developed some commonsense approaches to interviewing and understanding the needs of customers with disabilities. Below is a list of do's and don'ts for providers to use if they truly want to level the playing field between them and the people they serve. These are great tools to use to facilitate clear and meaningful communication between service providers and their customers with DD or ID:

Do's

1. Do consider the person as a person first, a customer second, and a consumer third.

2. Do make every effort to understand what the person with a speech impairment has to say.

3. Do take time to listen and don't assume you know what the person wants to say.

4. Do look at the person you are talking to and give him or her your full attention. This means don't fiddle with paper, read, or look at your watch.

5. Do be open-minded when the person is telling you what his or her vocational goal is.

6. Do keep your expectations high and believe the person has the ability to know his or her own capabilities.

7. Do communicate directly with the person even if he or she is accompanied by a parent, caseworker, or attendant.

8. Do be courteous to the person.

9. Do be encouraging and supportive when discussing educational goals or employment opportunities with the person. Avoid comments like "Come now, be realistic." "You know you'll fail if you try that." "My agency is not going to waste money on your pipe dreams."

10. Do be sensitive and willing to offer accommodations appropriate to the person's disability. For example, offer to read documents to the person with a visual impairment, have a sign interpreter for the deaf, and provide a solid writing surface for people who have difficulty using their hands.

Don'ts

1. Don't be negative when counseling a person with a severe disability. Negativity is stifling to people who aren't used to expressing themselves.

2. Don't be loud when conversing with a person with a disability who has no hearing impairment.

3. Don't bring preconceived notions into the counseling session before you get to know the person. Most textbooks on disability are written from a medical perspective and do not address factors such as determination or motivation.

4. Don't try to be a mind reader when you are listening to a person with a speech impairment. Believe me, this can be irritating as well as insulting.

5. Don't underestimate the determination of the person you are counseling.

6. Don't let the appearance of people influence your judgment of their abilities. A good rule to remember is the old saying "Don't judge a book by its cover."

7. Don't be overprotective and deny people their right to learn even if that means failing. Case managers can point out obstacles but should never force their opinions of what is and what is not possible.

8. Don't fail to offer appropriate accommodations if you are interviewing a person with a disability.

9. Don't position yourself in such a way as to make it difficult to maintain eye contact with the person.

10. Don't counsel a person with a speech impairment in a noisy environment.

11. Don't ever talk down to a person with a disability; this includes people with cognitive disabilities.

12. Don't be intimidating or judgmental when counseling. Never use your authority to stifle a person's dreams or goals.

By using and practicing the values discussed above, I believe service providers will see their customers in a different light and establish more meaningful partnerships. I am convinced these can be used with customers no matter how significant or profound their disabilities are. They may take a little more time to practice, but the service outcomes will be well worth the effort. As service delivery systems lean more and more toward customer choice, these values will become essential tools that providers must know how to use to facilitate maximum customer choice and satisfaction.

—Ed Turner

CHAPTER 13

Community-Based Vocational Training

Katherine Inge, Paul Wehman, and Stacy Dymond

LEARNING GOALS

Upon completion of this chapter, the reader will be able to

- describe what community-based instruction is and why it is an effective way to assist individuals with developmental disabilities in preparing for the transition from school to work

- list and briefly describe the five major steps in developing community-based training sites

- describe the key components of instructional strategies for implementing community-based instruction

- discuss the importance of using several different training sites in the community-based instruction process

Transition from school to work for students with significant disabilities should lead to competitive employment now that best practices such as person-centered planning, assistive technology, compensatory strategies, coworker supports, and systematic instruction have facilitated community inclusion. In order for integrated employment outcomes to become the norm rather than the exception, students must have increasing opportunities to participate in community-based training experiences as they progress through elementary, middle, and high school. Many professionals have recognized community-based vocational preparation as a best practice for teaching individuals with developmental disabilities (deFur, 1999; Moon & Inge, 2000; Wehman, 2001; Wehman & Revell, 1997).

Effective vocational preparation begins in the elementary school years with the focus on learning to follow a schedule, acquiring social skills, and learning to take responsibility (Moon & Inge, 2000). As the student progresses to middle school and high school, activities need to occur in the community where the skills will be used. The emphasis is on individualized training in real job sites, not field trips or simulated work activities within the school building. This instruction in real community settings should be balanced with teaching work-related academic skills and other age-appropriate curriculum content within school settings (Putnam, 1994; Stainback & Stainback, 1992). However, students must have the opportunity to participate in integrated business settings where production, quality, and social demands of the natural work environment can be addressed.

The opportunity to train in job settings may be the most critical for those students with significant disabilities who have difficulty generalizing skills acquired in one setting to another. Research has shown that students with significant disabilities do not generalize work skills learned in segregated school programs to community sites (Wehman, 1992). Due to this inability to generalize and to difficulties in learning new skills, the individual with developmental disabilities must be increasingly exposed to community-based training as he or she progresses through the school program (Renzaglia & Hutchins, 1988). The more difficulties displayed in skill transferral by an individual, the more he or she can benefit from instruction in natural or community environments.

Although community-based instruction has been identified as a needed curriculum component for students with developmental disabilities, many school systems continue to exclude students with the most significant disabilities. The presence of challenging behaviors may be one of the reasons that teachers hesitate to take some students into the community (Wehman, 1992). Issues of concern include the safety of the teacher, the employees, and the student if he or she becomes "uncontrollable" on a job site, as well as liability for damages to individuals or the environment. The simple solution for school districts, in some instances, is to continue training within the school setting rather than providing the much needed exposure to community work experiences. However, this practice will serve only to exclude individuals from critical skill training opportunities and eventually segregate them further from community participation and employment after graduation.

The steps in developing community-based training sites include (a) conducting a job-market analysis, (b) identifying businesses with the targeted jobs and contacting the personnel director or employer, (c) selecting and analyzing appropriate jobs for community-based training, (d) scheduling community-based vocational instruction, and (e) designing individualized instructional programs. These steps are explained in more detail in the following pages. Teachers may first want to contact adult service agencies within their communities to determine the location of supported employment placements. These sites may not be appropriate for community-based vocational training experiences, because the presence of unpaid students could confuse the employers and result in inappropriate work expectations and labor law violations (Moon & Inge, 1993). A detailed listing of the steps and activities involved in developing community-based training sites is provided in Table 13.1 (see also Moon & Inge, 1993; Moon, Inge, Wehman, Brooke, & Barcus, 1990; Moon, Kiernan, & Halloran, 1990; Pumpian, Shepard, & West, 1988).

STEP I: CONDUCT A JOB-MARKET ANALYSIS

Some students may be able to select a career path or identify possible jobs of choice in their person-centered plans (Inge, Malatchi, Armstrong, & Blankenship, 2001). However, students who have limited exposure will lack the life experiences necessary to know what they like and dislike (Smull, 1998). To support individual choice, it will be necessary to determine what environments or places students want to spend time in or avoid. What do they want to do, and what do they not want to do? As students have the opportunity to participate in community-based vocational training experiences, they can establish preferences and eventually make informed choices about their future career paths.

Participating in a number of training experiences that are reflective of the jobs available within a community can provide the needed life experiences. Therefore, the first step in setting up community-based vocational sites is an assessment of the local labor demands to determine the employment trends and to identify current and future job openings (Inge, Dymond, et al., 1993; Moon & Inge, 2000). Once these have been determined, job-training sites can be established in businesses. Initially, a school system may want to identify a task force of teachers to develop procedures for completing a community job-market analysis (Moon, Inge, et al., 1990). In some instances, the task force may appoint the transition coordinator to complete business contacts, or a special education teacher at the secondary level may take the lead. In any case, a plan of action should be developed to prevent duplication of effort.

Once school personnel have been identified to complete the market analysis, they may begin by surveying their local Chamber of Commerce or economic development office, looking in the telephone directory, reading the newspaper want ads, interviewing potential employers, completing follow-up contacts with school graduates, and contacting adult service agencies and supported employment

TABLE 13.1

Steps and Activities for Developing a Community-Based Vocational Training Program

Steps	Activities
1. Conduct a community job-market analysis.	1. Identify a school task force or individuals who will be responsible for completing the analysis. 2. Survey the telephone directory yellow pages. 3. Read the classified section of the newspaper. 4. Contact local business organizations (e.g., Chamber of Commerce). 5. Survey school graduates to determine jobs held by individuals with disabilities in the community. 6. Create a list of potential jobs, by job type, that are available to students with severe disabilities.

2. Identify businesses with the targeted jobs and contact the personnel director or employer.	1. Establish a school policy for contacting employers and businesses.
	2. Identify school personnel responsible for business contacts.
	3. Review and revise (as needed) school insurance/liability policy to cover community-based training sites and transportation.
	4. Outline school policy for meeting labor law regulations.
	5. Develop a contract for meeting the labor law requirements.
	6. Contact the business by letter or telephone:
	   a. Briefly describe the school's community-based program.
	   b. Discuss jobs that may be appropriate for training.
	   c. Schedule a time to visit and explain the program further.
	7. Visit the business in person:
	   a. Describe the purpose of vocational instruction.
	   b. Discuss the employer, teacher, and student responsibilities on the job site.
	   c. Explain the labor law regulations for nonpaid work experiences.
	   d. Discuss liability issues.
	   e. Develop a community-based training agreement.
	   f. Identify possible job tasks for training.
	   g. Schedule a time to observe the identified tasks to develop task analyses.
	   h. Send a thank-you note.
	8. Compile a file for each business visited.

3. Select and analyze appropriate jobs for community-based training.	1. Visit the job site. 2. Discuss the identified jobs with the site supervisor. 3. Discuss the job-site rules and regulations. 4. Observe the coworkers performing the job duties. 5. Select the tasks best suited for students with disabilities. 6. Develop a job duty schedule and task analyses for the activities selected. 7. Identify available times with the employer or department supervisor for training. 8. Request at least 1- to 2-hour blocks of time for each site identified. 9. Agree on a start date.

(continues)

TABLE 13.1 *Continued.*

Steps and Activities for Developing a Community-Based Vocational Training Program

Steps	Activities

4. Schedule community-based training.	1. Identify students to receive vocational training.
	2. Hold IEP/ITP meetings for students.
	  a. Identify student training needs.
	  b. Discuss purpose of community-based vocational training with transition team members.
	  c. Write vocational goals or objectives.
	3. Match students to available sites.
	4. Sign community-based training agreements (students, parents, employer, school representative).
	5. Develop a daily schedule.
	6. Develop a transportation schedule.
	7. Send a copy of the schedule to the school principal, special education supervisor, parents, employers, etc.
	8. Provide parents with information on individual insurance coverage for liability.

5. Design individual systematic instruction programs.	1. Modify job duty schedules and task analyses based on student characteristics. 2. Select a data collection procedure. 3. Take a baseline of student performance on all tasks to be taught. 4. Select an instructional procedure. 5. Select a reinforcer. 6. Implement the training program. 7. Take probe data on student performance. 8. Routinely review student data and modify program format as needed. 9. Review student goals and objectives for training and update as needed.

programs to determine job placements for individuals with disabilities. A list of contacts might include the following:

> state economic development office
> state employment commission
> Chamber of Commerce
> trade associations
> Better Business Bureau
> city and county employment offices
> Department of Labor
> One Stop Centers
> telephone book and newspaper classifieds
> business newsletters
> vocational rehabilitation agencies
> supported employment providers

civic clubs and organizations

friends and associates

STEP 2: IDENTIFY BUSINESSES WITH THE TARGETED JOBS AND CONTACT THE PERSONNEL DIRECTOR OR EMPLOYER

Once the local economy has been assessed to determine the possible job types for students with significant disabilities, the teacher must determine where instruction will occur. Each student should have the opportunity to experience a variety of jobs in a number of different settings to assist the student in developing a work history, determine his or her job preferences, identify future training needs, and determine skill characteristics for future job matching. The task force that completed the community job-market analysis should also identify the individual who will approach employers regarding use of their businesses for community-based training sites. Initial information to identify potential jobs within a business can be obtained from the personnel director or employer. Often this individual will be able to provide written job descriptions that can be useful in identifying job types.

However, observation of the actual work sites usually is more beneficial for job identification (Moon, Inge, et al., 1990). When selecting nonpaid work experiences, the teacher must be careful not to displace a worker within the job site to meet labor law requirements (Inge, Simon, Halloran, & Moon, 1993). The tasks targeted should provide enough space for the student and teacher to work alongside the regular employees. Other important issues to consider when establishing community-based vocational training experiences have been clearly defined in a policy statement issued by the U.S. Department of Education (1992). It includes the following criteria:

- Participants should be youth with disabilities for whom competitive employment at or above minimum wage is not immediately obtainable.
- Vocational exploration, assessment, and training activities in a community-based setting must be under the general supervision of the public school personnel.
- Community-based placements must be clearly defined as part of the student's educational program and included in the Individualized Education Program. Documentation as to the student's enrollment should be made available to the Departments of Labor and Education.
- The student and parent must be fully informed of the voluntary nature of the student's participation, with the understanding that this does not entitle the student to wages.
- The activities performed by the student on the job site do not benefit the business. Students must not displace other employees nor should other employees be freed up to do other activities while the student is present

on the job site. In addition, students must not fill vacant positions or perform additional services not ordinarily performed by employees that benefit the business.
- Students must be under the continued supervision of a school representative or employees of the business.
- Training activities performed by the student are completed according to the student's IEP and not to meet the labor needs of the business.

When completing community-based vocational training, a student cannot spend more than 120 hours per job experienced in any one school year. The maximum number of hours for vocational exploration is 5 hours, and for vocational assessment, the student cannot exceed 90 hours per job experienced.

Contacts with the personnel director or a company manager can be made by phone or letter to set up an appointment to discuss the school's program in detail. Additional methods for initial contacts may include visiting local business association meetings, attending employer breakfasts, and visiting regional business offices (Pumpian et al., 1988). Dropping in on employers without an appointment is not recommended.

STEP 3: SELECT AND ANALYZE APPROPRIATE JOBS FOR COMMUNITY-BASED TRAINING

Often, the initial contact made with a business is with an employer or management-level individual who will not be able to specifically assist the teacher in identifying jobs for training. The teacher will be referred to a supervisor who will be the actual contact person for community programming. Activities during this phase of setting up a community-based training site include observing the coworkers as they perform the job duties available, selecting tasks that are appropriate to the students who will be receiving training, and actually working the selected job duties.

When working with the supervisor to identify activities within the workplace, the teacher must consider the number of tasks that should be targeted for instruction. There is some debate as to whether it is more beneficial to provide students with many tasks, or to limit experience to one or two tasks (Sowers & Powers, 1991). This decision should be based on the characteristics of specific students, but it may be appropriate to limit the number of tasks for students with significant disabilities. Sowers and Powers suggest that providing instruction on a number of different tasks or moving students from task to task before skill learning occurs may not allow them to experience a sense of accomplishment.

A tentative schedule of the activities that the student will be performing should be developed, as well as task analyses for skills targeted. Both the schedule and the analyses may need modification once specific students are assigned to a work site. Finally, the teacher should negotiate the times for the student to be on site and a start date.

Job Duty Schedule

A job duty schedule outlines the specific work tasks that will be performed by the students, as well as the time the tasks will be performed. Figure 13.1 is a sample job schedule for a community-based training site. In addition to the job duty schedule, the teacher–trainer needs to determine if there are any special requirements that the employer has for the student on the job site. Answers to the following sample questions should be determined (Moon & Inge, 1993):

Community-Based Training Site: __Discount Clothing Store - Stock Room__

Area Supervisor: __Mrs. Mary Miller__

Teacher Completing Form: __Stacy D.__

☑ Daily
   (Training tasks remain the
   same from day to day)

☐ Varies day to day
   (If checked here, complete a separate form
   for each day's schedule)

If above box is checked, indicate day for which this form is completed:

☐   ☐   ☐   ☐   ☐
Mon   Tues   Wed   Thurs   Fri

Vocational Training Tasks	Approximate Time
Punch in, set up work area	1:00 P.M.–1:15 P.M.
Open clothing boxes	1:15 P.M.–1:30 P.M.
Put clothes on hangers	1:30 P.M.–2:00 P.M.
Break in employee lounge	2:00 P.M.–2:15 P.M.
Unpack boxes, fold items, put on shelves in stock room	2:15 P.M.–3:00 P.M.
Punch out - Go to McDonald's - Return to School	3:00 P.M.–3:30 P.M.

Comments: __Students should wear dark blue pants and a white shirt for this training site.__
__Report to Mrs. Miller upon arrival. If she is not in the stock room, call ext. 75 and report__
__to security. Students will work with Bill and Laura (coworkers) on all tasks.__

Signature/Title: _____ Date: _____

FIGURE 13.1. Sample community-based training schedule. From *Designing Community-Based Instructional Programs for Students with Severe Disabilities,* by K. Inge and P. Wehman (Eds.), 1993, Richmond: Virginia Commonwealth University, Rehabilitation Research and Training Center on Supported Employment. Copyright 1993 by Rehabilitation Research and Training Center on Supported Employment. Reprinted with permission.

- Does the employer or supervisor want the student to wear a uniform or specific clothing (e.g., white shirt with black pants)?
- What entrance should be used?
- Is it important to report to the supervisor or to a coworker upon arrival?
- Do employees have assigned lockers and can one be available to the student?
- Is there an identified break area and employee bathroom?
- Are there specific break times for employees?
- Are there any company benefits that may be available to the student (e.g., free lunch or soda)?
- Are there any restricted (hazardous) areas or activities that can be identified?
- Is there a company policy or procedure for reporting accidents on the job?

All of this information can be recorded and placed in a file that can be accessed by all school personnel. This file is particularly important during teacher absences when another school employee must supervise the site.

Task Analysis

Whatever activities are included in the job duty schedule, the teacher needs to complete a thorough task analysis of each activity prior to bringing the student to the work site. The teacher should observe the coworkers performing the task; identify each step that is completed; and then perform the job, modifying the steps as necessary. Finally, the teacher should check with the supervisor to ensure that the task is being performed correctly.

Each step of a task analysis should consist of one observable behavior that can be taught individually (Inge, 1997; Moon & Inge, 1993; Moon, Inge, et al., 1990). The steps should be worded in the second person so they can be used as verbal prompts during instruction (e.g., "Go to the desk") and should make references to things that are observable (e.g., "Push the green button"). A good task analysis assists the teacher in organizing instruction, providing consistent training, and evaluating the student's performance. Table 13.2 is a sample task analysis for entering data into a database.

There are several tips for developing and individualizing task analyses for vocational instruction to facilitate a student's skill acquisition and quality performance. First, the teacher should analyze a job to determine whether discrimination is part of the task and, if it is, how can it be built into the task analysis. For instance, many individuals with significant disabilities may be unable to distinguish clean from dirty. In the task analysis, the teacher could analyze cleaning the table and determine a pattern of wiping the top that would always result in a clean surface. These steps would then be broken down into smaller steps for instruction. For a student with discrimination difficulties, a sample step in the task analysis may be further analyzed as shown in Table 13.3.

TABLE 13.2

Sample Task Analysis: Entering Data

1. Press up arrow key.	11. Press enter key 2 times.
2. Press control key.	12. Type street.
3. Type F.	13. Press enter key 2 times.
4. Press shift key.	14. Type zip code.
5. Type first name.	15. Press enter key 2 times.
6. Press enter key.	16. Type today's date.
7. Press shift key.	17. Press enter key 3 times.
8. Type last name.	18. Type 1.
9. Press enter key.	19. Press enter key 3 times.
10. Type company name.	20. Begin next entry.

TABLE 13.3

Sample Step Analysis

8. Brush top of toilet. (Student wipes top one time, always working left to right.)

Place brush at back corner.
Move brush across top of toilet.
Place brush at front center.
Move brush across top.

Note. The information placed in parentheses serves as a cue to the trainer for consistency of prompting but is not used as a verbal cue to the student.

Another area that the teacher should address within the task analysis is chaining of activities or work tasks. For instance, the last steps of the task could be the first three steps of the next activity. In this manner, the teacher can write all of a student's task analyses to interconnect in order to sequence the work activities. This sequencing will help the student learn to move from one task to another and ultimately be independent on the job site.

Efficiency should also be considered when writing a task analysis. For instance, students with significant disabilities may avoid reaching across the midline of their body, using two hands together, or using one hand consistently. The teacher should observe the student and determine the most efficient way to complete the task based on his or her physical abilities. For instance, if no physical limitations prohibit the student's using both hands to complete a task, the task analysis should require the student to do so (e.g., picking up an armful of laundry with both arms vs. using one hand only). Systematic instruction then can be implemented to teach the student the physical requirements of the activity.

The use of natural cues or material prompts can also be built into the task analysis to facilitate skill acquisition. For instance, the student can be taught to use work supplies as a cue for task completion or assistance in moving from one step or work duty to another. An example might be putting the "pink" cleanser in all toilets that need to be cleaned, as the first step in the task analysis. The presence of cleanser in the toilet provides a cue that a bathroom stall has not been cleaned.

Completing a job to production standards or speed often will be an issue when teaching students with significant disabilities. Initial consideration when designing a task analysis can assist in eliminating this problem. For instance, students may continue to perform a step in a task even though it is not necessary (e.g., vacuuming the same area of the floor). Observation of the student may reveal that he or she is perseverating on steps in the task. Therefore, providing a systematic way of or pattern to vacuuming a room could assist the student in completing the task successfully. Even though most students with significant disabilities will not understand the concept of a pattern, or number of movements, repetition through systematic instruction can result in skill performance.

STEP 4: SCHEDULE COMMUNITY-BASED INSTRUCTION

Creative use of school personnel to schedule and transport students for community-based instruction will clearly be the greatest challenge for administrators and teachers of students with significant disabilities. A number of model demonstration programs across the country have identified solutions for scheduling and transportation issues (Baumgart & Van Walleghem, 1986; Hutchins & Talarico, 1985; Nietupski, Hamre-Nietupski, Welch, & Anderson, 1983; Wehman, Moon, Everson, Wood, & Barcus, 1988). Staffing solutions have included team teaching; use of volunteers, paraprofessionals, peer tutors, graduate students, and student teachers; heterogeneous grouping of students; staggered student training schedules; and utilization of support personnel providing integrated therapy services. Transportation issues have been resolved by the use of volunteers' or parents' cars with mileage reimbursement, coordination of training schedules with regular school bus schedules, use of public transportation, use of school district vehicles, and walking to sites within short distances. Each school system must select procedures that are effective for its specific needs. A rule of thumb to follow for scheduling purposes is no more than four students per training site per instructor; fewer would be more effective for skill development (Wehman et al., 1988).

Scheduling should also focus on providing a variety of experiences across the student's school year. Each transition team should decide what experiences are appropriate to a student's long-term objectives and make recommendations concerning training in the community. Keep in mind the labor law regulations and maximum number of hours in training and vocational experiences that have already been outlined in this chapter. Tables 13.4 and 13.5 show how the job duties and training schedule can be established for one group of students with significant disabilities who participate in community-based instruction.

TABLE 13.4
Vocational Job Duties for Community-Based Instruction

Training Site	Job Duties
Hechingers (hardware store)	1. Stock the shelves. 2. Front (organize) the shelves. 3. Straighten the bins. 4. Break down boxes. 5. Clean the bathrooms. 6. Straighten the battery section.
Shoney's (restaurant)	1. Empty the bus pan. 2. Wash the dishes. 3. Unload the dishwasher. 4. Bus the tables. 5. Roll the silverware. 6. Wipe tables.
Howard Johnson's (hotel)	1. Clean the vending machine area (wiping vending machines, sweeping and mopping the floor). 2. Clean the restroom (sinks, toilets, sweeping and mopping the floor). 3. Vacuum the lobby. 4. Fold linen. 5. Wash windows.

STEP 5: DESIGN SYSTEMATIC INSTRUCTIONAL PROCEDURES

Once the sites have been identified and a schedule for student placement determined, the teacher must design instructional programs outlining how each student will be taught job skills and other related vocational activities. Included in the design should be (a) specific training objectives, (b) individualized task analyses, (c) data collection guidelines, (d) instructional strategies, (e) reinforcement procedures, and (f) program modifications. The following sections outline each of these components in detail.

Write Vocational Training Objectives

Training objectives are written to include the observable behaviors that will be taught, the conditions under which they will occur, and the criteria that will be used to evaluate the student's performance (Snell & Grigg, 1986; Wehman et al., 1988). Each skill that is being taught on a job site should have a program

TABLE 13.5
Student Training Schedule

Student	Location	Time	Instructor
October 22–December 7			
R.M.	Shoney's	7:30–9:15 A.M.	Curtis
J.G.	Shoney's	9:45–11:45 A.M.	Curtis
L.R.	Shoney's	12:45–2:45 P.M.	Curtis
M.L.	Hechingers	7:30–9:15 A.M.	Chris
G.A.	Hechingers	9:45–11:45 A.M.	Chris
H.R.	Hechingers	12:45–2:45 P.M.	Chris
C.S.	Howard Johnson's	9:45–11:45 A.M.	Stacy
P.P.	Howard Johnson's	12:45–2:45 P.M.	Stacy
December 10–January 18			
P.P.	Shoney's	7:30–9:15 A.M.	Stacy
J.A.	Howard Johnson's	9:45–11:45 A.M.	Stacy
H.R.	Howard Johnson's	7:30–9:15 A.M.	Curtis
M.L.	Howard Johnson's	12:45–2:45 P.M.	Curtis
L.R.	Hechingers	7:30–9:15 A.M.	Chris
R.M.	Hechingers	9:45–11:45 A.M.	Curtis
J.G.	Hechingers	12:45–2:45 P.M.	Chris
C.S.	Shoney's	9:45–11:45 A.M.	Chris
January 8–March 8			
J.A.	Shoney's	7:30–9:15 A.M.	Stacy
M.L.	Shoney's	9:45–11:45 A.M.	Chris
H.R.	Shoney's	12:45–2:45 P.M.	Chris
J.G.	Howard Johnson's	7:30–9:15 A.M.	Curtis
L.R.	Howard Johnson's	9:45–11:45 A.M.	Curtis
R.M.	Howard Johnson's	12:45–2:45 P.M.	Curtis
P.P.	Hechingers	9:45–11:45 A.M.	Stacy
C.S.	Hechingers	7:30–9:15 A.M.	Chris

objective included in the student's Individualized Education Program (IEP) or Individualized Transition Plan (ITP). Table 13.6 is an example of one student's objective for folding a bath towel.

Develop Individualized Task Analyses

Although the teacher will have developed task analyses when he or she negotiated with the employer to set up the training site, each student will need them custom designed for his or her training. This customizing will occur during the first several days that the teacher and student are on a job site. For instance, the teacher may determine that a task needs to be broken down into more detailed steps or designed to eliminate a particular discrimination that the student cannot make. The process of altering or modifying a task analysis can be facilitated by the use of data collection. Data can point to a step in the task that the student is not learning and indicate that a change needs to be made in that area.

Collect Baseline and Probe Data

Data collection is an important part of any instructional program because it is necessary for monitoring a student's skill acquisition. However, it is a critical portion of community-based instruction, because the teacher–trainer must be able to demonstrate that a student's vocational placement is for training purposes in order to meet the U.S. Department of Labor regulations for nonpaid work experiences. In other words, data can indicate when the student is able to perform a work task to the standards or requirements of the work site. At this point in training, the student must receive payment for work completed, or he or she needs to be moved to another site for additional work experiences (Inge, Simon, Halloran, & Moon, 1993).

Once training begins, data collection is referred to as a probe and should be collected at least one time a week prior to the beginning of a training session. The critical component of both baseline and probe assessments is that the student is allowed to perform the task independently without feedback, reinforcement, or prompting (Moon & Inge, 1993; Moon, Inge, et al., 1990). Typically, a skill is considered learned when the student performs the task correctly for three or four consecutive probe trials without any assistance from the trainer (Wehman et al., 1988).

TABLE 13.6
Sample Behavioral Objective

Component	Example
Condition under which behavior will occur	Given a laundry basket of bath towels and the cue, "Fold the towels,"
Observable behavior	Janet will fold the towels
Criteria for evaluation of student performance	with 100% accuracy according to the steps in the task analysis for three consecutive probe trials.

Select an Instructional Strategy

Least Prompts

The majority of the literature on teaching vocational tasks to individuals with significant disabilities focuses on the use of least prompts as the teaching strategy of choice (Barcus, Brooke, Inge, Moon, & Goodall, 1987; Cuvo, Leaf, & Borakove, 1978; Test, Grossi, & Keul, 1988). This strategy is also referred to as a response-prompt hierarchy, because the trainer progresses from the least amount of assistance (usually a verbal prompt) to the most intrusive (usually a physical prompt) until one prompt stimulates correct responding.

Use of a least-prompt strategy can be very effective for teaching skills on community job sites. Teachers are encouraged to consider various types of prompts to use in addition to the traditional verbal–model–physical sequence. For instance, as a student becomes more proficient on a site, the teacher might try using an indirect verbal prompt in the sequence, such as, "What do you do next?" before using the verbal prompt specific to the step in the task analysis. This technique may also be effective for training students who have long been dependent on teachers for verbal instruction. In addition, gestures can be used instead of a full model prompt or partial physical assistance such as touching the student's arm.

Regardless of the types of prompts selected, the teacher should establish a latency period or time that he or she will wait for the student to respond before providing the next level of assistance. Usually a student should be given approximately 3 to 5 seconds to respond independently. Students with physical disabilities, however, may require longer latency periods based on their movement limitations, and this requirement should be determined on an individual basis (Inge, 2001; Sowers & Powers, 1991). Finally, the teacher is cautioned to deliver each prompt only once before moving to the next, more intrusive prompt. The following is a list of steps for using a least-prompt strategy:

1. Have the student move to the appropriate work area unless movement is part of the task analysis (TA).
2. Stand behind or beside the individual so that you can quickly provide prompts when necessary.
3. Provide the cue to begin the task (e.g., "Clean the mirror," "Sort the coat hangers").
4. Wait 3 seconds for self-initiation for Step 1 of the TA.
5. If the student completes the step independently, provide reinforcement and proceed to Step 2 of the TA. Score + or − on the data sheet.
6. If the student is incorrect or does not respond within 3 seconds, provide a verbal prompt specific to Step 1 of the TA (e.g., "Pick up the Windex").
7. If the student completes the step with a verbal prompt, provide reinforcement and move to Step 2. Record V (for verbal) on the data sheet.

8. If the student is incorrect or does not respond within 3 seconds, model the response (e.g., teacher picks up the Windex).

9. If the student completes the step with a model prompt, provide reinforcement and move to Step 2. Record M (for model) on the data sheet.

10. If the student is incorrect or does not respond within 3 seconds, physically guide him or her through the response (e.g., teacher guides the student's hand to pick up the Windex). Record P (for physical) on the data sheet.

11. Begin instruction on Step 2 of the TA.

12. Repeat this procedure for each step in the TA until the task is completed. Always interrupt an error with the next prompt in the least-prompt system.

Time Delay

The use of time delay on vocational training sites is another option for teachers of students with significant disabilities (Inge, Moon, & Parent, 1993; Moon, Inge, et al., 1990). There are several critical components to a time-delay procedure (Gast, Ault, Wolery, Doyle, & Belanger, 1988; Snell & Gast, 1981). First, the teacher must select a prompt that will consistently assist the student to perform the task correctly. Initially, the prompt is given simultaneously with the request to perform the job duty. Gradually, increasing amounts of time (usually seconds) are waited between giving the request to perform the task and providing the prompt to complete the task correctly. The number of trials at each delay level and the length of the delay should be determined prior to initiation of the program. By the teacher's pairing the prompt with the request to perform a work task, the student is not allowed to make errors initially. The delay procedure allows the teacher to gradually fade assistance until the student performs without prompting. For example, a set number of trials are designated for 0-second delay, the next set at 2 seconds, the next at 4 seconds, and so forth, until the student performs without assistance.

Unlike the system of least prompts, time delay requires that the teacher select one prompt for use during the instructional program. Therefore, the procedure would be particularly useful if a student has consistently demonstrated a preference for one type of prompt. For example, if a student has shown that he or she always responds to a model prompt without making errors, the teacher can select it to place on delay (Moon, Inge, et al., 1990).

If an error occurs during time delay, the teacher should implement an error-correction procedure. Typically, an error may occur as increasing amounts of time are waited before the prompt is provided. Usually, error correction consists of immediately interrupting the student's mistake and providing the prompt. If the student makes three or more errors in a row, the teacher may consider reverting to a number of trials at 0 seconds before again delaying the prompt. Monitoring of the training data is essential to ensure that the student is not constantly making errors during the procedure. If that is happening, the teacher should consider selecting another prompt in order to provide an error-less learning experience.

Identify Reinforcers and Determine Schedule of Delivery

Selection of reinforcers as well as the systematic delivery of reinforcement is critical for student success on community-based vocational sites. The most effective reinforcers are those that arise as a natural consequence of a given task or situation within the work environment (Wilcox & Bellamy, 1982). Therefore, the teacher should begin by attempting to identify items that are available in a specific community-based setting. For example, there may be a vending machine located within the employee break room that can be used to reinforce the student at the end of a training period, or an employee cafeteria where he or she can get a snack. However, the teacher should remember that not all individuals will be reinforced by the same items and that even the most preferred reinforcer used too frequently will lose its effectiveness (Falvey, 1989). Only after failing to identify a natural reinforcer should the teacher select more artificial items (Moon, Inge, et al., 1990). Teachers are also cautioned to select only age-appropriate materials for use on community sites. The following information may be helpful in identifying potential reinforcers for students (Barcus et al., 1987; Falvey, 1989; Moon, Inge, et al., 1990):

1. Survey individuals familiar with the student to determine likes and dislikes. Include leisure activities, tangible items, types of verbal reinforcement, and so forth.
2. Observe the student in several natural environments during his or her free time and record what he or she does.
3. Offer the student a chance to interact with several novel items and record what he or she does. Repeat the experience over several days and determine if there is a pattern to item selection.
4. Select an item and use it as a reinforcer for a behavior the student already performs independently. Observe to see if that behavior increases.

Timing

After items have been identified for use on community-based sites, a schedule of reinforcement should be determined. Ideally, all reinforcement should be given quickly and immediately following the occurrence of the desired behavior. However, it usually is not feasible on a job site to provide tangible or edible reinforcement immediately after a behavior occurs (Moon, Inge, et al., 1990). In addition, most students with significant disabilities will not understand the connection between work well done during the training session and the soda purchased at McDonald's before returning to school. In these instances, the teacher must develop a training program that utilizes exchangeable reinforcers on predetermined schedules. Exchangeable items include money, tokens, points on a card, and checks on a calendar.

Schedule of Delivery

Teachers can choose to reinforce students using two types of schedules: a predetermined number of responses (ratio schedule of reinforcement) or a predetermined period of time (interval schedule) (Moon, Inge, et al., 1990). When delivering reinforcement on a ratio schedule, the teacher may use a fixed-ratio or variable-ratio schedule. In a fixed-ratio schedule, reinforcement is provided after a set number of responses (e.g., after every three steps in the task analysis, after every five towels folded). It may be preferable to design programs with a variable-ratio schedule that requires delivery after an average number of responses. With this strategy, the student is reinforced on the average of a number of responses (e.g., on the average of every three steps in the task analysis, or on the average of every three towels folded). In this manner, the student is not able to anticipate when reinforcement will be delivered, a condition that may approximate that in the natural environment.

Use of an interval schedule is similar to a ratio schedule in that it too can be delivered on a fixed or variable basis. In this instance, the teacher designs the program to provide reinforcement based on time intervals. Using the fixed-interval schedule, the teacher may select to reinforce a student after every 5 minutes, at the end of the training session, at the end of the work week, and so forth. A variable schedule would occur on the average of a set period of time, such as on the average of every 10 minutes.

Regardless of the type of schedule the teacher selects, he or she must design a plan for fading the reinforcement to naturally occurring items on the job site. For instance, the teacher should always pair verbal praise with the delivery of a tangible item, fading the reinforcement to supervisor or coworker approval over the course of the program.

Make Program Modifications

Community-based instruction provides an excellent opportunity for teachers to determine the most effective training strategies to use with specific students in real work sites. By monitoring a student's progress through data collection, the teacher often can pinpoint what changes need to be made in an instructional program to assist a student in skill acquisition. Occasionally, it is difficult to determine exactly what needs to occur to facilitate success. In these instances, we suggest that several teachers or the student's transition team brainstorm solutions to problems encountered. Table 13.7 represents a list of brainstorming questions that can assist in program modifications.

Finally, the information generated during community-based vocational training should be shared with future teachers and adult service agencies to facilitate the transition process from school to work. The following case study is a description of how this type of training can be directly used to help a student with significant disabilities (Inge & Dymond, 1993).

TABLE 13.7
Brainstorming Solutions to Training Problems

1. Analyze the effectiveness of the training strategy.
   - Does the prompting procedure (e.g., least prompts, time delay) match the learning style of the student?
   - Is the student responding to the type of prompt(s) selected?
   - Is the student distracted by noise or people in the environment? Is he or she attending to task?
   - Can you reduce the number of skills being taught in order to provide repeated practice on a specific job duty?

2. Has the task analysis been individualized to match the student's abilities?
   - Has the task been broken down into small enough steps?
   - Have the physical limitations of the student been taken into consideration?
   - Does the task analysis eliminate the need to make quality judgments?
   - Can several steps of the task be taught rather than the whole task analysis?
   - Would the student benefit from a backward-chaining procedure?
   - Do the steps in the task analysis include any external cues or extra prompts that have been added to the task (e.g., turning the pages in a picture book)?

3. Have all the components of delivering reinforcement been considered?
   - Is the reinforcer individualized to the student's needs?
   - Has the student satiated to the selected reinforcer?
   - Is the timing of the reinforcer correct?
   - Is the schedule of reinforcement appropriate?
   - Have the naturally occurring reinforcers become meaningful to the student?

4. Can the task be modified for the specific problem area(s)?
   - Are there simple equipment adaptations that can be added to assist the student?
   - Can extra cues (e.g., visual or tactile) be added to the task?
   - Can coworkers provide assistance during a difficult portion of the task?
   - Can the location of task completion be modified to decrease distractions?

CASE EXAMPLE: BOBBY

Bobby was 21 years old with an IQ of 36 as measured by the *Stanford–Binet Intelligence Scale* (Thorndike, Hagen, & Sattler, 1986). This score placed him in the range of severe intellectual disability. His teacher described him as rarely interacting with others appropriately and as physically aggressive with self-stimulatory behaviors. Mellaril was prescribed for these behaviors. It was also noted that Bobby had great difficulty with any change in his routine and required daily consistency to be successful. His strengths were his good fine- and gross-motor skills and his ability to speak in clear sentences. His vocational program included working on cleaning tasks and collating, stapling, and folding paper within the school building. He had also been included in a janitorial crew that received training at a residential facility for youth with emotional disturbances. At the time of the program, Bobby lived at home with his mother, who had chronic mental illness and received services from the local mental health program.

Phase I: Initial Training Placement

Initially, Bobby was placed at a hotel, folding laundry and cleaning a small vending machine area from 12:45 P.M. to 2:45 P.M. on Mondays, Tuesdays, Wednesdays, and Thursdays for his community-based training. A structured instructional program based on a time-delay strategy with a physical prompt (Moon, Inge, et al., 1990) and reinforcement schedule were developed for him; however, within 5 days of placement, the teacher–trainer reported uncontrollable behaviors. These included running from the instructor and laughing, clinging to her arm, and running to the pool area of the motel.

A behavior management program was implemented in an attempt to keep Bobby at the training site. This included a strategy of differential reinforcement of other behaviors with checks that earned edible reinforcement. The data showed that Bobby was on task for only 5% of his training session by the fifth day of his community experience. His behaviors included

- swinging his body against the motel stair railings
- running down the guest corridors
- screaming
- climbing on cars in the parking lot
- physically resisting instruction

The staff met, discussed the problem, and determined that the behaviors had escalated to a level that could result in physical harm to the trainer or to Bobby. The team decided that he must be removed from the training site. A brainstorming session generated the following possibilities for consideration in designing a new program and training experience for Bobby.

The first step was to initiate instruction for Bobby within the school complex. The decision to return to school was based on two factors. First, it was necessary to immediately break the negative training cycle that was occurring between Bobby and the instructor at the job site. Second, with Bobby's return to school, the trainer could work with him in a familiar environment and provide one-on-one training while designing a new instructional program for returning to the community. This plan was seen as the better alternative to discontinuing training until a new program could be developed. Returning to the school environment was not seen as a necessary step to get Bobby "ready" for the community.

The community-based instructor identified several training activities for Bobby to complete at school: wiping down the vending machines, washing windows, cleaning tables, and sweeping the sidewalks. Time of day was changed to the first activity of Bobby's morning, and training time was decreased to 30 minutes. The primary objective was to provide time in a familiar environment for Bobby to adjust to the trainer–teacher. During the school-based training period, the instructor also changed her systematic instruction procedure from physical assistance on time delay to a system of least prompts. The team believed that Bobby did not respond well to the more intrusive physical assistance. Bobby's on-task behavior increased across an 8-day period to 90% on the 13th day of his first training experience.

At this point, the team decided that the new instructional procedures appeared to be effective and that Bobby should begin to resume his training in the community. A brainstorming session resulted in the decision to combine in-school instruction with the community component. Bobby would receive 2 hours of training daily, beginning as soon as he arrived at school. Initially, he would start work in this familiar environment, because he seemed to have the greatest amount of difficulty initiating activities with the trainer. Near the end of the 2 hours, he and the trainer would leave school and finish the session at Howard Johnson's.

Initially, the plan called for Bobby to stay at the hotel and work for only 5 minutes. As he was successful (with no occurrence of the behaviors), this time period would be increased by 3 to 4 minutes. The team projected that a gradual increase in time spent in the community would result in success with his vocational program. Bobby's on-task behaviors began to decrease as the training moved from school to include community programming. On Day 14 of his program, Bobby was on task for approximately 75% of the 5-minute training session. Day 15 showed a decline to 50% on-task behavior during a 12-minute training session. By Day 18, the trainer was unable to get Bobby in her car to go to the community training site.

This refusal to work coincided with the end of Bobby's first training experience, because the employer had agreed to provide a vocational training site for an 8-week period. At this time, the team decided that a new strategy was needed in order for Bobby to be successful in community-based training. Several issues were discussed during a planning session for Bobby:

- Bobby now associates the community-based trainer with work (something he does not like to do). The trainer and Bobby need to develop a positive relationship with no demands for work performance placed on Bobby.
- Although changes were made in his instructional program, the tasks remained the same at the hotel training site. A new site needs to be developed with different job types and responsibilities.
- Intensive one-on-one instruction needs to be reduced from the current 2-hour block of time. Reduce interaction with community-based instructor to ½ or 1 hour maximum.
- Initiate a training period that focuses on identifying and developing community reinforcers for Bobby. Currently, he does not appear to enjoy community access or activities.

After this discussion, the team decided to discontinue vocational training for a 6-week period and to substitute community instruction in nondemanding, "fun" activities. This time period would allow the trainer to identify community activities that could be used as reinforcers during later vocational training.

Phase 2: Community-Based Training

During Phase 2 of instruction, the primary objective was to provide successful experiences within the community while placing limited demands on Bobby. The main requirement was for him to stay within close physical proximity to the trainer without clinging to her body, throwing his body, or running from her. Tasks focused on low-demand activities that could provide an element of fun in order to build a rapport between the trainer and Bobby. Initially, he was only required to remain with the instructor for brief periods of time (i.e., 5 to 10 minutes) in the grocery store. As Bobby became successful in staying with the trainer, the number and type of community training sites as well as the number of demands to participate in the activity were expanded. Gradually, over the course of 6 weeks, he began to participate in shopping, going to fast-food restaurants, and using the post office. Whenever Bobby began to get excited or to laugh inappropriately, the trainer was able to calm him by looking at him and speaking a few words (e.g., "Settle down Bobby" or "Do you want to stay here?"). At the end of the 6-week period, it was determined that Bobby was able to remain with the trainer in a community setting for up to 30 to 45 minutes and to participate in activities without engaging in challenging behaviors. Some of the activities that were focused on during this community training included

- waiting in grocery line
- putting items on checkout counter
- paying for items
- waiting for change
- browsing in stores
- sitting quietly in a fast-food restaurant
- eating a snack

- using a self-serve soda machine
- posting a letter
- crossing the street

Throughout this phase of community-based instruction, the trainer kept a diary of anecdotal notes on Bobby's behavior. The following is an excerpt from this diary:

> 12/21 — Ukrops Cafe — 30 minutes: Another super day for Bobby! I asked him what he wanted to get for breakfast before we left his house, and he said, "Sausage biscuit." It was raining today, so it was hard to spend much time looking for cars before we crossed the road. Bobby waited in line for 4 minutes before placing his order. With a cue, "What do you want?" from me (not the store person), Bobby was able to say, "Sausage biscuit." When we got to the drink section, Bobby said he wanted a soda. (O.J. and milk were in front of him, along with cups for soda and coffee. Soda and coffee were on the other side of the wall out of view. Bobby was able to request something he couldn't see!) He needed assistance using the self-serve drink bar. I physically assisted him to press his cup against the ice and Coke dispensers. (He wanted to use his finger to push the lever.) It took him about 20 minutes to eat breakfast. Most of the time was spent drinking the soda and chewing all of the ice in the container. Halfway through eating (he was done with the biscuit and just working on his drink), he started to laugh loudly. I asked him if he was ready to go, and he quieted down immediately and remained quiet for the rest of the time we were there. When we got back to school, Bobby did something he's never done before. We've been working on locking my car door. He usually remembers to push the button down but forgets to hold the handle up when we close the door. I started to direct him back to fix the door when I noticed that he'd done it correctly before I had gotten around to his side! How exciting!! I used gestures and some physical assistance to teach that skill.

Phase 3: Community-Based Vocational Training at Hechingers

Setting, Time, and Training Tasks

A training placement at a large hardware store, Hechingers, was identified as the next vocational training placement for Bobby. This site was selected because the manager was extremely supportive and had already supported several students at his work site. In addition, the manager was receptive to having Bobby at Hechinger's with the understanding that he had numerous challenging behaviors and would be receiving training primarily on increasing his ability to remain in a community environment. The employer agreed to have Bobby work, beginning at 9:45 A.M. on Mondays, Tuesdays, Thursdays, and Fridays. The employee who was normally responsible for maintaining the bathrooms continued to perform that function in order to meet the Department of Labor's regulations for a nonpaid work experience.

Training tasks included cleaning the men's and women's bathrooms: wiping the sinks, counters, mirrors, urinals, toilets; and mopping the floors. The bathrooms were targeted because the instructor believed that she would have better control over Bobby's behaviors in a small, enclosed work environment. For instance, by positioning herself between Bobby and the door to the bathroom, she was able to prevent him from running out of the room. This setting was in contrast to that of his previous work experience at Howard Johnson's, where he could easily move about in large work areas and "escape" the environment.

Discussion

Critical to a review of this case study is a discussion of the continual brainstorming sessions and subsequent program revisions that led to Bobby's eventual success in community-based instruction. The instructor persisted in identifying reinforcers, changing instructional procedures, modifying expectations, and changing training sites until Bobby was able to respond to training for a 2-hour block of time on a community job site. Several key factors led to his success. First, the trainer was able to identify a community reinforcer, the soda break at McDonald's. Bobby learned to associate work with earning money that he could use to have access to a preferred activity.

The other critical element of this program was the gradual increase in expectations that occurred during Bobby's time at multiple work sites. All too often, teacher–trainers set objectives that students are unable to meet, a situation that subsequently results in failure and denied access to reinforcement. In this case study, Bobby was always successful in meeting his goal, and he learned to rely on the timer as a prompt to help him meet his goal for reinforcement. It should be mentioned, however, that criterion or goal levels would have been decreased if he had encountered problems. For instance, if Bobby had been unable to meet a specified goal for 2 consecutive days, the time would have been lowered in order for him to experience success.

When training in the community, teachers should not become discouraged if their students do not respond as successfully as in this example. Again, constant monitoring of the program data will provide information regarding how the student is performing in different community sites. It is hoped that Bobby's case example can provide guidelines and ideas for other students who previously have been denied access to community-based instruction.

FINAL THOUGHTS

Within the past decade, researchers and practitioners alike have determined the effectiveness of community-based training. This chapter has provided the details and guidelines for how to go about the program implementation in a local agency or school. We have used schedules, real job sites, and a real person as examples of how successful this approach is, yet how much time and planning are involved. Students will enter adulthood with more competency if they learn skills in the community.

REFERENCES

Barcus, M., Brooke, V., Inge, K., Moon, S., & Goodall, P. (1987). *An instructional guide for training on a job site: A supported employment resource.* Richmond: Virginia Commonwealth University, Rehabilitation Research and Training Center.

Baumgart, D., & Van Walleghem, J. (1986). Staffing strategies for implementing community-based instruction. *Journal of the Association for Persons with Severe Handicaps, 11*(2), 92–102.

Cuvo, A. J., Leaf, R. B., & Borakove, L. S. (1978). Teaching janitorial skills to the mentally retarded: Acquisition, generalization and maintenance. *Journal of Applied Behavior Analysis, 11,* 345–355.

deFur, S. (1999). Special education, transition, and school-based services. In S. H. deFur & J. R. Patton (Eds.), *Transition and school-based services: Interdisciplinary perspectives for enhancing the transition process* (pp. 15–50). Austin, TX: PRO-ED.

Falvey, M. A. (1989). *Community-based curriculum: Instructional strategies for students with severe handicaps* (2nd ed.). Baltimore: Brookes.

Gast, D. L., Ault, M. F., Wolery, M., Doyle, P. M., & Belanger, J. (1988). Comparison of constant time delay and the system of least prompts in teaching sight word reading to students with moderate retardation. *Education and Training in Mental Retardation, 23,* 117–128.

Hutchins, M., & Talarico, D. (1985). Administrative considerations in providing community integrated training programs. In P. McCarthy, J. Everson, S. Moon, & M. Barcus (Eds.), *School to work transition for youths with severe disabilities* [Monograph] (pp. 111–121). Richmond: Virginia Commonwealth University, Project Transition Into Employment.

Inge, K. J. (1997). Job site training. In V. Brooke, K. J. Inge, P. Wehman, & A. Armstrong (Eds.), *Supported employment handbook: A customer-driven approach for persons with significant disabilities* (pp. 159–200). Richmond: Virginia Commonwealth University.

Inge, K. J. (2001). Supported employment for individuals with physical disabilities. In P. Wehman (Ed.), *Supported employment in business: Expanding the capacity of workers with disabilities* (pp. 153–180). St. Augustine, FL: Training Resource Network.

Inge, K. J., & Dymond, S. (1993). Challenging behaviors in the work place: Increasing one student's access to community-based vocational instruction using a changing criterion design. In K. J. Inge & P. Wehman (Eds.), *Designing community-based vocational programs for students with severe disabilities* (pp. 81–121). Richmond: Virginia Commonwealth University, Rehabilitation Research and Training Center.

Inge, K. J., Dymond, S., Wehman, P., Sutphin, C., Johnston, C., & Fiana, M. (1993). Community-based vocational preparation for students with severe disabilities: Designing the process. In K. J. Inge & P. Wehman (Eds.), *Designing community-based vocational programs for students with severe disabilities* (pp. 1–50). Richmond: Virginia Commonwealth University, Rehabilitation Research and Training Center.

Inge, K. J., Malatchi, A., Armstrong, A., & Blankenship, T. (2001). *Whose life is it anyway? A look at person-centered planning and transition.* Richmond: Virginia Commonwealth University, Rehabilitation Research and Training Center.

Inge, K. J., Moon, M. S., & Parent, W. (1993). Applied behavior analysis in supported employment settings. *Journal of Vocational Rehabilitation, 3*(3), 53–60.

Inge, K. J., Simon, M., Halloran, W., & Moon, M. S. (1993). Community-based vocational instruction and the labor laws: A 1993 update. In K. Inge & P. Wehman (Eds.), *Designing community-based vocational programs for students with severe disabilities* (pp. 51–80). Richmond: Virginia Commonwealth University, Rehabilitation Research and Training Center.

Inge, K., & Wehman, P. (Eds.). (1993). *Designing community-based instructional programs for students with severe disabilities.* Richmond: Virginia Commonwealth University, Rehabilitation Research and Training Center on Supported Employment.

Moon, M. S., & Inge, K. (1993). Vocational training, transition planning, and employment for students with severe disabilities. In M. E. Snell (Ed.), *Systematic instruction of persons with severe disabilities* (4th ed., pp. 556–586). Columbus, OH: Merrill.

Moon, M. S., & Inge, K. J. (2000). Vocational preparation and transition. In M. E. Snell & F. Brown (Eds.), *Instruction of students with severe disabilities* (pp. 591–628). Upper Saddle River, NJ: Prentice Hall.

Moon, M. S., Inge, K. J., Wehman, P., Brooke, V., & Barcus, J. M. (1990). *Helping persons with severe mental retardation get and keep employment: Supported employment issues and strategies.* Baltimore: Brookes.

Moon, M. S., Kiernan, W., & Halloran, W. (1990). School-based vocational programs and labor laws: A 1990 update. *Journal of the Association for Persons with Severe Handicaps, 15*(3), 177–185.

Nietupski, J. A., Hamre-Nietupski, S., Welch, J., & Anderson, R. J. (1983). Establishing and maintaining vocational training sites for moderately and severely handicapped students: Strategies for community/vocational trainers. *Education and Training of the Mentally Retarded, 18*(3), 169–175.

Pumpian, I., Shepard, H., & West, E. (1988). Negotiating job-training stations with employers. In P. Wehman & M. S. Moon (Eds.), *Vocational rehabilitation and supported employment* (pp. 177–192). Baltimore: Brookes.

Putnam, J. W. (1994). *Cooperative learning and strategies for inclusion: Celebrating diversity in the classroom*. Baltimore: Brookes.

Renzaglia, A., & Hutchins, M. (1988). A community-referenced approach to preparing persons with disabilities for employment. In P. Wehman & M. S. Moon (Eds.), *Vocational rehabilitation and supported employment* (pp. 91–112). Baltimore: Brookes.

Smull, M. W. (1998). Revisiting choice. In J. O'Brien & C. L. O'Brien (Eds.), *A little book about person centered planning* (pp. 37–49). Toronto, Ontario: Inclusion Press.

Snell, M., & Gast, D. L. (1981). Applying delay procedures to the instruction of the severely handicapped. *Journal of the Association of the Severely Handicapped, 5*(4), 3–14.

Snell, M., & Grigg, N. C. (1986). Instructional assessment and curriculum development. In M. E. Snell (Ed.), *Systematic instruction of persons with severe handicaps* (pp. 64–109). Columbus, OH: Merrill.

Sowers, J., & Powers, L. (1991). *Vocational preparation and employment of students with physical and multiple disabilities*. Baltimore: Brookes.

Stainback, S., & Stainback, W. (1992). *Curriculum considerations in inclusive classrooms: Facilitating learning for all students*. Baltimore: Brookes.

Test, D. W., Grossi, T., & Keul, P. (1988). A functional analysis of the acquisition and maintenance of janitorial skills in a competitive work setting. *Journal of the Association for Persons with Severe Handicaps, 13*(1), 1–7.

Thorndike, R. L., Hagen, E. P., & Sattler, J. M. (1986). *Stanford–Binet Intelligence Scale* (4th ed.). Chicago: Riverside.

U.S. Department of Education. (1992). *Guidelines for implementing community-based educational programs for students with disabilities*. Washington, DC: U.S. Department of Labor.

Wehman, P. (1992). *Life beyond the classroom: Transition strategies for young adults with disabilities*. Baltimore: Brookes.

Wehman, P. (2001). *Life beyond the classroom: Transition strategies for young adults with disabilities* (3rd ed.). Baltimore: Brookes.

Wehman, P., Moon, M. S., Everson, J. M., Wood, M., & Barcus, M. (1988). *Transition from school to work: New challenges for youth with severe disabilities*. Baltimore: Brookes.

Wehman, P., & Revell, W. (1997). Transition into supported employment for young adults with severe disabilities: Current practices and future directions. *Journal of Vocational Rehabilitation, 8*(1), 65–74.

Wilcox, B., & Bellamy, G. T. (1982). *Design of high school programs for severely handicapped students*. Baltimore: Brookes.

CHAPTER 14

Positive Behavior Support

Dennis H. Reid and David A. Rotholz

LEARNING GOALS

Upon completion of this chapter, the reader will be able to

- Provide a general definition of positive behavior support
- Describe a basic difference between traditional behavior modification and positive behavior support
- Identify at least three core values of positive behavior support
- Identify three types of functional assessment strategies for assessing the motivational function of challenging behavior
- Describe the difference between behavior change procedures designed to reduce challenging behavior maintained by positive versus negative reinforcement

BACKGROUND

A major concern regarding quality of life among people who have developmental disabilities is the prevention and treatment of challenging behavior. Challenging behavior, or what historically has been referred to as behavior problems, is displayed in many forms. In the most extreme cases, challenging behavior is exemplified by self-injury and aggression that result in serious physical harm. Other types of challenging behavior—including, for example, property destruction, severe nonresponsiveness to instructional requests, and frequent repetitious or stereotypic behavior—impede learning and social development as well as opportunities to experience an inclusive and generally enjoyable lifestyle.

Challenging behavior interferes not only with the quality of life of many people with developmental disabilities, but also with that of their family members, peers, and support personnel. In a number of cases, challenging behavior has resulted in the use of highly restrictive procedures for protective purposes, such as application of restraint devices to prevent certain body movements. Challenging behavior is also a primary reason many people with developmental disabilities are administered potent medications, often with unintended and harmful side effects.

Because of the serious impact of challenging behavior, there has been a considerable amount of research on this type of behavior among people who have developmental disabilities. A major outcome of investigations in this area has been the development of *positive behavior support* as a currently recommended means of preventing and reducing challenging behavior. Positive behavior support is not a specific intervention per se, but rather an approach that involves the application of positive behavioral interventions and systems to achieve socially important behavior change among people who have developmental disabilities and challenging behavior (Sugai et al., 2000).

EVOLUTION

The essence of positive behavior support as a means of preventing and reducing challenging behavior cannot be adequately presented without considering how this approach has developed over time. As just indicated, positive behavior support has evolved in part as applied research has developed a technology for understanding and treating challenging behavior. Equally important, positive behavior support has evolved as the professional field and, to some extent, society at large have developed an increased sense of values regarding the personal dignity and rights of people with disabilities.

What is known today as positive behavior support progressed from its roots in applied behavior analysis in the late 1960s. From its beginnings, applied behavior analysis focused on producing socially important changes in the lives of individuals (Baer, Wolf, & Risley, 1968). These were changes in behavior that were meaningful to the individual whose behavior changed, and to those with whom the individual typically interacted (e.g., family, friends, teachers, employers).

Procedures for changing behavior within an applied behavior analytic framework are technological in nature in that they are described in sufficient detail to form a technology of behavior change. The various procedures are linked together conceptually by their basis in empirically established principles of learning, and are applied in an analytical fashion in terms of carefully analyzing and demonstrating their behavior change efficacy. The development of applied behavior analysis and the resulting technology of behavior change procedures as they relate to challenging behavior are perhaps best reflected in the accumulation of articles in the field's flagship journal, the *Journal of Applied Behavior Analysis,* from its inception in 1968 through its current existence. Other professional journals also reflect the early development of the field (e.g., *Behavior Modification, Education and Treatment of Children*), as well as more recent developments (e.g., *Journal of the Association for Persons with Severe Handicaps, Journal of Positive Behavior Interventions*).

Initially, applied behavior analysis interventions for challenging behavior typically focused on the use of consequences to change the behavior. This approach involved what is considered to be a *behavior modification* or *behavior management* paradigm. The primary intent was to modify or manage problem behavior that occurred. In most cases, a behavior modification approach involved positive reinforcement, in which a potent reinforcer was identified and then provided contingently upon the occurrence of an appropriate behavior in an attempt to increase the frequency of the behavior (e.g., Hall, Lund, & Jackson, 1968). If the goal was to decease problem behavior, reinforcement would be provided when an appropriate behavior occurred—preferably, a behavior that was incompatible with the problem behavior. In either case, the intended result of the reinforcement procedure was to increase the behavior that was followed by the reinforcer.

Another type of consequence-based procedure used in a behavior modification paradigm consisted of a punishment process. This involved identifying an event that was undesirable to the person exhibiting the problem behavior. The event would be provided to the person following display of the behavior in an attempt to decrease future occurrence of the problem behavior (e.g., Foxx & Azrin, 1973; Lovaas & Simmons, 1969).

As the field of applied behavior analysis evolved, there was a movement away from such a heavy reliance on consequence-based procedures to change problem behavior. This change in focus was a result of a developing recognition of the importance of understanding the motivating factors for an individual's behavior (i.e., the variables that occasioned and maintained the problem behavior), and how such an understanding enhanced the effectiveness of behavior change interventions. The focus on understanding the motivation for problem behavior—in essence, *why* an individual engages in problem behavior—also involved a fundamental shift away from viewing the person as having the problem to viewing the person's behavior in the context of the individual's surrounding environment. The role of environmental factors, such as, for example, the existing reinforcement in the routine environment, the type of teaching curriculum applied with the person, ongoing interpersonal interactions, and availability of preferred activities, on the presence and absence of challenging behavior began to receive much more emphasis. The importance of changing a broad array of features of the social and physical environment on the success of preventing and treating challenging behavior also became more apparent. An illustration of some of the key differences between the focus of earlier behavior modification interventions and more current approaches characteristic of a positive behavior support paradigm follows:

- *Sample behavior targeted to be changed*—self-injurious head slapping and accompanying destruction of task materials
- *More traditional behavior modification approach*—provide positive reinforcement for appropriate behavior (e.g., working on a task) and provide a punisher for the problem behavior (head slapping and destroying materials)
- *Positive behavior support approach*—(a) assess the variables that lead to, or maintain, the problem behavior of concern and the desired appropriate behavior, including but not limited to the ongoing reinforcement in the environment, communication skills of the individual, access to preferred items and events, and essentially what purpose or function the problem behavior serves for the individual; (b) develop and apply an intervention that removes or alters features of the environment that have been assessed to lead to the problem behavior, and help the individual attain desired functions with more socially acceptable behavior.

During the 1990s, behavioral approaches for addressing challenging behavior underwent additional changes that expanded the knowledge, methods, understanding, and in essence, the "person-centeredness" (Everson & Reid, 1999) of these approaches. The changes included enhanced means of assessing the motivation for challenging behavior through the development of an array of functional assessment procedures (O'Neill & Johnson, 2000); the role of an individual's communication skills on the occurrence of challenging behavior (E. G. Carr et al., 1994; Reichle & Wacker, 1993); the significance of, and procedures for, designing environments to match an individual's preferences (Reid, 2000); and determining how specific features of an environment affect an individual's behavior through stimulus control mechanisms (Luiselli & Cameron, 1998).

The changes that occurred in helping individuals with developmental disabilities overcome challenging behavior were well described in an early summary of the emerging field of positive behavior support provided by Horner and colleagues (1990). Elaboration on positive behavior support was subsequently detailed in the text *Positive Behavioral Support: Including People with Difficult Behavior in the Community* (Koegel, Koegel, & Dunlap, 1996), in which the essential features of this approach were described as "a grounding in person-centered values, a commitment to outcomes that are meaningful from the perspective of a person's preferred lifestyle, a reliance on individualized, functional assessments, and an appreciation and utilization of multiple interventions and support strategies" (p. xiii). A number of other sources regarding positive behavior support are also currently available (e.g., Bambara & Knoster, 1998; E. G. Carr et al., 1999; Scotti & Meyer, 1999).

BASIC COMPONENTS

To successfully practice positive behavior support to prevent and reduce challenging behavior among people who have developmental disabilities, a teacher needs to understand the core values on which this approach is based. It is also necessary to have a knowledge of the procedural characteristics that represent this approach to preventing and reducing challenging behavior.

Core Values

The core values of positive behavior support are aligned with the values encompassed within a person-centered approach to designing and providing supports and services for people with disabilities. Person-centered values are described in detail in a number of texts (e.g., Everson & Reid, 1999; Holburn & Vietze, in press), as well as in other chapters in this text. The most integral person-centered values that play a part in positive behavior support follow:

- *Supports and services are driven by the individual, family, and friends.* In contrast to more traditional service delivery systems that focus heavily on the opinions of professionals, person-centered approaches focus on the desires of the individual and the people who are most important in the individual's life; professionals still play a major role but not to the exclusion or near exclusion of the desires of the individual.
- *Community membership is an important goal.* A basic tenet is to support an individual to be as fully included in typical communities as possible.
- *An individual's gifts and capacities are emphasized.* In contrast to the more traditional focus on an individual's deficits and weaknesses, person-centered approaches attempt to identify an individual's unique capacities and to build on those capacities, as well as to identify support needs.
- *An individualized support plan is essential.* By focusing on an individual's unique desires, support plans must be highly individualized for each person.
- *Services are changed to be more responsive to individuals.* Person-centered approaches focus on identifying and designing environments that match a person's preferences, in contrast to changing an individual's behavior to "fit" into an existing environment.

Procedural Characteristics

Although positive behavior support is an approach to preventing and reducing challenging behavior in contrast to one specific treatment strategy, several key procedural features characterize how this approach is applied. These features represent both the behavior analytic and person-centered foundations of positive behavior support.

Focus on Behavior

The focus of positive behavior support is what a person does, or the individual's *behavior* (Reid, Parsons, Rotholz, Braswell, & Morris, in press). Previously, it was noted that positive behavior support developed as a means to help people with developmental disabilities overcome challenging behavior—that is, to prevent challenging behavior from occurring and to reduce or eliminate challenging behavior that does occur. However, positive behavior support does not address challenging behavior exclusively. Rather, this approach focuses on behavior that is beneficial to people with disabilities. The intent is not only to overcome challenging behavior but also to promote behavior that supports an individual in experiencing an enjoyable lifestyle and living as independently as possible. Positive behavior support assists an individual in living as normal a life as possible by participating in typical societal communities and functions.

To adequately practice positive behavior support, a teacher must carefully define the behaviors that are to be decreased and increased in accordance with the just noted goals. Behaviors of concern must be defined to the degree that people who interact with an individual with a developmental disability can easily agree when they occur and do not occur. As discussed in the next section, behaviors must also be defined sufficiently that they can be readily measured.

Reliance on Data

Sufficiently defining a person's behavior such that the behavior can be readily measured is necessary because of the reliance on *data* within a positive behavior support paradigm (Reid et al., in press). Objective data regarding measures of an individual's behavior are essential to understanding why a behavior occurs (see "Functional Assessment" below). Data are also necessary to evaluate whether a particular behavior support application is effectively changing the behavior of concern.

Behavioral measures can be obtained in a number of ways (Cooper, Heron, & Heward, 1987). Most of the ways involve direct observations of the person's behavior in the typical environments in which the individual lives, works, and plays. Most often, the measures involve *frequency counts* of the behavior, or how often the behavior occurs during a given time period. Other typical measures within a positive behavior support paradigm include *interval recording*, or whether the behavior occurs during a specific interval of time such as a day or week, and *duration recording*, or how long a behavior continues once it begins. Regardless of the measures used, objective data on the behavior's occurrence are vital to determining whether the behavior is getting better or worse—or occurring more or less often—once a behavior support procedure is applied.

Functional Assessment

One of the most defining procedural characteristics of a positive behavior support approach is the application of specific techniques to assess why an individual engages in challenging behavior. More precisely, attention is directed to the observable variables that occasion a given behavior, or that maintain the behavior once it occurs. It has become well recognized that challenging behavior occurs for a reason, that the behavior serves a function or purpose for the person

(Sugai et al., 2000). Before attempts are made to prevent or reduce the challenging behavior, attention should be directed to determining that purpose or function by conducting a *functional assessment.*

There are a variety of ways to conduct functional assessments of challenging behavior (O'Neill & Johnson, 2000). Typically, the most readily available and easily applied way is through an *interview* or *informant functional assessment.* In an interview functional assessment, people who are very familiar with an individual who displays challenging behavior are formally interviewed, or requested to complete a designated question-and-answer form, to determine the situations in which the individual is most and least likely to engage in the behavior. A number of formal interview instruments are available, including the *Motivation Assessment Scale* (Durand & Crimmins, 1988), the *Functional Assessment Interview Form* (O'Neill et al., 1997), and *Questions About Behavioral Function* (Paclawskyj, Matson, Rush, Smalls, & Vollmer, 2000). Currently, however, there is some controversy regarding the overall utility of interview functional assessment formats (e.g., Duker & Sigafoos, 1998). The most important issue in the controversy is whether a functional assessment should rely solely upon an interview format. Although the interview format can be useful in a number of situations (Knoster, 2000), it is also vulnerable to many sources of inaccuracy. These problems usually can be overcome with the use of systematic, direct observations of an individual's behavior, as described in subsequent paragraphs.

A second type of functional assessment is a *direct observation* assessment process. With this format, the individual's challenging behavior is directly observed in the individual's routine environments, with attention being directed to what occurs in the environment before, during, and after the challenging behavior occurs. Direct observation functional assessments are often conducted using an *antecedent–behavior–consequence,* or ABC, paradigm (Iwata, Kahng, Wallace, & Lindberg, 2000). With an ABC approach, the intent is to identify the antecedents to the behavior, or what environmental event tends to happen immediately before the behavior of concern. Likewise, the intent is to determine the consequence to the behavior, with a particular focus on what may be reinforcing the behavior's occurrence. For identifying both antecedents and consequences, the observational focus is on the patterns of behavior that occur over repeated episodes.

A third type of functional assessment is an *analogue functional analysis.* In an analogue functional analysis, an individual who displays challenging behavior is provided with a variety of environmental situations in a closely controlled, laboratory-type setting in an attempt to determine the situations in which the challenging behavior is most and least likely to occur (Iwata, Dorsey, Slifer, Bauman, & Richman, 1982). Common situations presented include frequent demands placed on the individual, such as instructions to do certain tasks; social attention presented when the behavior occurs; and a process in which no demands or attention are provided regardless of whether the behavior occurs.

Determining which type of functional assessment to conduct as part of the overall behavior support process depends on a number of factors. Currently, there are no well-established rules for deciding which approach to apply across all situations in which challenging behavior may be observed. However, as illustrated below, there are some general guidelines to consider (see also Knoster, 2000):

- *Available resources.* A practical consideration is the amount of personnel resources available for conducting the assessment. Generally, fewer resources are necessary to conduct an interview assessment than to perform a direct observational assessment. In turn, an observational assessment usually requires fewer resources than an analogue assessment.
- *Need for direct observation.* Although a formal observational functional assessment may not be feasible in every situation, at least some direct observation of the individual's challenging behavior in his or her routine environment should always occur (e.g., in addition to an interview or analogue assessment).
- *Severity of behavior.* Generally, the more severe or potentially harmful the behavior of concern is, the more formal the functional assessment should be. Observational assessments vary in degree of formality (e.g., an informal, clinical observation versus a structured, ABC assessment), and analogue analyses represent the most formal.
- *Effectiveness of previous interventions.* Often, functional assessments begin with less formal and less time-consuming approaches. If interventions derived from those approaches are not successful, more formal assessments are conducted.

Assessment-Based Interventions

Regardless of the type of functional assessment process used, the intent is to develop hypotheses regarding the likely environmental variables that occasion or maintain the challenging behavior, as well as more desired behavior. Subsequently, behavior change interventions are designed that take into account the relevant variables that are hypothesized to affect the behavior's occurrence. On a general level, such interventions are designed to alter the environmental variables that set the occasion for the challenging behavior or maintain the behavior once it occurs. This eliminates or at least reduces the reason for the problem. It also supports the individual in attaining a desired outcome without relying on problem behavior.

COMMON BEHAVIOR CHANGE PROCEDURES

Many behavior change strategies can be used within a positive behavior support paradigm to prevent or reduce challenging behavior, as well as to promote the occurrence of desirable behavior. In the prototypical positive behavior support process, a number of specific strategies are applied. The precise procedures used in a given situation depend in large part on the results of functional assessments regarding hypothesized variables that account for the occurrence and absence of the challenging behavior. All of the specific procedures, however, are based on principles of learning represented in the field of applied behavior analysis, from which positive behavior support evolved. The procedures usually involve principles of positive and negative reinforcement (see below). There is also an increasing tendency to attend to *establishing operations,* or those events preceding a behavior that may affect the behavior change efficacy of reinforcing consequences for the behavior (Smith & Iwata, 1997).

Positive Reinforcement

The process of positive reinforcement, in which a consequence follows a certain behavior and increases the future likelihood of the behavior's occurrence, was noted earlier. Much of the challenging behavior observed among people with developmental disabilities occurs because the behavior is positively reinforced by the consequence of the behavior. Applied research, and especially that involving functional assessments, has indicated that there are three general classes of consequences that singularly or in combination frequently function as positive reinforcers for challenging behavior, as well as desired behavior (Iwata et al., 1982). These classes include social attention, access to desired items or activities, and automatic consequences that appear to have little if any relationship to what is occurring in an individual's surrounding environment. Interventions designed to prevent or reduce challenging behavior that is maintained by positive reinforcement typically should be based on the types of consequences that reinforce the challenging behavior.

Challenging Behavior Reinforced by Attention

Challenging behavior often occurs because it functions to obtain attention for an individual. For example, an individual may periodically yell or scream because yelling and screaming result in someone (e.g., a teacher, parent, or support staff person) interacting with the person to determine what may be bothering the individual. The interaction provides attention to the individual. An individual may likewise engage in socially offensive language, remove clothing, or destroy items in the environment as a means of obtaining a reaction from someone. When a functional assessment indicates that a particular type of challenging behavior is functioning to obtain attention for an individual, a general behavior change intervention is to avoid providing attention when the behavior occurs, and to support the individual in obtaining attention through other, more appropriate behavior.

The principle behind withholding attention is that if no attention follows the behavior, the behavior will not be positively reinforced and will eventually cease to occur. However, within a positive behavior support paradigm, withholding attention following the behavior is rarely the only strategy applied. In such cases, the attention represents something that is desired by an individual. If the particular problem behavior does not obtain attention for the individual, the person is likely to seek attention in other ways, including through other types of challenging behavior. Hence, in positive behavior support, approaches to prevent or reduce challenging behavior that appears to be maintained by attention typically involve ensuring that the individual engages in social interactions with others in addition to withholding attention when the challenging behavior occurs.

Ensuring opportunities for social interaction include providing noncontingent attention—that is, attention that is not contingent on the targeted challenging behavior (J. E. Carr, Coriaty, Wilder, et al., 2000)—and teaching and otherwise supporting an individual in obtaining attention through socially acceptable behavior. The latter strategy often involves the teaching of what is considered to be replacement behavior (Knoster, 2000), such as various types of communication skills (e.g., using conventional speech, sign language, or voice output communication aids). The intent in teaching such skills is to replace the problem behavior with a more acceptable means of obtaining attention.

Challenging Behavior Reinforced by Access to Items and Activities

Problem behaviors also are positively reinforced when they enable the individual to obtain a desired item or activity. To illustrate, an individual may push someone off a bicycle because he or she wants to ride the bicycle, or may grab a video game from a peer in order to play with it. When functional assessments suggest that a problem behavior may be serving the purpose of obtaining a desired item or activity for an individual, the general intervention approach within a positive behavior support process is similar in concept to that described for problem behavior maintained by social attention. Attempts are made to prevent the item or activity from being obtained when the problem behavior occurs, and to support the individual in having access to the item or activity (or an alternative desirable item or activity) when the problem behavior is not occurring. Emphasis is likewise placed on teaching the individual useful skills for accessing what is desired without having to display problem behavior.

When focusing on teaching a replacement behavior that eliminates or reduces the reason for a challenging behavior to occur, it is important to ensure that the particular replacement behavior targeted is *more efficient* at producing the outcome desired by the person than is the challenging behavior (Horner & Day, 1991). That is, it should take less time for the person to use the replacement behavior to attain the desired outcome relative to using the challenging behavior. Otherwise, there is likely to be little motivation for the person to use the replacement behavior in lieu of the challenging behavior.

🚶 CASE EXAMPLE: TED

Ted is in a classroom for children with special needs at his neighborhood school. He sometimes exhibits the challenging behavior of screaming, which is quite disruptive to his class and annoying to his classmates. A functional assessment (including direct observation) revealed that he appears to display this behavior when he wants assistance from his teacher, so the teacher taught Ted the replacement behavior of raising his hand to seek assistance. However, this did not reduce the frequency of the screaming. Upon further analysis by the teacher, it became apparent that screaming results in immediate assistance, whereas when Ted raises his hand, the assistance is often delayed a few minutes (i.e., the teacher frequently acknowledges Ted vocally but does not immediately get to him to offer assistance). The teacher now provides Ted with immediate assistance when

he raises his hand, and the screaming has reduced to the point that it is no longer a problem.

Challenging Behavior Reinforced Automatically

In some cases, functional assessments reveal that challenging behavior does not appear to be reinforced by social attention or access to items or activities (and is not maintained by certain types of negative reinforcement—see the next section). In such cases, one explanation offered for the challenging behavior is that it is reinforced automatically (Vollmer, 1994). Automatic reinforcement means that the behavior results in a desired consequence that appears independent of the individual's environment, and is based on a presumed internal or physiological response. Automatic reinforcement is sometimes alternatively referred to as *nonsocially mediated reinforcement,* because the apparent reinforcement is not due to anything that anyone in the individual's environment does in response to the behavior (Vollmer, 1994). For example, pica behavior, or the ingestion of inedible substances, appears to be reinforced in a number of cases by an individual's physiological response to eating certain items (Piazza et al., 1998). Hand-mouthing among people who have profound disabilities also appears to be reinforced in a number of cases by the sensation of the hands being in the mouth (Turner, Realon, Irvin, & Robinson, 1996).

A number of behavior change strategies can be used with challenging behavior that appears to be reinforced automatically (J. E. Carr, Coriaty, & Dozier, 2000). One approach involves attempting to alter or remove the reinforcing properties of the consequence to the behavior. To illustrate, in some cases hand-mouthing is reduced when gloves are placed on an individual's hands, due to an apparent alteration in the sensation that results when mouthing occurs with gloves on the hands. Another approach involves attempting to provide a type of nonharmful consequence that is hypothesized to be similar to the consequence provided by the challenging behavior. Eye poking, for example, which apparently is reinforced by the visual sensation of pushing on the eye, may be reduced in some cases by providing enhanced visual sensation through use of lighted objects (e.g., computer screen images). More commonly though, within a positive behavior support approach, interventions are designed to provide frequent access to other types of reinforcers, such as attention and highly enjoyable activities that can compete with the reinforcers provided by the challenging behavior. In the latter situation, the attempt is to provide an individual with a highly enriched lifestyle that provides an array of enjoyable or reinforcing things to do that do not involve the challenging behavior.

Negative Reinforcement

The role of positive reinforcement in the occurrence of challenging behavior among people with developmental disabilities has been apparent since the beginnings of applied behavior analysis. More recently, the impact of *negative* reinforcement has become well established (Iwata, 1987). Like positive reinforcement, the process of negative reinforcement increases the likelihood that a particular behavior will occur due to the consequence that follows it. However, the type of consequence involved in negative reinforcement is quite different from that involved in positive reinforcement.

In essence, positive reinforcement increases the occurrence of behavior because the behavior is followed by something that is desirable for the individual, something the individual will act to obtain. In contrast, in negative reinforcement, the occurrence of a behavior is increased because the behavior results in removal, or avoidance, of something that is undesirable or negative for the person. Negative reinforcement results in a person escaping or avoiding something that is unwanted, something a person will act to escape or avoid. When presented with an instruction from a support staff member to perform an undesired task such as to clean one's room, for example, an individual may begin to be aggressive toward the staff person. The aggression can function to allow the individual to avoid having to clean the room because it terminates the staff person's instructional requests while the staff person responds to the aggressive behavior (or leaves the individual alone altogether to avoid being harmed by the aggression). Similarly, an individual may fall to the ground when being escorted to a van to take the individual from a group home to a job setting in order to avoid getting on the van and going to work (in this case, falling to the ground may be negatively reinforced because it allows the individual to avoid going to work). In educational settings, academic tasks that are disliked by an individual (e.g., because the tasks are difficult to perform or the individual has experienced unpleasant failure or boredom with them in the past) may be accompanied by material destruction, self-injury, or aggression by the individual in an attempt to avoid or discontinue working on the tasks. The challenging behavior is negatively reinforced in these situations because it functions to stop the task presentation while the staff attends or responds to the problem behavior.

There are a number of positive behavior support approaches for overcoming challenging behavior that appears to be maintained by negative reinforcement. As with behavior change procedures based on positive reinforcement, approaches are used rarely in isolation but rather in conjunction with other strategies. Often, the first approach is to determine whether the activity that produces the challenging behavior is something that is really important for the individual to perform. If not, then the challenging behavior can be prevented by discontinuing the demands or instructions to perform the activity. If the activity is something that *is* important, then a common approach is to make the activity more attractive to the individual such that the person will not attempt to avoid it. There are numerous ways to make an important activity (e.g., participating in a therapeutic exercise routine) more attractive, including the incorporation of choices into the activity, such as letting the individual decide when or where to perform it, interspersing more desired activities within it, and providing potent reinforcing events or items during or immediately after it (Green & Reid, 1999).

Another approach to overcoming challenging behavior that is apparently maintained by negative reinforcement is to persist with the activity despite the challenging behavior (J. E. Carr, Coriaty, & Dozier, 2000). With this approach, the individual does not experience the reinforcing consequence of having the activity terminated due to the challenging behavior. However, because this process can become unpleasant for both the individual and the support personnel who are presenting the undesired activity (e.g., the individual may intensify the challenging behavior to attempt to terminate the activity), it is usually accompanied by the other behavior change components just noted to make the activity more attractive for the individual.

CASE EXAMPLE: BESSIE

Bessie is a middle-aged woman who has many challenges. She has profound cognitive disabilities and multiple physical disabilities. Although she has very distinct likes and dislikes, it is extremely difficult for support staff to understand her expressions due to her significant communication challenges. Her person-centered team identified a support need involving daily exercises to maintain a range of motion with her arms and legs. However, whenever a staff person begins the exercises with her, she yells and physically withdraws from the staff person. Consequently, a behavior support plan was developed to help make the exercise routine more enjoyable for her. The plan included (a) beginning the routine with a highly preferred activity based on results of a systematic preference assessment, involving gently rubbing her arms; (b) presenting preferred music periodically during the routine; (c) briefly discontinuing the exercise and providing the music whenever she began to yell or pull away, and then returning to the exercise; and (d) following the entire exercise with 10 minutes of Bessie's most preferred activity, that of being rocked in a hammock. In addition, the entire exercise routine began to be conducted while she was in her hammock, which was a preferred location of hers, instead of while she was in her wheelchair. After the support plan was initiated, Bessie discontinued her yelling and withdrawal, and actually began to laugh during part of the exercise process (see Green & Reid, 1999, for more in-depth discussion).

Comprehensive Environmental Approaches

When considered in the context of positive and negative reinforcement, challenging behavior can be explained most simply as achieving something the person wants or getting rid of something the person does not want, respectively. When a functional assessment indicates which of these processes is operating, behavior change procedures such as those previously summarized can be applied to prevent or reduce the occurrence of the challenging behavior. However, it must be remembered that positive behavior support is a comprehensive approach to preventing and reducing challenging behavior, and involves much more than the application of a single behavior change strategy in any given situation. Positive behavior support involves analyzing the entire environment in which a person with a developmental disability lives, works, and plays and, where necessary, making significant changes in the environment or supporting an individual in experiencing new environments (E. G. Carr et al., 2002).

An integral component in the analysis and alteration of environments of people with developmental disabilities and challenging behavior as part of positive behavior support is that of ensuring that an individual experiences an enjoyable and meaningful lifestyle. Altering and developing environments to match the idiosyncratic preferences of an individual with a developmental disability is consistent with the person-centered values inherent in positive behavior support. Providing enjoyable and meaningful environments can have a major influence on the prevention and reduction of challenging behavior; people typically do not display problem behavior when they are enjoying themselves and are involved in meaningful experiences (Reid et al., in press).

There are many ways to design and provide enjoyable and meaningful environments for people with developmental disabilities. Several key components generally form the basis for such environments. These components include a reliance on person-centered planning, assessing and providing access to preferences, choice making, and opportunities to experience an inclusive lifestyle.

Relying on Person-Centered Planning

The relationship between positive behavior support and person-centered planning was discussed previously. The point of concern here is that applications of positive behavior support should be derived from, and form a part of, a person-centered plan. The essence of person-centered planning is to determine the desires of an individual with a disability, and then to support that person in fulfilling those desires. Such a process involves identifying or designing living, working, and recreational environments and experiences based on the desires of the individual (Everson & Reid, 1999).

Assessing and Accessing Preferences

Because many people with developmental disabilities, particularly individuals who have severe disabilities, experience difficulties expressing their preferences in ways that are easily understood by support personnel, there has been a considerable amount of research on assessing preferences among this population (Lohrmann-O'Rourke & Browder, 1998). A key component of positive behavior support is routinely assessing preferred items and activities and then ensuring that environments provide ready access to identified preferences. Routinely accessing preferred activities has many potential benefits, including increasing life enjoyment, enhancing educational and work performance, and generally decreasing the occurrence of challenging behavior (Lancioni, O'Reilly, & Emerson, 1996).

Choice Making

Closely related to accessing preferences is frequent opportunities to make choices regarding major lifestyle decisions such as where to live and work, as well as choices regarding routine and daily events such as what to eat and what to do during leisure time. Another basic component of positive behavior support is to build meaningful choice-making opportunities into the lives of people with developmental disabilities and challenging behavior (Reid et al., in press). Frequent opportunities to make choices have essentially the same beneficial effects as assessing and providing access to preferences.

Experiencing Inclusive Lifestyles

Having opportunities to live, work, and play in inclusive settings in which people without disabilities spend their time is another key aspect of positive behavior support (E. G. Carr et al., 2002). Participating in typical environments and settings allows people with developmental disabilities to interact and learn from people without disabilities, participate in meaningful activities, and generally experience an enriched lifestyle. Each of these outcomes of participating in inclusive settings can help prevent and reduce challenging behavior.

ENSURING QUALITY BEHAVIOR SUPPORT SERVICES

Qualifications for Developing Behavior Support Plans

When challenging behavior becomes an issue with an individual with a developmental disability, a behavior support plan is generally developed. The plan should be designed using person-centered, team-based approaches involving people who are important in the individual's life (E. G. Carr et al., 2002). The plan should be based on the values of positive behavior support and include behavior prevention or change procedures that have a sound empirical basis in applied behavior analysis. The plan should also be highly individualized, with concern directed to the motivating factors for the problem behavior (i.e., through a functional assessment) and the individual's particular preferences. The plan should likewise attend to the degree to which the individual's overall environment may be contributing to the challenging behavior and how that environment needs to be changed.

When considering the important features that go into developing a sound behavior support plan, it becomes apparent that significant skill and knowledge are necessary on the part of plan developers. Because of the importance of the skills and knowledge of plan authors and the fact that positive behavior support is a relatively new development in the prevention and treatment of challenging behavior, attention has been directed recently to specifying the qualifications of support plan authors. The American Association on Mental Retardation, with collaboration and endorsement of the American Psychological Association and the Association for Behavior Analysis, has developed a set of guidelines for identifying behavioral consultants (Rotholz & Jacobson, 2001). These guidelines represent important recommendations regarding qualifications for people responsible for developing behavior support plans. Core qualifications specified by the American Association on Mental Retardation are summarized below:

- a master's or doctoral degree in applied behavior analysis, or a closely related discipline (e.g., psychology, special education, human development) with an emphasis in applied behavior analysis
- experience implementing behavior analysis interventions for people who have intellectual disabilities or other developmental disabilities

- adherence to ethical principles of the American Psychological Association (independent of whether the person is a licensed psychologist or member of the association) and the ethical codes of one's respective affiliated chapter of the Association for Behavior Analysis; among other things, these ethical guidelines require professionals to provide only those services for which they have the appropriate training and experience
- adherence to the Right to Effective Treatment position statement of the Association for Behavior Analysis (Van Houten et al., 1988)

Training and Supervising People Who Implement Behavior Support Plans

Once a behavior support plan is developed for an individual who displays challenging behavior, the plan must be appropriately carried out by people who interact with the individual on a routine basis. People who are expected to implement a given support plan must first be trained in the plan's component procedures, as well as the rationale for the plan. Subsequently, they must be supervised in their implementation procedures.

Training and supervising of people charged with implementing a behavior support plan are often overlooked in human service agencies, or are conducted in a superficial or ineffective manner. A common scenario is that a clinician develops a behavior support plan, meets briefly with people expected to implement the plan to discuss the component procedures, and provides a written copy of the plan. Such a process is usually insufficient for ensuring that the plan is carried out adequately. This approach contradicts an extensive body of research on effective means of training and supervising the work performance of human service personnel (Reid & Parsons, 2000), as well as currently recommended standards of professional practice (Risley & Reid, 1991).

To ensure that personnel charged with implementing a behavior support plan are adequately prepared to implement the plan, training should be conducted in a performance- and competency-based manner with everyone expected to carry out the plan (Reid & Parsons, in press). Performance-based training means not only that the plan is explained to personnel, but that personnel are shown how to carry out the plan through physical demonstration. Performance-based training also means that personnel have opportunities to practice implementing the plan's procedures and receive feedback. Competency-based training means that these training procedures are continued until each person is observed to carry out the plan at a designated level of proficiency.

Once trained, support staff should be actively supervised in implementing the plan. Both the author of the plan and the staff's regular supervisor should be involved in providing the supervision. The supervisory process should include at a minimum frequent observations of staff's proficiency in implementing the plan, along with frequent provision of supportive and corrective feedback as necessary to ensure proficient implementation. A detailed discussion of supervisory and consultative procedures for ensuring that behavior support plans are effectively carried out by human service personnel is provided by Reid and Parsons (in press).

FINAL THOUGHTS

Challenging behavior continues to be a serious issue for many people with intellectual disabilities. Positive behavior support has evolved as an effective and socially acceptable means of helping prevent and reduce challenging behavior. Stemming from behavior analytic research, behavior change procedures constituting positive behavior support approaches have a sound evidence base to substantiate their effectiveness. Application of those procedures within the person-centered philosophy of positive behavior support enhances the relevance to individuals with intellectual disabilities and respects their dignity. Ongoing and future research with positive behavior support should continue to offer more opportunities for people with disabilities to live an enjoyable life without challenging behavior.

REFERENCES

Baer, D. M., Wolf, M. M., & Risley, T. R. (1968). Some current dimensions of applied behavior analysis. *Journal of Applied Behavior Analysis, 1,* 91–97.

Bambara, L. M., & Knoster, T. (1998). *Designing positive behavioral support plans.* Washington, DC: American Association on Mental Retardation.

Carr, E. G., Dunlap, G., Horner, R. H., Koegel, R. L., Turnbull, A. P., Sailor, W., Anderson, J. L., Albin, R. W., Koegel, L. K., & Fox, L. (2002). Positive behavior support: Evolution of an applied science. *Journal of Positive Behavior Interventions, 4,* 4–17.

Carr, E. G., Horner, R. H., Turnbull, A. P., Marquis, J. G., McLaughlin, D. M., McAtee, M. L., Smith, C. E., Ryan, K. A., Ruef, M. B., & Doolabh, A. (1999). *Positive behavior support for people with developmental disabilities: A research synthesis.* Washington, DC: American Association on Mental Retardation.

Carr, E. G., Levin, L., McConnachie, G., Carlson, J., Kemp, D. C., & Smith, C. E. (1994). *Communication-based intervention for problem behavior: A user's guide for producing positive change.* Baltimore: Brookes.

Carr, J. E., Coriaty, S., & Dozier C. L. (2000). Current issues in the function-based treatment of aberrant behavior in individuals with developmental disorders. In J. Austin & J. E. Carr (Eds.), *Handbook of applied behavior analysis* (pp. 91–112). Reno, NV: Context Press.

Carr, J. E., Coriaty, S., Wilder, D. A., Gaunt, B. T., Dozier, C. L., Britton, L. N., Avina, C., & Reed, C. L. (2000). A review of "noncontingent" reinforcement as treatment for the aberrant behavior of individuals with developmental disabilities. *Research in Developmental Disabilities, 21,* 377–391.

Cooper, J. O., Heron, T. E., & Heward, W. L. (1987). *Applied behavior analysis.* Columbus, OH: Merrill.

Duker, P. C., & Sigafoos, J. (1998). The Motivation Assessment Scale: Reliability and construct validity across three topographies of behavior. *Research in Developmental Disabilities, 19,* 131–141.

Durand, V. M., & Crimmins, D. B. (1988). Identifying variables maintaining self-injurious behavior. *Journal of Autism and Developmental Disorders, 18,* 99–117.

Everson, J. M., & Reid, D. H. (1999). *Person-centered planning and outcome management: Maximizing organizational effectiveness in supporting quality lifestyles among people with disabilities.* Morganton, NC: Habilitative Management Consultants.

Foxx, R. M., & Azrin, N. H. (1973). The elimination of autistic self-stimulatory behavior by overcorrection. *Journal of Applied Behavior Analysis, 6,* 1–14.

Green, C. W., & Reid, D. H. (1999). Reducing indices of unhappiness among individuals with profound multiple disabilities during therapeutic exercise routines. *Journal of Applied Behavior Analysis, 32,* 137–147.

Hall, R. B., Lund, D., & Jackson, D. (1968). The effects of teacher attention on study behavior. *Journal of Applied Behavior Analysis, 1,* 1–12.

Holburn, S., & Vietze, P. (in press). *Research in person-centered planning.* Baltimore: Brookes.

Horner, R. H., & Day, H. M. (1991). The effects of response efficiency on functionally equivalent competing behaviors. *Journal of Applied Behavior Analysis, 24,* 719–732.

Horner, R. H., Dunlap, G., Koegel, R. L., Carr, E. G., Sailor, W., Anderson, J., Albin, R. W., & O'Neill, R. E. (1990). Toward a technology of "nonaversive" behavioral support. *Journal of the Association for Persons with Severe Handicaps, 15,* 125–132.

Iwata, B. A. (1987). Negative reinforcement in applied behavior analysis: An emerging technology. *Journal of Applied Behavior Analysis, 20,* 361–378.

Iwata, B. A., Dorsey, M. F., Slifer, K. J., Bauman, K. E., & Richman, G. S. (1982). Toward a functional analysis of self-injury. *Analysis and Intervention in Developmental Disabilities, 2,* 3–20.

Iwata, B. A., Kahng, S. W., Wallace, M. D., & Lindberg, J. S. (2000). The functional analysis model of behavioral assessment. In J. Austin & J. E. Carr (Eds.), *Handbook of applied behavior analysis* (pp. 61–89). Reno, NV: Context Press.

Knoster, T. P. (2000). Practical application of functional behavioral assessment in schools. *Journal of the Association for Persons with Severe Handicaps, 25,* 201–211.

Koegel, L. K., Koegel, R. L., & Dunlap, G. (1996). *Positive behavioral support: Including people with difficult behavior in the community.* Baltimore: Brookes.

Lancioni, G. E., O'Reilly, M. F., & Emerson, E. (1996). A review of choice research with people with severe and profound developmental disabilities. *Research in Developmental Disabilities, 17,* 391–411.

Lohrmann-O'Rourke, S., & Browder, D. M. (1998). Empirically based methods to assess the preferences of individuals with severe disabilities. *American Journal on Mental Retardation, 103,* 146–161.

Lovaas, O. I., & Simmons, J. Q. (1969). Manipulation of self-destruction in three retarded children. *Journal of Applied Behavior Analysis, 2,* 143–157.

Luiselli, J. K., & Cameron, M. J. (Eds.). (1998). *Antecedent control: Innovative approaches to behavioral support.* Baltimore: Brookes.

O'Neill, R. E., Horner, R. H., Albin, R. W., Sprague, J. R., Storey, K., & Newton, J. S. (1997). *Functional assessment and program development for problem behaviors: A practical handbook.* Pacific Grove, CA: Brooks/Cole.

O'Neill, R. E., & Johnson, J. W. (2000). A brief description of functional assessment procedures reported in *JASH* (1983–1999). *Journal of the Association for Persons with Severe Handicaps, 25,* 197–200.

Paclawskyj, T. R., Matson, J. L., Rush, K. S., Smalls, Y., & Vollmer, T. R. (2000). Questions about behavioral function (QABF): A behavioral checklist for functional assessment of aberrant behavior. *Research in Developmental Disabilities, 21,* 223–229.

Piazza, C. C., Fisher, W. W., Hanley, G. P., LeBlanc, L. A., Worsdell, A. S., Lindauer, S. E., & Keeney, K. M. (1998). Treatment of pica through multiple analyses of its reinforcing functions. *Journal of Applied Behavior Analysis, 31,* 165–189.

Reichle, J., & Wacker, D. P. (1993). *Communicative alternatives to challenging behavior: Integrating functional assessment and intervention strategies.* Baltimore: Brookes.

Reid, D. H. (2000). Enhancing the applied utility of functional assessment. *Journal of the Association for Persons with Severe Handicaps, 25,* 241–244.

Reid, D. H., & Parsons, M. B. (2000). Organizational behavior management in human service settings. In J. Austin & J. E. Carr (Eds.), *Handbook of applied behavior analysis* (pp. 275–294). Reno, NV: Context Press.

Reid, D. H., & Parsons, M. B. (in press). *Working with staff to overcome challenging behavior among people who have severe disabilities: A guide for getting support plans carried out.* Morganton, NC: Habilitative Management Consultants.

Reid, D. H., Parsons, M. B., Rotholz, D. A., Braswell, B. A., & Morris, L. A. (in press). *The Carolina curriculum on positive behavior support.* Washington, DC: American Association on Mental Retardation.

Risley, T. R., & Reid, D. H. (1991). Management and organizational issues in the delivery of psychological services for people with mental retardation. In J. W. Jacobson & J. A. Mulick (Eds.), *Manual of diagnosis and professional practice in mental retardation* (pp. 383–391). New York: Pergamon.

Rotholz, D. A., & Jacobson, J. (2001, February). *Behavioral consultants: Who are they and how do I find the right one?* Retrieved January 31, 2002, from the American Association on Mental Retardation Web site: http://aamr.org/groups/div/ps/flyer1.htm

Scotti, J. R., & Meyer, L. H. (Eds.). (1999). *Behavioral intervention: Principles, models, and practices.* Baltimore: Brookes.

Smith, R. G., & Iwata, B. A. (1997). Antecedent influences on behavior disorders. *Journal of Applied Behavior Analysis, 30,* 343–375.

Sugai, G., Horner, R. H., Dunlap, G., Hieneman, M., Lewis, T. J., Nelson, C. M., Scott, T., Liaupsin, C., Sailor, W., Turnbull, A. P., Turnbull, H. R., Wickham, D., Wilcox, B., & Ruef, M. (2000). Applying positive behavior support and functional behavioral assessment in schools. *Journal of Positive Behavior Interventions, 2,* 131–143.

Turner, W. D., Realon, R. E., Irvin, D., & Robinson, E. (1996). The effects of implementing program consequences with a group of individuals who engaged in sensory maintained hand mouthing. *Research in Developmental Disabilities, 17,* 311–330.

Van Houten, R., Axelrod, S., Bailey, J. S., Favell, J. E., Foxx, R. M., Iwata, B. A., & Lovaas, O. I. (1988). The right to effective behavioral treatment. *Behavior Analyst, 11,* 111–114.

Vollmer, T. R. (1994). The concept of automatic reinforcement: Implications for behavioral research in developmental disabilities. *Research in Developmental Disabilities, 15,* 187–207.

CHAPTER 15

Supported Employment for Persons with Intellectual and Developmental Disabilities

Paul Wehman, W. Grant Revell,
Valerie Brooke, and Wendy Parent

LEARNING GOALS

Upon completion of this chapter, the reader will be able to

- list and describe five core values underlying supported employment
- delineate the 10 critical factors for determining the effectiveness of supported employment
- discuss what workplace supports are and describe six workplace supports and how they help persons with severe disabilities go to work
- describe the "paradigm shift" when related to employment for persons with disabilities

t was in the early 1980s when initial published reports began to appear on supported employment as a means to assist people with significant disabilities become competitively employed. During these past 20 years, we have learned a great deal about what works in supported employment and what does not work (Mank, Cioffi, & Yovanoff, 1997, 2000; Wehman, 2001). We have also learned that there are many challenging implementation issues, as well as persistent philosophical differences, that have created major barriers to full implementation. We have seen greater amounts of deinstitutionalization (Hayden & Albery, 1994), the closing of state institutions (Stancliffe & Lakin, 1999), the downsizing of sheltered workshops and selective reallocation of funds targeted from segregated programs to integrated programs (Murphy, Rogan, Handley, Kincaid, & Royce-Davis, 2002), and a more significant voice given to people with disabilities via the statutes and the advocacy movement (Wehmeyer & Lawrence, 1995). We have seen changes in the way individuals with intellectual disabilities are classified by the American Association on Mental Retardation (Luckasson et al., 1992), with a movement away from intelligence quotient labels that are derived from tests and a movement toward a description of the supports, both level and intensity, that are required by persons with cognitive disabilities (American Association on Mental Retardation [AAMR], 2002).

In the past 2 decades, we have seen that the demystification of disability is the most significant contribution generated through the evolution of supported employment and other programs that define themselves in a context of supports. Too often and with too many people in our society, perceptions related to disability are immediately linked to descriptors such as *handicapped, impairment, unable to, dependent,* and *less qualified.* The gift of supported employment is its focus on the abilities of individuals with disabilities to be valued and productive at the workplace. Supported employment reduces the impact of disability, even if it is only during the time frame that the individual is at work. Once that individual departs the workplace, he or she may well be forced into "putting back on" the physical disability or intellectual disability label because needed supports are not present at home or other places in the community.

For example, consider Marci, a woman with cerebral palsy and an intellectual disability. Marci has limited speech and requires some personal assistance services throughout the day. When Marci works at Circuit City placing security scanners on the CDs in the electronics department, she earns $8.40 an hour, receives health benefits, and participates in the profit-sharing plan. With supports at work, she reduces or neutralizes the effects of her disability label. In fact, she is not disabled at all during the workday. In the eyes of her coworkers and manager as she performs her job duties, she is not disabled because they are depending on her to complete her work assignments. However, once her work shift ends, she is totally dependent on and at the mercy of the local transit system that serves people with physical disabilities. Once Marci leaves Circuit City, she must again "put on her label" and be dependent. The more the concepts of supports can permeate not only the human service system, but also communities and society as a whole, the more individuals with disabilities such as Marci will become infused into the mainstream of daily life in the community.

When we review the progress made in supported employment over the last 2 decades, we must always return to our core values. These core values have not only defined supported employment, they have also created the substantial spillover effect of supports equaling reduction of disability. No one is independent. We are all interindependent (Condeluci, 1991). The concept of true independence does not truly exist. We may all feel that we are completely independent at one time or another in our lives, but invariably we need others to help combat the physical, emotional, and intellectual disabilities that crowd into our lives. Understanding that we are all interdependent helps pave the way for understanding the role and impact of supports in designing systems aimed at elevating people to a higher level.

The core values that have permeated supported employment are inclusion; informed choice; career plan; parity in wages, hours of employment, and benefits; parity in work style options and choices; and the opportunity to be employed in the quickest, most efficient manner possible. These core values are in stark opposition to the opportunities available to an individual with a significant disability being limited to participating in segregated day programs and living in a nursing home or other congregate setting. These are discussed in more detail later in this chapter.

SUPPORTED EMPLOYMENT: GROWTH, IMPLEMENTATIONS, AND VALUES

Within less than a decade, the number of people participating in supported employment in the United States increased from 9,800 to over 140,000 (Wehman, Revell, & Kregel, 1998). McGaughey, Kiernan, McNally, Gilmore, and Keith (1994) report that approximately 18% of all individuals with developmental disabilities in adult day programs participate in integrated employment. Historically, these are individuals who were confined to adult activity centers, sheltered workshops, nursing homes, and institutions. Competitive employment was not likely to be in their futures as long as they participated in segregated employment. The use of trained employment specialists, informed coworkers, mentors, and technological supports, together with enlightened legislation such as the Americans with Disabilities Act of 1980 (ADA), have greatly enhanced the employment possibilities for people with significant disabilities.

A recent policy change by a major federal employment service funding agency is a critically important example of the movement toward increasing opportunities for achievement of competitive employment outcomes by people with a significant disability. On January 22, 2001, the Rehabilitation Services Administration of the U.S. Department of Education amended the regulations governing the state Vocational Rehabilitation Program to redefine the term *employment outcome* to mean "an individual with a disability working in an integrated setting" (*Federal Register*, January 22, 2001, pp. 7249–7258). For decades with state Vocational Rehabilitation (VR), extended employment (sometimes referred to as nonintegrated or sheltered employment) was an approved potential employment outcome for individuals with a disability who received VR services. Because extended or sheltered employment utilizes nonintegrated work settings, the redefining of employment outcome removes extended or sheltered employment as an approved potential employment outcome for Vocational Rehabilitation services.

The purpose of the Vocational Rehabilitation Program, as stated in the Rehabilitation Act of 1973, as amended, is to enable individuals with a disability to achieve an employment outcome in an integrated setting (*Federal Register,* January 22, 2001, pp. 7249–7258). In response to the priority on employment outcomes in integrated settings, first highlighted in the 1992 Amendments to the Rehabilitation Act of 1973, the decade of the 1990s was marked by a continual decrease in the use of sheltered employment as an employment outcome by Vocational Rehabilitation agencies. For example, VR agencies nationally closed 11,605 people with disabilities in sheltered employment in fiscal year (FY) 1990; by FY 1998, the number of sheltered employment VR closures dropped 34% to 7,633. In contrast, the number of individuals closed by VR in supported employment, an employment outcome marked by the use of integrated work settings, rose steadily during the 1990s. For example, VR closed approximately 9,528 individuals in supported employment in FY 1991, then 13,950 in FY 1994, and 23,056 in FY 1998 (Rehabilitation Services Administration, 2001).

Wage opportunities are a key factor in the movement by VR away from sheltered employment to more integrated employment outcomes. The average wage for individuals closed in sheltered employment by VR in FY 98 was $2.54 per hour or $64.51 per week; the corresponding wage information for persons closed by VR in supported employment during the same time period was $5.88 per hour or $142.93 per week. These wage differences are consistent across various disability groupings. For example, individuals with a primary disability classification of moderate mental retardation closed in sheltered employment by VR in FY 98 earned on average $2.04 per hour or $50.71 per week; the corresponding wage information for persons in this disability classification closed by VR in supported employment during the same time period was $5.24 per hour or $112.09 per week (Rehabilitation Services Administration, 2001). The federal minimum wage increased from $4.75 to $5.15 per hour as of September 1, 1997, one month before the start of federal FY 1998.

The growth of competitive employment outcomes over the last decade through use of supported employment is an important milestone in the movement, fostered by the Americans with Disabilities Act (ADA), to full community integration of people with a disability at work and elsewhere in their lives (Wehman, 1993). The ADA was the reason the Supreme Court upheld the case of *Olmstead v. L.C.* (1999), a major community integration landmark decision. However, the actual impact of this growth in competitive employment outcomes is relatively small in terms of the full array of programs serving people with disabilities in nonintegrated settings. For example, *The State of the States in Developmental Disabilities: 2002 Study Summary* (Braddock, Hemp, Parish, & Rizzolo 2002) reports that in FY 2000, state mental retardation/developmental disabilities (MR/DD) agencies served approximately 361,000 individuals in day, work, and sheltered employment programs that did not involve supported competitive employment. In comparison, approximately 108,000 persons were served by these agencies in supported competitive employment, an approximate 3:1 ratio of noncompetitive to competitive work outcomes for persons served by MR/DD agencies. Although this FY 2000 participation rate of 23% in supported competitive employment is an improvement over the corresponding 21% rate found for FY 1998 (Braddock et al., 2000), it is clear that noncompetitive employment settings still dominate state developmental disabilities service systems.

For individuals served through the Medicaid Home and Community Based Services (HCBS) Waiver, West, Wehman, and Revell (2002) indicated that in FY 1999, only about 15% of the more than 130,000 persons receiving day habilitation services through the HCB Waiver were in supported employment. The rest were in a variety of day habilitation service categories that were not competitive work oriented and frequently not community integrated. These reports dramatically demonstrate that for many people with significant disabilities, being served in nonintegrated settings continues to be the dominant experience. Unfortunately, hundreds of thousands of people with disabilities remain left behind in segregated centers. Many more are on waiting lists for employment despite the fact that people with significant cognitive, physical, and behavioral challenges have demonstrated their competence in the workplace.

CORE VALUES UNDERLYING SUPPORTED EMPLOYMENT

Increasingly, most people agree on the benefits of individuals with significant disabilities having opportunities for real integrated work as a primary option. All parties involved benefit from competitive employment. Such employment provides the individual with a disability with a real job, benefits, and the dignity that arises from gainful employment. The employer gets a good worker and receives specialized support to train and maintain the individual. The family is able to see its family member in a fully competent role in the workplace. Finally, taxpayers spend less money than they would to support the individual in a segregated day program year in and year out. However, several questions remain: Why do the vast majority of individuals with mental and physical disabilities remain in segregated day programs? What values are service providers and advocates following? And what are the factors that best reflect quality employment outcomes?

The answers to these questions lie partially in the inability of advocates and people with disabilities to adequately marshal their collective efforts to increase work opportunities (Wehman & Kregel, 1995). The adult service systems in the world remain deeply entrenched, as they have been for several decades (Albin, Rhodes, & Mank, 1994). Changing this way of providing services is extremely difficult, particularly in times of reduced funding resulting from a recessionary economy. Hence, there is an overwhelming necessity to market the positive attributes of supported employment for people with significant disabilities.

Table 15.1 lists nine values that have guided supported employment efforts from the early 1980s and provides a brief description of each. These values

TABLE 15.1
Supported Employment Values

Values	Values Clarification
Presumption of employment	A conviction that everyone, regardless of the level or the type of disability, has the capability of performing and right to a job.
Competitive employment	A conviction that employment occurs within the local labor market in regular community businesses.
Control	A conviction that when people with disabilities choose and regulate their own employment supports and services, career satisfaction will result.
Commensurate wages and benefits	A conviction that people with disabilities should earn wages and benefits equal to that of coworkers performing the same or similar jobs.
Focus on capacity and capabilities	A conviction that people with disabilities should be viewed in terms of their abilities, strengths, and interests rather than their disabilities.
Importance of relationships	A conviction that community relationships both at and away from work lead to mutual respect and acceptance.
Power of supports	A conviction that people with disabilities need to determine their personal goals and receive assistance in assembling the supports necessary to achieve their ambitions.
Systems change	A conviction that traditional systems must be changed to ensure customer control, which is vital to the integrity of supported employment.
Importance of community	A conviction that people need to be connected to the formal and informal networks of a community for acceptance, growth, and development.

reflect the themes discussed at the beginning of this chapter; they have been increasingly reflected in rehabilitation legislation, as well as the *Olmstead* decision. Presumption of employment, person-centered control, wages, supports, interdependence, and connecting within the community are the underlying values that are reflected in an excellent employment program. Without these values, a program has no beacon to follow in its daily operations. Without these values, a program will wander from funding source to funding source, dependent on the current fad or whim of the moment. Without clear values, a program will dilute its efforts and lose focus.

Questions remain, however: How do values become translated into real operational quality factors for programs to guide themselves? What are the benchmarks by which program staff, consumers, and advocates can discern the value of one program over another? These questions take on special merit when one considers, for example, the emergence of the Ticket to Work and Work Incentive Improvement Act of 1999, a program intended to financially empower individuals who receive Social Security disability benefits to utilize funding from the Social Security Administration to select their own employment program and pay for needed services and supports. What is the best way to assess whether competitive employment services are being used by individuals with disabilities who hold a Ticket to Work or a funding agency seeking positive employment outcomes for the dollars spent on services? What follows is a description of 10 factors that can be used in assessing the quality of a supported employment program.

MEASURING THE EFFECTIVENESS OF SUPPORTED EMPLOYMENT PROGRAMS

The goal of supported employment programs is to assist people with the most significant disabilities to be successful in paid employment in the integrated work setting of their choice. However, what exactly is the functional meaning of the phrase "paid employment in an integrated setting"? Current federal regulations, issued by the Rehabilitation Services Administration to govern the national Vocational Rehabilitation Program, define *integrated setting* as a setting typically found in the community where individuals with a disability interact with nondisabled individuals, other than the nondisabled individuals who are providing services to the individuals with a disability, to the same extent that nondisabled individuals in comparable positions interact with other persons (*Federal Register,* January 17, 2001, pp. 4379–4435).

The general wording in this regulation of the phrases "setting typically found in the community" and "interact with nondisabled individuals to the same extent as nondisabled persons in comparable positions" allows for various interpretations on what actually constitutes paid employment in an integrated setting. Jobs can be considered competitive employment when the single measure of integration is the presence of coworkers who are not disabled, without consideration of other key measures of settings typically found in the community. As a result, Vocational Rehabilitation and other supported employment funding agencies, providers of employment services, and individuals with disabilities served by supported employment programs are uncertain over just what is meant by an outcome to supported employment services generally characterized as paid employment in an integrated work setting. It is clear that the uncertainty surrounding both the regulatory meaning and community-level application of the phrase "paid employment in an integrated setting" severely compromises the usefulness of general references to "paid employment" and "an integrated setting" as measures of the quality of an employment outcome. Clearly defined, carefully described factors to assess the quality of supported employment programs are needed.

Table 15.2 contains 10 factors that can help serve as effective measures of the quality of a supported employment program. These 10 factors address quality of a supported employment program from a variety of critical perspectives. The first perspective is the point of view of individuals with a disability who turn to a supported employment program for support in getting and retaining a job. Do individuals served by the supported employment program consistently achieve truly meaningful job outcomes? Who selects these jobs, and do these employment opportunities reflect informed customer choice and control? The factor must also reflect the perspective of employers. Are employers satisfied with the work produced by the individuals in supported employment and the quality of the ongoing support services received from the supported employment program? The factors must be responsive to the agencies funding the supported employment program. Does the provider have a well-coordinated job retention support system in place, and does the program's management information system accurately track and monitor employment outcomes? Finally, the combined set of factors must serve as a means for self-assessment by the supported employment program itself to help identify areas of strength that can be used in marketing and areas that need priority attention for improvement. In the discussion that follows, each of the 10 factors recommended in Table 15.2 is described in terms of its importance as a quality measure for a supported employment program.

Factor I: Meaningful Competitive Employment in Integrated Work Settings

An individual in supported employment works in a competitive job in an integrated work setting. What in fact characterizes the true quality of competitive work in an integrated setting? The preamble to the 1997 Vocational Rehabilitation regulatory announcement frames paid employment in integrated settings in the context of the *parity principle* by asking the question: Is the experience of the person with a disability at parity with the experiences of the nondisabled coworker (*Federal Register,* February 11, 1997, p. 6311)? The importance of this parity principle is supported by the research of Mank and his associates on the positive relations of typical employment features and coworker involvement with higher wage and integration outcomes for individuals in supported employment (Mank et al., 1997, 1999, 2000). Consideration of the parity of experiences between the worker with a disability and the nondisabled coworker leads directly to the following questions as functional indicators of the quality of the paid employment outcome:

- How are people with disabilities hired? Are they hired by the business where the work is being performed, or are they an employee of an employment services organization?
- How are people with disabilities supervised? Are they supervised by an employee of the business where the work is being performed or by an employee of an employment service organization?

TABLE 15.2

Quality Factors for Supported Employment Programs

Factors	Example of Functional Measures for Factors
Meaningful competitive employment in integrated work settings	Employee with a disability is hired, supervised, and paid directly by business where job setting is located; receives wages and benefits commensurate with those of nondisabled coworkers.
Informed choice, control, and satisfaction	Employee selects own service provider and job coach; selects job and work conditions; is satisfied with job and supports.
Level and nature of supports	Program is skilled in identifying workplace support options and developing workplace support options.
Employment of individuals with truly significant disabilities	Program is serving individuals whose intermittent competitive work history, disability profile, functional capabilities, and other barriers to employment are truly reflective of people who need ongoing workplace supports to retain employment.
Number of hours worked weekly	Program is achieving employment outcomes at 30 or more hours per week consistently. Individuals receiving support are satisfied with their hours of competitive employment.
Number of persons from program working regularly	Program currently has a majority of its participants working in competitive employment. Individuals receiving support are satisfied with their program of services.
Well-coordinated job retention system	Program maintains regular contact with its employed customers to monitor job stability and can respond effectively to both planned and unplanned job retention support needs. Program replaces individuals who do not retain employment.
Employment outcome monitoring and tracking system	Program maintains an information system that provides information readily to its customers on employment status, longevity, wages, benefits, hours of employment, and jobs.
Maximizing integration and community participation	Employees with a disability work in jobs where the work environment facilitates physical and social interaction with coworkers. Employees are satisfied with the quality of their work and community integration.
Employer satisfaction	Program is viewed as an employment service rather than a human service provider. Employers are seen as a customer of the service, and the program designs policies and procedures that are responsive to the needs of the business community.

- Are people with disabilities paid comparable wages *and* benefits to those of coworkers who are not disabled?
- Do employees with disabilities have the same career advancement opportunities within the work site as coworkers who are not disabled, as well as equal access to resources at the workplace such as Employee Assistance Programs?
- Is there full social access to coworkers who are not disabled, and is there an absence of a congregation of persons with disabilities within the work site?

These are important questions to be considered.

Factor 2: Informed Choice, Control, and Satisfaction

The opportunity to make choices concerning employment, living arrangements, and recreation has been limited or nonexistent for many individuals with disabilities (Gilson, 1998). It has become increasingly evident that the powerlessness and lack of direction frequently felt by people with disabilities are related to attitudes and practices of service providers, caregivers, funding agencies, and society in general, rather than any true limitations as a result of an individual's disability (Brooke, Wehman, Inge, & Parent, 1995; Browder, Wood, Test, Karvonen, & Algozzine, 2001; Wehman, 1981). High-quality supported employment programs avoid this trap by empowering their customers to make choices and to take control of their career paths. A critical factor in assessing the overall quality of a supported employment program is analyzing the data to determine if the customers of the service have choice over the process and are truly in control of their rehabilitation outcomes. Organizations that support choice and control shape their service delivery practices by the wants and needs of their customers. Key features or factors of a supported employment program would assess informed choice and control by reviewing the following factors to determine the level of involvement by customers.

Factor 3: Level and Nature of Supports

Supported employment is perhaps best characterized as employment with supports or special assistance. Detailed job analysis, identification and use of community and workplace supports, systematic instruction, compensatory strategies, orientation training, and workplace accommodations have always been the cornerstones of a well-developed plan of support (Inge & Tilson, 1997; Parent, Wehman, & Bricout, 2001). The term *natural supports* was first noted in federal policy with the 1992 Rehabilitation Act Amendments that included that phrase as a possible source of ongoing (§ 7.33.C. vii) and extended services (§ 635, 6.C. vii). However, quality supported employment service providers must move beyond the language used in federal policy and attempt to provide the exact type and intensity of support needed across all aspects of their services. For example, an employment specialist would not want to provide any more or less support than what was actually necessary to assist the supported employment customer in obtaining, learning, or maintaining employment. Supported employment providers, in consultation with their customers, would always approach a task by discussing the least intrusive approach and only move to a more intrusive level of support if that was the desire of the customer and was needed to achieve the desired outcome.

The task of identifying, selecting, and facilitating supports that promote independence and employment stability is complex with multiple factors that must be considered. Working with the supported employment customer, the employment specialist must be skilled at analyzing data results along with supervisor and coworker comments to determine the exact nature and level of support that will best match the employment situation. When this process is done correctly, supported employment customers are assured a high-quality supported employment service.

Factor 4: Employment of Individuals with Truly Significant Disabilities

The 1986 Amendments to the Rehabilitation Act of 1973 included Title VI-C, which designated supported employment as a program. However, it was not until the 1992 Reauthorization of the Rehabilitation Act that the regulations made major changes to the eligibility provisions and included language that clearly stated that the program was designed for people with the *most* significant disabilities. Supported employment was never intended to serve the typical vocational rehabilitation customer. Rather, this service option was created for those people who experience truly significant disabilities and traditionally were not able to obtain competitive employment through vocational rehabilitation services. The 1992 reauthorization further describes customers of supported employment as those individuals who have obtained intermittent employment but have not been successful in maintaining competitive employment, and who need long-term support to achieve competitive employment. Supported employment service providers need to work with potential customers and rehabilitation counselors to ensure that the organization is marketing their service to the appropriate customers (Green & Brooke, 2001).

Factor 5: Number of Hours Worked Weekly

Number of hours worked weekly is a critical quality indicator for a supported employment program for a number of reasons. First, on an individual customer basis, hours of weekly employment establish the base for a number of meaningful employment outcomes. Lower hour, part-time jobs are usually characterized by lower pay and limited benefits. In comparison, employment of 30 or more hours per week brings better access to higher wages and potential benefits such as health coverage, vacation and sick leave, and insurance coverage. Higher hours of weekly employment also improve access to work-related training provided through the employer and social interaction with coworkers. From a program perspective, supporting a high percentage of customers in lower hour jobs creates a variety of possible strains on the program. What are the program's funded responsibilities for helping its customers fill nonwork hours? Many funding agencies require a certain level of program involvement per week; lower hours of employment can create situations where programs turn to more center-based, segregated services to fill hours. This practice perpetuates center-based services, ties down staff who could be shifted to supporting customers in the community, and creates confusion among program participants and their families as customers move back and forth between community-integrated work and set-apart, center-based services.

On a customer-to-customer basis, hours worked per week should reflect the preferences and choices of each individual. An individual might choose to work under 30 hours a week because of concerns over maintaining Social Security disability benefits, because of work preferences, or because of work tolerances reflecting the residual effects of the disability and the supports needed for that person to work. For example, an individual who needs personal assistance services at work might have limited hours of this service available and will therefore work a more limited number of hours. Overall, however, the hours of weekly employment consistently achieved by participants are a valid indicator of the quality of a supported employment program.

Factor 6: Number of Individuals from the Program Working Regularly

Earlier in this chapter, reference was made to the approximate 3:1 ratio of noncompetitive to competitive work outcomes for persons served by MR/DD agencies nationally (Braddock et al., 2002). A large number of persons with significant disabilities have very limited access to competitive employment. The negative impact of nonemployment on the lives of people with disabilities is substantial. Participation in noncompetitive work programs by people with a disability severely limits earnings, as demonstrated by the disparity between earnings from sheltered employment and earnings through supported employment reported previously in this chapter. It restricts personal choices, in terms of both available resources and opportunities. It creates unnecessary dependency and perpetuates the myths and stereotypes related to disability and nonproductivity. And maintaining noncompetitive programs locks down resources within more segregated settings, resources that are needed to provide community-integrated workplace supports.

Identifying the number of persons from a program working regularly should not be limited to those individuals who are in the supported employment program. Many supported employment programs are a component of larger agencies that offer multiple services, sometimes including noncompetitive employment services (Wehman et al., 1998). The true measure of the quality of supported employment outcomes achieved by a program is reflected in the percentage of individuals in its overall enrollment who are working regularly in competitive employment. With an enrollment of 100 individuals, if 75 are involved in noncompetitive activities while 25 are working regularly in competitive employment, a program is stuck at the national 3:1 ratio and fails this quality indicator.

Factor 7: Well-Coordinated Job Retention System

The provision of ongoing supports as long as needed after employment is the core characteristic of supported employment that differentiates it from other employment services. There is strong evidence that the maintenance of ongoing supports after employment is a characteristic of successful supported employment programs that generate better employment outcomes (Bond et al., 2001). Well-coordinated job retention systems provide ongoing individualized supports that assist the employee with a disability in areas such as structuring needed workplace accommodations, monitoring and assessing job stability, adjusting supports to address changing needs both at and away from the job site, and providing other supports that enhance job retention (Ridgway & Rapp, 1998). Well-coordinated job retention systems provide replacement assistance in situations of job loss or job enhancement.

Supported employment providers face a substantial challenge in operating a well-coordinated job retention system that extends into the extended-services phase of supported employment services after the time-limited funding from Vocational Rehabilitation ends. Although few studies have focused on extended services, there is evidence that many supported employment providers have limited access to funding for extended services. Extended-services funding frequently does not cover the cost for providing these services, and monthly follow-along services are often funded from other program revenues (West, Johnson, Cone, Hernandez, & Revell, 1998). This limited commitment of funding agencies to extended services continues despite the findings from a recent study citing clear evidence that maintaining employment supports well into the job tenure and beyond the limited period of VR funding is often critical to addressing work-related problems. This same study noted the increases in the contact time that occur in extended services during the 3- to 6-month tenure in employment to address non–work-related problems and career advancement interests (West, Wehman, & Revell, 2002). Although funding for job retention services continues to be a problem for supported employment agencies, it is clear that the most successful supported employment programs are those that can operate a well-coordinated job retention service.

Factor 8: Employment Outcome Monitoring and Tracking System

Traditionally, supported employment programs have developed standards, objectives, and processes in an effort to build and promote quality supported employment services. Program managers and staff design standards and factors to assist in gauging the success of their program services. The typical areas assessed include philosophy, mission, administration, fiscal management, image, community resources, personnel, job or career development, job training and support, long-term supports, and employee relations.

With many programs, the primary reason for organizational assessment is to meet an agency need for supported employment provider certification. This certification is required to become a local vendor for supported employment and to qualify for state or local funding. Most supported employment organizations recognize the need for assessing quality and are committed to providing excellent services, yet many supported employment personnel report that collecting and analyzing data on factors is an unrealistic expectation. For this reason, some programs have stopped collecting the data necessary for an accurate assessment of the overall quality of their service organization. Collecting and analyzing data on supported employment service outcomes does not have to be difficult or time consuming. Without accurate and consistent data, it is impossible to accurately assess the quality of a supported employment program, particularly in the core factors of serving persons with significant disabilities, achieving meaningful employment outcomes, customer choice and employer satisfaction, and job retention.

Factor 9: Maximizing Integration and Community Participation

Integration and community participation are important outcomes of quality services. The idea that individuals with significant disabilities can and should work in regular business environments and participate fully in the life of their communities is the guiding philosophy behind supported employment. Work is a highly valued activity in U.S. culture and offers wage earners numerous benefits. Having a job and paying taxes can enhance an individual's status in the community and offer the employee an opportunity to interact with coworkers and develop a host of relationships at work and in the community.

Multiple factors can be examined when determining whether an employee is integrated in the workplace and participating in the community. Analyzing a business site to determine whether the company offers an opportunity for integration is important, as is the need to repeat the analysis periodically as the customer becomes more familiar to his or her coworkers. In addition, the employee's work area, work hours, and satisfaction level play important roles in assessing that customer's integration and community participation. A negative answer to any of the following questions could be an indicator that intervention is necessary to improve the overall quality of the employment situation and, consequently, the services of the supported employment program:

- Does the company offer opportunities for physical and social integration, such as common break areas and company social functions?

- Does the employee's work area facilitate physical and social inter-actions through close proximity of coworkers, shared responsibilities, unrestricted communication, and so forth?
- To what extent is the customer integrated? Does he or she work and socialize with others or in isolation?
- In what activities does the customer engage in the community, such as going out with friends and participating in clubs and groups?
- Is the customer satisfied with the job and the level of community integration?

Factor 10: Employer Satisfaction

Supported employment service providers must not view themselves as human service providers, but rather as employment service agencies. This is a significant paradigm shift for many supported employment organizations that emphasizes a competitive and valued offering of needed services to employers. The language must be business to business; the message must be clear: "Our company will fill your personnel needs!" This shift establishes an approach that presents the service, as well as the person with a significant disability, in a competent and respected manner. In addition, it focuses the organization's resources on the business community and is designed to satisfy employment needs (Green & Brooke, 2001).

Job placement personnel with rehabilitation programs are still fairly hidden from the business community. Businesses looking to recruit and hire people with disabilities cannot seem to find the rehabilitation programs in the community, nor do they know how to recruit people with disabilities who want to work (Peck & Kirkbride, 2001). It is fair to say that most rehabilitation professionals assisting people with disabilities in obtaining employment do not see themselves as customer representatives with direct responsibility for building ongoing relationships with the business community. However, the task of customer relationships should be the primary responsibility for all rehabilitation personnel. Programs can measure the quality of their service to employers by reviewing the following factors:

- Does the supported employment program develop business profiles complete with business culture notations and language specific to the identified business?
- Does the supported employment program provide staff development training for rehabilitation personnel?
- Has the supported employment program established a sense of urgency that is responsive to the business community?
- Does the supported employment program do community outreach and provide training on disability awareness?
- Does the supported employment program serve as a liaison for the business and people with disabilities?

• Does the supported employment program involve the business community in the development of the organization's policy?

Summary

These 10 factors of quality supported employment programs ensure that the
community rehabilitation program is developing strong strategies for developing productive business relationships. These are the key areas that, if not met,
will block productive relationships between business and rehabilitation programs (Egan, 2001).

People with significant disabilities are beginning to work more, to earn
better wages, and to be more empowered (e.g., Blanck, 1998). At the same time,
employment service providers have tended to approach the needs of workers
with disabilities and the needs of employers from the mutually exclusive perspectives of addressing perceived deficits on one side, and capitalizing on workplace potential on the other. Too often the rehabilitation needs of workers with
disabilities are identified without simultaneously acknowledging the many potential work supports available with the assistance of employers. Frequently, employment service providers have not looked closely enough at the different types
of supports that are available to persons with disabilities in the workplace. The
use of a paid job coach has been heavily relied upon by many providers—often
with success; however, providers need to broaden their perspectives.

Table 15.3 presents four major categories of work supports and the sub-
categories within them. These categories include supports that are agency mediated, business mediated, government mediated, and family and community mediated. These supports can all be identified, implemented, and evaluated in the
workplace environment. However, they will usually be initiated from different
starting points and with different entities mediating resources and services. As
the basis for designing this taxonomy, we provide the following short literature
review and discussion of each category of work supports.

WORKPLACE SUPPORTS THAT CAN HELP
FACILITATE JOB RETENTION

Agency-Mediated Supports

Because most human services funding for rehabilitation flows through a single,
common agency, the human service agency that provides supported employment
services is an important starting point for examining workplace supports. One of
the services that may be provided by such agencies is to coordinate services with
other entities, be they employers, government, or providers of specialized services such as mental health treatment, vocational rehabilitation, or education.
Historically, the rehabilitation agency mediated the flow of supports. A number

TABLE 15.3

Taxonomy of Work Supports

Agency-Mediated Supports

1. Job coach assistance
   - specialized training
   - compensatory strategies
2. Compensatory strategies (e.g., memory aids)
3. Assistive technologies
4. Counseling
5. Substance abuse services
6. Medical services
7. Specialized transportation
8. Vocational rehabilitation counselor

Business-Mediated Supports

1. Job restructuring
2. Workplace accommodations
   - environmental modifications
   - assistive technology
   - task modification
   - schedule modification
3. Coworker mentoring
   - job task training and support
   - social support
4. Job creation
5. Employee Assistance Programs
6. Employment consultant (hired by business)

Government-Mediated Supports

1. Social Security work incentives
   - plan for achieving self-support
   - impairment-related work experience
2. Tax credits
   - work opportunity tax credit
   - disabled access credit
   - tax deduction to remove transportation and architectural barriers

Family- and Community-Mediated Supports

1. Personal care attendant
2. Peer mentors
3. Family members as job developers
4. Friends and neighbors
5. Social support networks

---

of different types of supports mediated by agencies are reported in the literature. The various types are listed below.

Job Coach Support

The majority of the work support literature has focused on the job coach (individual placement) model of supported employment. This approach was initially presented by Wehman (1981) and further articulated by Wehman and Kregel (1989). Since then, Bond (1998) and Drake (1998) have built significantly on this approach, focusing on persons with psychiatric disabilities. The process is the same, regardless of the population of consumers: provide support services at the job site, rather than treatment-centered support at a clinic or elsewhere. Many researchers have written supporting the job coach/individual placement approach (e.g., Bond, Dietzen, McGrew, & Miller, 1995; Kregel, Wehman, & Banks, 1989; MacDonald-Wilson, Revell, Nguyen, & Peterson, 1991; Shafer, Banks, & Kregel, 1991; Sinnott-Oswald, Gliner, & Spencer, 1991; Wehman, Kregel, West, & Cifu, 1994; Wehman et al., 1990). In fact, the individual placement/job coach model of supported employment appears to be the predominant practice of vocational service agencies in the field as well, and has been viewed as something of a gold standard of services for many persons with severe disabilities (West, Kregel, Hernandez, & Hock, 1997).

Compensatory Strategies

Compensatory strategies represent one avenue of support for overcoming the gap that sometimes occurs between worker abilities and environmental demands. Compensatory strategies are plans, behaviors, or materials that help workers with disabilities compensate for functional impairments. Certainly, others in addition to the agency can initiate compensatory strategies as supports. In fact, the person with the disability will usually be a driving force in selecting a compensatory strategy. The person with the disability will often help the agency or job coach identify what compensatory strategies or tasks makes the best sense, given the situation and available resources.

Examples for workers with cognitive disabilities include memory aids and strategies, additional time to complete tasks, verbal rehearsals, checklists, and location markers (Adelman & Vogel, 1993; Briel, 1996). For persons with traumatic brain injury, compensatory strategies for cognitive remediation can be achieved using systematic task analysis (Giles & Shore, 1989; Kreutzer, Gordon, & Wehman, 1989; Kreutzer, Wehman, Morton, & Stonnington, 1988). The job coach conducts an intensive analysis of all job tasks until the constituent parts can be identified and listed sequentially. Compensatory strategies are then developed on the basis of the task analysis and the supported employee's abilities (Kreutzer et al., 1989; Kreutzer et al., 1988). Compensatory strategies can be developed that match the supported employee's presenting problems by integrating information from several sources in a graduated process of testing and modification (Briel, 1996). An evaluation of learning and memory abilities is conducted, followed by a situational working assessment and on-site job training feedback, with employee needs, preferences, and concerns an ongoing part of the process (Briel, 1996). Similar supports are possible using assistive technologies. Assistive technologies can be considered specialized supports aiding the supported employee in his or her adaptation to the environment. These assistive technologies complement the supports provided by specialized professional services, such as mental health education and treatment, and other disability-specific services. The discussion will begin with a brief consideration of assistive technologies.

Assistive Technologies

One of the most influential definitions of assistive technologies is provided by a federal statute, the Technology-Related Assistance for Individuals with Disabilities Act of 1988 (Wallace, Flippo, Barcus, & Behrman, 1995). The act can be paraphrased as stating that with respect to employment, assistive technologies are low- and high-technology devices, services, and adaptations that enable some persons with disabilities to participate in, contribute to, and interact in work life in much the same fashion as nondisabled coworkers. Although agency-mediated supports are the focus of this section, it is important to note that government, and more particularly, the federal government is a major funding source for assistive technologies (Parette & VanBiervliet, 1992). Supported employment provider agencies play a pivotal role in assistive technologies because job coaches have considerable input in the selection, procurement, implementation, and evaluation of assistive technologies used as work supports.

Assistive technologies can be of either low or high technology. Several examples from both will help make the picture of assistive technologies more clear. One example of a low-technology assist is a communications book. Such a book was used to help integrate workers with severe disabilities in a competitive workplace (Storey & Provost, 1996). This device consists of pictures bound together in a book or wallet and used to facilitate conversations with nondisabled coworkers. Two workers with severe disabilities using a communications book were able to increase their number of interactions with nondisabled coworkers in some circumstances (Storey & Provost, 1996). Recalling that services and adaptations are part of assistive technologies in addition to devices, another interesting example is found in the training of an adult with a brain injury to use bus transportation to and from work (Newbigging & Laskey, 1996). A combination of daily planning sessions and *in vivo* training on the bus resulted in the worker's being able to develop lasting bus riding skills.

In the realm of high-technology devices, an 18-inch-long head pointer, together with an angled control panel and a touch-sensitive screen, enables a worker with cerebral palsy to operate a copy machine as part of his job (Smith, 1992). Another copier innovation, an attached computer and voice synthesizer, allows a worker with a visual impairment to operate the equipment (Smith, 1992). A robotic device to assist workers with severe motor impairments to their upper and lower limbs has significantly reduced the amount of time per work unit that an assistant is needed, although at some loss of productivity (Birch et al., 1996). High-technology devices must sometimes be adapted to real-life situations that require a coordination of efforts between machine, supervisor, worker, and coworkers.

Specialized Agency Services

Supported employees can also benefit from multidisciplinary expertise in their adaptation to the competitive workplace. This holds true for disability-related functional impairments, as well as for the design and implementation of assistive technologies. Some combination of resources and coordination of efforts, between the employment service provider and the disability-related service provider is desirable (LaRocca, Kalb, & Gregg, 1996). Examples of specialized, disability-related service providers include psychological counseling, substance abuse programs, medical programs, mental health programs (Rogers, Anthony, & Danley, 1989), taxi or shuttle transportation, and developmental disabilities programs (McGaughey et al., 1994). Vocational rehabilitation providers may play the same role in mediating disability-related specialized services as supported employment providers. Nonetheless, their roles diverge inasmuch as it is possible for a supported employment provider to act as the specialized service provider for a vocational rehabilitation service. For the moment, however, supported employment programs and vocational rehabilitation services will be considered equal vocational service providers, with other providers lending their specialized expertise on the management and treatment of the disability in question. A case example of the way vocational and specialized providers can influence the employment outcomes of workers with disabilities may bring these issues into sharper focus.

CASE EXAMPLE: SIMON

Simon, a worker with a psychiatric disability, receives specialized services from mental health providers in accordance with his disability-related needs and his goals. He receives counseling and medication from a mental health provider to manage his illness. These treatments will help him achieve success in his employment goal. Simon has just landed his preferred job. He and his job coach have determined that coworker aid is a critical work support for success in this job. The mental health services he receives will enable him to have successful social interactions with coworkers after he has received some additional social skills training from his job coach. The job coach is able to successfully complete social skills training with Simon because mental health treatments have increased Simon's receptivity.

As this example suggests, it is not only the supported employee who benefits from the efforts of the specialized service provider; the job coach does, too. When the specialized provider services are provided separately from vocational services, they are called brokered services. Particularly with respect to psychiatric disabilities, brokered services have been found to produce less effective employment outcomes and poorer customer service than integrated services (Drake, Becker, Xie, & Anthony, 1995). Ideally, integrated services are characterized by seamless customer-centered services and resources, together with cross-training and/or education of vocational and specialized service staff (Bybee, Mowbray, & McCrohan, 1995; Drake et al., 1995; Drake, McHugo, Becker, Anthony, & Clark, 1996).

Business-Mediated Supports

Even though agencies have traditionally initiated the work support process, an ever-increasing number of professionals are concluding that employers should also be initiating work supports (Hanley-Maxwell & Millington, 1992; Harper, 1993; Sandow, Olson, & Yan, 1993; Test & Wood, 1996). Businesses are a vital source of in-house work supports, including people (e.g., supervisors and coworkers), practices (e.g., flexible scheduling), policies (e.g., early return to work), and environmental supports (e.g., accessible work spaces) (Fabian & Leucking, 1991; Rhodes, Sandow, Taliaferro, & Mank, 1993; Shoemaker, Robin, & Robin, 1992; Sowers, Kouwenhoven, Sousa, & Milliken, 1997). Businesses can also lead collaborations with human service providers (Rhodes et al., 1993). As Golden (1995) notes, businesses can tap into government-sponsored services such as those provided under the Job Training Partnership Act, federal employ-ment-related funding such as the Disabled Access Tax Credit, and nonprofit funds such as those provided by the Association for Retarded Citizens' wage reimbursement program.

A wide variety of programs designed to meet the support needs of work-ers with disabilities have been sponsored by businesses. Businesses have entered into partnerships to hire and provide supports for workers with disabilities with public entities, nonprofit organizations, insurance companies, and other busi-nesses (Akabas & Gates, 1993; Miano, Nalven, & Hoff, 1996; Tilson, Luecking, & West, 1996). Finally, businesses also have contracted with employment con-sultants and Employee Assistance Programs to provide work supports (Kiernan & McGaughey, 1992). In each of these instances, business is the mediator through which work support programs, practices, policies, and procedures for disabled workers are realized.

Workplace Accommodations

Accommodations such as assistive technologies, job modification, environmental modification, job restructuring, and schedule modification can often be achieved at a low cost. It is estimated that about 80% of accommodations cost between $100 and $500, whereas half of accommodations cost little or no money (John-son, 1992). Moreover, the federal government offers businesses tax incentives to cover part of the cost of removing many barriers (Johnson, 1992). The cost of job creation, another accommodation possibility, could be justified by seasonal variations in product demand, the labor pool, or unmet company needs. At the same time, free accommodations, such as schedule modification or job restruc-turing, may contain a hidden cost in the burdens or perceived inequities that they impose on coworkers, supervisors, and employers (Frierson, 1992). The need to have business personnel buy in to work supports and accommodations hints at why these individuals are themselves important work supports.

Coworker and Employer Supports

Coworker support has been identified as critical to the work performance and job satisfaction of all employees, disabled and nondisabled alike (Curl, Hall, Chisholm, & Rule, 1992; Fabian & Leucking, 1991). An important dimension of coworker support is social integration, which has been linked to both social sup-port (important to job satisfaction) and mentoring (important to job perfor-mance) (Curl, Fraser, Cook, & Clemmons, 1996; Gaylord-Ross, Park, Johnston, Lee, & Goetz, 1995; Storey & Provost, 1996). In addition to providing social sup-port and mentoring, coworkers can provide formal training for workers with disabilities, and have done so successfully in a number of circumstances (Curl et al., 1996). Supervisors and employers provide training and mentoring sup-port as part of their role, although they may provide more varied, extensive, and intensive training for workers with disabilities than for nondisabled workers. Su-pervisors and employers also provide work supports such as flexible scheduling, task modifications, job restructuring, and job sharing. Studies have indicated that employers do not object to providing additional task-related support for workers with disabilities (Adelman & Vogel, 1993). However, employers have reported objections to providing additional support of a personal or emotional nature (Adelman & Vogel, 1993). Another source of supports is found in specialized in-house and contracted disability-related programs and policies.

Employer-Sponsored Programs and Policies

Return-to-work policies, disability case management, and rehabilitation have been identified as cost-saving procedures for employers because of the high costs of disability claims and replacement labor. Disability management programs are one response to the high cost of worker disablement (Akabas & Gates, 1993). Such programs seek to identify and manage job-related stressors, along with workplace environmental limitations in order to create a productive fit between the requirements of the job and the worker (Akabas, 1994; Akabas & Gates 1993). Supervisory support, job accommodations, supportive policies, training, evaluation, and prevention are integral components of a successful disability management program (Akabas, 1994).

In addition to internal policies about family and medical leave, there are two federal statutes of importance to employers of workers with disabilities: the Americans with Disabilities Act (ADA) and the Family and Medical Leave Act of 1993 (Akabas, 1994). The ADA has required an early return-to-work policy of employers (Shoemaker et al., 1992). It is not known to what degree employers have implemented or even adopted such a policy, although a 1992 study in Michigan found a minority of respondents had either adopted or implemented such a policy (Shoemaker et al., 1992).

Several business-sponsored projects, however, have successfully implemented the model of in-house hiring and support for workers with disabilities (Miano et al., 1996; Rhodes et al., 1993). These projects used the supported employment or natural supports models (Miano et al., 1996; Rhodes et al., 1993). For instance, one corporation sponsored a project team of professionals and employees who assessed the workplace environment for the special needs of a group of deaf workers (Berkay, 1993). The recommendations of this team resulted in a number of adaptations and accommodations and inspired a model called the Assessment Center Deaf Exercise Adaptation Model (Berkay, 1993). The professionals in this team served as paid consultants for the corporation.

Businesses also use paid professionals with expertise in the issues affecting workers with disabilities in Employee Assistance Programs (Hanley-Maxwell & Millington, 1992). Employee Assistance Programs (EAPs) can be either in-house or contracted. In addition to serving employees with a disability directly, EAPs can be designed to serve the front line supervisor and coworkers who have family members with a disability (Kiernan & McGaughey, 1992). Research indicates that EAPs provide effective supports to employees with disabilities (Kiernan & McGaughey, 1992). It is thought that the ADA will encourage the growth of employee supports for workers with disabilities, such as the EAP (Kiernan & McGaughey, 1992). Once again, as in the instance of the job audits, tax incentives, program funding, and workplace disability policies, federal statutes and initiatives loom large. Government is both a source and a mediator of work supports.

Government-Mediated Supports

Government-mediated supports are those policies and practices that enhance the likelihood that persons with disabilities will find and maintain employment. Examples of government supports include selected Social Security policies, U.S. Department of the Treasury tax policies, civil rights legislation, and other laws targeted specifically at the employment of persons with disabilities.

Consider, for example, the Targeted Job Tax Credit (TJTC), a law passed by Congress and administered by the U.S. Department of the Treasury for the purpose of enticing employers to hire persons with disabilities. Zivolich and Aivilich (1995) studied the effects of the TJTC and found it to be a useful support. Similarly, the Social Security Administration (SSA) has implemented a number of supports to help individuals with disabilities who want to work. Referrals to state Vocational Rehabilitation services, trial work periods, continuing eligibility for Medicare, deduction of impairment-related work expenses from taxable earnings, and development of a Plan for Achieving Self-Sufficiency (PASS) are all strategic elements of an effort to support and promote the employment of individuals with disabilities. Some of these incentives or supports have been difficult for many beneficiaries to access or understand, and thus many of these supports have been underutilized.

Only recently has there been another effort to greatly improve the viability of the PASS program. SSA provided a new set of guidelines to make PASS supports more viable. They include the following:

- PASS evaluations and notices will make a clear distinction between the feasibility of the goal (based on an individual's reasonable expectations of performing the work) and the viability of the plan for achieving it (based on the steps necessary to achieve the goal).
- Unless there is evidence to the contrary, the Social Security Administration's PASS specialists will presume an occupational goal to be feasible, and the plan for achieving it to be viable, if any of certain state or private professionals in the field of vocational rehabilitation and employment develops the PASS. If the PASS specialist cannot approve a PASS, he or she will discuss the matter with the individual as well as with the plan's preparer.
- Instructions regarding the limit on occupational goals will make it clear that this limit is not the strict entry-level limit that many, both in and outside of SSA, perceive it to be. The SSA policy stipulates that, within the business, trade, or profession the individual has chosen, the occupational goal cannot exceed the earliest point on the career path that would generate sufficient earnings to enable the individual to pay for his or her own living expenses, uncovered medical expenses, and work-related expenses.
- Allowable expenses for major purchases will not be limited to down payments. Funds set aside for installment payments will be excluded to the extent that the expense remains related to and supportive of an approved occupational goal, and earnings do not negate the need to continue the exclusion.
- The PASS specialist will play an earlier and expanded role in the PASS application or review, and he or she and the customer will be able to communicate directly with each other throughout the process.

Medicaid and Medicare reforms at the federal and state levels also have had significant impacts on health benefits and employment for persons with disabilities, as well as the way in which Medicaid funds are distributed. For example, in 1997, Congress amended the Medicaid statute to make funds for supported employment available for Medicaid-eligible clients who were not previously institutionalized and who wish to enter supported employment. This is a major government support that may open the door to supported employment for 150,000 new clients (West, Revell, Kregel, & Bricout, 1999). The Home and Community Based (HCB) Waiver can be seen as a major government support adopted by states across the nation (West et al., 1999).

In 1994, 135,000 individuals participated in MR/DD waiver programs—triple the number of participants in 1990. State and federal outlays for those programs totaled $3.5 billion in 1994. Twice as many people with developmental disabilities participate in the HCB Waiver program as reside in public MR institutions (West et al., 1999). By 1995, the number of individuals who participated in MR/DD HCB Waiver programs had exceeded the number served in all types of intermediate care facilities for persons with mental retardation (ICFs/MR) (West et al., 1999). States are continually increasing the number of services and supports offered in their programs, including supported employment. The number of people participating in disability HCB Waiver programs likely will grow at an annual rate of 10% to 15% for the next 3 to 5 years (West et al., 1999).

Perhaps the most far-reaching government support, however, can be found in the Americans with Disabilities Act, a law passed in 1990 that provides a host of civil rights and protections for persons with disabilities. For example, in Title I of the ADA, employment access is ensured through nondiscrimination protections in the workplace. This act was followed by a comprehensive set of regulations published exactly 1 year later (*Federal Register,* July 26, 1991, pp. 11234–11241). These regulations provide for accessibility, nondiscrimination, greater integration, and participation in workplaces, in community facilities, in the use of public transportation, and in telecommunication use. As a consequence of the ADA's success in bringing about some of these outcomes, young adults have been able to participate in a world that is less discriminatory against people with disabilities than that faced by previous cohorts. The ADA is a critical government-mediated social policy that brings needed support to the enhancement of employment opportunities for persons with a disability.

Under Title I of the ADA, employers are prohibited from discriminating against otherwise qualified individuals with disabilities during recruitment, hiring, evaluation, promotion, and any other facet of employment. Employers are further required to provide "reasonable accommodations" to enable qualified individuals with a disability to successfully perform their jobs. Such accommodations are to be provided to the extent that the employer does not sustain "undue hardship." Reasonable accommodations may include such things as restructuring jobs or work schedules, modifying equipment or providing assistive devices, providing an interpreter or reading aids, or improving the overall accessibility of the work site. Employers found to be in violation of the law face the same legal penalties as those found guilty of discrimination based on gender or race. Another piece of federal legislation providing critical supports to workers with a disability is the so-called Tech Act of 1994.

The Technology-Related Assistance for Individuals with Disabilities Act Amendments of 1994, also referred to as the Tech Act, was signed into law on March 9, 1994. This law provides access to assistive technology services and devices for individuals with disabilities of all ages. The following are specific purposes of the Tech Act:

- to provide discretionary grants to states to assist them in developing and implementing a "consumer-responsive, comprehensive, statewide program of technology-related assistance for individuals with disabilities of all ages"
- to fund programs of national significance related to assistive technology
- to establish and expand alternative financing mechanisms to allow individuals with disabilities to purchase assistive technology devices and services

With the passage and 1994 reauthorization of the Tech Act, Congress acknowledged the powerful role that assistive technology can play in maximizing the independence of individuals with disabilities. This law has the potential to open many new opportunities for individuals with disabilities and their families to receive appropriate assistive technology services. The Tech Act places the emphasis on being responsive to the needs of consumers and their families.

The state grants program under Title I of the Tech Act served as a catalyst for statewide systems to increase access to appropriate assistive technology devices and services. These funds were used to support systems change and advocacy activities to increase the availability of assistive devices and services (Wallace et al., 1995).

Consumer- and Family-Mediated Supports

In a consumer-driven system of human services, persons with disabilities should be the true customers of supported employment. Brooke and her colleagues (1995) outline a series of steps and strategies for consumers and families that help them take more power and responsibility for the supports they need. As discussed in the following sections, however, the literature on this topic is still developing.

Family Supports

Families play an important role in the quality of life, adjustment, and health outcomes of persons with disabilities (Kelley & Lambert, 1992). Families can provide informal care that ranges from general psychosocial support to job-related skills training (Prosser & Moss, 1996; Turner & Alston, 1994; Urbain, 1997). The ethnic group and culture to which the person with a disability belongs may have an impact on how strongly the family influences consumer life choices and decisions, with some groups and cultures emphasizing independence more than others (Parette, 1997; Turner & Alston, 1994). Individual differences and context (e.g., employment) may also influence the degree of independence from family that a person with disabilities displays (Mowbray, Bybee, Harris, & McCrohan, 1995). However, family continues to be an important mediator of various work supports (Killam, Petranek, & Harding, 1996; Kutty, 1993; Parette, 1997; Prosser & Moss, 1996). For instance, family members have an important role to play in the selection and implementation of assistive technology devices and services (Parette, 1997). Parents have successfully managed a supported employment program for persons with severe disabilities (Killam et al., 1996). Parents trained by professionals have also been involved in providing vocational services at community-based programs (Kutty, 1993).

On the basis of experience from six projects nationwide, Urbain (1997) of the PACER Center in Minneapolis has formulated a comprehensive approach for parental involvement in fostering natural supports in the supported employment process. She envisions parents as both facilitators and skills trainers. For instance, as facilitators, parents can use their unique access to interpersonal networks, including relatives, neighbors, friends, business contacts, and others, to provide the job developer with a broader range of employment possibilities. Parents can also act as skills trainers by actively encouraging successful work-related behaviors at home, such as timeliness, task completion, and following instructions (Urbain, 1997).

It is not easy, however, to generalize about the relationship of family support to actual employment outcomes. In fact, the influence of family support on employment outcomes appears to be uneven. Some investigators have found positive associations of family support to favorable employment outcomes (see Kelley & Lambert, 1992; Siegel & Gaylord-Ross, 1991); others have reported negative associations of family support to favorable employment outcomes (e.g., Mowbray et al., 1995). Further research needs to take place that clearly specifies the degree of collaboration between family and supported employee, as well as specifying what constitutes family support, before any conclusions can be drawn on the influence of different kinds of family support on employment outcomes. It has already been suggested that the interpersonal supports available to supported employees extend beyond family to include coworkers, supervisors, and mentors with a stake in an individual's employment success. Disabled peers and other friends and acquaintances may also have an important role to play in providing work supports for persons with disabilities (Kelley & Lambert, 1992).

Consumer, Friend, and Peer Support

An important force in enhancing the working potential and choices of persons with disabilities is found in the independent living movement. The independent living movement grew out of a desire to increase the autonomy and community participation of persons with disabilities (Asher, Asher, Hobbs, & Kelley, 1988). Independent living was intended to provide a barrier-free, self-directed environment and an alternative to institutionalization, medicalization, and dependence (Boland & Alonso, 1982; Budde & Bachelder, 1986). Independent living was first conceived as a model for persons with severe physical disabilities but came to serve persons with a wide range of disabilities, including many with intellectual disabilities (Budde & Bachelder, 1986). Increasing the employability of persons with disabilities has always been one goal of independent living, within the broader goals of consumer decision-making control and community participation (Asher et al., 1988; Asher, Asher, Hobbs, & Kelley, 1991), or as it is sometimes called total rehabilitation (Boland & Alonso, 1982).

Personal attendants, also called personal care workers, are vital to successful independent living for many consumers (Atkins, Meyer, & Smith, 1982). Personal attendants make it possible for persons with disabilities to live in their own residence and to work in the community (Budde & Bachelder, 1986). Attendants help consumers with domestic chores, personal hygiene and dress, cooking, and other daily living tasks (Asher et al., 1991; Budde & Bachelder, 1986). The services of the attendant can also be modified to include the role of advocate, adviser, or coach (Budde & Bachelder, 1986).

FINAL THOUGHTS

In closing, all those who are interested in how supported employment has evolved over the past 20 years (e.g., Wehman, 2001) must ask how successful the field has been in adopting this contemporary model of employment support services. Invariably, the issue of the shift from center-based programs to industry- or community-based work arises and is known as the "paradigm shift."

The paradigm shift refers to movement from center-based day program services to business- or industry-based employment services. This term has also been used (Bradley, Ashbaugh, & Blaney, 1994) to discuss community living with the thought that deinstitutionalization of persons with disabilities would lead to integrated community living in apartments and other supported living arrangements. Clearly, the dream of most of the advocates, going back to Boggs (1959), Wolfensberger (1972), Taylor (1988, 2001), Brown and York (1974), and Wehman (1981), has been to see this paradigm shift occur in service delivery—that is, to greatly reduce all services that occur in specialized settings exclusively for persons with disabilities and instead use normal community services. The philosophy and, of late, the research (e.g., Mank & Revell, 2001) support this approach as the best way to help persons with disabilities be independent and maximize their potential. More important, as Gilson (1998) has noted and as ADA establishes, this is what persons with disabilities want: their own empowerment and the capacity and opportunity to choose the quality of life they want. The U.S. Supreme Court has upheld this belief through the classic *Olmstead* decision rendered in 1999.

From an empirical standpoint, the research in integrated employment, unfortunately, does not support that the paradigm shift has occurred. This is not rocket science. One only has to glance at literature from Rizzolo, Hemp, Braddock, and Pomeranz-Essley (2004) or Wehman et al. (1998) or McGaughey et al. (1994) to see that the shift has not happened yet. The U.S. Department of Education's supported employment systems-change grants, initiated in 1986, got things started in a positive way (Mank & Revell, 2001). Clearly, however, there has been a lack of follow-through by both the federal government and the states with policies to strongly encourage full implementation. Mank (1994) and Wehman and Kregel (1995) term this problem "underachievement" or "being at the crossroads"; Wehman (1996) also called for 250,000 persons to be placed in supported employment. By some counts, this has occurred, but even this achievement falls far short of a full paradigm shift of numbers of people when one looks at the overall base of individuals remaining in segregated centers.

So what positive things have occurred to give some reason for hope that a paradigm shift in employment services can and will occur? There are several reasons for cautious optimism. To begin with, the first wave of people with significant disabilities are actually working for the first time, and their participation in competitive employment has gone from being exclusively episodic to being widespread across the entire country (Wehman et al., 1998). This gives other programs and advocates and consumers something to work from and sets the bar of expectation higher than it was previously.

Second, the legislation and court decisions from the federal government seem to be moving in the right direction. ADA, the amended Rehabilitation Act, and the new Ticket to Work Act with the Medicaid buy-in option (Cheek, 2001) are all positive. In addition, the New Freedom Initiative policies of the present administration and the *Olmstead* court decision seem to favor and be supportive of integrated competitive employment.

Third, the level of awareness about disability from the business community, persons with disabilities, and families seems to be at the highest level in 20 years. There will always be a shortage of human service funds and funds that are not spent efficiently, but if the collective power of persons with disabilities and their families in conjunction with business is put forward at a grassroots community level, a true paradigm shift in the next 5 to 10 years is much more probable.

The overall key to breaking the existing cycle in our view is to concentrate and focus much more extensively on the youth with disabilities in America. All efforts from the One-Stop Career Centers, rehabilitation selection process, school employment and career building priorities, and Social Security incentives should be focused most heavily on youth and young adults ages 16 to 25. This is where the cycle needs to be broken once and for all. As more and more young people refuse to go to segregated programs and their families or guardians refuse to accept these programs as a base for services, states and localities will have no choice but to create new service vendors to provide supports for people with disabilities working in competitive employment.

Depending on the existing providers is a major mistake. They have had 25 years to change their services, and they have failed for the most part to make the change. It is time for colleges and universities, One-Stop Career Centers, medium and large businesses such as Manpower, Inc., and others to step up. The federal government needs to fund new vendors of services, and persons with disabilities need to step in and run their own programs. The Centers for Independent Living need to more aggressively move in the area of providing employment programs and workplace supports. The next 5 years hold tremendous potential. The opportunity and technical skill level are there. Now we need to do it.

REFERENCES

Adelman, P. B., & Vogel, S. A. (1993). Issues in the employment of adults with learning disabilities. *Learning Disability Quarterly, 16*(3), 219–232.

Akabas, S. H. (1994). Workplace responsiveness: Key employer characteristics in support of job maintenance for people with mental illness. *Psychosocial Rehabilitation Journal, 17*(3), 91–101.

Akabas, S. H., & Gates, L. B. (1993). *Stress and disability management project: Final report.* New York: Columbia University, School of Social Work, Center for Social Policy and Practice in the Workplace.

Albin, J. M., Rhodes, L., & Mank, D. (1994). Realigning organizational culture, resources, and community roles: Changeover to community employment. *Journal of the Association for Persons with Severe Handicaps, 19*(2), 105–115.

American Association on Mental Retardation. (2002). *Mental retardation: Definition, classification and systems of support.* Washington, DC: Author.

Americans with Disabilities Act of 1990, 42 U.S.C. § 12101 *et seq.*

Asher, C. C., Asher, M. A., Hobbs, W. E., & Kelley, J. M. (1988). A preliminary investigation of the independent living movement in Pennsylvania. *Journal of Rehabilitation, 54*(2), 34–39.

Asher, C. C., Asher, M. A., Hobbs, W. E., & Kelley, J. M. (1991). On consumer self-direction of attendant care services: An empirical analysis of survey responses. *Evaluation and Program Planning, 14*(3), 131–139.

Atkins, B. J., Meyer, A. B., & Smith, N. K. (1982). Personal care attendants: Attitudes and factors contributing to job satisfaction. *Journal of Rehabilitation, 48*(3), 20–24.

Berkay, P. J. (1993). The adaptation of assessment group exercises for deaf job applicants. *Journal of the American Deafness and Rehabilitation Association, 27*(1), 16–24.

Birch, G. E., Fengler, M., Gosine, R. G., Schroeder, K., Schroeder, M., & Johnson, D. L. (1996). An assessment methodology and its application to a robotic vocational assistive device. *Technology and Disability, 5*(2), 151–165.

Blanck, P. (1998). *The emerging workforce: Employment integration, economic opportunity, and the Americans with Disabilities Act; Empirical study from 1990–1996.* Washington, DC: American Association on Mental Retardation.

Boggs, E. M. (1959). *Decade of decision* (Report prepared for the 1960 White House Conference on Children and Youth). New York: National Association for Retarded Children.

Boland, J. M., & Alonso, G. (1982). A comparison: Independent living rehabilitation and vocational rehabilitation. *Journal of Rehabilitation, 48*(1), 56–59.

Bond, G. (1998). Principles of the individual placement and support model: Empirical support. *Psychiatric Rehabilitation Journal, 22,* 11–23.

Bond, G. R., Becker, D. R., Drake, R. E., Rapp, C. A., Meisler, N., Lehman, A. F., Bell, M. D., & Blyler, C. R. (2001). Implementing supported employment as an evidenced-based practice. *Psychiatric Services, 52,* 313–322.

Bond, G. R., Dietzen, L. L., McGrew, J. H., & Miller, L. D. (1995). Accelerating entry into supported employment for persons with severe psychiatric disabilities. *Rehabilitation Psychology, 40,* 91–111.

Braddock, D., Hemp, R., Parish, S., & Rizzolo, M. (2002). *The state of the states in developmental disabilities: 2002 study summary.* Boulder: University of Colorado, Coleman Institute for Cognitive Disabilities and Department of Psychiatry.

Bradley, V. J., Ashbaugh, J. W., & Blaney, B. C. (1994). *Creating individual supports for people with developmental disabilities: A mandate for change at many levels.* Baltimore: Brookes.

Briel, L. W. (1996). Promoting the effective use of compensatory strategies on the job for individuals with traumatic brain injury. *Journal of Vocational Rehabilitation, 7*(2), 151–158.

Brooke, V., Wehman, P., Inge, K., & Parent, W. (1995). Toward a consumer-driven approach of supported employment. *Education and Training in Mental Retardation and Developmental Disabilities, 30*(4), 308–319.

Browder, D., Wood, W., Test, D., Karvonen, M., & Algozzine, B. (2001). Reviewing resources on self-determination: A map for teachers. *Remedial and Special Education, 22*(4), 233–244.

Brown, L., & York, R. (1974). Developing programs for severely handicapped students: Teacher training and classroom instruction. *Focus on Exceptional Children, 6*(2), 2–11.

Budde, J. F., & Bachelder, J. L. (1986). Independent living: The concept, model and methodology. *Journal of the Association for Persons with Severe Handicaps, 11*(4), 240–245.

Bybee, D., Mowbray, C. T., & McCrohan, N. M. (1995). Towards zero exclusion in vocational services for persons with severe psychiatric disabilities: Prediction of service receipt in a hybrid vocational/case management service program. *Psychosocial Rehabilitation Journal, 18*(4), 73–78.

Cheek, M. (2001). *Medicaid buy-in programs for employment persons with disabilities: Going forward. 2000 SSI annual report.* Baltimore: Social Security Administration.

Condeluci, A. (1991). *Interdependence: The route to community.* Delray Beach, FL: St. Lucie Press.

Curl, R. M., Fraser, R. T., Cook, R. G., & Clemmons, D. (1996). Traumatic brain injury vocational rehabilitation: Preliminary findings for co-worker as trainer project. *Journal of Head Trauma Rehabilitation, 11*(1), 75–85.

Curl, R. M., Hall, S. M., Chisholm, L. A., & Rule, S. (1992). Coworkers as trainers for entry-level workers: A competitive employment model for individuals with developmental disabilities. *Rural Special Education Quarterly, 11*(1), 31–35.

Drake, R. (1998). Individual placement and support [*Special issue*]. *Psychiatric Rehabilitation Journal, 22*(1).

Drake, R. E., Becker, D. R., Xie, H., & Anthony, W. A. (1995). Barriers in the brokered model of supported employment for persons with psychiatric disabilities. *Journal of Vocational Rehabilitation, 5*(2), 141–149.

Drake, R. E., McHugo, G., Becker, D. R., Anthony, W. A., & Clark, R. E. (1996). The New Hampshire study of supported employment for people with severe mental illness. *Journal of Consulting and Clinical Psychology, 64*(2), 391–399.

Egan, K. (2001). Staffing companies opening new doors to people with disabilities. *Journal of Vocational Rehabilitation, 16*, 93–96.

Fabian, E. S., & Luecking, R. G. (1991). Doing it the company way: Using the internal company supports in the workplace. *Journal of Rehabilitation Counseling, 22*(b), 32–35.

Federal Register. (1991, July). Washington, DC: U.S. Government Printing Office.

Federal Register. (1997, February). Washington, DC: U.S. Government Printing Office.

Federal Register. (2001, January 17). Washington, DC: U.S. Government Printing Office.

Federal Register. (2001, January 22). Washington, DC: U.S. Government Printing Office.

Frierson, J. G. (1992). An employer's dilemma: The ADA's provisions on reasonable accommodation and confidentiality. *Labor Law Journal, 43*(5), 308–312.

Gaylord-Ross, R., Park, H. S., Johnston, S., Lee, M., & Goetz, L. (1995). Individual social skills training and co-worker training for supported employees with dual sensory impairments: Two case examples. *Behavior Modification, 19*(1), 78–94.

Giles, G., & Shore, M. (1989). A rapid method for teaching severely brain injured adults how to wash and dress. *Archives of Physical Medicine and Rehabilitation, 70*, 156–158.

Gilson, S. F. (1998). Choice and self-advocacy: A consumer's perspective. In P. Wehman & J. Kregel (Eds.), *More than a job: Securing satisfying careers for people with disabilities.* Baltimore: Brookes.

Golden, T. P. (1995). *Employer incentives for hiring workers with disabilities: How job developers can consult with business to access supports for employees with disabilities.* St. Augustine, FL: Training Resource Network.

Green, H., & Brooke, V. (2001). Greater success through new partnerships: The business connection. In P. Wehman (Ed.), *Supported employment in business: Expanding the capacity of workers with disabilities.* St. Augustine, FL: Training Resource Network.

Hanley-Maxwell, C., & Millington, M. (1992). Enhancing independence in supported employment: Natural supports in business and industry. *Journal of Vocational Rehabilitation, 2*(4), 51–58.

Harper, J. (1993). Securing a role for people with disabilities in the work force. *Journal of Vocational Rehabilitation, 3*(4), 70–73.

Hayden, M., & Albery, B. (Eds.). (1994). *Challenges for a service system in transition.* Baltimore: Brookes.

Inge, K., & Tilson, G. (1997). Ensuring support systems that work: Getting beyond the natural supports vs. job coach controversy. *Journal of Vocational Rehabilitation, 9,* 133–142.

Johnson, S. E. (1992). Creating a barrier-free work environment. *HR focus, 69,* 15.

Kelley, S. D. M., & Lambert, S. S. (1992). Family support in rehabilitation: A review of research, 1980–1990. *Rehabilitation Counseling Bulletin, 36*(2), 98–119.

Kiernan, W. E., & McGaughey, M. (1992). Employee assistance: A support mechanism for the worker with a disability. *Journal of Rehabilitation, 58*(2), 56–63.

Killam, S. G., Petranek, I., & Harding, G. (1996). Parents in charge of the system: Strategies for increasing supported employment opportunities for individuals with severe disabilities. *Journal of Vocational Rehabilitation, 6*(1), 41–45.

Kregel, J., Wehman, P., & Banks, P. (1989). The effects of consumer characteristics and type of employment model on individual outcomes in supported employment. *Journal of Applied Behavioral Analysis, 22,* 407–415.

Kreutzer, J. S., Gordon, W. A., & Wehman, P. (1989). Cognitive remediation following traumatic brain injury. *Rehabilitation Psychology, 34,* 117–130.

Kreutzer, J. S., Wehman, P., Morton, M. V., & Stonnington, H. (1988). Supported employment and compensatory strategies for enhancing vocational outcome following traumatic brain injury. *Brain Injury, 2*(3), 205–224.

Kutty, A. T. T. (1993). Parents associations for vocational training and employment of persons with mental retardation. *Indian Journal of Disability and Rehabilitation, 7*(1), 53–58.

LaRocca, N. G., Kalb, R. C., & Gregg, K. (1997). A program to facilitate retention of employment among persons with multiple sclerosis. *Work, A Journal of Prevention Assessment and Rehabilitation, 7*(1), 37–46.

Luckasson, R., Coulter, D. L., Polloway, E. A., Reiss, S., Schalock, R. L., Snell, M. E., Spitalnik, D. M., & Stark, J. A. (1992). *Mental retardation: Definition, classification, and systems of supports* (9th ed.). Washington, DC: American Association on Mental Retardation.

MacDonald-Wilson, K., Revell, W. G., Nguyen, N., & Peterson, M. (1991). Supported employment outcomes for people with psychiatric disability. *Journal of Vocational Rehabilitation, 1,* 30–44.

Mank, D. (1994). The underachievement of supported employment: A call for reinvestment. *Journal of Disability Policy Studies, 5*(2), 1–24.

Mank, D., Cioffi, A., & Yovanoff, P. (1997). An analysis of the typicalness of supported employment jobs, natural supports, and wage and integration outcomes. *Mental Retardation, 35*(3), 185–197.

Mank, D., Cioffi, A., & Yovanoff, P. (1999). Impact of coworker involvement with supported employees on wage and integration outcomes. *Mental Retardation, 37*(5), 383–394.

Mank, D., Cioffi, A., & Yovanoff, P. (2000). Direct support in supported employment and its relation to job typicalness, coworker involvement, and employment outcomes. *Mental Retardation, 38*(6), 506–516.

Mank, D., & Revell, G. (2001). Systemic change for supported employment: Old lessons and new possibilities. In P. Wehman (Ed.), *Supported employment in business: Expanding the capacity of workers with disabilities.* St. Augustine, FL: Training Resource Network.

McGaughey, M., Kiernan, W. E., McNally, L., Gilmore, D., & Keith, G. (1994). *Beyond the workshop: National perspectives on integrated employment.* Boston: Children's Hospital, Institute for Community Inclusion.

Miano, M. N., Nalven, E. B., & Hoff, D. (1996). The Pachysandra Project: A public–private initiative in supported employment at the Prudential Insurance Company of America. *Journal of Vocational Rehabilitation, 6*(1), 107–118.

Mowbray, C. T., Bybee, D., Harris, S. N., & McCrohan, N. (1995). Predictors of work status and future work orientation in people with a psychiatric disability. *Psychiatric Rehabilitation Journal, 19*(2), 17–29.

Murphy, S. T., Rogan, P. M., Handley, M., Kincaid, C., & Royce-Davis, J. (2002). People's situations and perspectives eight years after workshop conversion. *Mental Retardation, 40,* 30–40.

Newbigging, E. D., & Laskey, J. W. (1996). Therapy methodology. Riding the bus: Teaching an adult with a brain injury to use a transit system to travel independently to and from work. *Brain Injury, 10*(7), 543–550.

Olmstead v. L.C., 119 U.S. 2176 (1999).

Parent, W., Wehman, P., & Bricout, J. (2001). Supported employment and natural supports. In P. Wehman (Ed.), *Supported employment in business: Expanding the capacity of workers with disabilities.* St. Augustine, FL: Training Resource Network.

Parette, H. P. (1997). Assistive technology devices and services. *Education and Training in Mental Retardation and Developmental Disabilities, 32*(4), 267–280.

Parette, H. P., & VanBiervliet, A. (1992). Tentative findings of a study of the technology needs and patterns of persons with mental retardation. *Journal of Intellectual Disability Research, 36*(1), 7–22.

Peck, B., & Kirkbride, L. T. (2001). Why businesses don't employ people with disabilities. *Journal of Vocational Rehabilitation, 16,* 71–75.

Prosser, H., & Moss, S. (1996). Informal care networks of older workers with an intellectual disability. *Journal of Applied Research in Intellectual Disabilities, 9*(1), 17–30.

Rehabilitation Act Amendments of 1992, 29 U.S.C. § 701 *et seq.*

Rehabilitation Services Administration. (2001). *Rehabilitation cases in selected work status at closure.* Unpublished report. Washington, DC: Author.

Rhodes, L., Sandow, D., Taliaferro, W., & Mank, D. (1993). *Final report: The community employment development project, April, 1993.* Eugene: University of Oregon, Specialized Training Program.

Ridgway, P., & Rapp, C. (1998). *The active ingredients in achieving competitive employment for people with psychiatric disabilities: A research synthesis.* Lawrence: University of Kansas, School of Welfare.

Rizzolo, M. C., Hemp, R., Braddock, D., & Pomeranz-Essley, A. (2004). *The state of the states in developmental disabilities.* Washington, DC: American Association on Mental Retardation. Retrieved August 5, 2004, from http://www.cu.edu/ColemanInstitute/stateofthestates/

Rogers, E. S., Anthony, W. A., & Danley, K. S. (1989). The impact of collaboration on system and client outcomes. *Rehabilitation Counseling Bulletin, 33*(2), 100–109.

Sandow, D., Olson, D., & Yan, X. Y. (1993). The evolution of support in the workplace. *Journal of Vocational Rehabilitation, 3*(4), 30–37.

Shafer, M. S., Banks, P. D., & Kregel, J. (1991). Employment retention and career movement among individuals with mental retardation working in supported employment. *Mental Retardation, 29*(2), 103–110.

Shoemaker, R. J., Robin, S. S., & Robin, H. S. (1992). Reaction to disability through organization policy: Early return to work policy. *Journal of Rehabilitation, 58,* 18–24.

Siegel, S., & Gaylord-Ross, R. (1991). Factors associated with employment success among youths with learning disabilities. *Journal of Learning Disabilities, 24*(1), 40–47.

Sinnott-Oswald, M., Gliner, J. A., & Spencer, K. C. (1991). Supported and sheltered employment: Quality of life issues among workers with disabilities. *Education and Training in Mental Retardation, 9,* 388–397.

Smith, B. (1992). Technology gives workers greater freedom in the office. *HR Focus, 69,* 12–13.

Sowers, P. C., Kouwenhoven, K., Sousa, F., & Milliken, K. (1997). *Community-based employment for people with the most severe disabilities: New perspectives and strategies.* Durham: University of New Hampshire, Institute on Disability.

Stancliffe, R. J., & Lakin, K. C. (1999). A longitudinal comparison of day program services and outcomes of people who left institutions and those who stayed. *Journal of the Association for Persons with Severe Handicaps, 24*(1), 44–57.

Storey, K., & Provost, N. (1996). The effect of communication skills instruction on the integration of workers with severe disabilities in supported employment settings. *Education and Training in Mental Retardation and Developmental Disabilities, 31*(2), 123–141.

Taylor, S. J. (1988). Caught in the continuum: A critical analysis of the principle of the least restrictive environment. *Journal of the Association for Persons with Severe Handicaps, 13*(1), 45–53.

Taylor, S. J. (2001). The continuum and current controversies in the USA. *Journal of Intellectual & Developmental Disability, 26*(1), 15–33.

Technology-Related Assistance for Individuals with Disabilities Act Amendments of 1994, 29 U.S.C. § 2201 *et seq.*

Test, D. W., & Wood, W. M. (1996). Natural supports in the workplace: The jury is still out. *Journal of the Association for Persons with Severe Handicaps, 21*(4), 155–173.

Ticket to Work and Work Incentive Improvement Act of 1999, 42 U.S.C. § 1305 *et seq.*

Tilson, G. P., Luecking, R., & West, L. L. (1996). The employer partnership in transition for youth with disabilities. *Journal for Vocational Special Needs Education, 18*(3), 88–92.

Turner, W. L., & Alston, R. J. (1994). The role of the family in psychosocial adaptation to physical disabilities for African Americans. *Journal of the National Medical Association, 86*(12), 915–921.

Urbain, C. (1997). *Supported employment using a natural supports approach: A handbook for parents.* Minneapolis: PACER Center.

Wallace, J. F., Flippo, K. F., Barcus, J. M., & Behrman, M. (1995). Legislative foundation of assistive technology policy in the United States. In K. F. Flippo, K. J. Inge, & J. M. Barcus (Eds.), *Assistive technology: A resource for school, work and community* (pp. 3–22). Baltimore: Brookes.

Wehman, P. (1981). *Competitive employment: New horizons for severely disabled individuals.* Baltimore: Brookes.

Wehman, P. (1993). *The ADA mandate for social change.* Baltimore: Brookes.

Wehman, P. (1996). *Life beyond the classroom: Transition strategies for young people with disabilities* (2nd ed.). Baltimore: Brookes.

Wehman, P. (2001). *Supported employment in business: Expanding the capacity of workers with disabilities.* St. Augustine, FL: Training Resource Network.

Wehman, P., & Kregel, J. (1989). *Supported employment and transition: Focus on excellence.* New York: Plenum Press.

Wehman, P., & Kregel, J. (1995). Supported employment: At the crossroads. *Journal of the Association for Persons with Severe Handicaps, 20*(4), 286–299.

Wehman, P., Kregel, J., West, M., & Cifu, D. (1994). Return to work for patients with traumatic brain injury: Analysis of costs. *American Journal of Physical Medicine and Rehabilitation, 73*(4), 280–281.

Wehman, P., Kreutzer, J., West, M., Sherron, P., Zasler, N., Groah, C., Stonnington, H., Burns, C., & Sale, P. (1990). Return to work for persons with traumatic brain injury: A supported employment approach. *Archives of Physical Medicine and Rehabilitation, 71*(13), 1047–1052.

Wehman, P., Revell, W. G., & Kregel, J. (1998). Supported employment: A decade of rapid growth and impact. *American Rehabilitation, 24*(1), 31–43.

Wehmeyer, M. L., & Lawrence, M. (1995). Whose future is it anyway? Promoting student involvement in transition planning. *Career Development for Exceptional Individuals, 18*(2), 68–84.

West, M., Johnson, A., Cone, A., Hernandez, A., & Revell, G. (1998). Extended employment support: Analysis of implementation and funding issues. *Education and Training in Mental Retardation and Developmental Disabilities, 33,* 357–366.

West, M., Kregel, J., Hernandez, A., & Hock, T. (1997). Everybody's doing it: A national study of the use of natural supports in supported employment. *Focus on Autism and Other Developmental Disabilities, 12*(3), 175–181, 192.

West, M., Revell, G., Kregel, J., & Bricout, J. (1999). The Medicaid Home and Community-Based Waiver and supported employment. *American Journal of Mental Retardation, 104*(1), 78–87.

West, M., Wehman, P., & Revell, G. (2002). Extended services in supported employment: What are providers doing? Are customers satisfied? In D. Dean, P. Wehman, & J. Kregel (Eds.), *Achievements and challenges in employment services for people with significant disabilities: A longitudinal impact of workplace supports.* Richmond: Virginia Commonwealth University, Rehabilitation Research and Training Center on Workplace Supports.

Wolfensberger, W. (1972). *Principles of normalization.* Toronto: National Institute for Mental Retardation.

Zivolich, J. S., & Aivilich, S. (1995). If not now, when? The case against waiting for sheltered workshop changeover. *Journal of the Association for Persons with Severe Handicaps, 20,* 311–312.

CHAPTER 16

Independent Living for People with Intellectual and Developmental Disabilities

Wendy Strobel and Douglas J. Usiak

LEARNING GOALS

Upon completion of this chapter, the reader will know

- the legislative basis for Centers for Independent Living as they exist today
- the role the courts have had in ensuring the independent living rights of people with intellectual disabilities
- the core services provided by Centers for Independent Living and the underlying philosophy of these centers
- the role personal assistant services play in facilitating independent living and the responsibilities the person with an intellectual disability has in the management of these services
- how assistive technology can facilitate independent living

I n today's society, "independent living" is not only a description of a person's living arrangement, but a declaration of individual freedom and choice. Unfortunately, many people with developmental disabilities never get the opportunity to realize the dream of living independently. Many people believe that it is perfectly reasonable to expect this segment of the population to stay in the home until the parents can no longer care for their adult child. Sadly, adults with developmental disabilities are often viewed as eternal children by their parents and other caregivers. Often, people even view these adults as "burdens" on the aging parents.

 ## CASE EXAMPLE: SUE

Sue lived in the Bronx with her mother for 26 years. Sue's mother served as her primary caregiver during the time they lived together. She sent Sue to special schools for kids with disabilities and, after she "graduated," to a work activity center. Unfortunately, when Sue's mom passed away in the winter of 1980, no provision had been made for Sue's living arrangements. Faced with the task of caring for her in their homes, her aunts and uncles decided that she would be placed in a nursing home. After all, not only did she have cerebral palsy, but she also had an intellectual disability. It was reasoned that she would receive the attention she needed only with 24-hour care. The family's goal of nursing home placement was achieved within a year.

The good news is that Sue was not left to languish in the nursing home for very long. A long-time family friend got wind of her incarceration and began a 2-year battle to free her. The friend took custody of Sue, and Sue was able to move in with the friend's family. However, Sue was not satisfied. She wanted to live in her own apartment and prove once and for all that she was able to care for herself. She decided to contact a cousin in Buffalo who had ties to the Western New York Independent Living Center (ILC). Sue and her cousin worked with the ILC staff to locate an affordable apartment that Sue could pay for with her Social Security check. After the apartment was located, she and her cousin packed up a U-Haul, and Sue moved to Buffalo, New York.

As this story illustrates, it took a great deal of perseverance for Sue to obtain her independence. Had she at any point abandoned the notion that she was a strong person who was capable of great things, her goal would not have been achieved. We will discuss Sue's case more fully later in the chapter. It is also important that other important issues surrounding independent living are discussed. These issues include legislation surrounding the independent living movement, advocacy and self-determination, support services, long-range planning, and community inclusion.

RELEVANT LEGISLATION

In 1963, President John F. Kennedy outlined the need for community facilities and services for the mentally retarded in a speech to Congress (American Presidency Project, 1963). He stated that the development of these community-based services would end the "reliance on the cold mercy of custodial isolation" and replace it with "the open warmth of community concern and capability." He further called for a reduction, over a number of years, and by hundreds of thousands, in the number of people confined to institutions. Unfortunately, it has taken many years for President Kennedy's vision to begin to come to life in American communities. A number of important legislative events have promoted this dream. In the following pages, you will find an outline of some of these major legislative events. Please note that this is not meant to be a comprehensive review of all disability-related legislation, but it does include legislation that is most relevant to the independent living movement.

Mental Retardation Facilities and Community Mental Health Centers Construction Act

The Mental Retardation Facilities and Community Mental Health Centers Construction Act was signed into law in 1963, after President Kennedy's plea to Congress to establish community-based services for individuals with mental retardation and mental illness in their neighborhoods. This act, renamed in 1984 as the Developmental Disabilities Act, continues to exist, with the most recent version signed into law by President Clinton (Policy Almanac, 2000). The original form of this law authorized grants for assistance in the construction of community mental health centers. In its current form, Title I of the law, known as the Developmental Disabilities Assistance and Bill of Rights Act of 2000 (Public Law [P.L.] 106-402), establishes and funds Developmental Disabilities Councils; Protection and Advocacy Systems; University Centers for Excellence in Developmental Disabilities Education, Research, and Service; and Projects of National Significance. The purpose of Title I is to create partnerships between state, local, and nonprofit agencies that can enhance the independence, productivity, and community inclusion of people with disabilities. Title II authorized the Family Support Act, which gives states greater flexibility in establishing family support services. Title III creates support programs for direct care workers who serve people with developmental disabilities (Arizona Technical Assistance Program, 2001). President Clinton made the following statement concerning this act: "This crucial investment has provided the structure to assist people with developmental disabilities to pursue meaningful and productive lives. These programs have made community living possible for individuals across our nation with significant disabilities" (White House, 2000).

Vocational Rehabilitation Act

The Smith-Fess Act (P.L. 66-236), also known as the Civilian Vocational Rehabilitation Act, was temporary legislation that established the first Vocational Rehabilitation program for civilians. This law, which was passed on June 2, 1920, provided funds to states on a 50–50 match basis to provide vocational guidance, education, occupational adjustment, and placement to people with physical disabilities who were "totally or partially incapacitated for remunerative occupation" (Rubin & Roessler, 1995, p. 47). Although the original version of this law was temporary, it continues to exist today as a major piece of legislation that promotes the independence and earning capacity of people with disabilities.

The "Findings and Purposes" section of the Vocational Rehabilitation Act states that disability is a natural part of the human experience and in no way diminishes the right of individuals to live independently; enjoy self-determination; make choices; contribute to society; pursue meaningful careers; and enjoy full inclusion and integration into the economic, political, social, cultural, and educational mainstream of American society (Legal Information Institute [LII], 2003a). It further states that one purpose of the law is to empower individuals with disabilities to maximize employment opportunities, economic self-sufficiency, independence, and inclusion and integration into society. Independent Living Centers are established as one way to carry out this goal.

The first appearance of a need statement for independent living occurred in the Rehabilitation Act of 1973 (P.L. 93-112) with the authorization of six independent living rehabilitation (ILR) demonstration projects (Rubin & Roessler, 1995). It was through this legislation that funding for the first consumer-operated Center for Independent Living (CIL) at Berkeley was authorized, along with five other centers that were not consumer run. Through the 1973 Rehabilitation Act, federal funding for 286 CILs and 44 satellites was established at $58 million (National Council on Independent Living [NCIL], 2003).

Title VII, Part B, of the amendments passed in 1978 established a grant program for federal–state ILR programs for people whose "ability to function independently in family or community services is severely limited" (p. 47). Part C authorized independent living services specific to individuals who were blind. The following services were authorized with Part B of this legislation (Rubin & Roessler, 1995):

- attendant care
- independent living skills services
- peer counseling
- assistance with housing and transportation

This set of amendments also authorized important civil rights for people with disabilities in Sections 501 through 504 (see Table 16.1). Section 504, which is most relevant to the independent living movement, was added in 1974. It addressed discrimination against people with disabilities in employment, housing, health care, and education (General Services Administration–Office of Governmental Policy, 2002).

The amendments to this act, published in 1992 (P.L. 102-569), expanded the role and responsibilities of statewide CILs, creating a full partnership with vocational rehabilitation agencies in the independent living process (Richards,

1995). Part C of this law establishes the purpose of the CIL program, stating that it is in the CILs' charter

> to promote a philosophy of independent living, including a philosophy of consumer control, peer support, self-determination, equal access, and individual and system advocacy, in order to maximize the leadership, empowerment, independence, and productivity of individuals with significant disabilities, and the integration and full inclusion of individuals with significant disabilities into the mainstream of American society by providing financial assistance to develop and support Statewide networks of CILs. (U.S. Department of Education, 1994)

The 1998 amendments of the Rehabilitation Act (P.L. 105-220) strengthened issues surrounding consumer control and informed choice, concepts that are vital in planning for independent living (Wehmeyer, 2003).

Medicaid Home and Community Based Waiver Program

Medicaid is a joint federal and state program that was first funded in 1965 under Title XIX of the Social Security Act. It is an entitlement program that pays for medical services for people who have a low income, are elderly, or have qualifying

TABLE 16.1

Items Addressed in Sections 501 Through 504
of the Rehabilitation Act Amendments of 1973

Section	Issue Addressed
501	Affirmative Action in federal hiring—To establish the federal government as a model agency for "recruiting, hiring, and advancing people with disabilities."
502	Accessibility—Established the Architectural and Transportation Barriers Compliance Board (ATBCB) to enforce the Architectural Barriers Act of 1968.
503	Affirmative Action by federal contract recipients—For contracts that exceeded $2,500; established the Department of Labor's Office of Federal Contract Compliance as its enforcement agency.
504	Prohibits the exclusion based on disability of otherwise qualified individuals from participation in federal programs or activities or from any program or activity receiving federal assistance; also created the requirement to consider reasonable accommodation in hiring decisions.

disabilities. It is the largest medical assistance program in the United States targeted toward people with low income and resources (Center for Medicare and Medicaid Services [CMS], 2002). Eligibility requirements vary from state to state, as states are given broad federal guidelines but have a great deal of flexibility in the way they administer these programs. Despite these state-to-state differences, Medicaid's orientation to care has been in the context of a medical model. As a result, care has been provided primarily in institutional settings such as nursing homes and intermediate care facilities for individuals with mental retardation (ICFs/MR) (Harrington & LeBlanc, 2001).

To remedy this institutional bias, Congress passed the Home and Community Based Services (HCBS) Waiver program in 1981, under Section 1915(c) of the Social Security Act (SSA). The authorization of the HCBS Waiver program verified the belief that many people who would traditionally be placed in an institution could be cared for in their own homes and communities, preserving their independence, as well as ties to families and friends, at an equal or lesser cost than institutional placement (CMS, 2003). The assurance that the cost of community care would not exceed the cost of care provided in an institution is necessary to secure approval for an HCBS Waiver program. By 2002, the HCBS Waiver program was approved for all states and the District of Columbia, with the exception of Arizona, which runs an equivalent program under the SSA's Section 1115 waiver authority. Only 33.9% of the waivers operational in 1997 targeted a 1915(c) waiver program to people with developmental disabilities (Miller, Ramsland, & Harrington, 1999). This number remains low despite the fact that care under the HCBS Waiver program is provided at an average annual expenditure of $33,528 for the 259,561 people with disabilities served (CMS, 2003). The cost of care for people in ICF/MR facilities is $78,369 (Lankin, Anderson, & Prouty, 1999). According to CMS (2002), there are no specific services that must be covered under an HCBS waiver, but they generally include some of the following:

- case management
- home health services
- personal care
- skilled nursing assistance
- residential care
- vocational training
- environmental modification
- transportation

Many states have a long waiting list for Medicaid HCBS Waiver services. These lists are created when states open only a limited number of HCBS Waiver slots in an effort to keep costs to a minimum. Additional problems occur when states fail to fill all of the allocated waiver slots (Perkins & Kulkarni, 2000). Perkins and Kulkarni also state that a change may come only through well-placed litigation that challenges a state's ability to limit these important services. Despite these challenges, the demand for waiver services continues to grow; between 1990 and 2000, spending for HCBS Waiver services grew by 80.6% (Lankin, Braddock, & Smith, 2001). Lankin et al. (2001) state that this expansion may lead states to provide HCBS Waiver funding to support people who live with their families.

Fair Housing Act Amendments of 1988

The Fair Housing Act was introduced in Title VIII of the Civil Rights Act of 1968. It

> prohibits discrimination in the sale, rental, and financing of dwellings, and in other housing-related transactions, based on race, color, national origin, religion, sex, familial status (including children under the age of 18 living with parents of legal custodians, pregnant women, and people securing custody of children under the age of 18), and handicap [disability]. (U.S. Department of Housing and Urban Development [HUD], 2003)

The Fair Housing Act Amendments passed in 1988 extended the antidiscrimination mandate for people with disabilities to housing. No funds accompanied this mandate (Rubin & Roessler, 1995). The 1988 amendments gave HUD the responsibility of evaluating claims of discriminatory housing practices (HUD, 2003).

Americans with Disabilities Act of 1990

The ADA was the most sweeping civil rights legislation for people with disabilities passed in recent history (Rehabilitation Research and Training Center on Independent Living Management [RRTC-ILM], 2001). It mandated nondiscrimination in hiring practices, nondiscrimination in state and local government services, nondiscrimination in public accommodations and commercial facilities, increased access to telecommunications, and other miscellaneous provisions (Rubin & Roessler, 1995). In Title II, discrimination proscription, public entities are required to administer services in the most integrated setting appropriate to the needs of qualified individuals with disabilities (LII, 1999). Title II of the Americans with Disabilities Act of 1990 (ADA) extends the requirement by the Rehabilitation Act Amendments of 1973 to cover all government agencies, including those that do not receive federal funds, stressing that people with disabilities and their known associates should have equal access to services and benefits of public entities. It also encourages reasonable modification to permit this access (U.S. Department of Justice [DOJ], 1992). Rubin and Roessler (1995) state that ADA was intended to prevent public entities from developing "segregationist policies." Title II further ensures access to public transportation, requiring that fixed-route bus services must provide an accessible transportation system and that newly constructed facilities for public transportation must also be accessible (Rubin & Roessler, 1995). Title III "prohibits discrimination on the basis of disability by public accommodations and requires places of public accommodation and commercial facilities to be designed, constructed, and altered in compliance with the accessibility standards established by this part" (DOJ, 2002). Title IV increases access to telecommunications (DOJ, 2002). These portions of the ADA are important to independent living because they ensure equal access to community goods and services for people with disabilities.

Medicaid Community-Based Attendant Services and Supports Act of 2001 (MiCASSA)

MiCASSA reforms Title XIX of the Social Security Act by allowing individuals who currently receive care in ICF/MR facilities to choose "community-based attendant services and support." It also allows the funds that would have supported the individual in the institutional setting of the ICF/MR to follow the individual into the community (American Disabled for Attendant Programs Today, 2001). This act also authorizes states to fund system change grants to programs that promote choice for people with disabilities. When MiCASSA becomes permanent, it will offer states financial assistance to reform their long-term service and support systems to provide services in the most integrated setting (NCIL, 2003).

The most remarkable attribute of this law is the power it gives to people with disabilities to manage their own personal care in their own communities. It gives people the authority to decide who provides services and what services they should receive. To facilitate transfer to the community, MiCASSA provides monies for people to move from an ICF/MR to a community setting. Specifically, it will pay for "rent and utility deposits, bedding, basic kitchen supplies and other necessities required for transition" (NCIL, 2003).

The MiCASSA Act of 2003 has been introduced in the Senate for reauthorization. The "Findings and Purposes" section of this proposed law states that long-term services and supports programs must meet the ability and personal choices of individuals with disabilities and older Americans, including the choice to live in one's own home or with one's family and to become a productive member of the community. The proposed legislation cites that only 9% of the long-term care funds expended under Medicaid pay for services and supports in home and community-based settings. It further states that the nation's goal is to provide people with disabilities with

- a meaningful choice of receiving long-term services and supports in the most integrated setting appropriate to their needs
- the greatest possible control over the services received and, therefore, their own lives and futures
- quality services that maximize independence in the home and community, including the workplace

This is important legislation in that it directly legislates the right of people with disabilities to receive care in their communities with the support of the Social Security Program as outlined in Title XIX.

New Freedom Initiative

The New Freedom Initiative was announced by President George W. Bush on February 1, 2001, as part of an effort by the United States to eliminate barriers to community living (U.S. Department of Health and Human Services, 2003). The Department of Health and Human Services labels the initiative as part of a "comprehensive plan that represents an important step in working to ensure that all Americans have the opportunity to learn and develop skills, engage in productive work, make choices about their daily lives and participate fully in community life." The initiative has been designed to support a number of the goals that surround the independent living movement in this country. It promotes home ownership, expands transportation options, and promotes full access to community life for people with disabilities, as outlined in the *Olmstead, Commissioner, Georgia Department of Human Resources, et al. v. L.C. & E. W.* decision (LII, 1999).

RECENT LANDMARK JUDICIAL DECISIONS

In addition to the landmark legislation discussed above, a number of legal decisions have affected the independent living movement.

Helen L. v. Snider (1995)

The U.S. Court of Appeals Third Circuit ruled that a disabled woman from Pennsylvania had her civil rights violated under the ADA as a result of continued institutional placement that was not medically necessary and because home care was an option. Disability rights advocates perceived this ruling as a landmark decision regarding the rights of people with disabilities in nursing homes to personal assistant services (RRTC-ILM, 2001).

Olmstead, Commissioner, Georgia Department of Human Resources, et al. v. L. C. and E. W. (1999)

In what is now known as the *Olmstead* decision, the Supreme Court ruled that individuals with disabilities must be offered services in the most integrated settings (RRTC-ILM, 2001). The respondents were two people who were living at the Georgia Regional Hospital even after their treatment teams determined that both women could be cared for appropriately in a community setting. They alleged that the State of Georgia had violated their civil rights under Title II of the ADA by failing to provide community placement (LII, 1999). The LII (1999) reported that the Court decided in favor of the two women and stated that "unnecessary institutional segregation constitutes discrimination per se." The Court encouraged states to comply with the ADA in a two-step process. First, they should establish an effective plan for placing people with disabilities in the least restrictive setting. Second, they should establish a waiting list for community-based services to ensure that services will be provided and people will be moved off the list at a reasonable pace (Fox-Grage, Folkemer, & Lewis, 2003). Moving people off the waiting list at a reasonable pace is a problem encountered by states in the HCBS Waiver services. In response, several states are implementing *Olmstead* plans. According to Fox-Grage et al. (2003), 21 states have issued plans or reports, 12 states plan to issue reports in 2003, 4 states have task forces that are focusing on projects related to *Olmstead* but do not plan to write a report, and 6 states have not specified whether they intend to develop a plan or write a report. (For information on your state, see your state's *Olmstead*-related Web site.)

CHOICE, ADVOCACY, AND SELF-DETERMINATION

Despite the mandates of self-determination and choice found in the legislation, many people with disabilities continue to have everyday choices, such as what to eat or what to wear, made for them by well-meaning caregivers (Shapiro, 1994). In many cases, this custodial treatment of people with intellectual and developmental disabilities causes them to become passive participants in their own lives (Turner, 1995). Not only do people with intellectual or developmental disabilities expect to have everyday decisions made for them, but because they have no experience in making choices on their own, it can be difficult to know how to choose when a choice is presented. Therefore, the concept of choice must be taught.

Part of teaching choice is mastering the ability to listen. Although many people may not be able to voice a preference for one item over another, they may send signals in body language or conversation that clearly illustrate a preference. By recognizing these signals, it is possible to begin to support an individual's ability to make real choices.

It is important that the choices presented to people with disabilities should not force them to decide between the lesser of two evils, such as the following:

- Would you like to live in an institution with 50 people? or
- Would you like to live in an institution with 25 people?

The questions in this example do not really represent a choice at all, especially if the person is interested in living in a community. An improved scenario might provide a choice between remaining in the family home, getting an apartment with a roommate, or living in an apartment independently. Along with this improved scenario, information must be provided to support positive decisions by individuals with developmental or intellectual disabilities. For example, living with a roommate has both pros and cons. It is true that there is someone in the house to share financial responsibilities and chores, but there is a chance that the roommate will not meet his or her financial obligations, or he or she might enjoy having uninvited guests over on a regular basis despite repeated protests. Living alone has its advantages, but the sole tenant will be responsible for taking care of all of the finances, cleaning, and shopping. Having this information will certainly impact a person's choice.

In some cases, an informed choice can be made only after people are allowed to experience each element of the decision. If they have never been exposed to the elements of the choice, such as what food they would like to eat, it is impossible to determine what they would rather have. Only by trying the food in question can a decision be reached. *Informed choice* is a phrase used to refer to awareness and context of decisions. As a person learns to make decisions using informed choice, he or she can begin to move into the next phase of speaking for him- or herself.

Self-determination and advocacy are vital factors in achieving and maintaining independent living. Self-determination is defined by Fullerton (1995) simply as a self-awareness that allows a person to be aware of both one's goals and the method of achieving those goals. The construct of self-determination can be further clarified as not only the ability to know oneself, but also the ability to engage in goal-directed, self-regulated, autonomous behavior (Field, Martin, Miller, Ward, & Wehmeyer, 1998). Self-advocacy, as defined by Pennell (2001) is the ability to stand up for oneself by "speaking up, speaking out, and speaking loud" (p. 223). It takes a great deal of time to gather the courage to take a stand against the conventional wisdom propagated by those in authority. Turner (1995) writes that some people who are placed in situations where others are making choices for them that they do not approve of begin to "question the passive role and start to exhibit self-determination" (p. 330). Consider Sue, who allowed her family to place her in an institution after the death of her mother but began a crusade to live independently shortly thereafter.

Just as in Sue's case, sometimes people need a strong advocate to set them on the road to self-determination. An advocate serves as a voice for people who have not yet learned to use their own. Advocates are generally mindful of the desired outcome of any given situation. In effect, the advocate is a person who is capable of teaching and promoting the important concepts of choice and self-determination. Many times, an advocate empowers people to begin to make their own choices. After the friend's intervention to get Sue out of the nursing home, Sue was able to use her own voice to seek the move to Buffalo and achieve her goal of having her own apartment in a community.

There are important components to becoming a self-advocate. A training program known as the Self Advocacy Institute, which was designed and implemented at the Rehabilitation Research and Training Center on Workplace Supports, teaches that there are five levels to self-advocacy (Turner, 1995). The instructors, who are themselves people with disabilities, teach that the first level of self-advocacy is to talk to your family about the choices that you would like to make. The second step encourages people to discuss choices in the context of social and recreational activities. At the third step, the instructors encourage that self-advocates speak to teachers or counselors about their desires in courses of study. Vocational counselors, case managers, and employers are added at the fourth level of self-advocacy. Finally, people with disabilities are taught to let people in the community know of their wishes and desires (Turner, 1995).

It is not always individual advocates who promote the ability of individuals with intellectual or developmental disabilities to speak up on their own behalf. Organizations such as People First and Centers for Independent Living give people voices and the peer support to use them. These grassroots organizations spring up as the desire to make personal choices, needs, and desires becomes known. As T. J. Monroe put it at the first ever convention of People First, held in Connecticut in 1990, "This is a free county. You can talk for yourself. You may need some help, but you can talk for yourself" (Monroe, as cited in Shapiro, 1994, p. 187). The Connecticut chapter still exists, and its Web site (http://www.wecahr.org/people.htm) promotes the following rights for its members and others with disabilities:

- You have a right to dignity and good care. When people treat you with dignity, they respect you.
- You have the right to privacy, privacy to decide for yourself what you want to share and with whom. You do not have to share what is personal. You have the right to be alone.
- You have the right to attend the religious institution of your choice.
- You have the right to have friends.
- You have the right to be free from harm and to have a safe and comfortable place to live.
- You have the right to get services and supports in the community.

The Connecticut chapter, along with all of the international chapters of People First, still promotes the idea of independent living and the right to community homes and care.

Although authorized and funded by the federal and state governments, CILs also continue to exist as grassroots organizations. They promote ideas and concepts that began in the late 1960s as individual efforts and in 1972 as institutional efforts when Ed Roberts and others took a philosophy and built a home for it in Berkeley, California. CILs advance the idea of persons with disabilities making their own choices, deciding what they want, how to get it, and when to do it. Independent living is a major component of the services that these centers provide, as indicated by their names.

As an individual learns to be a self-advocate, he or she begins the journey to self-determination. Pennell (2001) eloquently describes four tenets of self-determination:

1. Freedom is the ability of individuals and freely chosen family and friends, to dream and plan a life with necessary support rather than to purchase a preplanned program from the system;
2. Authority is the ability for a person with a disability, with a social or support network if necessary, to control a certain sum of dollars in order to purchase supports;
3. Support is the arranging of resources and personnel, both formal and informal, that will assist an individual in everyday living; and
4. Responsibility is the acceptance of building a valued life in a person's

community through competitive employment, organizational affilia-
tions, spiritual development, and general caring for others in the community, as well as accountability for spending public dollars in ways
that are life-enhancing. (p. 2)

As programs such as the Medicaid HCBS Waiver continue to grow, the opportunities for people to promote self-determination within the service system will
increase.

SUPPORT SERVICES

Centers for Independent Living

Independent living is often promoted through a series of support services that
enable people with intellectual or developmental disabilities to live in communities. CILs are a major source of that support in local communities. The history of
CILs began with the Center for Independent Living in Berkeley, which was the
first organization with "independent living" in its name. At the same time, other
groups of persons with disabilities were forming, organizing, and implementing
change in Illinois, Michigan, New York, and Massachusetts. People with disabilities were taking their futures into their own hands, and they began to change their
environment, open up employment opportunities, reduce attitudinal barriers,
and develop services and programs that would increase their capacity to live their
own lives in settings that they chose. Education, empowerment, and equality
were goals for people with disabilities, and one way to achieve them was through
a new, rapidly growing industry of Centers for Independent Living. Today, there
are over 620 CILs, providing services to over 250,000 persons with disabilities of
all ages and with all disabilities. A recent study conducted by the Rehabilitation
Research and Training Center on Independent Living Management found that
18,118 people with intellectual or developmental disabilities received independent living services from CILs in fiscal year 2002. According to the Rehabilitation
Act of 1973 and its amendments,

> The purpose of the Centers for Independent Living (CILs) program is to
> promote a philosophy of independent living, including a philosophy of con-
> sumer control, peer support, self-determination, equal access, and individual
> and system advocacy, in order to maximize the leadership, empowerment,
> independence, and productivity of individuals with significant disabilities,
> and the integration and full inclusion of individuals with significant disabil-
> ities into the mainstream of American society by providing financial assis-
> tance to develop and support statewide networks of CILs.

Centers for Independent Living are community-based organizations with volun-
teer boards of directors whose composition must be at least 50% people with disabilities. Not only does at least half the board have to be made up of people with
disabilities, it also must reflect the community's racial and ethnic demographics

and have representation of the five functional limitations (physical, mental–emotional, cognitive, sensory, and multiple disabilities). Although the board sets policies for the CILs, the majority of supervisors and staff must also be persons with disabilities.

A unique circle of control, direction, and implementation is created for program settings and community involvement when the board of directors is composed of persons with disabilities, the management and staff include persons with disabilities, and consumers who participate in the programs and services have the opportunity to become members of the board. Simply stated, people who are planning and working for CILs are also eventually working for themselves. The independent living philosophy that CILs embrace and promote is regulated in both federal and many state laws, and is described and outlined in the 725 standards laid out in the Rehabilitation Act Amendments of 1992 (P.L. 102-559). These standards are the guide for federally funded CILs. They are as follows:

1. The center shall promote and practice the independent living philosophy of—
(a) consumer control of the center regarding decision making, service delivery, management, and establishment of the policy and direction of the center;
(b) self-help and self-advocacy;
(c) development of peer relationships and peer role models; and
(d) equal access of individuals with severe disabilities to society and to all services, programs, activities, resources, and facilities, whether public or private and regardless of the funding source.

2. The center shall provide services to individuals with a range of severe disabilities. The center shall provide services on a cross-disability basis (for individuals with all different types of severe disabilities, including individuals with disabilities who are members of populations that are unserved or underserved by programs under this Act). Eligibility for services at any center for independent living shall not be based on the presence of any one or more specific severe disabilities.

3. The center shall facilitate the development and achievement of independent living goals selected by individuals with severe disabilities who seek such assistance by the center.

4. The center shall work to increase the availability and improve the quality of community options for independent living in order to facilitate the development and achievement of independent living goals by the individuals with severe disabilities.

5. The center shall provide independent living core services and, as appropriate, a combination of any other independent living services specified in section 7(30)(B).

6. The center shall conduct activities to increase the capacity of communities within the service area to meet the needs of individuals with severe disabilities.

7. The center shall conduct resource development activities to obtain funding from sources other than this chapter. (LII, 2003b)

Any federally funded center that meets the 725 standards also has the flexibility to provide a variety of programs and services as long as all programs, regardless of funding, continue to operate according to the standards. Centers can explore and take advantage of almost any funding opportunity and provide its services to the entire community. In reviewing the standards, one notes that the CIL does not focus only on individual services; CILs take a macro approach to people with disabilities, not just a micro rehabilitation effort. Education to the consumer of services is important, but education to the community is equally critical. CILs work extensively in the community to promote the capabilities, contributions, and requirements of people with disabilities, in their effort to empower the customer through their services.

Once the person with a disability and the community have reached a level of understanding, both are empowered to take the next step and ensure that equality for the person with a disability becomes a reality. Once the consumer understands that he or she has the right to access all events, activities, and public accommodations in the community, and the community embraces that concept, the person with a disability is able to become a full partner in the community, sharing the responsibility and promoting future growth for all community members.

The process begins when a person with a disability contacts a CIL for assistance. The consumer is informed that he or she is a full partner in the process and will be in charge of determining individual goals and the path to achieving those goals. All efforts are concentrated on the consumer's ability to achieve those goals. Each consumer develops an Independent Living Plan (ILP) that allows him or her to set individual goals and take the steps necessary to achieve those goals, or a consumer may choose to waive an ILP and still pursue his or her goals with full assistance from the center. Consumers are notified before any service of their rights as a consumer or a CIL customer. They are also provided with information as to how to appeal a decision by the CIL, a process known as filing a grievance. Customers of a CIL do not have to provide medical documentation of their disability to get services, although specific funding sources may request such information to access services.

The Rehabilitation Act Amendments define a number of services that a CIL can provide. However, the services offered at each individual CIL will differ. Service options include the following:

- *Advocacy and legal services.* Assistance and representation in obtaining access to benefits, services, and programs to which a consumer may be entitled.
- *Assistive devices and equipment.* Provision of specialized devices and equipment such as communication devices, wheelchairs and lifts, and assistance to obtain these devices and equipment from other sources.
- *IL skills training and life skills training.* These may include instruction to develop independent living skills in areas such as personal care, coping, financial management, social skills, and household management. They may also include education and training necessary for living in the community and participating in community activities.
- *Peer counseling.* Counseling, teaching, information sharing, and similar kinds of contact are provided to consumers by other people with disabilities.
- *Personal assistance.* This includes, but is not limited to, assistance with personal bodily functions; communicative, household, mobility, work,

emotional, cognitive, personal, and financial affairs; community participation; parenting; leisure; and other related needs.

- *Rehabilitation technology.* Provision of, or assistance to obtain through
other sources, adaptive modifications that address the barriers confronted
by individuals with significant disabilities with respect to education,
rehabilitation, employment, transportation, independent living, and
recreation.

Although CILs offer extensive services to individuals, a great deal of their
activities promote open communities for persons with disabilities by advocating
community change, collaborating with other organizations, and producing educational campaigns, for a few examples. CILs routinely assist consumers in re-
locating from nursing homes or other institutions into the community. Other
activities that promote community integration include working with public and
private entities to establish new community options or capacities to meet the
needs of consumers, or revising the charter of those organizations to include
people with significant disabilities in existing community options or capacities
that have not previously served individuals with intellectual or developmental
disabilities. CILs often participate in activities that foster collaboration and development of new coalitions to maximize use of community resources or to open
new resource development opportunities.

Personal Assistant Services and Home Health Care

Personal assistant services (PAS) assist people with disabilities with activities of
daily living that they would perform for themselves if not for the presence of the
disability (Turner, West, Strobel, & Barcus, 2000). These activities do not differ
from the personal grooming tasks that millions of Americans perform for themselves before they leave the house in the morning. A focus group conducted in
1998 by the RRTC on Workplace Supports at the National CIL meeting in Washington, D.C., revealed that people with disabilities viewed PAS as assisting with
the following activities:

- grooming tasks
- getting food and beverages
- toileting
- travel and transportation
- dressing (Turner et al., 2000)

Additional tasks may include cooking, cleaning, shopping, and paying bills. Lyle
O'Brien (1992, p. 1) stated that PAS form the "foundation of a decent and dignified life for people with significant disabilities." The simple fact is that PAS allow people with disabilities to perform the tasks that would otherwise preclude
them from reaching their goals in independent living. Not only do these services
improve the quality of life for people with disabilities, but they also meet the
least restrictive environment mandates found in the legislation. According to

Hanchett (2001), PAS evolved as an effective way for states to reduce the increasing costs of traditional home care and institutionalization.

The values of PAS were formed by grassroots organizations of people who use these services, much in the way self-determination found its roots. The World Institute on Disability, which was founded by Ed Roberts, Judy Heumann, and Joan Leon in 1983, has established 10 values of PAS (Turner & Barrett, 2000; Turner et al., 2000):

1. No medical supervision is required.
2. The services provided include personal maintenance and hygiene such as catheterization, mobility, and household assistance.
3. The maximum service limit should not exceed 20 hours per week.
4. Service is available 24 hours a day, 7 days a week.
5. The income limit for eligibility is greater than 150% of the poverty level. Further, individuals who are severely disabled and whose income exceeds that established for eligibility should be allowed to buy into an insurance policy that provides attendant care. Marital status and subsequent financial circumstances should not govern access to personal assistant services.
6. Individual providers can be utilized by the consumer.
7. The consumer hires and fires the assistant.
8. The consumer pays the assistant.
9. The consumer trains the assistant.
10. The consumer participates in deciding on the number of hours and type of services he or she requires.

Obviously, a number of these requirements demand a certain level of skill. In some cases, training for the person with a disability is required to effectively manage a personal assistant. Many times, CILs offer these training programs to enhance a person's ability to find and maintain quality personal assistants. In other cases, a case manager or family member may assist with the process. Many steps must be taken to find a qualified personal assistant. The first step is generally creating a detailed job description that will help the person with a disability to determine if the applicant is capable of performing all elements of the job (Turner & Barrett, 2000). For many people with disabilities, this means that they will have to take a realistic look at what tasks they can and cannot perform in their living environment. Also, time requirements for identified tasks must be considered to ensure that accurate estimates can be provided upon hire of a personal assistant. Advertisements that encourage people with the necessary skills to apply for open positions must be created. Most important, effective interviews must be completed to screen out candidates who are not suitable for the position (Turner, 2001). Determining the capabilities of PAS applicants requires that a number of skills be evaluated during the application and interview process and that certain questions be asked (e.g., about the person's work history, and about whether he or she has been fired in the past, and, if so, for what reason). Experience with people with disabilities is also an important issue; many times, applicants may have a family member or friend who has a disability, or they may not have had any related experience. It is very important when discussing issues related to providing services to ensure that the applicant does not have a custodial attitude toward people with disabilities. The strongest candidates will believe in the abilities of a person with a disability to be independent. They must also believe in a person's ability to be a contributing member of the community. These characteristics will ensure that an employee will see the duties outlined in the job description as important, just as a personal assistant in an office would. Strong (2001) lists a number of other tasks that are required to effectively manage a personal assistant:

- contract preparation
- determining pay rates and maintaining payroll
- providing feedback
- scheduling
- clarification of job responsibilities
- dispute resolution
- termination

Finding and maintaining effective personal assistants when there are often shortages of qualified individuals is a daunting process. High turnover rates plague the field because of low wages, lack of benefits, and limited opportunity for promotion (Strong, 2001). Therefore, a contract is vital to ensure that all duties, wages, time requirements, benefits, and other financial incentives are clearly expressed. A sample contract for a personal assistant is presented in Figure 16.1.

In some cases, supervision by a trained nurse or physician is vital to the care needs of the person with a disability. In these cases, consumer-directed home care (CDHC) is an effective method to provide long-term home-based support for individuals with more involved medical needs (Hanchett, 2001). In CDHC, the person with a disability has the same responsibilities to hire, fire, train, and pay the caregiver, but unlike personal assistance, that caregiver is a trained nurse or a nurse's aide who is supervised by a nurse or physician. These services continue to offer considerable cost savings when compared to nursing home or hospital care due to a reduction in overhead costs and elaborate program requirements (Benjamin, Matthias, & Franke, 2000). This model is based on the concept of self-care, in which nurses help consumers to find their own solutions, mobilize their own resources, and focus on their own goals and needs (Rice, 1998). According to Rice, the primary components of self-care include

- health teaching
- psychological, sociological, and physical care
- case management

For example, nurses may instruct a person with an intellectual or developmental disability on how to take important medication. They may also devise a system that allows the person to do that without a great deal of thought. The nurse would be responsible for addressing complex physical care needs but would also provide support to the person on how to cope with medical concerns. Most im-

This is a legally binding document. Be sure you understand everything in this contract **BEFORE** you sign it.

The assistant will perform the following services for [the person with a disability]. Activities include, but are not limited to [insert job duties here].

- [Insert name], hereafter known as assistant, will be supervised by and is wholly responsible to [insert name], hereafter known as the employer.
- Assistant will respect the confidentiality of the employer.
- Assistant will complete the duties as outlined in the agreed upon schedule.
- Three absences without prior notification and/or three late arrivals will result in termination.
- Assistant will work [insert schedule].
- The employer will pay the assistant [insert wage and pay schedule].
- Transportation with or for employer will be reimbursed at the rate of [insert reimbursement rate] if the assistant uses his or her own vehicle.
- Salary [does or does not] include paid vacation or sick leave.
- In the event of an emergency, the employer or assistant will notify the other as soon as possible and/or before the assistant is expected at work.
- Assistant will be notified three times of unacceptable behavior [insert definition of unacceptable behavior] before termination occurs. In the event that such behavior endangers the employer's health or safety, the assistant will be terminated without notice.
- Each party will give two weeks' notice before the termination of this contract.

The assistant is working as an independent contractor and is solely responsible for keeping adequate records and making tax and other payments related to this contract. Assistant acknowledges that no money will be withheld by the employer for payment of assistant's local, state, or federal taxes.

Signature of Employer _____ Date _____

Signature of Assistant _____ Date _____

FIGURE 16.1. Sample contract for a personal assistant. *Note.* From *Personal Assistance in the Workplace: A Consumer-Directed Guide,* by E. Turner, G. Revell, and V. Brooke (Eds.), 2001, Richmond: Virginia Commonwealth University, Rehabilitation Research and Training Center on Workplace Supports. Copyright 2001 by Virginia Commonwealth University. Reprinted with permission.

portant, the nurse would serve as a case manager, facilitating the person's team to manage health concerns.

A cooperative relationship must be established with a nurse to successfully promote independent living. Rice (1998) defines this relationship as a mutual partnership, in which the nurse and the person with a disability have equal power and are interdependent. Rice also speaks of the importance of trust in a self-care relationship; both parties must be secure in the knowledge that the other is responsibly carrying out the tasks that were arranged during the visit.

In many cases, a person with an intellectual or developmental disability will also involve his or her family in the self-care relationship in order to ease concerns about health-related issues. The independent living model in which self-care is promoted insists that disability does not equal disease, and that people with disabilities must be active participants in or directors of resolving their basic service needs (Hanchett, 2001).

Whether PAS is provided by a personal assistant, nurse's aide, or nurse, the underlying philosophy remains the same. There must be a belief that these services allow people with disabilities to exercise independent choice and autonomy in selecting how best to use PAS to complete activities of daily living (Hanchett, 2001). In whatever form PAS is provided, three essential qualities must be present (Lyle O'Brien, 1992):

- PAS must be available to everyone who, on the basis of functional need, requires them.
- PAS must be comprehensive enough to offer a genuine alternative to living in a nursing facility or other institution.
- PAS must be controllable by people with disabilities to allow them to tailor services to individual circumstances.

Although PAS services are cost-effective and generally successful in terms of consumer satisfaction, there are still considerable problems that must be addressed. Many personal assistants are often late or do not bother to come to work at all. In other cases, low-quality assistance is provided that does not meet the needs of the consumer of the services. A person with a disability must be well versed in the management process to address these issues effectively. In cases of emergency, when the personal assistant is not available, a back-up plan should exist. This plan may mean that a group of family members or friends are available for assistance on an emergency basis. A schedule with contact numbers and availability should be kept by the phone to ensure that assistance is available if needed.

Assistive Technology

Assistive technology (AT) is another tool that enables people with disabilities to function independently across all environments. AT is defined in the Assistive Technology Act of 1998 (Tech Act) as "any item, piece of equipment, or product system, whether acquired commercially off the shelf, modified, or customized, that is used to increase, maintain, or improve the functional capabilities of individuals with disabilities" (29 U.S.C. § 3, S2431, [5]).

Although AT seems as if it would consist primarily of high-technology, high-cost items, it can actually be quite simple. For example, Black & Decker recently announced a new electric jar opener in its line of new home appliances. This product opens jars without requiring hand strength or the ability to use both hands (Black & Decker, 2003). If a person is unable to open a jar to prepare a meal, this simple device offers a way to get the job done with no assistance. Other examples of low-tech devices might consist of an electric razor for someone who cannot use a standard blade, electric toothbrushes to ensure good oral hygiene, and pans with heat-resistant handles to improve kitchen safety.

In some cases, higher tech devices are required, such as communication devices that allow people who cannot verbalize to have a voice of their own. Environmental control units, which allow remote access to electric devices, are also considered high tech. These high-tech items are generally more expensive and require more training to use effectively. The Tech Act also calls for the provision of AT services. AT service is defined as "any service that directly assists an individual with a disability in the selection, acquisition, or use of an assistive technology device" (29 U.S.C. § 3, S2431, [5]). This definition allows for a wide variety of services to enhance the ability of people with disabilities to use AT. These services include (a) evaluation of the needs of an individual with a disability, including a functional evaluation of the individual in his or her customary environment; (b) purchasing, leasing, or otherwise providing for the acquisition of AT devices by individuals with disabilities; (c) selecting, designing, fitting, customizing, adapting, applying, maintaining, repairing, or replacing AT devices; (d) coordinating and using other therapies, interventions, or services with AT devices, such as those associated with existing education and rehabilitation plans and programs; (e) training or technical assistance for an individual with disabilities or, where appropriate, the family of an individual with disabilities; and (f) training or technical assistance for professionals (including individuals providing educational and rehabilitation services, employers, or other individuals who provide services to, employ, or are otherwise substantially involved in the major life functions of individuals with disabilities) (29 U.S.C. § 3, S2431, [5]).

There are a number of resources that people with disabilities and their families can access when searching for information on assistive technology. First and foremost, it is advisable to contact the CIL in one's area. The Tech Act also authorized a series of assistive technology service centers in each state; a listing can be found at the Rehabilitation Engineering & Assistive Technology Society of North America (www.resna.org). RESNA also has a listing of assistive technology practitioners and their contact information if individual assistance is needed. The World Wide Web is also an excellent source of information. AbleData (www.abledata.com) and Closing the Gap (www.closingthegap.com) are databases filled with technology devices and ideas.

PLANNING FOR INDEPENDENT LIVING

It is important to plan carefully to ensure successful community living. If independent living services are provided by a CIL, staff will generally help to prepare a plan. These plans, known as Independent Living Plans (ILPs), delineate the services that the person with a disability will receive from the CIL. For example, Sue's plan called for the provision of the following services:

- cooking
- cleaning

- shopping
- identification of funding for independent living
- money management
- community orientation

The ILP service plan culminated in many activities that CIL staff performed with Sue when she arrived in Buffalo. The CIL began to work by enrolling Sue in the subsidized housing rolls. They were also able to research information regarding Sue's eligibility for benefits through her deceased parents. This research allowed Sue to receive a Social Security check that was twice as large as her Supplemental Security Income check, as well as a $6,000 back payment, as a result of her father's death. She was also able to qualify for the low-income Home Energy Assistance Program and food stamps to offset her living costs. To teach Sue to cook, CIL staff began to provide cooking classes so she could prepare meals in her apartment. They also taught her how to clean her apartment.

Money management was identified as a key component to Sue's success in the community. As a result, CIL staff trained her in the use of a calculator that she could keep in her purse to calculate change and other simple transactions. She was also taught to maintain a log to keep track of her purchases and review it with her IL specialists at least once a month and weekly if she thought necessary. She learned to review her utility bills and identify whether an error had occurred. If she found anything that appeared incorrect, she consulted with a CIL specialist. She opened a checking account and was taught how to write checks and mail her payments. She was taught how to put a shopping list together and look for the best buys. Comparison shopping was taught not only for groceries but for clothing and other items as well.

In the process of Sue's instruction on community living, she decided that she would like to have a roommate. She decided to invite her long-time friend Gloria to live with her. Gloria, who was living with her mother and father in the Bronx, accepted Sue's offer and completed many of the same programs and services as Sue received. Sue and Gloria complement each other's strengths and weaknesses. While Gloria enjoys cooking and cleaning, Sue is able to manage the money and outside shopping.

If a person with an intellectual or developmental disabilitiy is moving into a community without the assistance of a CIL, family members should assist in the development of a similar plan. These plans are important to ensure that success is possible in the community. The plan should consist of the following elements (adapted from Brooke, Inge, Armstrong, & Wehman, 1997):

1. a primary support person and his or her contact information
2. additional support people and their contact information
3. a list of needs identified as necessary to ensure success
4. potential options for addressing each need
5. the preference of the consumer
6. primary support option
7. back-up support
8. where necessary, the identification of funding options

Using a format such as this to plan for independent living ensures that the person can be systematically taught each skill he or she will need to ensure success in the community. The identification of a primary support person will also provide the independent living team with a list of duties that people have agreed to perform. It is important to note that signing up for a task on this list does not necessarily mean that the support person will be primarily responsible for teaching that task; it only means that he or she will assist the person in locating resources for learning on that task. For example, the person with an intellectual or developmental disability may choose to complete a community cooking class instead of private cooking instruction at home. (However, follow-up should be provided to determine whether the task has been sufficiently understood.)

It is also important to consider the independent living plans of individuals who currently reside with an aging parent or other family member. This planning will prevent unnecessary confusion in the event that the primary caregiver can no longer carry out the necessary tasks, whether due to illness, accident, or death. Careful planning as to the desires of a person with a developmental disability before these emergencies occur will allow a solid plan to be in place if needed.

BECOMING PART OF THE COMMUNITY

Many people who reside in communities across the country are isolated from friends and neighbors. Because having a disability is often isolating in and of itself, it is important that careful steps be taken to ensure that community inclusion will occur. Pearpoint makes some powerful points about what inclusion is:

- Inclusion is about living full lives, about learning to live together.
- Inclusion makes the world our classroom for a full life.
- Inclusion treasures diversity and builds community.
- Inclusion is about our abilities, our gifts, and how to share them.
- Inclusion is not just a disability issue.
- Most important, inclusion means *with* and not just *in*. (2003, What Is Inclusion? ¶ 1)

These guiding principles serve as a reminder of the importance of working with people to help them become part of their communities. That may mean that neighbors get to know each other and are able to watch out for each other's best interests. It may also mean that individuals work and shop in their own communities, participate in community activities such as yard sales or block parties, or offer to help a neighbor who is shoveling a sidewalk. In many cases, people will initiate these activities independently. In others, it may be necessary to facilitate these relationships by introducing a person who is living in the community for the first time to neighbors, or teaching the person to introduce him- or herself. In Sue's case, she began community orientation by walking around her neighborhood identifying stores and other points of interests, and introducing herself to her neighbors. She later learned how to access the bus system and travel to area malls as well as to the homes of her extended family.

FINAL THOUGHTS

The information presented in this chapter outlines some of the key issues in successful independent living. Legislation related to independent living is slowly encouraging people with disabilities to become part of their communities and the courts are supporting their rights to do that. It may take many years to undo the damage created in the years of institutionalization and segregation, but change is coming. As for Sue and Gloria, they still live together, although they have since decided to move to the suburbs. They have a case service coordinator to assist in those issues they cannot deal with directly. Sue is able to contact her family to help when needed. She also knows when to recognize problems and ask for assistance when needed. She has gone to Florida to visit the family that helped her out of the nursing home, and travels to New York City with Gloria to visit her parents. The two women attend family gatherings and entertain guests and relatives regularly. Both have significant others in their lives.

REFERENCES

American Presidency Project. (1963). *John F. Kennedy: Special message to the Congress on mental illness and mental retardation.* Retrieved June 23, 2004, from http://www.presidency.ucsb.edu/site/docs/pppus.php?admin=1963&id=50

American Disabled for Attendant Programs Today. (2001). *Medicaid Community-Based Attendant Services and Supports Act of 2001 (S. 1298): A Summary.* Retrieved June 23, 2004, from http://www.adapt.org

Arizona Technical Assistance Program. (2001). *The Developmental Disabilities Assistance and Bill of Rights Act of 2000 (P.L. 106-402).* Retrieved June 23, 2004, from http://www.nau.edu/ihd/aztap/ddabra/shtml

Assistive Technology Act of 1998, 29 U.S.C. § 2201 *et seq.*

Benjamin, A., Matthias, R., & Franke, T. (2000). Comparing consumer directed and agency models for providing supportive services at home. *Health Services Research, 35*(1), 351–366.

Black & Decker. (2003). *Lids Off Automatic Jar Opener.* Product description retrieved June 23, 2004, from http://www.blackanddeckerappliances.com/

Brooke, V., Inge, K. J., Armstrong, A. J., & Wehman, P. (1997). *The supported employment handbook.* Richmond: Virginia Commonwealth University, Rehabilitation Research and Training Center on Supported Employment.

Center for Medicare and Medicaid Services. (2002). *Medicaid: A brief summary.* Retrieved June 23, 2004, from http://www.cms.hhs.gov/publications/overview-medicare-medicaid/default4.asp

Center for Medicare and Medicaid Services. (2003). *Home and community-based services waiver program: How to obtain approval.* Retrieved June 23, 2004, from http://www.cms.hhs.gov/Medicaid/1915c/obtainapp.asp

Field, S., Martin, J., Miller, R., Ward, M., & Wehmeyer, M. (1998). *A practical guide to teaching self-determination.* Austin, TX: PRO-ED.

Fox-Grage, W., Folkemer, D., & Lewis, J. (2003). *The states' response to the Olmstead decision: How are states complying?* Washington, DC: National Conference of State Legislatures.

Fullerton, A. (1995). Promoting self-determination for adolescents and young adults with autism. *Journal of Vocational Rehabilitation, 5*(4), 337–346.

General Services Administration–Office of Governmental Policy. (2002). *Section 504 of the Rehabilitation Act.* Retrieved June 23, 2004, from http://www.section508.gov/index.cfm?Fuse Action=Content&ID=15

Hanchett, M. (2001). What you need to know about consumer-directed homecare. *Home Healthcare Nurse, 19*(11), 681–686.

Harrington, C., & LeBlanc, A. J. (2001). *Disability statistics report: Medicaid home and community based services.* San Francisco: U.S. Department of Education, Office of Special Education and Rehabilitative Services.

Lankin, K. C., Anderson, L., & Prouty, R. (1999). Medicaid HCBS "waiver" recipients are now twice the number of Medicaid ICF/MR residents. *Mental Retardation, 37*(4), 341–343.

Lankin, K. C., Braddock, D., & Smith, G. (2001). Medicaid long-term services for people with developmental disabilities: That was then, this is now. *Mental Retardation, 39*(6), 488–491.

Legal Information Institute, Supreme Court Collection. (1999). Olmstead v. L.C. (98-536) 527 U.S. 581 (1999) 138 F.3d 893, affirmed in part, vacated in part, and remanded. Retrieved June 23, 2004, from http://supct.law.cornell.edu/supct/html/98-536.ZS.html

Legal Information Institute. (2003a). Title 29, Chapter 16, Section 701, general provisions of the Vocational Rehabilitation Act Amendments. Retrieved August 8, 2004, from http://www4 .law.cornell.edu/uscode/29/701.html

Legal Information Institute. (2003b). Title 29, Chapter 16, Section 786f-4, standards and assurances for centers for independent living. Retrieved July 15, 2004, from http://www4.law .cornell.edu/uscode/29/796f-4.html

Lyle O'Brien, C. (1992). *Evaluating personal assistant services.* Syracuse, NY: University of Minnesota Research and Training Center on Community Living.

Miller, N. A., Ramsland, S., & Harrington, C. (1999). Trends and issues in the Medicaid 1915(c) waiver program. *Health Care Financing Review, 20*(4), 139–160.

National Council on Independent Living. (2003). Take the initiative, invest in freedom: Position on the reauthorization of the Rehabilitation Act of 1973, as amended. Retrieved June 23, 2004, from http://www.ncil.org/rehab03.htm

Pearpoint, J. (2003). *What is inclusion? Inclusion is about all of us.* Retrieved July 19, 2004, from http://www.inclusion.com/inclusion.html

Pennell, R. L. (2001). Self-determination and self-advocacy: Shifting the power. *Journal of Disability Policy Studies, 11*(4), 223–227.

People First, Connecticut Chapter. (2003). *People first: Real rights for real people.* Retrieved June 23, 2004, from http://www.wecahr.org/people.htm

Perkins, J., & Kulkarni, M. (2000). *Addressing home and community-based waiver waiting lists through the Medicaid program.* Retrieved June 23, 2004, from the National Health Law Program Web site: http://www.healthlaw.org/medicaid.shtml

Policy Almanac. (2000). *Clinton signs Developmental Disabilities Act.* Retrieved July 20, 2004, from http://www.policyalmanac.org/social_welfare/news/disability-2000.shtml

Rehabilitation Act of 1973, 29 U.S.C. § 701 *et seq.*

Rehabilitation Act Amendments of 1992, 29 U.S.C. § 796e.

Rehabilitation Research and Training Center on Independent Living Management. (2001). *Disability rights timeline.* Retrieved June 23, 2004, from http://www.wnyilp.org/RRTCILM/ dissemination/DISABILITYRIGHTSTIMELINE.doc

Rice, R. (1998). Key concepts of self-care in the home: Implications for home care nurses. *Geriatric Nursing, 19*(1), 52–54.

Richards, L. (1995). *Composition of statewide independent living councils.* Retrieved June 23, 2004, from the Independent Living Research Utilization at TIRR Web site: http://www.ilru.org/ilnet/files/faqs/compo.html

Rubin, S. E., & Roessler, R. T. (1995). *Foundations of the vocational rehabilitation process* (4th ed.). Austin, TX: PRO-ED.

Shapiro, J. P. (1994). *No pity: People with disabilities forging a new civil rights movement.* New York: Times Books.

Strong, J. (2001). Training a person with a disability to use PAS. In E. Turner, G. Revell, & V. Brooke (Eds.), *Personal assistance in the workplace: A consumer-directed guide.* Richmond: Virginia Commonwealth University, Rehabilitation Research and Training Center on Workplace Supports.

Turner, E. (1995). Self-advocacy: A key to self-determination. *Journal of Vocational Rehabilitation, 5*(4), 329–336.

Turner, E. (2001). Using a self-assessment in finding the right personal assistant. In E. Turner, G. Revell, & V. Brooke (Eds.), *Personal assistance in the workplace: A consumer-directed guide.* Richmond: Virginia Commonwealth University, Rehabilitation Research and Training Center on Workplace Supports.

Turner, E., & Barrett, C. (2000). *Finding a qualified personal assistant. The customer is right.* Richmond: Virginia Commonwealth University, Rehabilitation Research and Training Center on Workplace Supports.

Turner, E., Revell, G., & Brooke, V. (Eds.). (2001). *Personal assistance in the workplace: A consumer-directed guide.* Richmond: Virginia Commonwealth University, Rehabilitation Research and Training Center on Workplace Supports.

Turner, E., West, M., Strobel, W., & Barcus, M. (2000). Personal assistant services: A vital workplace support. In M. Barcus, T. Blankenship, E. Turner, P. Wehman, & G. Galloway (Eds.), *Advocacy and supported employment for people with disabilities: A guide and workbook for individuals with disabilities and service providers.* Richmond: Virginia Commonwealth University, Rehabilitation Research and Training Center on Workplace Supports.

U.S. Department of Education. (1994). *Centers for independent living: Biennial evaluation report, FY 93–94.* Retrieved June 23, 2004, from http://www.ed.gov/pubs/Biennial/330.html

U.S. Department of Health & Human Services. (2003). *The new freedom initiative.* Retrieved June 23, 2004, from http://www.hhs.gov/newfreedom/init.html

U.S. Department of Housing and Urban Development. (2003). *Fair housing—it's your right.* Retrieved June 23, 2004, from the Consumer Law Page Web site: http://consumerlawpage.com/brochure/fair-hse.shtml

U.S. Department of Justice. (1992). *ADA: Title II technical assistance manual.* Washington, DC: Author.

U.S. Department of Justice. (2002). ADA, Title III Regulations, 28 CFR Part 36: *Nondiscrimination on the basis of disability by public accommodations and in commercial facilities.* Washington, DC: Author.

Wehmeyer, M. (2003). Self-determination, vocational rehabilitation, and workplace supports. *Journal of Vocational Rehabilitation, 19*(2), 727–728.

White House. (2000). Statement by the President. Retrieved June 22, 2004, from http://www.aucd.org/legislative_affairs/Presidentssignstate.html

Social Security Disability Benefit Programs

Susan O'Mara and John Kregel

LEARNING GOALS

Upon completion of this chapter, the reader will be able to

- define what Social Security is, specifically the Supplemental Security Income and Disability Insurance Programs
- discuss how an individual's Social Security cash benefits can be affected by earnings from a job
- review two work incentives—Plan for Achieving Self-Support and Impairment-Related Work Expenses—that can be used to help people with severe disabilities obtain or retain employment
- identify the barriers to employment inherent in the Social Security system
- discuss key employment supports contained in the Ticket to Work and Work Incentive Improvement Act of 1999

The Social Security Administration (SSA) administers two separate income support programs for persons with disabilities: Supplemental Security Income (SSI, or Title XVI) and the Social Security Disability benefit programs under Title II of the Social Security Act. To be eligible for monthly cash payments under the SSI and Title II disability benefit programs, an individual must meet the SSA's statutory definition of disability, as well as other nondisability-specific requirements.

A first step in understanding the SSA disability standard is to understand how disability is defined in the Social Security Act:

> The inability to engage in any substantial gainful work activity, by reason of any medically determinable physical or mental impairment, that has lasted or is expected to last for a continuous period of at least 12 months, or is expected to result in death.
>
> An individual shall be determined to be under a disability only if his physical or mental impairment or impairments are of such severity that he is not only unable to do his previous work, but cannot, considering his age, education, and work experience, engage in any other kind of substantial gainful work which exists in the national economy, regardless of whether such work exists in the immediate area in which he lives, or whether a specific job vacancy exists for him, or whether he would be hired if he applied for work.

Several basic conditions are contained in this lengthy definition. First, the individual must have a disability that can be documented by a qualified medical examiner, and the disability must be considered severe. Second, the disability must be expected to last 12 or more months or be expected to result in death. Third, the individual cannot be working at the time of application or, if working, cannot be earning more than the Substantial Gainful Activity (SGA) level of $800 for individuals with a disability other than blindness, or $1,330 if they are blind. (These dollar figures represent the SGA guideline for 2003.)

Substantial Gainful Activity is a measure of a person's ability to work at a substantial level. Individuals engaging in SGA-level work at the time of initial application will not be considered disabled under Social Security law.

The process used to determine whether an individual meets the SSA's definition of disability is the same for both the Title II disability programs and Supplemental Security Income. Essentially five questions determine whether one meets the criteria contained in this definition:

1. Is the individual engaging in substantial gainful work activity?
2. Does the person have a physical or mental impairment that can be documented by a qualified medical examiner? In addition, has the disability lasted, or is it expected to last at least 12 months or to result in death?
3. Does the person's impairment meet or equal a certain level or severity of disability as outlined in the SSA's listing of impairments?
4. Given the work-related abilities that the individual has retained, is he or she able to perform any past relevant work? This refers to any jobs that

the individual has had during the last 15 years. What is being evaluated here is the ability of the individual to continue in or return to previous types of work in spite of the limitations he or she now has as a result of the disability.

5. Finally, if the person is unable to perform any of his or her previous work, given age, education, and work history, is he or she able to perform any other work that exists in the national economy?

In deciding whether a person is disabled, these five questions must be addressed in the order listed. The evaluation stops at any step in the process if a decision of "disabled" or "not disabled" can be made.

It is important to keep in mind that "engaging in SGA," or substantial work, is not just earning over the specific dollar amount that is currently designated as the SGA guideline. Instead, SGA is a decision that is made about the actual value of the work the person is performing. In some instances, a beneficiary's gross earnings may be above the SGA guideline, but the person is unable to sustain work at a substantial level over a period of time.

In making the SGA determination, SSA considers a variety of factors, including pay, the nature of the job duties, hours worked, productivity, and any other factors related to the value of the work performed. The Social Security claims representative looks at the work performed by the individual, calculates its gross value, and then takes deductions allowed under the law to see if that work is substantial. A beneficiary is determined to be engaging in SGA only if that person has a sustained work effort valued over the current SGA earnings guideline after all of the deductions are made.

Four categories of deductions are considered in the SGA decision-making process to help SSA more accurately assess the true value of the work performed:

• *Impairment-Related Work Expenses.* IRWEs are any work-related expenses that a person with a disability would have as a result of physical or mental impairment. These are expenses that (a) are directly related to enabling the person with a disability to work and (b) would not be necessary for individuals who are not disabled for gaining and maintaining employment. The purpose of the IRWE work incentive is to enable persons with disabilities to recover some or all of the costs of expenses incurred as a result of disability to support their work. Many different types of expenses are allowable as IRWEs. Examples include supported employment services, special transportation services, and attendant care support on the job or assisting the individual to get to and from work, medical support devices, work equipment, and more. In addition, these costs are deductible even if the item or service is also needed to carry out daily living unrelated to the individual's work. The dollar amount of IRWEs is deducted from an individual's gross monthly earnings before the SGA determination is made.

• *Subsidy.* Subsidy allows the SSA to not consider, or ignore, earnings that are not representative of the person's ability to work. Sometimes a person's disability will result in the need for extra assistance, a reduced production rate, frequent breaks, or fewer job duties than coworkers in a similar job. When that happens, the individual's income not only is pay for their work product but also represents either direct help from someone else, like a supervisor or job coach, or full pay for lower productivity than other employees.

SSA is only interested in assessing earnings that can be attributed directly to the individual and the earnings potential if those supports were not in place. Therefore, the SSA adjusts the value of the income by deducting the cost attributed to the extra help or special situation that each person experiences.

For example, say someone with a severe disability earns $20 per hour. The SSA determined, however, that the individual's productivity is only half that of nondisabled coworkers who are performing the same job. In this circumstance, the SSA may decide that the person really earns only $10 per hour, and will ignore the other 50% of the earnings for the SGA determination.

• *Income averaging.* When an individual's earnings or work activity varies from month to month, the SSA is able to average the earnings over a specific period of work. Income averaging can possibly result in a current month's wages that are above the SGA guideline being considered non-SGA when averaged with other lower wage months within the specific work period.

• *Unsuccessful work attempt.* An unsuccessful work attempt is an effort on the part of a beneficiary to work at a substantial level that is either stopped or reduced below the SGA earnings guideline after a short period of time (no more than 6 months). To qualify as an unsuccessful work attempt, the work effort must be stopped either because of the individual's disability, or because special circumstances needed by the person to work at a substantial level ended. For example, special conditions end if the person no longer has a job coach and is not able to perform the job without the job coach support. In this circumstance, the SSA does not consider the person to have performed SGA. In making the SGA decision, the SSA claims representative looks at the amount of the beneficiary's gross earnings. If gross earnings are above the current SGA guideline, the claims representative will evaluate and apply all appropriate deductions before making the final SGA determination.

SSI PROGRAM RULES

The Supplemental Security Income program was established in 1974 to provide benefit assistance to individuals who demonstrate economic need and who are 65 or older or have a disability. The primary goals of Congress in establishing the SSI program include the following:

1. to provide a uniform, minimum income level that is at or above
    the poverty line
2. to establish uniform, national eligibility criteria and rules
3. to provide fiscal relief to the states
4. to provide efficient and effective administration

Prior to 1974, states provided public assistance to individuals with disabilities to varying degrees depending on the state. Unlike the Social Security Disability Insurance (SSDI) program, SSI is funded through the general revenues of the federal treasury. As a result, to be eligible for an SSI cash benefit, it is not necessary for a person to have a past history of employment and payroll tax contributions. Instead, eligibility for SSI is based solely on meeting specific income, resource, and disability eligibility criteria. Eligible individuals can receive both SSDI and SSI.

As previously explained, a cornerstone to meeting the disability criteria for eligibility to the SSI program is the Substantial Gainful Activity standard. Prior to July 1, 1987, the performance of SGA (monthly gross earnings over $500) after initial eligibility was established as a basis for ceasing SSI entitlement and, for many individuals, access to Medicaid as well. Addressing this severe disincentive to return to work, the Employment Opportunities for Disabled Americans Act of 1986 (P.L. 99-643) established on a permanent basis two special status benefits for SSI recipients under Section 1619 of the legislation. Section 1619A enables individuals who continue to be disabled to continue receiving an SSI cash benefit and health care coverage under Medicaid when earnings exceed the SGA level. If an SSI recipient continues to meet all eligibility requirements, when earnings exceed the SGA level but remain lower than the break-even point, he or she will automatically move into 1619A status. Eligibility for a 1619A cash benefit and Medicaid continues until earnings fall below the SGA level, at which point the person automatically moves back into 1611 status and receives a regular 1611 check, or until gross earnings exceed the break-even point, at which time the SSI cash benefit ceases. Section 1619B of the 1987 legislation provides for continued Medicaid eligibility when a person's income is too high to qualify for an SSI cash benefit but is not high enough to offset the loss of Medicaid and any publicly funded attendant care services. An individual is eligible for the 1619B protected Medicaid status only if the sole cause for SSI benefit cessation is increased earnings over the break-even point. A second criterion for 1619B status is that an individual's gross earnings fall below certain limits called threshold amounts. Earnings at or above the threshold amount are considered to be sufficient to replace the cost of Medicaid coverage. A final criterion for 1619B requires that an individual must need Medicaid in order to work. Compliance with this criterion is established through the individual's statements to the Social Security Administration regarding his or her use of Medicaid in the last 12 months, expected use within the next 12 months, or need for Medicaid if he or she becomes injured or ill within the next 12 months.

Section 1619B is an extremely important provision of the Social Security Act because it not only protects an individual's Medicaid coverage but also maintains his or her eligibility for receiving an SSI cash benefit in any future month that countable income falls below the allowable limits (the break-even point for 1619A and the current SGA guideline for 1611), provided that the individual continues to meet all other eligibility requirements for SSI. Because 1619B status maintains an active SSI case standing for an indefinite period, an individual may work for several years above the allowable levels for an SSI cash benefit and then be reinstated automatically if loss of employment or reduction of earnings below the allowable levels occurs.

Because SSI is an economic need-based program, it is intended to supplement any income or resources an individual already possesses to ensure a minimum level of income. Therefore, the dollar amount of the SSI benefit received on a monthly basis varies from person to person. In January of each year, Congress establishes the Federal Benefit Rate (FBR), which is the maximum dollar amount that an individual or couple can receive in SSI cash benefit on a monthly basis.

The amount of an individual's SSI payment may be reduced below the FBR level, on the basis of the person's earned and unearned income. The more earned or unearned income received, the greater the reduction in the SSI payment. Not all income a person receives, however, is considered in determining the amount of the benefit. The Social Security Administration allows a $20 general exclusion that is subtracted from a person's income regardless of its source. In addition to the general exclusion, a $65 earned-income disregard is subtracted from earned income. After the earned-income disregard is applied, one half of the remaining earned income is counted by the Social Security Administration in adjusting the benefit amount. The remaining amounts of earned and unearned income after exclusions are combined to determine the total countable income. This total is the dollar amount of an individual's SSI benefit reduction.

Persons receiving an SSI benefit are subject to two separate review processes to ensure continued compliance with eligibility criteria. Redeterminations are nonmedical reviews, which occur annually for persons in statuses 1611, 1619A, and 1619B. The purpose of redetermination reviews is to update nonmedical information that affects SSI eligibility and cash payment amounts. A second review process for SSI recipients is the Continuing Disability Review. The Social Security Administration is required by law to determine periodically whether a recipient continues to be disabled and is therefore eligible to continue receiving benefits.

SOCIAL SECURITY DISABILITY PROGRAM RULES

The following Social Security disability programs provide benefits to individuals with disabilities if all applicable eligibility requirements are met:

- SSDI, or Social Security Disability Insurance
- CDB, or Childhood Disability Benefits
- DWB, or Disabled Widow(er)s Benefits

All of these programs, established under Title II of the Social Security Act, are designed to supplement the income of workers and their families when the worker loses earnings from work due to retirement, disability, or death. It is important to keep in mind that the Social Security benefits are an insurance program, and, therefore, to qualify, one must meet an insured status test.

Social Security Disability Insurance is a monthly cash benefit paid to a worker or former worker who is under the age 65 and has a disabling condition. The SSDI program enables these individuals who become disabled and are unable to continue working at a substantial level to receive monthly cash benefits and Medicare insurance. To qualify for SSDI, individuals must have "insured status," meaning that they have contributed a sufficient amount to the Social Security Trust Fund through past work in employment covered by Social Security, are medically disabled according to SSA's standard of disability, and, finally, apply for the benefit.

There is no minimum age at which a person can begin receiving SSDI cash benefits on their work record. In fact, establishing eligibility for SSDI can happen quite quickly for younger people because fewer "work credits" are needed for insured status for those who become disabled before the age of 24.

Social Security Childhood Disability Benefits (CDB) are benefits paid to an adult with a disability who does not have sufficient work credits for insured status on his or her own work record but receives a Title II benefit based on a parent's insured status. To be eligible for CDB, individuals must be at least 18 years old; be disabled by SSA's definition before the age of 22; be the child of an insured worker who is either deceased, retired and collecting SSA benefits, or disabled and drawing an SSDI benefit; and be unmarried (with some exceptions). This program was previously referred to as "Disabled Adult Child," or DAC, benefits.

There are several important features of the Title II disability benefit programs to keep in mind. First, because SSDI is not based on economic need, unearned income and resources are not considered and have no bearing on eligibility or payment amount. This is a significant difference between the Title II disability programs and SSI.

Second, the monthly amount of the Title II disability benefit received by an individual depends on the level of contributions that individual made to the program (i.e., how much that person earned and how long that person worked). Therefore, the amount of the monthly cash benefit varies significantly from person to person.

Third, earnings from a job or self-employment *will* affect ongoing eligibility for the Title II benefit. For Title II disability beneficiaries, engaging in SGA-level work after eligibility is established continues to be a major factor in loss of the benefit.

Finally, unlike the SSI program, there is no provision for a gradual reduction in the cash benefit as earnings increase. Instead, a Title II beneficiary will receive either the full cash benefit in a given month or no income support at all.

To encourage individuals who receive Title II disability benefits to work, several special provisions or work incentives are provided. Two of these incentives, known as the trial work period (TWP) and extended period of eligibility (EPE), provide a graduated safety net for persons as they take steps to move from benefit support to employment and greater self-sufficiency.

Unless medical recovery is expected, individuals receiving Social Security Disability Insurance are entitled to a 9-month TWP, which provides opportunities to test work skills while maintaining full benefit checks regardless of any income earned. As SGA is not material during the trial work period, earnings over the current SGA limit will not have any impact on the benefit. The cash benefit will continue regardless of level of earnings.

The TWP begins the first month that an individual is entitled to an SSDI or CDB benefit, or files applications for disability benefits, whichever is later. Only those months during which an individual earns over the current trial work period guideline ($570 in 2003) are counted as TWP months.

The TWP ends only when an individual has performed 9 months (not necessarily consecutive) of trial work within a rolling period of 60 consecutive months. TWP months must be carefully tracked, as the 36-month EPE begins immediately after the 9-month TWP. All individuals who continue to have their original disabling condition are eligible for an EPE.

The EPE is a further extension of the safety net for beneficiaries who work. As its name suggests, the extended period of eligibility enables the beneficiary to retain eligibility or connection to the program throughout the period of 36 consecutive months. Unlike during the trial work period, the ability of the individual to perform SGA-level work is considered during the EPE and has a bearing on whether a beneficiary will receive a cash benefit in a given month. The first month of the EPE in which a beneficiary earns more than the SGA level is known as the cessation month. During the cessation month and the following 2 months, the individual will receive his or her cash benefit regardless of earnings level. For the remainder of the 36-month EPE, no cash benefits are paid for months in which the beneficiary earns more than the SGA amount. However, even in months that cash benefits are not received during the EPE, the individual's case with SSA remains open and health insurance under Medicare continues.

Following the EPE, benefit eligibility ends after the first month that a person earns more than SGA. At that point, the person's case with SSA is closed. Any subsequent disability benefit payments require either expedited reinstatement of the benefit or a new application.

As is the case during the initial eligibility process, in making SGA determinations during the EPE, the Social Security claims representative will consider any impairment-related work expenses or subsidies that the person may have. The dollar amount of IRWEs and subsidies is subtracted from an individual's gross earnings before the SGA determination is made. Once the dollar amount of IRWEs and subsidies is excluded, if the person's earnings are valued at less than the current SGA level, he or she will be determined not to be engaging in SGA and, therefore, to be eligible for a cash benefit.

Additionally, income averaging and unsuccessful work attempt may be considered during the EPE as long as the cessation month has not occurred. After an individual's first month of SGA during the extended period of eligibility, income averaging and unsuccessful work attempt can no longer be considered when deciding if earnings are substantial.

In spite of the fact that an individual may have one or more months with no cash payment during the EPE due to SGA-level earnings, as long as the individual is in the 36-month EPE, a new application will not be necessary for cash benefits to resume when earnings fall below SGA. The EPE is a safety net for beneficiaries who return to work, enabling them to keep their beneficiary status intact although they may have months when they receive no cash benefit due to SGA. Because the person continues to be eligible, cash benefits can be started again by simply informing the SSA regarding the loss of or reduction in earnings below SGA.

Given that a beneficiary may be eligible for a cash benefit during some months of the EPE and not eligible during other months, promptly reporting changes in earnings to the SSA becomes critical to minimize overpayment or underpayment.

Individuals who receive a Title II benefit based on disability are eligible for medical insurance coverage under Medicare. A 5-month waiting period from the month of disability onset must be completed before Social Security cash benefits begin. An additional 24-month waiting period (known as the Medicare Qualifying Period) after SSDI benefits begin is required before an individual is entitled to receive Medicare coverage.

Medicare has two parts: hospital insurance (Part A) and medical insurance (Part B). Hospital insurance helps pay for inpatient hospital care and certain follow-up care. This part of the Medicare program is automatic for Social Security beneficiaries upon completion of the 24-month Medicare qualifying period.

Medical insurance helps pay for doctors' services and a variety of other medical services and supplies that are not covered by hospital insurance. Medical insurance is voluntary and is financed by the monthly premiums of individuals who enroll. Enrollment occurs automatically for those receiving Social Security at the time when hospital insurance begins.

If a beneficiary chooses to purchase medical insurance, the monthly premium is deducted from the monthly Social Security cash benefit. If the person is not due a cash benefit for a particular month or months, he or she will be billed on a quarterly basis for the premium.

INCENTIVES FOR EMPLOYMENT

The legislative history pertaining to both SSI and SSDI programs shows that Congress wished to provide every opportunity and encouragement to individuals with disabilities to return to gainful employment. Although SSA has frequently promoted SSI and the Title II disability programs as "stepping stones or springboards to employment and greater economic self-sufficiency," reports on employment outcomes for beneficiaries and recipients indicate that extremely limited numbers of individuals have actually opted to return to work once disability benefits are awarded. In an effort to encourage employment for beneficiaries, the federal government and the SSA have responded during the past 30 years with legislative and regulatory changes in the SSI and Title II programs. These changes, or work incentives, are aimed at reducing the risks and costs associated with the loss of benefit support and medical services as a result of returning to work.

The goals of the work incentive programs are to assist individuals to achieve gainful employment, to increase independence, to facilitate empowerment, and to assist individuals to acquire self-support. Work incentive provisions can help people with disabilities in two significant ways: First, they can help individuals pay for services or items they need in order to work. Second, they make it feasible for individuals to maintain, or even increase, their cash benefits until they are stable in employment. The Plan for Achieving Self-Support (PASS), Impairment-Related Work Expense (IRWE), and Blind Work Expense (BWE) are several work incentives that enable people with disabilities to recover expenses they incur while working toward greater economic self-sufficiency.

Plan for Achieving Self-Support

The PASS work incentive was part of the original Supplemental Security Income program enacted by Congress in 1972 (Social Security Act Amendments, 1972). A plan for achieving self-support is an SSI work incentive under which persons with disabilities can set aside income or resources to be used to achieve specific, individualized vocational goals. A PASS can be established for education, vocational training, starting a business, or purchasing job coach and job-support services that enable a person to work. The purpose of a PASS is to increase the individual's income-producing capacity and thus to reduce reliance on government benefit support in the long run.

The income or resources used to pay for goods and services under a PASS are not counted in determining a person's eligibility for SSI or in calculating the amount of the SSI benefit that he or she will receive. By excluding this income or resources in a PASS, the individual is able to meet the income and resources test, thereby qualifying for SSI. Likewise, an individual who already receives SSI can maintain that SSI in the same amount or even receive a larger SSI benefit by setting aside his or her income or resources in a PASS. For a PASS to be approved by the SSA, the following criteria must be met:

1. The plan must be especially designed for the individual and have a designated and feasible occupational objective.
2. A specific time frame must be established for an objective to be achieved.
3. The plan must state the sources and the amounts of income or resources to be set aside to achieve the goal.
4. The plan must state how the money set aside will be spent to achieve the goal.

Impairment-Related Work Expense

An impairment-related work expense is an expense directly related to enabling a person with a disability to work, which is incurred because of the individual's physical or mental impairments and would not be incurred by unimpaired individuals in similar circumstances. The purpose of the IRWE work incentive is to enable individuals with disabilities to recover some of the costs of the expenses incurred to support their work as a result of their disability.

The SSA's list of allowable expenditures under IRWE is extensive and includes costs of adaptive equipment or specialized devices, attendant care, and special transportation costs, as well as the cost of job coach services. This work incentive applies to both SSI recipients and SSDI beneficiaries and allows for certain costs or expenses to be excluded in calculating earnings and SGA. For an

SSI recipient, deducting the cost of an IRWE from monthly gross wages increases the SSI cash payment he or she can receive. For an SSDI beneficiary, deducting an IRWE may keep monthly gross earnings below SGA and thus enable the individual to maintain SSDI eligibility. The cost of IRWEs can also be deducted from gross earnings during initial SSI and SSDI application processes, a deduction enabling an individual to meet the SGA requirement as well as the income test for SSI.

Blind Work Expense

The Blind Work Expense is a work incentive available to individuals who receive SSI because of blindness. This provision allows for the cost of work expenses to be deducted from individuals' earnings before the SSI payment amount is computed, whether or not the expenses are necessary as a result of the disability. Using the Blind Work Expense, individuals pay for expenses using their earned income. This income is not counted in determining their SSI cash benefit, allowing them to recover some part, or in some instances, all of the cost of the expense.

INCENTIVES PROVIDED THROUGH THE TICKET TO WORK AND WORK INCENTIVES IMPROVEMENT ACT OF 1999

The Ticket to Work and Work Incentives Improvement Act of 1999 (TWWIIA) was signed into law by President Clinton on December 17, 1999. At the signing, the president described the act as "one of the most important legislative advances for people with disabilities since the enactment of the Americans with Disabilities Act." The act contains numerous components. In combination, the components of TWWIIA are designed to enable beneficiaries who are interested in entering or reentering the workforce to (a) pursue their employment goals without jeopardizing their ability to provide for their basic needs, (b) maintain health care coverage throughout their period of employment, and (c) access the employment services and supports they need to acquire and maintain employment.

Several key provisions in the act are described below, including the Ticket to Work and Self-Sufficiency Program, health care incentives, and specific work incentive enhancements. Other key provisions of the act related to the development of a comprehensive work incentive support structure are discussed at a later point in this chapter.

The Ticket to Work and Self-Sufficiency Program

The Ticket to Work and Self-Sufficiency Program (TTW program) is a vocational voucher program that provides an opportunity for individuals with disabilities to exert greater choice and control of the employment services and supports they receive. This program is also intended to promote innovation and competition among agencies providing employment services for individuals with disabilities. The TTW program is a *voluntary* program in which an individual may assign a "ticket" to obtain vocational rehabilitation services, employment services, or other types of services necessary to assist him or her in obtaining or regaining employment. The individual deposits the ticket with an employment network or State Vocational Rehabilitation Agency (i.e., a qualified provider or network of providers). The employment network accepting the ticket is responsible for providing the individual with services and supports necessary to support his or her employment, as specified in an individual work plan. Most individuals between the ages of 18 and 64 who presently receive SSI or SSDI benefits are eligible to participate in the TTW program.

The TTW program began a 3-year phase-in period in February 2002. Thirteen states implemented the program then; another 20 states plus the District of Columbia began the program in November 2002; and the remaining states and territories were scheduled to implement the program 9 to 12 months after the Phase 2 states. The 13 states included in the Phase 1 rollout were Arizona, Colorado, Delaware, Florida, Illinois, Iowa, Massachusetts, New York, Oklahoma, Oregon, South Carolina, Vermont, and Wisconsin. Phase 2 rollout states were Alaska, Arkansas, Connecticut, Georgia, Indiana, Kansas, Kentucky, Louisiana, Michigan, Mississippi, Missouri, Montana, Nevada, New Hampshire, New Jersey, New Mexico, North Dakota, South Dakota, Tennessee, Virginia, and the District of Columbia.

Expanded Availability of Health-Care Services

Expanded availability of health-care services is provided for under Title II of TWWIIA. An important change to the Medicare program for working beneficiaries with disabilities significantly extends the amount of time beneficiaries who lose entitlement because of substantial work may receive premium-free Part A Medicare and premium-based Part B. The new rule, referred to as the extended period of Medicare coverage (EPMC), applies to anyone who currently has Medicare coverage based on disability benefits, provided that the disabling condition continues. Prior to the creation of the EPMC, premium-free Medicare could only be extended for 39 months after the completion of the trial work period (TWP). The new rules under TWWIIA allow this coverage to continue for at least 93 months after the TWP ends, an addition of at least 54 months of Medicare coverage. One should keep in mind that Medicare will never end before the month after the month of the termination notice, regardless of the reason benefits are being ceased.

Medicaid options available to states were also expanded under the Ticket legislation. One important provision addressed under the act relates to the Medicaid buy-in program. Medicaid buy-in first appeared as an option for states under Section 4733 of the Balanced Budget Act of 1997. The buy-in is designed to provide Medicaid to working people with disabilities, who, because of relatively high earnings, cannot qualify for Medicaid under one of the other statutory provisions. Section 4733 allows states to provide Medicaid to these individuals by creating a new optional categorically needy eligibility group.

The Medicaid buy-in program allows working individuals with disabilities to "buy in" to their state's Medicaid program by paying a premium or cost-share amount similar to the manner in which they would purchase health coverage on the private market. Any working individual with a disability that meets his or her state's specific eligibility requirements for the buy-in may enroll in the program. A person is not required to be a current or previous recipient or beneficiary of Social Security disabilities benefits or Medicaid to be eligible under the Medicaid buy-in provision. However, if a person is not receiving disability benefits from Social Security, the state must make a determination as to whether the person meets the definition of disability as defined in the Social Security Act. The fact that the individual is working will not be considered when making the disability decision for this law.

As indicated above, eligibility for the Medicaid buy-in will vary significantly from state to state given that states have a great deal of flexibility in designing their programs. States are provided with the option of using the standard income (both earned and unearned) and resource standards for the SSI program, or they may choose to establish their own income and asset limits for the buy-in.

Many of the states currently operating buy-in programs have opted to establish more liberal income and resource criteria for the program. Examples of these income provisions include the exclusion of unearned income and/or income from a spouse, and the application of earned income disregards for employment and other disability-related expenses necessary for work.

In addition to increasing the asset limit from the current $2,000 figure for an individual, a number of states have also established an opportunity for resources to be accumulated in approved accounts for retirement, medical savings, and independence. A concern related to the accumulation of resources in such accounts relates to the ability of individuals to access health care under the regular Medicaid program in the event that employment and, therefore, access to the buy-in is lost. Some states have addressed this issue by including a provision for individuals to continue receiving Medicaid for a specific period of time following termination of employment to allow for a spend-down of assets below the limits for the state's regular Medicaid program.

In addition to establishing their own income and resource standards for the program, states have the option to establish and require a payment of premiums or other cost-shares on a sliding fee scale for access to the program. The premium rate is required by law to be structured according to income. A provision under the Ticket to Work and Work Incentives Improvement Act of 1990 provides that states may require payment of 100% of the premium for individuals with incomes over 250% but below 450% of the federal poverty level, except that the premium cannot exceed 7.5% of the individual's income.

Other Medicaid options made available to states under the TWWIIA include the following: States can choose to provide Medicaid to employed individuals who participate in the Medicaid buy-in program but later lose their eligibility due to medical improvement, but continue to have severe medically determinable impairments. Additionally, states may apply for grants to run a time-limited demonstration project to extend Medicaid to working individuals with potentially severe disabilities who, without health care, would likely progress to disability status.

While the Balanced Budget Act of 1997 and the TWWIIA of 1999 established and liberalized options for states in the development of Medicaid buy-in programs, it is important to keep in mind that these provisions are optional and not mandatory. In other words, it is up to the individual states to develop and submit an amendment to the Health Care Financing Agency for approval of a Medicaid buy-in. Medicaid buy-in programs involve an amendment to the state's Medicaid plan. Requirements for approval of the amendment and buy-in program are that Medicaid buy-in plans must be statewide and must provide the same comprehensive health-care package as the state's regular Medicaid plan.

Work Incentive Enhancements

Work incentive enhancements are addressed under Title 1 of the Ticket legislation and provide protections from Continuing Disability Reviews (CDRs) for some Title II beneficiaries, as well as for individuals who have a ticket "in use" under the Ticket to Work and Self-Sufficiency Program.

Additionally, the legislation makes available an important new work incentive called Expedited Reinstatement, or EXR. EXR, which became effective in January 2001, is a way to return more easily to SSI or Social Security disability benefits when work is significantly reduced or stopped because of an individual's original disabling condition.

EXR enables individuals who meet all of the necessary criteria to return to disability benefits more quickly and without filing a new application. While waiting for the EXR request to be processed, individuals may receive up to 6 consecutive months of provisional benefits and health insurance coverage. Additionally, after being paid 24 months of reinstated benefits, Title II beneficiaries are given a new trial work period, extended period of eligibility, and another 60-month period in which to request EXR if benefits are lost due to SGA-level work.

ISSUES, OBSTACLES, AND CHALLENGES

Current SSI Disincentives to Employment

Legislative changes made under the Employment Opportunities for Disabled Americans Act of 1986 and the Ticket to Work and Work Incentives Improvement Act of 1999 have eliminated many of the disincentives to work for SSI recipients. Because work activity is no longer a consideration for cessation of SSI eligibility, a person receiving SSI is assured of an overall increase in net income as earnings increase. The ability to move freely between the 1611 and 1619A statuses as earned income fluctuates likewise provides a financial safety net in the event that employment stability is threatened. Section 1619B provides assurance that medical services under Medicaid will be protected despite the fact that cash benefits are suspended when earnings exceed the break-even point. Additionally, for individuals in many states, once eligibility for continued Medicaid is exhausted under 1619B, health care coverage may be accessed through a Medicaid buy-in program. Despite these significant improvements in the SSI program, several barriers to employment remain unaddressed.

The SGA consideration remains a key criterion in establishing initial eligibility for SSI benefits. An individual must first prove that he or she is unable to work at the SGA level to qualify for benefits. This initial emphasis on limited work capacity forces individuals to limit any current work activity to qualify and may in fact provide an inaccurate message to recipients that future earnings at the SGA level will endanger their ability to maintain SSI support.

A second concern for SSI recipients returning to work relates to the requirement of additional medical reviews precipitated by increasing earnings. Although an increase in earnings will not result in termination of SSI due to SGA, it may indirectly result in the loss of benefits due to a determination of medical recovery. Because they recognize that movement into 1619 status due to increased earnings may precipitate a review of their medical files, individuals receiving SSI may choose to limit earnings to avoid further scrutiny of their disability status and a potential loss of eligibility. The CDR protection for Title II beneficiaries under TWWIIA was not extended to SSI recipients.

Current Social Security Disability Benefit Disincentives to Employment

Despite the issues just addressed, the incentives for SSI recipients to engage in work far outweigh those provided to Title II disability beneficiaries. The risk of reduction in overall net income is a justified concern for these beneficiaries given that SGA continues to be a primary factor not only in establishing initial eligibility, but also in maintaining eligibility after benefits are awarded. The average SSDI cash benefit in 2003 was $834. A beneficiary may lose this monthly cash benefit if gross monthly earnings are determined to be in excess of the SGA guideline following completion of the trial work period.

During the past 13 years, the SSA has taken several steps to diminish the disincentives surrounding SGA determinations. In 1990, SSA implemented a change in program rules that increased the level of gross earnings that constitute SGA from $300 to $500 a month. This change resulted in limited improvement to the system given that the $200 increase accounted solely for the growth in wages since 1980, when the SGA level had last been adjusted. A second proposed rule change in 1990, which was not implemented, was a plan to index the SGA level to average wage growth in future years. The failure to implement such an index was particularly damaging, in view of the subsequent increase in the federal minimum wage level. Subsequent program rule changes resulted in a further increase of the SGA guideline to $700 in July of 1999, and, finally, in January 2001, a change providing for an annual adjustment of the SGA guideline to reflect wage growth.

In spite of these enhancements, Title II disability beneficiaries still face the possibility of benefit loss due to SGA. Clearly, the most effective resolution to the dilemma is removal of the SGA criteria altogether. A legislative change proposed in 1989 suggested the removal of the SGA disincentive by allowing SSDI beneficiaries who return to work and earn above the SGA level to be considered "disabled and working." Persons qualifying for this status, who would otherwise lose cash benefits due to SGA, would be eligible for cash and Medicaid benefits under Section 1619 of the SSI program. The formula used to adjust monthly cash benefits as earnings increase for SSI recipients would apply to persons in disabled and working status. This proposal, intended to be a parallel to the Section 1619 provisions of the SSI program, was not adopted by Congress.

This tremendous work disincentive continues to cause concern among disability advocates on a national level, and as a result of concerted advocacy efforts, Title III of the TWWIIA of 1999 requires that SSA conduct a specific demonstration study on the impact of instituting a cash benefit offset ($1 reduction in benefits for every $2 earned) for the SSDI program. While not eliminating the SGA requirement entirely, this approach would provide for a gradual reduction in benefits as earnings increase over the current SGA guideline.

Arguably, one of the greatest obstacles to employment for both SSI and SSDI beneficiaries is the complexity of the disability programs and the misinformation and misconceptions that surround them. Concern regarding both the real and perceived disincentives in both programs is readily expressed by individuals with disabilities and their families. Beneficiaries must carefully consider the risk factors involved when weighing the uncertainties of success in employment against the consistent support of benefit income. Their willingness to use the work incentives and return to work depends in large part on their perceptions and understanding of the work incentives available to them. The system of Social Security regulations, policies, and procedures as they have evolved are complex and confusing. For most, mastery of the regulations and system is an unattainable goal. Many of these individuals are hesitant to return to work not only because they are unaware or unsure of the work incentive options but also because they lack confidence in their ability to advocate for resolution of potential benefit complications caused by increased earnings.

The critical need for complete and accurate benefit information and assistance is addressed in Section 121 of the Ticket to Work and Work Incentives Improvement Act. Specifically, SSA is directed to (a) establish a comprehensive work incentive support structure that includes as primary components an internal corps of work incentive specialists within SSA, (b) establish a network of community-based benefits planning and assistance agencies, and (c) establish a protection and advocacy grant program for beneficiaries of Social Security.

The SSA's awareness of and concern with the problems created by lack of understanding or misinformation about the benefit programs and work incentives has been evidenced in past years by its efforts to build effective working relations with advocacy groups and service provider organizations. Well in advance of the Ticket to Work legislation's requirement that the SSA develop an internal corps of trained work incentive specialists, the Social Security Administration had positioned work incentive liaisons in each local SSA district office across the country. In many localities, these individuals have served as a primary contact for rehabilitation professionals and agencies who work with people with disabilities and have been a valuable source of information regarding the work incentives. A significant drawback to this effort, however, has been the limited amount of time and resources that the work incentive liaisons have been able to devote to their additional work incentive job assignment given their other job duties.

A second approach to providing work incentive information and support was tested by the SSA in its piloting of an employment support representative, or ESR, position in 2001. A total of 32 field staff serving as ESRs received intensive training in Social Security work incentives and other SSA programs that can help beneficiaries make their transition to careers. Following training, ESR duties included processing disability work issue caseloads, serving as a technical resource for other SSA employees, and providing information and training about SSA's employment support programs through outreach to SSDI and SSI beneficiaries with disabilities who want to work or keep working, as well as their families, advocates, service providers, other organizations who assist people with disabilities, and possible employers.

In spite of a November 2001 report recommending that the ESR position be established as permanent and implemented on a nationwide basis, the SSA recently adopted a plan to designate existing field staff as work incentives specialists. The work incentives specialists will be delegated their new work incentive duties in addition to their existing duties. It is anticipated that this approach will once again make it difficult for these field staff to be responsive to the needs of beneficiaries and other community members.

As the SSA takes steps to develop its internal cadre of work incentive specialists, another key work incentive support component has made tremendous strides in delivering information and direct support to beneficiaries. Authorized by Section 121 of the Ticket Act, 116 Benefits Planning, Assistance, and Outreach (BPAO) programs are providing services to SSA beneficiaries in all 50 states and five territories. Collectively, the 116 BPAO projects employ over 450 benefit specialists and have served over 80,000 individuals since implementation in early 2001.

The purpose of the BPAO initiative is to provide SSA disability beneficiaries with accurate and timely information about SSA work incentives and other federal efforts to remove regulatory and programmatic barriers to employment for persons with disabilities. Trained benefits specialists in local BPAO programs work with individual beneficiaries to explain the myriad of regulations, provisions, work incentives, and special programs that complicate an individual's decision to enter or reenter the workforce. The BPAO programs are not funded to make decisions for individuals or tell them what to do. Instead, they allow beneficiaries to make their own informed decisions based on complete and accurate information. In addition, they support individuals who choose to enter employment by assisting them to comply with all relevant regulations and reporting procedures.

The BPAO program has the potential of assisting hundreds of thousands of beneficiaries by allowing Ticket participants to make informed choices about their employment and health care coverage. However, if beneficiaries receive incomplete or inaccurate information from BPAOs, it can have dire consequences for the individual's independence and well-being.

Protection and Advocacy for Beneficiaries of Social Security

Under a program authorized by Section 1150 of the Ticket to Work and Work Incentives Improvement Act, the Social Security Administration awarded grants to Protection and Advocacy Systems (P&As) in every state, in the District of Columbia, in five U.S. territories, and to the P&A for Native Americans. The Protection and Advocacy for Beneficiaries of Social Security (PABSS) programs are designed to assist beneficiaries with disabilities in obtaining information and advice about receiving vocational rehabilitation and employment services, as well as advocacy and other services that a disabled beneficiary may need to secure or regain gainful employment. In addition, Section 411.605 requires that Employment Networks vendored to provide services to Ticket holders must inform SSI and SSDI beneficiaries of the availability of assistance from P&As in dispute resolution. Disputes may focus on issues such as Ticket assignment or reassignment, Individual Work Plan development, legal issues, or related topics.

FINAL THOUGHTS

The information provided in this chapter provides a basic framework for understanding the current program rules and regulations governing the Social Security disability benefit programs, as well as the various incentives and supports available to promote a smooth transition to work and greater economic self-sufficiency for people with disabilities. While building awareness and understanding of these programs is an important first step, it is critical to remember that successful use of work incentives and smooth benefit transitions ultimately depend on cooperative working relationships between the Social Security Administration, people with disabilities, Benefits Planning, Assistance and Outreach Projects, and other rehabilitation professionals.

REFERENCES

Employment Opportunities for Disabled Americans Act of 1986, 42 U.S.C. 1382 *et seq.*, 100, 3575–3580.
Federal Register. (1989, April). Washington, DC: U.S. Government Printing Office.
Omnibus Budget Reconciliation Act of 1987, 101 Stat. 1330 (December 22, 1987).
Omnibus Budget Reconciliation Act of 1989, 42 U.S.C. 1396 *et seq.*, 103, 2253–2273.

Social Security Act Amendments of 1972, 86 Stat. 1329 (October 30, 1972).

Social Security Act Amendments of 1980, 94 Stat. 444 (June 9, 1980).

Social Security Administration. (1993, Spring). Shifting the cost of self-pay for SSI workers in supported employment. *Social Security Bulletin, 56*(1), 45.

Social Security Administration. (1994, September). *Developing a world-class employment strategy for people with disabilities.* Washington, DC: Author.

Ticket to Work and Work Incentives Improvement Act of 1999, 106 U.S.C. 113 Stat. 1860.

U.S. Department of Health and Human Services. (1985, May). *Program operations manual system.* Washington, DC: Author.

CHAPTER 18

Using One-Stop Career Centers for Employment Services and Supports

Beth A. Bader

LEARNING GOALS

Upon completion of this chapter, the reader will be able to

- describe how the key principles that guide the implementation of the Workforce Investment Act of 1998 apply to serving people with disabilities in One-Stop Career Centers

- describe the three levels of service delivery at One-Stop Career Centers and identify which services would most likely be useful to individuals with intellectual disabilities

- describe ways in which One-Stop Career Centers can be used by individuals with intellectual disabilities

- describe the components of One-Stop Career Centers that are successful in serving individuals with disabilities

- identify issues that may present as barriers to participation in One-Stop services by individuals with intellectual disabilities and describe strategies that can be used to deal with the barriers

S ince the passage of the Workforce Investment Act of 1998 (WIA), people with disabilities have been "testing the waters" to see if they can get the training and support needed to become employed or better employed through the One-Stop Career Center system. As with any service system, some people have been successful using One-Stop services and others have not. The purpose of this chapter is to provide a realistic view of what services people with developmental disabilities can expect from One-Stop Career Centers and how they can use the One-Stop services as part of the employment process.

An overview of the principles that guide service delivery in One-Stop Career Centers, information on how One-Stops are operated under the mandates of WIA, and specific services that can be readily used by people with intellectual disabilities are included in this chapter. Two case examples that illustrate how One-Stop Centers are being accessed are also included to assist people with intellectual disabilities, their families, and service providers in their use of One-Stop Centers in their home communities.

EMERGENCE OF ONE-STOP CAREER CENTERS UNDER THE WORKFORCE INVESTMENT ACT

One-Stop Career Centers emerged in the early 1990s in response to concerns that the nation's workforce was not being adequately prepared or trained to compete in an increasingly technology-based marketplace (Gilson, 2000). The U.S. Department of Labor (DOL) developed a One-Stop Career Center initiative to meet the needs of both the employers who required a workforce trained in current technologies, and job seekers who needed training or retraining to be able to compete in the employment marketplace. It was not until August 7, 1998, that Senate Bill 1385 was passed by Congress, finally creating what is now the Workforce Investment Act of 1998. Known as WIA, this act set the stage for One-Stop Career Centers to become the focal point of workforce development reform across the United States. One-Stop Centers were intended to be a single location where an applicant would find all of the information needed to choose an occupation, find access to training, be placed in a job, and obtain all of the public services necessary to continue in employment (Sar Levitan Center for Social Policy Studies, 1998).

Training and employment programs under the U.S. Department of Labor preceded the development of the current One-Stop Career system. The Manpower Development Training Act of 1962, the Comprehensive Employment and Training Act of 1973, and the Job Training Partnership Act of 1982 were all aimed at addressing the issues of an economy changing from a focus on production to one of automation and technology. None of these initiatives excluded people with disabilities, but they did have eligibility criteria that limited the scope of services that were available as well as access to the full array of programs.

Individuals with disabilities have been given the opportunity through WIA to receive the same employment services as the general public, but the impact of these services will affect employment outcomes only if these individuals have access to, and choose to use, the programs within the One-Stop service delivery system. It is widely acknowledged that people with disabilities are in need of the same services and supports as any other job seeker, but they have historically been relegated to using only the employment services offered by disability service provider agencies. Once a person is labeled as having a disability, it usually means a lifetime of using specialized services based on disability diagnosis and level of functioning, not the type of service that is needed. Not only have people with disabilities been consigned to specialized services, they have been prevented from using the generic employment service system because of established or assumed eligibility criteria. What makes the service system created under WIA different is that there are no exclusionary disability eligibility criteria for One-Stop Career Center use. This has set the stage for people with disabilities to have the potential of getting in the same "front door" to employment services and supports as their nondisabled peers in the general public (Presidential Task Force on Employment of Adults with Disabilities, 2000).

KEY PRINCIPLES OF WIA
FOR PEOPLE WITH DISABILITIES

Contained within the WIA are the following four principles that guide the implementation of One-Stop Career Centers.

• *Universality.* The intent of the WIA is for all services available through a One-Stop Career Center to be accessible to everyone who needs them. For example, people with disabilities should be able to use the same information resources and services as their nondisabled peers. Similarly, non–English-speaking citizens must be able to access the services without language being a barrier. Through the One-Stop Center, it is the intent of WIA for every individual to be able to "obtain job search assistance as well as labor market information about job vacancies, the skills needed for occupations in demand, wages paid, and other relevant employment trends in the local, regional and national economy" (Workforce Investment Act Implementation Taskforce Office, 1998).
• *Customer choice.* Under the WIA, individuals are to be "empowered to obtain the services and skills they need to enhance their employment opportunities" (Workforce Investment Act Implementation Taskforce Office, 1998). Through self-directed use of available core services and being able to choose the support services and qualified training programs that best meet their needs, customers of One-Stop Career Centers have increased control in the planning and implementation of their employment and training programs.
• *Integration of services.* "Multiple employment and training programs will be integrated at the 'street level' through the One-Stop delivery system" (Workforce Investment Act Implementation Taskforce Office, 1998). Although not all of the 154 employment programs that existed in 1994 have been pulled under the One-Stop umbrella, those that can make the most difference in the lives of the greatest numbers of people have been consolidated. Attempts have been made at integrating service delivery, but the funding mechanisms remain separate for most programs.

• *Accountability for results.* The WIA specifically identifies performance standards that One-Stop Career Center operators, as well as training service providers, must meet to continue to receive funding. These indicators include job placement rates, earnings, retention in employment, skill gains, and credentials earned (Workforce Investment Act Implementation Taskforce Office, 1998). The first full year of collecting this information from the One-Stop systems within each state did not occur until 2001.

Although One-Stop Career Centers from their inception were never targeted toward meeting the employment needs specifically of individuals with disabilities, there are stipulations within Section 188 of WIA (nondiscrimination assurances) that require states to provide assurance that people with disabilities, including those with intellectual disabilities, will not be discriminated against within its One-Stop service system.

There are guidelines contained within WIA that require states to make their One-Stop systems universally accessible to all citizens, but it is left to the governor of each state to set the policies that govern the extent to which universality is expected and achieved. A governor may choose, because of budget constraints, to establish very narrow eligibility requirements for intensive and training level services. These services may be further limited if the definition of eligibility is narrowed to require that an individual have the aptitude for a successful employment outcome in a specific field before training commences. This would be a barrier for many individuals with disabilities who, when put in a standardized testing situation, would have difficulty scoring high enough in any area to show a significant level of job aptitude. Nor is it likely that these individuals have had a chance to demonstrate their potential for success in employment settings without having received the necessary training and support that would be available through intensive and training services. Therefore, people with disabilities may be able to get in the front door of a One-Stop Center, but the policies developed may not require that the programs have unrestricted eligibility requirements or be provided in such a way as to be useful to them in obtaining employment.

Since the passage and implementation of WIA, One-Stop system coordination among agencies occurs at the federal, state, and local levels. The federal agencies designated under the WIA include the Department of Labor, the Department of Education, the Department of Health and Human Services, and the Department of Housing and Urban Development. Coordination is also encouraged under the WIA with the Department of Agriculture, Department of Transportation, and AmeriCorps (Maguire, 2000). Notably, the Social Security Administration was not mentioned in the WIA, but it has figured prominently in a number of cooperative ventures with the DOL that influence the service delivery of One-Stop Career Centers (Workforce Investment Act Implementation Taskforce Office, 1998).

At the state level, the governor is responsible for appointing a Workforce Investment Board on which he or she sits as a member. In addition to the governor, the board includes two members of each chamber of the state legislature and other appointed representatives, with a majority being representatives of the business sector. The governor also designates local workforce investment areas within his or her state, taking into consideration factors such as consistency with labor market areas (Workforce Investment Act Implementation Taskforce Office, 1998). A local elected official sits on the board, as well as representatives of educational providers, labor organizations, community service providers (including disability service providers), economic development agencies, and local representatives of each of the required partners.

It is the local Workforce Investment Board (WIB) that selects the One-Stop providers and eligible providers of training services. Selection of One-Stop providers is done through a competitive process. Both public and private providers can apply to become One-Stop operators, or a number of agencies can make application together as a consortium (Workforce Investment Act Implementation Taskforce Office, 1998). All mandatory partners and other agencies that become partners within each One-Stop system are required to have in place a memorandum of understanding (MOU) with the local WIB that outlines the responsibility of the partner agency (Workforce Investment Act Final Rule, 2000). The topics that the MOU covers include the job search services that the partner will provide, referral relationships, "as well as policies covering co-location in One-Stop Career Centers, cost allocation, performance management and conflict resolution" (Funaro & Dixon, 2002, p. 3). WIA requires at least one physical One-Stop Career Center in each workforce investment area. Because the number of designated areas in each state varies, there exists a need to provide access to One-Stop Centers for individuals who may not live within easy travel distance to a center. Service coverage is usually provided to less populated areas through One-Stop satellite centers.

SERVICES OFFERED THROUGH ONE-STOP CAREER CENTERS

It is explicitly stated within WIA that One-Stop Career Centers are to provide three levels of services: core, intensive, and training (Silverstein, 2000). Table 18.1 lists the services that are to be provided at each of the levels (Workforce Investment Act of 1998). Although the legislation designates which services are to be included at the core level, service availability becomes less clear at the intensive and training levels. WIA has left it to local Workforce Investment Boards to determine how individuals move from one level to the next among the core, intensive, and training levels in One-Stop Centers (U.S. General Accounting Office, 2001). Each governor-appointed state Workforce Investment Board is responsible for setting the policies that ensure access to all three levels of One-Stop service delivery. Yet the actual operation of One-Stop Career Centers and the distribution of funds are left to the discretion of the locally created WIBs. This creates the possibility that access to programs within One-Stop Career Centers could vary from state to state and from one One-Stop to another within any given state (Gilson, 2000).

TABLE 18.1
One-Stop Levels of Service

Core Services	Intensive Services	Training
Eligibility determination	Diagnostic testing	Individuals use their Individual Training Accounts (ITAs) at an "approved" educational or training program of their choice
Intake/orientation	Development of individual employment plans	
Initial assessment		
Job search/placement assistance	Group counseling, individual counseling, and career planning	Occupational skills training
Career counseling	Case management	On-the-job training
Provide labor market information	Short-term prevocational services	Skills upgrading
Other information: training providers, performance outcomes, One-Stop information, unemployment insurance, support services		Adult education
		Customized training for employers
		Training services must be directly linked to occupations that are in demand in the local area

CHOOSING TO USE GENERIC RATHER THAN DISABILITY-SPECIFIC EMPLOYMENT SERVICES

People with intellectual and other developmental disabilities seeking employment services have traditionally been referred to vocational rehabilitation, private disability employment providers, or mental health/mental retardation service systems. They have traditionally been excluded from the programs that the general public uses to seek training and employment services. There are at least two reasons that can be identified for this underrepresentation. First, providers are thought to need special knowledge and skills to be able to work successfully with a disabled population (Berkowitz, 1987; Schriner, Rumrill, & Parlin, 1995). Generic employment service providers, such as technical or vocational schools, community colleges, and temporary employment agencies often serve individuals with nonvisible disabilities, but do not know it because of nondisclosure on the part of the job seeker. Thus, because of lack of awareness on their part, generic service providers might believe that they could not meet the needs of clients with disabilities, or that the disability-related problems that might be encountered would be beyond the scope of their regular service delivery.

Second, available public funding has been delegated, for the most part, to disability-specific employment services, with state Vocational Rehabilitation agencies receiving the largest mix of federal and state dollars, accompanied by the expectation that it serve people eligible under the Rehabilitation Act of 1973, as amended in 1998 (Berkowitz, 1987). Even within the WIA legislation, Vocational Rehabilitation is the only disability-related employment entity to be identified as a mandated "partner agency" to be represented on state and local WIBs.

One of the cornerstones of the WIA legislation is choice (Presidential Task Force on Employment of Adults with Disabilities, 1999). WIA gives people with disabilities the ability to choose between receiving services from the traditional disability service system and the array of services and supports used by the nondisabled public when seeking jobs. Lack of choice in what services are desired and delivered by providers specifically selected by the customer has historically been a barrier in the disability service delivery system (Racino, 1998). The mechanisms that have been used for the allocation of federal and state funds for employment services have limited the scope of those services and the pool of potential service providers. With the implementation of WIA, customer choice, inclusion, and self-determination have become possible for many people with disabilities who may no longer have to depend on a specialized service system to obtain employment.

Vocational Rehabilitation and the Employment Rate of People with Disabilities

With the industrialization of the United States at the beginning of the 20th century came public policies that segregated people with disabilities away from their indigenous communities and placed many of them into institutions (Scotch, 2001). World Wars I and II marked "superficial advancement" (Mackelprang & Salsgiver, 1999, p. 40) of people with disabilities in the sense that the passage of federal rehabilitation legislation produced money for treatment of veterans disabled by the wars in preparation for employment outside of institutional settings. Scotch (2001) comments that "while the importance of institutions has waned over the past four decades, segregated programs persist and a separate community of people with disabilities continue to be reinforced by 'special' service strategies and the stigma that pervades our culture" (p. 389). The federal- and state-funded vocational rehabilitation system that continues to exist in the United States is an example of this.

Berkowitz (1987) maintains that vocational rehabilitation and other disability programs are locked into an institutional structure that has proved resistant to change, "even though the programs have failed to serve those they were intended to help" (p. 10). Scotch (2001) points out that vocational rehabilitation has remained isolated from income support programs and that effective relationships never existed among the various disability programs. He further maintains that even though Congress was given the expectation that unemployed individuals with disabilities would enter or reenter the workforce after being provided with services, few beneficiaries of income maintenance programs have gone to work through state Vocational Rehabilitation programs.

Major changes were attempted in the mid-1980s when "the philosophy that provided the foundation for day and employment services for individuals with severe disabilities shifted from support of facility-based employment toward integrated, community-based employment with supports" (Butterworth & Kiernan, 1996, p. 245). This began with the introduction of supported employment as one of the options available to people with disabilities, especially those with severe disabilities who had not achieved success within the traditional vocational rehabilitation service delivery system (Butterworth & Kiernan, 1996; Wehman, 1988). Unfortunately, funding at the federal and state levels has continued to be allocated to the more traditional, short-term service model, rather than to supported employment that provides long-term supports that may be needed at any point during the career of a person with a disability (Wehman, 1988). Even though supported employment has increased employment service options for individuals with disabilities, it is still a specialized, nongeneric service requiring specialized funding resources.

Alternatives to State Vocational Rehabilitation Services

Recommendations have been made as to what is needed as an alternative to traditional vocational rehabilitation services in order to impact the unemployment rate of people with all types of disabilities. The National Choice Demonstration, conducted under the auspices of the Rehabilitation Services Administration of the U.S. Department of Education from 1993 to 1998, examined strategies to increase the role of informed choice by people with disabilities in the rehabilitation employment process. Callahan (2000), in his qualitative evaluation of the project, reported that across the seven demonstration sites, 3,148 persons with disabilities received services. Sixty-six percent of those individuals became successfully employed as a result of using choice-based services (i.e., control of resources, control of selecting providers, control in targeting outcomes, control of deciding what is relevant) rather than the traditional services provided by state Vocational Rehabilitation agencies. Eleven percent of the successfully employed group chose self-employment, which exceeds the percentage of self-employed persons in traditional vocational rehabilitation programs, as well as the percentage of self-employed persons in the general public. In his reflections on the meaning of choice, Callahan (2000) states that "choice goes beyond choosing providers and controlling resources; it also involves determining the degree of privacy, disclosure, outside participation and personal effort one wants to embrace in order to become employed" (p. 1).

Barnow and King (2000) recommend that employment and training programs should focus on occupational training rather than immediate employment, and that the training provided should be intensive rather than short term. They further state that "Programs should offer a full range of supportive services as part of their program mix" (p. 339). This would include individualized case management and various postemployment services provided when participants require and choose to use the services (Barnow & King, 2000). West (1996) suggests that money should follow the consumer as he or she moves from one service option to another through the use of vouchers redeemed by the provider. Service vouchers are thought to put more control in the hands of consumers to be able to choose the types of work environments and support methods they want. Finally, rehabilitation or employment services must prepare and promote diverse work settings for people with disabilities. Daly (2001) states that the workforce in America is made up of people of diverse racial and ethnic backgrounds that must be recognized, and seen not for their differences, but rather "for the improvement of performance and efficiency that can also result by including people with disabilities (PWD) rather than excluding them based on their differences" (p. 29).

ISSUES AND POTENTIAL BARRIERS TO SERVING PEOPLE WITH DISABILITIES

Through the WIA and its One-Stop Career Center system, there is the potential that the recommendations made by Barnow and King (2000), West (1996), and Daly (2001), as well as those contained in the evaluation of the National Choice Demonstration (Callahan, 2000), can be met using the same employment services as those available to the general public. One-Stop Career Centers can either be a widely used employment resource that upholds the values of inclusion, choice, and diversity, or it can remain a conduit for traditional, specialized disability employment services that have had only limited success in impacting the employment rate of people with disabilities.

Kregel (1999) voices concern that emphasis to date has focused almost entirely on the physical accessibility of One-Stop systems, with very little emphasis being placed on ensuring that personnel are knowledgeable about the needs of people with disabilities. A nationwide survey of One-Stop Centers to determine their accessibility status and the ways the workforce development system under WIA is serving people with disabilities was done by Storen, Dixon, and Funaro (2002). Of the 175 One-Stop managers and operators from 36 states who responded to the study's Internet survey, 94% stated that their One-Stop Center was physically accessible, but far fewer had fully accessible computer workstations (55%) and sign language interpretation or alternative format of written materials (37%) available. Surprisingly, 85% of the respondents to the survey received frontline staff training on serving people with disabilities, and 90% received policy statements on how people with disabilities should be served. What is not known from this survey, which had a response rate of only 16%, is the type of training that was received and whether it was specific to assisting individuals with disabilities in obtaining employment.

In a study done by Funaro and Dixon (2002), 80% of survey respondents agreed that most people with disabilities entering the One-Stop system are referred to the state Vocational Rehabilitation agency or to other disability-specific agencies. The authors postulate that this could be due to Vocational Rehabilitation's protectiveness over its clients or to the belief that disability agencies are most qualified to serve people with disabilities.

Bennici, Mangum, and Sum (2000) express their concern that "WIA's primary emphasis seems to be on a work-first strategy and relatively short-term training" (p. 42) that will likely have a very limited effect in raising postprogram earnings of One-Stop participants. There may be a focus in the One-Stop system on getting participants jobs rather than assisting them in preparing for occupations that are part of a career path. Farley, Schriner, and Roessler (1988) have found that individuals with disabilities have little work experience, limited information about occupations, and few opportunities to make career decisions. Thus, participants with disabilities who come to the One-Stop Center looking for different employment or increased earnings may find only another job unrelated to their skills and interests.

Although it is too soon since the initiation of the One-Stop system under WIA to accurately document use rates by people with disabilities, there is concern that One-Stop Centers and the program services that are available through them are not widely known. One of the results of the Funaro and Dixon (2002) study was that One-Stop managers and operators ranked outreach and marketing low on the list of issues that are important in serving participants with disabilities. For the One-Stop system to be successful in providing employment resources needed by people with disabilities as well as the general public, there needs to be improved outreach (Cheney, 2001). After surveying businesses in six communities in the United States, Cheney further recommends that employers need to know how to access One-Stop Career Center services.

HOW ONE-STOP CAREER CENTERS CAN BE USED BY PEOPLE WITH INTELLECTUAL DISABILITIES

 ## CASE EXAMPLE: HERB

Herb has recently returned to his community's sheltered workshop after working for the past 6 years in a small manufacturing company. The company that he worked for was recently bought by a large corporation. Two weeks ago, Herb and all of his fellow workers received a "pink slip" in their paycheck envelope. A coworker told Herb what the note said and explained what it meant. The company had no human resource manager, so there was no one but the president of the company available to provide information as to what the employees could do. And all that the president could do was shake his head as he drove off the company grounds for the last time.

For 5 of the past 6 years, Herb has lived in his own apartment, where his rent and utility bills are sometimes more than half of his monthly income. Although he has tried to save money, in reality he has been living paycheck to paycheck. At first, his elderly parents were very opposed to his

leaving the sheltered workshop, but his supported employment job coach helped them work through their fears, and before supported employment services ended, both Herb and his parents were very pleased with his community-based job. When he called his parents the evening after he received his layoff notice from his employer, his dad's first response was to tell Herb to go to the sheltered workshop the next Monday and see if they would take him back. This probably was somewhat of a "panic response," because Herb's parents also lived on a very limited income and had depleted all of their savings months earlier. They knew that they were in no position to help their son financially. With very little paperwork or procedural requirements, Herb began employment at the workshop the following Tuesday.

Unfortunately, the County Board of Mental Retardation and Developmental Disabilities had no funds available to fund supported employment services for any new or "reopened" customer until the following fiscal year. Herb's case manager at the workshop knew this, but she also knew that there might be an alternative through state Vocational Rehabilitation (VR) services. The case manager called the county VR office and was told to tell Herb to visit One-Stop A, where a VR counselor would open or reopen his case file. Herb doesn't read, so he never knew that the building he passed every day on his way to his old job was a One-Stop Career Center, a place where anyone could walk in and get information about getting a job.

When Herb entered One-Stop A, the receptionist asked how he could be of assistance. Within 15 minutes, a VR counselor came to the waiting room after being called by the receptionist, introduced herself, and asked Herb to follow her. On the way to her office, she pointed out the resource room—a large room with many computers, a few telephones, and lots of written signs and brochures hanging on the walls. After getting some general information from Herb, the VR counselor told him that not only could he apply for VR services while he was at the One-Stop, but he could also receive other help because he was a dislocated worker (people who are laid off from their jobs, a designated special population under WIA). Dislocated workers are entitled to services under WIA that are coordinated by workforce development specialists (staff paid by WIA funds, sometimes also known as case managers or WIA staff). The VR counselor completed the VR application and then went across the hall and spoke to a workforce development specialist (WDS) who immediately walked over to meet Herb.

The WDS asked Herb if he had been to the resource room and tried searching for job openings using the computers. Herb said no. He was directed to go to the resource room and check back with the WDS before he left the One-Stop. Herb went to the room and sat in front of a computer, not having any idea what to do next. After about half an hour, a resource room staff person noticed Herb and asked if he needed assistance. At that point, Herb was pretty overwhelmed and couldn't explain why he was sitting there. The resource room staff person asked Herb if he needed

a job, and from the information that he gave her, she was able to figure out that he was someone who needed assistance and who had a disability. So the resource room staff person called the One-Stop's disability resource specialist.

Now, it might appear that Herb was getting the runaround, but his experience is really what should happen at One-Stops with any customer. A person walks in and is asked what he or she needs. If they ask for a certain person or office, they are directed to that specific provider. Most "partners" in a One-Stop want to make sure that customers know exactly what is available, so they want to link people with One-Stop staff, the specialists, who are responsible for directing people to first try and see if they can find the information they need using the self-service resource room. If further assistance is needed, a WDS is called, or in the case of an individual with an apparent disability, a disability resource specialist (if the One-Stop has such a designated staff person) is asked to meet with the customer. All of this can occur within a very short amount of time and usually on the same day that the customer walks in the door of the One-Stop.

Because Herb is a dislocated worker, he is entitled to training to learn skills that are needed by employers with job openings in the area. But before he can access the funds that can pay for this training, he must try and see if he can get a job on his own by using the resource room. The resource room and initial meeting with staff to determine what is needed are considered to be core services. If Herb is unable to get reemployed through the use of core services, a WDS will do an assessment and help him enroll in workshops and classes to improve things such as interview skills, writing résumés, and job search skills. These services come under the category of intensive services. If after trying out the intensive services available at the One-Stop, Herb is still not employed but he knows the type of job that he wants and there is a need for this type of job in the region where he lives, then he can apply for an Individual Training Account (ITA). An ITA is a specified amount of money that has to be used with an approved provider, usually for classroom training, within a specified period of time (usually within 2 years).

The problem that Herb and people with cognitive disabilities face is that ITAs are usually designed to be used for training provided at community colleges or private vocational technical schools—training in a group setting where most of the individuals are not disabled. This is not always the case, but the training for which ITAs are used must be a type of educational experience that leads to a degree or some kind of certification or credential.

Herb is lucky in many ways. Although he cannot read or write, he has good manual dexterity and over the years has acquired the ability to follow directions that are depicted through simple drawings. He was a pipe cutter in the manufacturing firm and learned that skill by watching a coworker who was good at demonstrating rather than using just words to describe what he was doing. After working with both the disability resource specialist and the WDS at One-Stop A, Herb thought he would like to learn to be a bricklayer, a job skill that was definitely needed and which had job openings in the area where he lived. A barrier that Herb encountered was that the bricklaying course was only 8 weeks long and required simple math and reading. To be able to take advantage of this training, he would need a "coach" to participate in the class with him and would need longer than 8 weeks to be able to learn to do everything that was required to earn his bricklayer certificate.

Rather than just applying for an ITA to go to bricklaying school, Herb ended up with training through the use of blended funding. VR funds were used to pay for the tuition for the first 8 weeks of the course, and WIA picked up an additional 8 weeks of tuition at the technical school so that Herb could repeat the course. VR also paid for a full-time job coach for the first 8 weeks and then gradually faded these services during the second phase of training. Through one of its external contractors, VR was able to pay for all of the written materials to be put in alternative formats, either pictorial diagrams or actual photographs of the bricklaying task that Herb was to learn. Once Herb learned the skills being taught in the course, and practiced his skills, he had no trouble taking the final exam, which was to build a brick wall in a specified amount of time, and earning his certificate. The technical school assists all students who successfully complete its bricklaying course to find jobs, and did so for Herb, which allowed his remaining VR-funded job coach hours to be used for on-the-job support rather than job search activities.

Herb's experience is far different from what usually occurs at One-Stop Career Centers when people with disabilities go for employment assistance. It is what should happen and what does happen at those One-Stops that are committed to serving all individuals who seek services and are creative in their use of resources. It is more likely that people with similar or more severe disabilities will get the services needed if the One-Stop director has an understanding of disability service issues and is willing to seek different funding sources for specialized services. Another attribute of One-Stops that serve people with disabilities is that they have staff, including those of the One-Stop partners, that communicate informally and are creative in problem solving and blending funding to meet the additional support needs of individuals with disabilities who are seeking One-Stop services. These best practices, along with the presence of a disability resource specialist staff person, are beginning to emerge at the One-Stops that welcome people with disabilities, including those with intellectual and other developmental disabilities.

♠ CASE EXAMPLE: LADAWN

Ladawn is 22 years of age and is ready to leave school with a special education certificate. Professionals consider her to be an individual with significant disabilities, both cognitive and physical. Her expressive language skills are limited, she uses an electric wheelchair, and she can recognize only single words—the ones that are on the communication device attached to her wheelchair. Ladawn has indicated that she wants to work, but what that means to her is the same "work" experience that she has had for the past 2 years at school. Unfortunately, she cannot remain at that work site once she leaves school.

Ladawn is on a waiting list for employment services offered by the local disability employment service provider. Most of her classmates expect a wait of up to 3 years before they will get served. This is unacceptable to Ladawn's mother, who knows that her daughter will lose skills if she does not use them. Ladawn and her mother took a school-sponsored tour of their local One-Stop Career Center (One-Stop B) last fall. Her mother knows that the vocational training available at One-Stop B for individuals who are not disabled will not work for her daughter. From the reaction of staff during the tour, it was apparent that they do not know how to work with someone with multiple severe disabilities, and there is no disability resource specialist on site at the One-Stop. Another factor is that the funds available to the One-Stop are extremely limited and are prioritized to be used with individuals who can participate in existing core, intensive, and training services without the need for special accommodations or modifications.

What One-Stop B can offer Ladawn is the use of extensive assistive technology in its resource room to search for jobs that are available and identify those that she is interested in and has the skills for, or that she could do some part of if the job could be modified or "carved out." There are many adaptive computer software programs, an adjustable workstation that increases access to the computer keyboard and screen, and magnification devices usually available in those One-Stops that have taken advantage of special funding initiatives primarily through the U.S. Department of Labor. Although One-Stop B does not have staff that can sit with Ladawn and provide hands-on assistance, it does welcome individuals who bring others with them to provide the one-on-one contact. Resource room staff can show Ladawn's assistant, in this case a teacher's aide from school, how the software and hardware are used but can spend only a short time explaining how job searches and other tutorial programs are done.

One-Stop B will never provide Ladawn intensive or training-level services that she can use, but it can provide her with information about jobs that are available. Having this information, as well as an idea of the jobs that are of most interest, will make a job coach's task much easier and less time consuming. Hopefully, by the time it is Ladawn's turn to receive supported employment services, she will be ready and have the information of what job possibilities she would like to pursue. In the meantime, she can also pursue activities available through One-Stop B's Youth Services and participate in them to the extent possible given her need for assistance and accommodation.

A recent research study conducted by Bader (2003) found the following practices, or components, in One-Stop Career Centers identified as leaders in the United States in serving people with disabilities.

• The presence of disability resource specialists provides individuals with disabilities with a point of contact within One-Stop Career Center systems to obtain assistance needed to access core, intensive, and training services when they are unable to do it by themselves. Disability resource specialists also assist staff, management, and partner agencies in the One-Stops by providing information to facilitate the removal of barriers and increase the inclusion of people with disabilities in service delivery.

• One-Stop Career Centers that pursue special funding initiatives are able to use these funds to address access issues that may, in the past, have prevented individuals with disabilities from being included in many of the services provided through the centers.

- Strong leadership provided by a One-Stop director who understands disability issues facilitates timely removal of physical access barriers within the center and creates an environment whereby partner staff can work together to eliminate the problems that prevent individuals with disabilities from having access to the programs they need.
- The co-location of benefits planning and assistance providers at One-Stop Career Centers, or having timely access to benefits counseling services, provides individuals with disabilities with the resource information they need to make decisions regarding employment.
- Availability of benefits planning services at One-Stop Centers serves as a catalyst to draw individuals with disabilities into the centers, and exposes them to the other services that are offered.
- One-Stop Career Centers that creatively blend funding sources are able to provide intensive and training services, as well as the supports that are needed, to individuals with disabilities beyond those that would be available through limited WIA funds.

FINAL THOUGHTS

Since the passage of the Workforce Investment Act of 1998, states and localities have been implementing a formal system of One-Stop Career Centers that serve as a single point of information and skill training for individuals wanting to enter or reenter the workforce, as well as for employers who need a retooled workforce. There are over 2,000 comprehensive One-Stop Career Centers across the United States, all of which are guided by WIA's four principles: universality, customer choice, integration of services, and accountability for results. From the beginning of the implementation of WIA, it has been widely acknowledged that these principles, especially universality, need to be incorporated into all service levels in the One-Stop Career Center system if people with disabilities are to be included in service delivery. The mission of the One-Stop Career Centers is not clear at this time. It is not consistent from one One-Stop to the next. For some individuals, the One-Stop Career Center is a place to go for information regarding unemployment and other public benefits, to find out what jobs are currently available in the area, and to learn how to prepare for job interviews. Other individuals go to the One-Stop Centers expecting personal assistance in finding a job and the support needed to become employed. Still others go to the One-Stop Centers to gain skills through training. At some One-Stop Career Centers, there is little that is useful for individuals with disabilities, especially those who do not have average cognitive skills, whereas at other One-Stops, people with disabilities find the accommodations needed to participate in core, intensive, and training services alongside their nondisabled peers.

Even though One-Stop Career Centers do not yet have a clear mission, there are practices that are assisting people with disabilities in accessing some, if not all, of the services they need to become employed, to become better employed, or to become reemployed. The "best practices" that are emerging are a result of the commitment and success of the One-Stop Career Centers in implementing the WIA principles, as well as their creativity in dealing with the obstacles that have been encountered.

With the implementation of WIA, customer choice, inclusion, and self-determination have become possibilities for many people with intellectual and other developmental disabilities who may no longer have to depend on a specialized service system to obtain employment. Individuals with disabilities have been given the opportunity through WIA to receive the same employment services as the general public, but these services will affect employment outcomes only if there is access to, and people have choice in using, the programs within the One-Stop service delivery system.

REFERENCES

Bader, B. A. (2003). *Identification of best practices in One-Stop Career Centers that facilitate use by people with disabilities seeking employment.* Unpublished doctoral dissertation, Virginia Commonwealth University, Richmond.

Barnow, B. S., & King, C. T. (2000). Strategies for improving the odds. In B. S. Barnow & C. T. King (Eds.), *Improving the odds: Increasing the effectiveness of publicly funded training* (pp. 335–345). Washington, DC: Urban Institute Press.

Bennici, F., Mangum, S., & Sum, A. M. (2000). The economic, demographic, and social context of future employment and training programs. In B. S. Barnow & C. T. King (Eds.), *Improving the odds: Increasing the effectiveness of publicly funded training* (pp. 19–48). Washington, DC: Urban Institute Press.

Berkowitz, E. D. (1987). *Disabled policy: America's programs for the handicapped.* Cambridge, England: Cambridge University Press.

Butterworth, J., & Kiernan, W. E. (1996). Access to employment of all individuals: Legislative, systems, and service delivery issues. In D. H. Lehr & F. Brown (Eds.), *People with disabilities who challenge the system* (pp. 243–281). Baltimore: Brookes.

Callahan, M. (2000). *The meaning of choice: Implications for systems and providers.* Unpublished manuscript. Washington, DC: Presidential Taskforce on Employment of Adults with Disabilities.

Cheney, S. (2001). *Keeping competitive: Hiring, training, and retaining qualified workers.* Washington, DC: U.S. Chamber of Commerce, Center for Workforce Preparation.

Comprehensive Employment and Training Act of 1973, 29 U.S.C. § 801 *et seq.*

Daly, T. (2001). Diversity and disability: A paradox? *Generations, 29*(2), 29–44.

Farley, R., Schriner, K., & Roessler, R. (1988). The impact of the Occupational Choice Strategy on the career development of rehabilitation clients. *Rehabilitation Psychology, 33,* 121–125.

Funaro, A., & Dixon, K. A. (2002). *How the One-Stop system serves people with disabilities: A nationwide survey of disability agencies* [Report prepared by the John J. Heldrich Center for Workforce Development]. New Brunswick, NJ: Rutgers University.

Gilson, B. B. (2000). One-Stop Career Centers: Will they be used by people with disabilities? *Focus on Autism and Other Developmental Disabilities, 15*(1), 30–36.

Job Training Partnership Act of 1982, 29 U.S.C. §§ 1501–1781, 49, 49a-49 note, 96 Stat. 1322.

Kregel, J. (1999). Promoting employment opportunities for individuals with cognitive disabilities: A time for reform. In A. Tymchuk, C. Lakin, & R. Luckasson (Eds.), *A forgotten generation: The status and challenges of adults with mild cognitive impairments in American society.* Baltimore: Brookes.

Mackelprang, R. W., & Salsgiver, R. O. (1999). *Disability: A diversity model approach in human service practice.* Pacific Grove, CA: Brooks/Cole.

Maguire, S. (2000). *Surviving, and maybe thriving, on vouchers.* Retrieved June 23, 2004, from Public/Private Ventures Web site: http://www.ppv.org/ppv/publications/publications_description.asp?search_id=6&publication_id=96

Manpower Development and Training Act of 1962, 42 U.S.C.

Presidential Task Force on Employment of Adults with Disabilities. (1999). *Re-charting the course: If not now, when?* [Second Annual Report to the President of the United States]. Washington, DC: Author.

Presidential Task Force on Employment of Adults with Disabilities. (2000). *Re-charting the course: Turning points* [Third Annual Report to the President of the United States]. Washington, DC: Author.

Racino, J. A. (with Whittico, P.). (1998). The promise of self-advocacy and community employment. In P. Wehman & J. Kregel (Eds.), *More than a job: Securing satisfying careers for people with disabilities* (pp. 47–69). Baltimore: Brookes.

Sar Levitan Center for Social Policy Studies. (1998, July 1). *The public employment service in a One-Stop world.* Retrieved June 23, 2004, from http://www.icesa.org/articles/template.cfm?results_art_filename=pesmenu.html

Schriner, K., Rumrill, P., & Parlin, R. (1995). Rethinking disability policy: Equity in the ADA and the meaning of specialized services for people with disabilities. *Journal of Health and Human Services Administration, 17*(4), 478–500.

Scotch, R. K. (2001). American disability policy in the twentieth century. In P. K. Longmore & L. Umansky (Eds.), *The new disability history: American perspectives* (pp. 375–392). New York: New York University Press.

Silverstein, R. (2000). *A description of the Workforce Investment Act from a disability policy perspective.* Washington, DC: Author.

Storen, D., Dixon, K. A., & Funaro, A. (2002, February). *One-Stop accessibility: A nationwide survey of One-Stop centers on services for people with disabilities* [Report prepared by the John J. Heldrich Center for Workforce Development]. New Brunswick, NJ: Rutgers University.

U.S. Department of Labor. (1998). *White Paper: Implementing the Workforce Investment Act of 1998* [Message from the secretary of labor, Alexis Herman]. Retrieved June 23, 2004, from http://www.doleta.gov/usworkforce/documents/misc/wpaper3.cfm

U.S. General Accounting Office. (2001, October). *Workforce Investment Act: Better guidance needed to address concerns over new requirements* [GAO-02-72]. Washington, DC: Author.

Wehman, P. (1988). Supported employment: Toward zero exclusion of persons with severe disabilities. In P. Wehman & M. S. Moon (Eds.), *Vocational rehabilitation and supported employment* (pp. 3–16). Baltimore: Brookes.

West, M. (1996). Promoting self-determination for individuals with severe disabilities in employment services. In D. J. Sands & M. L. Wehmeyer (Eds.), *Self-determination across the life span: Independence and choice for people with disabilities* (pp. 311–328). Baltimore: Brookes.

Workforce Investment Act of 1998, 112 Stat. 936.

Workforce Investment Act Final Rule, 20 U.S.C. 927(c) § 662.300 (2000).

Workforce Investment Act Implementation Taskforce Office. (1998, November 12). *Implementing the Workforce Investment Act of 1998.* Available online from http://usworkforce.org/wpaper3.htm

CHAPTER 19

Postsecondary Education for Students with Significant Disabilities

Elizabeth Evans Getzel

LEARNING GOALS

Upon completion of this chapter, the reader will be able to

- describe the issues in accessing postsecondary programs for students with significant disabilities
- define the concept of universal instructional design and explain how it benefits students with significant disabilities in postsecondary education
- describe the current types of postsecondary programs available to students with significant disabilities
- describe the challenges students with significant disabilities face when adjusting to a postsecondary environment and explain how the use of accommodations and technology can help to address these challenges
- identify the steps needed for planning a successful postsecondary experience for students with significant disabilities

Obtaining an advanced degree or training beyond high school is essential for individuals to be competitive in today's labor market. Whether it is college, adult and continuing education, or technical preparation, postsecondary education plays a major role in preparing persons for employment and career opportunities (Gajar, Goodman, & McAfee, 1995; Getzel, Briel, & Kregel, 2000; Getzel, Stodden, & Briel, 2001). Students who continue their education after high school are more prepared to meet the challenges of a changing marketplace. Increased numbers of students with disabilities are entering postsecondary education to obtain further skills and knowledge as a result of a combination of legislative, academic, and social changes. Research demonstrates that persons with disabilities find postsecondary education a means to enhance their chances of (a) obtaining and maintaining employment, (b) earning a higher annual income, and (c) creating a pathway to lifelong independence and a greater quality of life (Fairweather & Shaver, 1991; "Only Skills Training," 1995; Wilson, Getzel, & Brown, 2000).

Although the number of students with disabilities entering postsecondary programs has increased, their rate of enrollment is still significantly lower than that of the general population (Getzel et al., 2001). Furthermore, Hart, Zafft, and Zimbrich (2001) cite U.S. Department of Education data that shows that students attending postsecondary education programs are generally those with sensory, mobility, and learning disabilities and not those with intellectual, autism, or multiple developmental disabilities. There are still challenges and issues around accessing postsecondary programs, especially for those students with more significant disabilities. Understanding the range of educational supports needed, the specific accommodations appropriate for students, and the critical institutional structures needed to support students with significant disabilities are just a few of the challenges that must be addressed. Furthermore, few studies have been done concerning the participation or lack of participation of students with significant disabilities, especially those with intellectual disabilities (Grigal, Neubert, & Moon, 2001), easily the least studied disability group in postsecondary settings (Babbitt & White, 2002; Hall, Kleinert, & Kearns, 2000).

ACCESS TO POSTSECONDARY EDUCATION

Among the individuals who face the greatest challenges when attempting to participate in and exit postsecondary programs to pursue their self-chosen careers are students with significant disabilities. Research has shown a strong positive relationship between disability, level of education, and adult employment (Benz, Doren, & Yovanoff, 1998; Blackorby & Wagner, 1996; Gilson, 1996; Reis, Neu, & McGuire, 1997). Stodden (1998) found that employment rates for individuals with disabilities show a stronger positive correlation between level of education and rate of employment than is seen in statistical trends for the general population. Therefore, access to postsecondary programs for students with significant disabilities becomes even more critical.

Issues in Accessing Postsecondary Programs

What challenges do students with significant disabilities face when trying to access postsecondary education programs? One primary issue is the lack of preparation for college as a result of lower expectations of these students. This begins early in students' educational experiences, and as a result they are not provided with the necessary information or skills leading to a goal of entering postsecondary programs (Hart et al., 2001; Wehman, Getzel, & Thoma, 2002; Weir, 2001). By the time students with significant disabilities enter high school, a transition goal of postsecondary education often is not viewed as a viable outcome.

A second challenge faced by students is the requirements for entry into a program, which include placement tests or other entrance requirements (Hart et al., 2001; Weir, 2001). Students who are not able to move through the standard application and approval process for college are often viewed as incapable of participating in postsecondary education. Coupled with this challenge is the lack of training and preparation of support personnel and faculty in postsecondary settings. The lack of understanding on how to support and educate students with significant disabilities creates further barriers to success of these students on college campuses. This creates a perceived lack of "ability to benefit" from further educational opportunities (Weir, 2001). Students with significant disabilities are viewed as unable to have meaningful experiences and learning in postsecondary education.

A final barrier concerns eligibility for financial aid or other financial assistance while in college (Wehman et al., 2002; Weir, 2001). Students with significant disabilities often lack the appropriate high school credentials to be eligible for financial aid. They also become ineligible as a result of auditing courses or going part time. This limits their access to financial aid resources that could help to offset some of the expenses related to attending college. In some instances, the opportunity to attend postsecondary education is achieved through parent brokering with a community college or other college, enabling students to audit classes. Another option involves occupational opportunities, in which vocational rehabilitation funds are blended with funds from the family (Hart et al., 2001; Wehman et al., 2002; Weir, 2001). Access to financial assistance remains a substantial obstacle for greater numbers of students with significant disabilities to participate in postsecondary programs.

The barriers discussed thus far concern service and support issues involved in including students with significant disabilities in postsecondary settings. Perhaps the overarching issue around educating these students in college settings involves a philosophical question about the purpose of postsecondary education and the role it can play in the lives of students with significant disabilities. Currently, students attending college are enrolled to complete a specific certificate or degree program. For some students with significant disabilities, this outcome might not be possible. However, the experience of being in a postsecondary environment could have other benefits. For example, students could obtain a certain set of skills or knowledge without completing an entire program. The experience of living on campus, providing opportunities to interact with their peer group, could assist students with significant disabilities to become more included in their community and increase their independent living skills. Creative thinking and approaches on the benefits or outcomes for these students if they are not enrolled in a typical degree or certificate program will be continuing subjects of demonstration projects and research.

As this section has described, a number of issues need to be addressed in postsecondary education to enable more students with significant disabilities access to the programs, services, and supports available in college. Table 19.1 summarizes some of the issues that have been identified as barriers to participation in higher education by students with significant disabilities, including students with intellectual disabilities (Wehman et al., 2002).

Ideas and Approaches for Overcoming Access Barriers

Secondary School Programs in Higher Education

As documented previously, higher education has a significant impact on the career attainment of individuals with disabilities. Regrettably, little research has been done that demonstrates the participation and involvement of students with significant disabilities in postsecondary settings (Grigal, Neubert, & Moon, 2001). However, valuable information has been obtained through existing literature that focuses on program descriptions and case studies conducted on a small number of individuals who participated in postsecondary programs through public school programs established with postsecondary schools (Dolyniuk et al., 2002; Grigal et al., 2001, 2002; Hart et al., 2001; Neubert, Moon, Grigal, & Redd, 2001; Weir, 2001). For example, Grigal and colleagues (2002) describe the important components needed to ensure that students with significant disabilities successfully participate in postsecondary settings. These authors discuss establishing

TABLE 19.1
Barriers to Participating in Postsecondary Programs

Funding (especially if students are auditing courses or not going full time)

Inadequate preparation of students to enter college because of low expectations

Lack of career planning

Lack of infrastructure and guidelines to educate students in postsecondary (especially 4-year) schools

Lack of support staff in universities and colleges

Lack of structure to share strategies, support, and ideas among university and college programs

Failure to resolve issues around housing, transportation, work, and other complementary supports and services

---

planning committees, conducting needs assessments, writing action plans, deciding where services should be provided, and managing logistics. Grigal and colleagues (2001) also emphasize the critical role of the public schools in the preparatory process for these students. They studied students in 13 postsecondary programs and highlighted from their study issues that were critical for success. Hart and colleagues (2001) discuss their work with students with significant disabilities in Massachusetts using the model of a secondary school program collaborating with a postsecondary school. In all of these efforts, logistics are critical. They are the details necessary to successful implementation.

To achieve the level of planning necessary for the smooth transition of students with significant disabilities, a strong collaborative relationship between secondary and postsecondary education is essential. The participation of the disability support services (DSS) coordinator is key in helping to facilitate the transition of these students. All too often, college representatives, such as the DSS coordinator, do not attend transition-planning meetings (Getzel et al., 2001; deFur, Getzel, & Trossi, 1996). Ensuring that all the services and supports are coordinated between the two educational sites, and completing the necessary documentation to receive services on campus are critical for the smooth transition into postsecondary education (Grigal et al., 2001, 2002; Hart, 2002; Hart et al., 2001). To accomplish this level of collaboration, training opportunities are needed so that all parties involved, including students with disabilities, family members, secondary education personnel, DSS coordinators, and agency personnel, understand their roles and responsibilities.

Universal Instructional Design

As previously indicated, few published research or program description articles exist on persons with significant disabilities, especially students with intellectual disabilities, going to college. However, with the concept of universal instructional design, the type of disability may be less important than the nature of a college environment and supports (Wehman et al., 2002). The concept of universal instructional design (UID) in postsecondary environments is developing and changing as faculty members learn more about its application and the outcomes achieved by students. The idea of universal design began with architecture, making buildings and communities more accessible (Bowe, 2000; Johnson & Fox, 2003). Essentially the curb cuts on street corners that are now such a familiar sight in our communities are a result of the universal design movement. This concept of universal design began to be studied in terms of its applicability to instruction in higher education in the late 1990s (Silver, Bourke, & Strehorn, 1998). In essence, educators began looking at the possibility of designing "curb cuts" in teaching, making the curriculum and materials more accessible for all students (Johnson & Fox, 2003). The appeal of using universal instructional design techniques in postsecondary settings is that it creates an accessible academic learning experience for all diverse learners, including students with disabilities. A faculty member who uses universal design strategies provides information to students using a variety of methods, including multimedia and videos, field trips and service learning projects, and access to lecture notes and information (Johnson & Fox, 2003). Students are able to demonstrate their knowledge of the course material using their strongest learning style, which could include oral presentations, hands-on demonstrations, or written materials. The key to the use of universal instructional design is the flexibility that faculty have in the presentation of course content and the evaluation of student progress (Johnson & Fox, 2003). The material or information that students are required to learn is not "watered down" or significantly altered; it is the method used to present the material that is varied to meet the learning needs of all students (Hart et al., 2001; Johnson & Fox, 2003). For students with more significant disabilities, UID can be an effective means for inclusion of these students in postsecondary settings.

Need for Further Research

The inclusion of students with significant disabilities, especially students with intellectual disabilities, is a growing movement in the education field. Further research is needed on effective strategies and techniques for educating these students, appropriate supports that need to be in place, and the level of collaboration among service providers needed to effectively meet their educational and personal support needs (Center on Disability Studies, 2002; Hart et al., 2001; Wehman et al., 2002). In addition, continuing discussion and exploration of the purpose and outcome of postsecondary education for students with significant disabilities will play a tremendous role in the design and implementation of new approaches in postsecondary settings (Grigal et al., 2001, 2002). Table 19.2 identifies some of the strategies and ideas needed in overcoming barriers to postsecondary education programs for students with significant disabilities (Wehman et al., 2002).

TABLE 19.2

Possible Solutions to Overcoming Barriers

Research-specific interventions or models used to gather outcome data.

Train disability support services staff in accommodating students.

Train faculty members in teaching strategies and methods involving universal design, hands-on learning, use of technology, and so on.

Create flexibility in the use of resources for students.

Fund model demonstration projects to gather best practices for replication in other postsecondary programs.

Begin student preparation for college needs early—teach needed critical skills and competencies beginning in elementary school.

Inform parents about college opportunities beginning in the early years of students' educational experience.

Think creatively about and develop innovative approaches to what can be learned in college outside of a typical degree or certificate program.

PREPARING STUDENTS FOR POSTSECONDARY EDUCATION

Postsecondary education programs are offered in a variety of settings, including trade or business schools, vocational-technical schools, community colleges, universities and colleges, and specialized training in business and industry (Wille-Gregory, Graham, & Hughes, 1995). Effective planning and preparation are needed to ensure that students with significant disabilities are able to successfully enter postsecondary programs and receive the appropriate supports and services they need. Unfortunately, these students typically are not included in transition planning (Getzel & deFur, 1997; Hart et al., 2001). Increased involvement of students with significant disabilities in planning their transition from high school to postsecondary education or employment is essential. Using person-centered planning strategies and increasing students' self-determination and self-advocacy skills are just two examples of ways to increase and include their voices in the transition process. To help students with disabilities prepare for their transition to higher education, three primary areas of consideration emerge: exploring opportunities in postsecondary educational settings, setting career goals, and identifying skills needed by students for a successful transition.

Exploring Opportunities in Postsecondary Education Settings

In spite of the limited capacity in postsecondary education settings to serve students with significant disabilities, including students with intellectual disabilities, there remains a growing movement among professionals, parents, and students to engage them in postsecondary education opportunities. Hart (2002) describes three program models that are currently in place on some postsecondary campuses around the country. These program models could be implemented using secondary education funds, creating a school program based on a college campus or a program developed on campus using a variety of funding strategies, including family resources, community agency funds, and secondary school funds. They include the following:

- *Separate programs.* These programs are significantly separate and are typically referred to as life skills or transition programs based on college campuses.
- *Mixed programs.* Again, these programs are significantly separate from other campus programs, but the students with significant disabilities in these programs have some interaction with the general student population and may take a college course.
- *Individual support model.* Students are provided with individualized services and supports; all services are student centered and based on student choices and preferences.

Another example of an approach that has been developed for students with learning, psychiatric, and physical disabilities is a supported education model that has been implemented at Virginia Commonwealth University (VCU) within the current DSS structure on campus (Getzel, McManus, & Briel, 2003). The supported education model, or the VCU Academic Strategies for Achievement Program (ASAP), works with students with disabilities who are admitted to the university through the regular application process. The model uses an individualized approach to facilitate student learning and is designed to assist students who are at risk of failing or dropping out of college. These students are typically on academic probation, failing two or more courses a semester, or exhibiting problems in a clinical or internship setting. The model is designed to provide intensive, individualized services and supports a student-directed approach. Figure 19.1 outlines how students enter the process for obtaining services through this model. The model uses various levels of services that students with disabilities may need while in college. Examples of Level 1 services are note takers in class, extended time on tests, and a quieter or distraction-free setting for taking exams. Level 2 services are a little more involved and may require technology or more specialized types of services—for example, screen readers, books on tape, and sign language interpreters. The figure identifies Level 3 services as supported education; this level provides individualized services, including specific academic strategies, technology such as personal digital devices (PDAs), and an individualized time management plan. Students with disabilities can move among these three levels or receive services from more than one level, depending on their academic needs.

Students participating in the supported education model are responsible for working with staff members to design and implement an education plan that describes the specific services and supports that students need. The staff and students work together using a variety of strategies that include technology software programs, time management and study skill techniques, and accessing services on campus or in the community (e.g., counseling services, career services, advocacy groups). Table 19.3 provides a summary of some of the students served through the VCU supported education model and the services they received. A case study of a VCU student enrolled in the ASAP program is included to provide a more in-depth picture of how the process works for a specific student.

🧍 CASE EXAMPLE: TODD

Todd is an undergraduate student at Virginia Commonwealth University and hopes to obtain a degree in social work or education. He receives services through the Disability Support Services office on campus after registering with that office. Todd has multiple disabilities, which include a learning disability, traumatic head injury, and a psychological disability. During his sophomore year, he was experiencing problems in his psychology class, specifically with take-home tests and time management. He talked with his psychology professor about the difficulties he was experiencing in class, and the faculty member suggested that he seek services through the VCU Academic Strategies for Achievement Program. Information on this program had been distributed to all faculty members, so the professor was able to give Todd the name and number of someone to contact.

Todd contacted the ASAP staff, and a meeting was arranged. During the initial meeting with

(*text continues on page 517*)

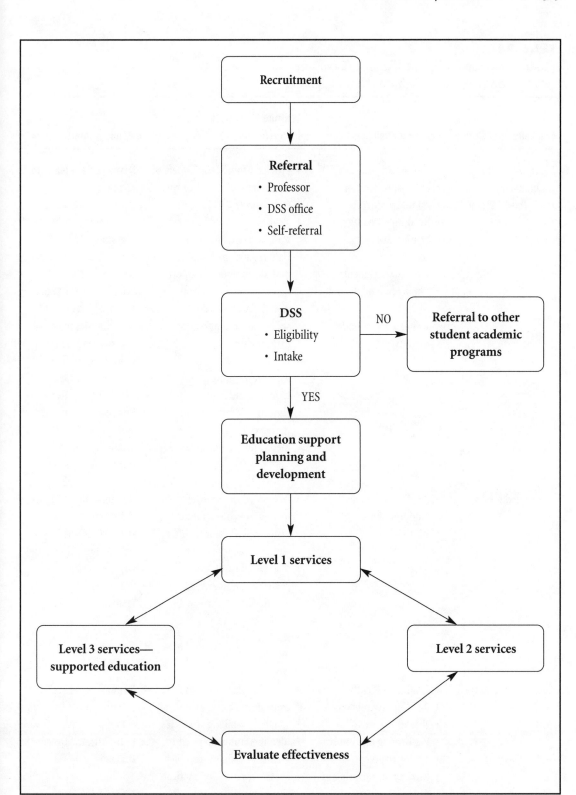

FIGURE 19.1. How students obtain services through the Academic Strategies for Achievement Program model for college students with disabilities at Virginia Commonwealth University. *Note.* DSS = Disability Support Services.

TABLE 19.3

Student Participants in the Virginia Commonwealth University
Academic Strategies for Achievement Program

Disability	Learning Challenges	Learning Strategies Interventions	Technology Interventions
Learning disability, traumatic brain injury, posttraumatic stress disorder	• Self-awareness • Disclosure decisions • Auditory processing • Reading difficulty • Writing difficulty • Test taking • Time management • Application of clinical skills • Visual discrimination • Anxiety	• Provided counsel on understanding disability; learning style; effective ways to disclose to professors, clinical staff, and employers • Held regular meetings to provide emotional support, discuss stress management, verbally process new skills, plan and prioritize assignments • Identified effective electronic test-taking strategies • Explored and identified clinical accommodations • Referred to physician for medication management	• Developed templates for recording information • Demonstrated and provided screen-reading and study-skills software for reading textbooks, writing, and test taking • Scanned several textbooks • Explored features of screen reader to enlarge and space text and to proof writing assignments • Demonstrated speech recognition software • Provided personal digital assistant (PDA) to manage coursework and explore transfer to work setting
Learning disability	• Reading textbook • Studying skills • Writing skills	• Developed timeline for memorizing dates for art history; used color to differentiate time periods • Made flash cards, defined pertinent information; practiced flash cards with staff • Explored strategies to proofread papers	• Demonstrated and provided screen-reading and study-skills software for reading textbooks and writing papers • Scanned art history textbook
Learning disability	• Reading difficulty • Reading comprehension • Test taking • Performing tasks in lab • Typing papers • Anxiety over passing courses	• Organized information using graphic organizers • Taught test-taking strategies • Identified tutors to provide further assistance in applying information to practical situations	• Demonstrated Kurzweil software; provided technical support with software • Demonstrated Dragon Dictate

(continues)

TABLE 19.3 *Continued.*
Student Participants in the Virginia Commonwealth University
Academic Strategies for Achievement Program

Disability	Learning Challenges	Learning Strategies Interventions	Technology Interventions
Learning disability (*continued*)	• Memorizing information • Writing papers • Self-advocacy • Math	• Coordinated with Disability Support Services office to type papers; performed task analysis; made study plan; made to-do list; suggested discussing concerns with program adviser; referred for individualized psychological counseling • Discussed mnemonics; incorporated tactile learning strategies to recall body parts • Discussed disability and the effectiveness of using accommodations • Identified tutor to assist with basic math computations	• Instructed student on the use of graphic organizers to organize information

ASAP staff, Todd expressed his frustration about not being able to convey what he has learned in class, especially on take-home exams. He stated that the tests were confusing, and as a result, he was doing poorly on them. After examining several take-home tests, the ASAP staff determined that Todd was having difficulty with the short-answer essays with multiple parts. He was experiencing problems with reading comprehension and visual discrimination. The ASAP staff recommended that Todd use a screen reader during take-home exams. Todd arranged with his professor to send the test to him electronically. Once he received the exam, he enlarged the font and broke the essay questions into manageable parts in order to answer the entire question. He then used the screen reader to aid in the comprehension of the test questions and to proofread answers. He was able to significantly increase his grade on the next test. Todd and the ASAP staff members determined that the screen reader and books on tape would be effective strategies for reading and comprehending textbook material.

Todd also worked on improving his time management skills. He spent time with the ASAP staff developing a semester "to do" list, establishing weekly plans for academic assignments and using a paper planner. Readings and papers were prioritized, and assignments were broken into manageable tasks. Although the use of the paper planner was somewhat effective, Todd needed prompting to review the planner on his own. He is currently exploring using a personal digital assistant (PDA) to see if it works better for him than the paper planner. The ASAP staff recommended that Todd consider using a PDA for time management because of the alarm notification feature to remind him of upcoming events. He was also encouraged to look at how technology could be used in his future career to assist him in meeting the

demands of the work setting. Todd continues to do well and meets regularly with the ASAP staff to review his progress and use of technology and other learning strategies.

_____

Setting Career Goals for Successful Transition Planning

Students with significant disabilities, including students with intellectual disabilities, need opportunities to explore a variety of career options and the skills required. Students need work experience during high school to help develop social interaction skills and to further explore vocational interests (Benz, Lindstrom, & Yovanoff, 2000; Frank & Sitlington, 2000). Such opportunities will assist students to determine their future goals and what type of educational programs can best meet their needs.

Prior to enrolling or participating in a postsecondary program, students with significant disabilities need to explore potential employment outcomes as a result of their involvement in postsecondary schools. Students need to explore job sites through community-based programs to interact with individuals in those settings and learn about what they do. There are also a number of software programs and CDs that provide students with role models of individuals with disabilities employed in a variety of occupational areas. This information can be invaluable as students prepare to set their education and employment goals.

Identifying Skills Needed for Successful Transition

It is essential that students with significant disabilities engage in a planning process that assists them in identifying their interests, goals, and support needs in postsecondary education settings. Hart and colleagues (2001) describe a model that includes person-centered planning, creating a menu of services and supports designed specifically for the individual entering postsecondary education, and implementing ongoing services and supports once the student has entered a program. In a study to identify components of programs serving students with intellectual disabilities in higher education, an emphasis on self-determination skills was found to be an essential element in all of the programs (Grigal et al., 2001). Self-advocacy and self-determination skills are critical for all students with disabilities entering postsecondary education. They have been found to be particularly helpful to youth transitioning to college (Durlak, Rose, & Bursuck, 1994). Students who exercise personal choice options help to empower themselves and enhance their willingness to persist.

ADJUSTING TO POSTSECONDARY EDUCATION PROGRAMS

Once students with significant disabilities have started their postsecondary program, they must be prepared to face new challenges as they adjust to a different environment and educational process. Individualized services and supports must be in place to increase their chances of successfully adjusting to college life. Preparation around such areas as accommodations on campus and use of assistive technology devices is critical during planning. It is essential that students with significant disabilities have access to curriculum that includes multiple instructions and material formats and technology (Hart et al., 2001).

Postsecondary education is different from secondary education, and some of the differences are especially important for students with significant disabilities who are attending postsecondary education that is not part of a high school program under the Individuals with Disabilities Education Act. Services and supports offered through secondary education programs are provided under IDEA. Under this law, students with significant disabilities are entitled to services once they are found eligible for special education services. In postsecondary education, students with disabilities are covered under the Americans with Disabilities Act and Section 504 of the Rehabilitation Act. However, under these laws, students with disabilities are guaranteed access to needed supports and services once students have been determined eligible for these services. Students with disabilities transitioning from secondary education to postsecondary education move from an entitlement program to an eligibility program. In many ways, the changes in how services and supports are provided impact any student with a significant disability entering postsecondary education. For instance, a student who is attending a postsecondary program through a secondary program will need to ensure that services and supports are coordinated between the two programs. This would especially be the case if the student received an education coach as part of the secondary education program but in addition requested that faculty provide specific accommodations in a course (Hart et al., 2001). The DSS coordinator on campus would develop the accommodations and the process used by students with disabilities covered under ADA and Section 504 once the student is found eligible for these services. This is the reason coordination between the secondary and postsecondary programs is so critical. The roles and responsibilities of each educational program must be clearly spelled out in order for students to fully benefit from their college experience.

In college, students with disabilities are expected to be more independent and to display self-determination and self-advocacy skills. Regardless of the type of program in which students with significant disabilities participate at the postsecondary level, each of these programs, whether separate or individualized, emphasizes the need for students to achieve a higher level of independence (Grigal et al., 2001; Hart et al., 2001). These skills will assist students in their college programs as well as in the workplace.

Accommodations on Campus

Access to services and supports while a student is attending postsecondary programs is vital to the successful completion of classes or programs. Students with significant disabilities need to be involved in the planning of supports to obtain an understanding of how the supports will be implemented. To learn about available services and resources, students should take advantage of orientation sessions that are available during the summer or early in the semester. An increasing number of colleges are setting aside time during general orientation for students with disabilities to meet with college staff, learn about resources on campus, and network with other students (Getzel et al., 2001; Hart et al., 2001; Page & Chadsey-Rusch, 1995).

Building a relationship with the Disability Support Services (DSS) office on campus is another important part of the adjustment process. Hart and colleagues (2001) used current information available through the DSS office on practices and procedures, which helped to simplify some of the college orientation information. The DSS office also provided recommendations on what courses to take to maximize students' strengths and decrease the impact of their disability. In the description of their model, Hart and colleagues (2001) state that students used the same procedures as all students with disabilities do to obtain some of the accommodations needed. Examples of key accommodations include tape recorders and note takers to capture new material, creative methods for textbook reading, extended time for tests using a reader and scribe, hands-on learning, weekly meetings with support staff members, and educational coaches in the classroom when available. A DSS coordinator on a college campus will play a critical role in the design of accommodations for students. In addition, the coordinator can assist in facilitating the discussion with faculty and staff on how to implement the accommodations into their coursework. Table 19.4 provides ideas on how the DSS coordinator can help to facilitate the inclusion of students with significant disabilities in college (Wehman et al., 2002).

Use of Technology Devices

Learning about available technology is critical for students with disabilities who are entering postsecondary programs. Students need access to technology in order to explore what is available to them and how they can best use these resources. The use of technology can greatly facilitate student learning. Screen readers, spell check, enlarging font size, and highlighting materials in color are just a few examples of uses of readily available technology for students with significant disabilities (Getzel et al., 2003; Hart et al., 2001). Students need opportunities to explore the use of technology to learn how to incorporate it into their learning. Having teaching materials and activities in digital formats allows for arranging information so that it is more accessible to diverse learners (Hart et al., 2001; Rose & Meyer, 2000). Continuing to educate faculty and staff about various technology and software and how to incorporate it into their curricula is

TABLE 19.4

Assistance to Disability Support Services (DSS) Staff

DSS staff members need to be invited to transition planning meetings to better understand the transition process and to plan for postsecondary education.

Training is needed for DSS staff to better understand the types of supports and services needed.

Guidelines and policies need to be developed by DSS staff to provide methods for assisting students entering college (documentation requirements, etc.), progressing through the university (if not going full time or in a specific degree program), and coordinating services and supports among other university entities and community agencies.

DSS staff must have access to current information and research concerning the assessment of college environments for students; successful transition models; and accommodation supports, strategies, and methods to use with faculty and staff.

---

also critical. The use of technology can greatly enhance the learning and application of knowledge by students with significant disabilities.

PLANNING FOR SUCCESS IN POSTSECONDARY SCHOOLS

This chapter has discussed several issues facing students with significant disabilities entering postsecondary programs, ideas and strategies for overcoming obstacles, and skills needed by students to successfully participate in these settings. This section will highlight important components of the planning process that need to be in place to ensure that students with disabilities have the greatest chance for succeeding in college.

Determine Students' Interests and Goals

It is critical that students with significant disabilities participate fully in the process to identify their postsecondary interests and goals. Using person-centered planning is an effective process for assisting students to express their interests and needs (Hart et al., 2001; Weir, 2001). A discussion of the potential outcomes of attending a postsecondary program should be part of this planning process. As a result of the information obtained, an individualized plan can be developed to facilitate the transition from secondary to postsecondary education.

Choose a Postsecondary Program

Once interests and goals have been established, it is important for students with significant disabilities, family members, and school personnel to determine the appropriate program for a student. The selection of a program will be based on a variety of factors, including the following:

- the interests of the student and how they match with existing coursework offered by the school
- the outcome a student will achieve as a result of enrolling in a program or course
- the requirements for entering a program or the process that a student must complete before entering the program
- the types of services and supports currently available on campus

Identify All Transition Participants

The Individualized Education Program (IEP) transition team or support team must be representative of everyone who is needed to ensure that a student will successfully transition to and remain in college. The DSS coordinator will play a critical role on the team. As indicated previously, representatives from postsecondary education typically do not participate on IEP transition teams. Input from postsecondary members will play a tremendous role in planning the logistics of enrolling students, determining courses to take, and identifying accommodations or services that will be provided.

Ensure That Students Have the Necessary Skills

As described earlier, self-determination skills are critical for students with significant disabilities entering postsecondary education (Grigal et al., 2001). These skills will help students to function more independently in a new environment that is very different from that of secondary education, and ultimately in a job setting. Academic preparation is also critical. Preparing students for possible participation in postsecondary education must begin early in their education.

Conduct Up-Front Planning

Students need to participate in an orientation to familiarize themselves as much as possible about the campus. Issues around transportation, documentation, services, and supports must all be addressed prior to entering a program or course (Hart et al., 2001). The specific services or supports that each player on the IEP transition team or support team will provide must be identified. The DSS coordinator, faculty members, community agencies, secondary education staff, students with disabilities, and family members should all be included in these discussions.

Use Flexibility and Creative Problem Solving

Providing opportunities in postsecondary education for students with disabilities is a relatively new educational frontier. Flexibility in planning and using creative problem-solving skills are essential. It is important that everyone involved in assisting students on campus communicates about issues or concerns that need to be addressed. Faculty members, DSS providers, students, family members, and community agencies must all work together to determine appropriate strategies to ensure that students can take full advantage of the opportunities available to them.

FINAL THOUGHTS

Increasing numbers of students with significant disabilities are seeking post-secondary education experiences to further their interests and career goals. This chapter has provided an overview of some of the current challenges and issues facing these students. In addition, strategies and ideas for resolving some of these issues have been discussed. The continuing advance of technology and the use of new teaching strategies such as universal instructional design will help in-crease the diversity of students in postsecondary education, as well as improve the outcome of their postsecondary experience. One group among this diverse population is students with significant disabilities. Their growing presence on college campuses will broaden awareness of their strengths and abilities, helping to expand their educational and career opportunities.

REFERENCES

Babbitt, B. C., & White, C. M. (2002). Helping students assess their readiness for postsecondary education. *Teaching Exceptional Children, 35*(2), 62–66.

Benz, M., Doren, B., & Yovanoff, P. (1998). Crossing the great divide: Predicting productive en-gagement for young women with disabilities. *Career Development for Exceptional Individu-als, 21*(1), 3–16.

Benz, M., Lindstrom, L., & Yovanoff, P. (2000). Improving graduation and employment outcomes of students with disabilities: Predictive factors and student perspectives. *Exceptional Chil-dren, 66*, 509–529.

Blackorby, J., & Wagner, M. (1996). Longitudinal postschool outcomes of youth with disabilities: Findings from the National Longitudinal Transition Study. *Exceptional Children, 62*, 399–413.

Bowe, F. G. (2000). *Universal design in education: Teaching nontraditional students.* Westport, CT: Bergin & Garvey.

Center on Disability Studies. (2002, December). Preparation for and support of youth with cogni-tive disabilities in postsecondary education. *Proceedings of the Second Summit of the Coali-tion for the Support of Individuals with Significant Disabilities in Postsecondary Education.* Boston: Author.

deFur, S. H., Getzel, E. E., & Trossi, K. (1996). Making the postsecondary education match: A role for transition planning. *Journal of Vocational Rehabilitation, 6*, 231–241.

Dolyniuk, C. A., Kamens, M. W., Corman, H., DiNardo, P. O., Totaro, R. M., & Rockoff, J. C. (2002). Students with developmental disabilities go to college: Description of a collabora-tive transition project on a regular college campus. *Focus on Autism and Other Develop-mental Disabilities, 17*(4), 236–241.

Durlak, C. M., Rose, E., & Bursuck, W. D. (1994). Preparing high school students with learn-ing disabilities for the transition to postsecondary education: Teaching the skills of self-determination. *Journal of Learning Disabilities, 27*(1), 51–59.

Fairweather, J. S., & Shaver, D. M. (1991). Making the transition to post-secondary education and training. *Exceptional Children, 57,* 264–268.

Frank, A. R., & Sitlington, P. L. (2000). Youth adults with mental disabilities—Does transition planning make a difference? *Education and Training in Mental Retardation and Developmental Disabilities, 35,* 119–134.

Gajar, A., Goodman, L., & McAfee, J. (1995). *Secondary schools and beyond: Transition of individuals with mild disabilities.* New York: Macmillan.

Getzel, E. E., Briel, L. W., & Kregel, J. (2000). Comprehensive career planning: The VCU career connections program. *Journal of Work, 14,* 41–49.

Getzel, E. E., & deFur, S. (1997). Transition planning for students with significant disabilities: Implications for student-centered planning. *Focus on Autism and Other Developmental Disabilities, 12*(1), 39–48.

Getzel, E. E., McManus, M. S., & Briel, L. (2003, February). *VCU's supported education model for students with LD and ADHD.* Symposium conducted at the meeting of Pac Rim Collaboration & Change: A Future of Choices for Mind, Body, & Spirit, Waikiki, HI.

Getzel, E. E., Stodden, R. A., & Briel, L. W. (2001). Pursuing postsecondary education opportunities for individuals with disabilities. In P. Wehman (Ed.), *Life beyond the classroom: Transition strategies for young people with disabilities.* Baltimore: Brookes.

Gilson, S. F. (1996). Students with disabilities: An increasing voice and presence on college campuses. *Journal of Vocational Rehabilitation, 6,* 263–272.

Grigal, M., Neubert, D. A., & Moon, M. S. (2001). Public school programs for students with significant disabilities in post-secondary settings. *Education and Training in Mental Retardation and Developmental Disabilities, 36*(3), 244–254.

Grigal, M., Neubert, D. A., & Moon, M. S. (2002). Postsecondary options for students with significant disabilities. *Teaching Exceptional Children, 35,* 68–73.

Hall, M., Kleinert, H. L., & Kearns, J. F. (2000). Postsecondary programs for students with moderate and severe disabilities. *Teaching Exceptional Children, 32,* 58–65.

Hart, D. (2002). *Preparation for and support of youth with cognitive disabilities in postsecondary education.* Symposium conducted at the meeting of Pac Rim Collaboration & Change: A Future of Choices for Mind, Body, & Spirit, Waikiki, HI.

Hart, D., Zafft, C., & Zimbrich, K. (2001). Creating access to college for all students. *Journal for Vocational Special Needs Education, 23*(2), 19–30.

Johnson, D. M., & Fox, J. A. (2003). Creating curb cuts in the classroom: Adapting universal design principles to education. In J. L. Higbee (Ed.), *Curriculum transformation and disability: Implementing universal design in higher education* (pp. 7–21). Minneapolis: Center for Research on Developmental Education and Urban Literacy.

Neubert, D. A., Moon, M. S., Grigal, M., & Redd, V. (2001). Post-secondary educational practices for individuals with mental retardation and other significant disabilities: A review of the literature. *Journal of Vocational Rehabilitation, 16,* 155–168.

Only skills training can counter growing income inequality. (1995). *Vocational Education Weekly, 8*(3), 3–4.

Page, B., & Chadsey-Rusch, J. (1995). The community college experience for students with and without disabilities: A viable transition outcome? *Career Development for Exceptional Individuals, 18*(2), 85–96.

Reis, S., Neu, T., & McGuire, J. M. (1997). Case studies of high-ability students with learning disabilities who have achieved. *Exceptional Children, 63,* 463–479.

Rose, D., & Meyer, A. (2000). Universal design for individual differences. *Educational Leadership, 58*(3), 39–43.

Silver, P., Bourke, A., & Strehorn, K. C. (1998). Universal instructional design in higher education: An approach for inclusion. *Equity & Excellence in Education, 2,* 47–51.

Stodden, R. A. (1998). School-to-work transition: Overview of disability legislation. In F. R. Rusch & J. G. Chadsey (Eds.), *Beyond high school: Transition from school to work* (pp. 60–76). Belmont, CA: Wadsworth.

Wehman, P., Getzel, E. E., & Thoma, C. A. (2002). *Postsecondary education for youth with intellectual disabilities.* Unpublished manuscript, Virginia Commonwealth University, Richmond.

Weir, C. (2001). *Individual supports for college success.* Retrieved June 24, 2004, from University of Maryland, On-Campus Outreach Web site: http://www.education.umd.edu/oco/resources/factsheet7.html

Wille-Gregory, M., Graham, J. W., & Hughes, C. (1995, Spring). Preparing students with learning disabilities for success in postsecondary education. *Transition Linc,* pp. 1–6. [Center for Innovations in Special Education, University of Missouri-Columbia, College of Education].

Wilson, K., Getzel, E., & Brown, T. (2000). Enhancing the post-secondary campus climate for students with disabilities. *Journal of Vocational Rehabilitation, 14*(1), 37–50.

CHAPTER 20

Legal Rights and Benefits

D. Michael Malone

LEARNING GOALS

Upon completing this chapter, the reader will be able to

- identify the central laws that provide legal rights and benefits to children with disabilities and their families
- reflect upon the cases provided relative to the laws discussed
- understand strategies that help parents advocate for their children's legal rights and benefits
- discuss options parents have when their children's legal rights are not met
- understand the importance of estate planning and describe strategies for effective planning
- provide responses to questions commonly asked by parents
- identify resources that parents and professionals can draw on to help them become informed advocates for children

P arenting is a journey filled with many joys and challenges. Unfortunately, for parents with children who experience developmental concerns, the challenges can, at times, overshadow the joys. The realization that their child might be experiencing problems, the process of formal diagnosis, weathering emotional adjustments, becoming knowledgeable about their child's particular concerns, determining their child's needs, and locating resources can be overwhelming and stressful. What does this mean for Chris, now and later? Where can I get information on Jody's condition? Am I on my own with this? Who do I go to for help? What will other people think about Kisha? How will she be treated? How much will Jon's services cost? Are there programs that can help me with Jenny? Although a child's welfare is ultimately the responsibility of the parents, several federal programs have been designed to help families support their child's needs (Malone & Orthner, 1988). This chapter describes these programs and how parents and children may benefit from them. It discusses several programs that guarantee child and family rights. It also advises parents about advocating for legal rights and benefits and about estate planning.

CASE EXAMPLE: JONATHAN

Jonathan was born prematurely and had many medical complications before his discharge from the hospital at 2 months of age. His teenage mother, Tina, was not employed and did not have medical insurance to cover Jonathan. With the help of the hospital staff, she applied for Supplemental Security Income (SSI), which also provided Medicaid health insurance. Jonathan was diagnosed with cerebral palsy at 6 months of age, and through the Child Find program in her community, Tina was able to enroll him in an early intervention program in which a physical therapist and early childhood educator visited him at home weekly. Jonathan continued to require special education programs and to need special equipment when he entered elementary school. Tina used the SSI funding to help purchase a van with a wheelchair lift and to construct a ramp and widen doorways in her house. As school progressed, Tina was generally satisfied with the Individualized Education Program (IEP), but sometimes she felt that not all of Jonathan's needs were being adequately addressed. She learned to advocate on his behalf and on one occasion requested a hearing and brought legal representation to obtain services she believed were necessary. During Jonathan's early school years, Tina went to college and eventually became a realtor. Although her income improved significantly, she was able to maintain Jonathan's Medicaid coverage through a waiver based on his disability rather than her income. When she changed jobs for a better position, Jonathan was covered by a COBRA policy until the new health policy became active. Tina set up a will that both provided financially for Jonathan and identified his grandparents as guardians in the event of Tina's death. Jonathan is now 14, and although he has significant physical disabilities, he also has many cognitive strengths. He is being evaluated for vocational rehabilitation services to plan for accommodations and training to help him successfully enter the workforce after he finishes his education. Although Tina needed help at first, over time she has become an expert in navigating the system to identify Jonathan's rights and benefits and has been empowered by the experience.

♦ CASE EXAMPLE: KATIE

Although Katie's parents knew that she could be rigid and controlling at times, their awareness of the difficulty she had in managing her impulses and interacting with other people grew when they enrolled her in preschool. Katie's teacher noticed that she seemed to be overwhelmed during times when there were moderate to high amounts of movement and noise, such as during transitions and group activities. At such times she might withdraw, resist, or act out. Observations of Katie and discussions between her parents and professionals resulted in the conclusion that she was experiencing problems with sensory overload. An intervention plan was developed that everyone believed would help her manage the typical classroom environment. The plan, which included strategies such as the use of a weighted vest and "brushing" followed by joint compression prior to transitions, was effectively imple-

mented in her preschool program. The success of the intervention plan was challenged, however, when she transitioned to kindergarten. In spite of the past success of the intervention strategies, a formal diagnosis by qualified professionals, and an IEP, the kindergarten teacher and school psychologist were resistant to both Katie's enrollment in the "regular" kindergarten and providing her with the supports she needed to manage that school setting. The passage of a year, continual meetings with school personnel, advocacy by professionals in the community who know Katie and her family, and a new teacher willing to implement IEP goals with the help of a teacher's aide resulted in Katie's receiving the supports she needed and enjoying a successful school year in an inclusive first-grade program. As for the next year ...

SUPPORTS PROVIDED BY FEDERAL PROGRAMS

The challenges faced by Jonathan and Katie and their families are not unique. Parents of children with disabilities are faced with understanding the resultant problems, determining what services and supports are needed, and learning about and negotiating with community agencies and programs that may not automatically address their concerns and needs. This section provides an overview of specific federal programs designed to offer supports to children with disabilities and their families, focusing on the rights and benefits that parents and children are entitled to under each program.

The Rehabilitation Act and Amendments

The Rehabilitation Act of 1973 was designed as a civil rights law that would protect people with disabilities from discrimination in areas such as employment, architectural accessibility, and transportation. The purpose of the law is to "empower individuals with disabilities to maximize employment, economic self-sufficiency, independence, and inclusion and integration into society." Section 504 of the Rehabilitation Act was implemented to ensure individuals with disabilities of participation in, access to benefits of, and protection from discrimination under programs receiving federal financial assistance. These rights are extended to children in schools. Disability is defined in Section 504 as a physical or mental impairment that substantially limits one or more major life activities. Physical and mental impairments include speech, hearing, visual, and orthopedic impairments; cerebral palsy; epilepsy; muscular dystrophy; multiple sclerosis; cancer; diabetes; heart disease; intellectual disability; emotional illness; specific learning disabilities (including perceptual impairments); brain injury; dyslexia; minimal brain dysfunction (now known as attention-deficit/hyperactivity disorder); and the communication disorder developmental aphasia. Major life activities include self-care, seeing, hearing, speaking, breathing, learning, walking, and performing manual tasks.

Section 504 ensures that children with disabilities are provided a free and appropriate public education (FAPE) in the most natural setting possible, such as a general education classroom. The law also requires schools to develop an educational plan that will meet the needs of children with disabilities. Parents must be notified about any identification, evaluation, or significant change in placement related to their child. Section 504 evaluation and placement procedures require the use of multiple information sources, formal documentation, team-based decision making, and periodic reevaluation. Section 504 also provides protection under due process for children in the event that the school does not fulfill its legal obligations. Schools must provide an impartial hearing for parents who disagree with the identification, evaluation, or placement of their child. Parents have the right to participate in any part of the hearing process and to be represented by legal counsel. Schools may use the IEP required by the Individuals with Disabilities Education Act (IDEA) to meet the Section 504 planning requirement. A Section 504 plan, however, is less complex than an IEP, so the school may develop and implement the simpler Section 504 plan if a child is eligible for Section 504 but not IDEA. Finally, specific funding and policy procedures related to Section 504 are the responsibility of local school districts.

Developmental Disabilities Assistance and Bill of Rights Act and Amendments

The Developmental Disabilities Assistance and Bill of Rights Act of 2000 (DD Act) was designed to promote the independence, productivity, and inclusion of people with disabilities into all facets of community life. The intent of the law is accomplished through support of state developmental disabilities (DD) councils, state protection and advocacy systems (P&As), and university-affiliated programs for persons with developmental disabilities (UAPs). The goals of the DD councils are to promote system-wide change to enhance individual capability and advocacy activities and to produce a responsive, family-centered, coordinated, and comprehensive system of services and supports for individuals with disabilities and their families. The P&As exist to protect the legal and human rights of individuals with disabilities and their families. UAPs are designed to provide interdisciplinary preservice training to students, to conduct community service activities, and to disseminate information and research findings about developmental disabilities. Finally, the DD Act provided the first entirely functional definition of developmental disabilities, removing the need for a person to receive a specific diagnostic label in order to be eligible for services. The DD Act defines developmental disability as a severe or chronic condition that can be attributed to a mental or physical impairment that is evidenced before an individual reaches the age of 22 years and that results in significant functional limitations in three or more major life activities, including self-care, receptive and expressive language, learning, mobility, self-direction, capacity for independent living, and economic self-sufficiency. For children under the age of 5 years, developmental disability is considered a significant delay in development or a specific congenital or acquired condition that would likely result in a developmental disability if services are not provided. Such a definition allows services to be provided to meet functional needs across all categories of disability. Any of these three programs can serve as a resource to parents and professionals for information, guidance in networking, and assistance in advocating for children.

Americans with Disabilities Act

The Americans with Disabilities Act of 1990 (ADA) is a civil rights law designed to protect people with disabilities from discrimination in employment, public services and accommodations, public transportation, and telecommunications. The ADA was designed to complement the Rehabilitation Act by using the same terms and definitions. The ADA does extend the protection of people with disabilities to all public services, programs, and activities, regardless of whether these services, programs, or activities receive federal financial assistance. As does the Rehabilitation Act, the ADA extends protection to any person who has a formal record of, or who is generally considered to have, a "physical or mental impairment that substantially limits one or more major life activities." Although the ADA does not specifically address the issue of FAPE, Title II of the ADA does state that "no qualified individual with a disability shall ... be excluded from participation in, or denied access to, programs or activities; denied benefits or services; or be subjected to discrimination by any public entity." This protection applies to children in day care and in private schools that are not administered by religious organizations or entities. Unfortunately, the ADA does not provide for funding of mandates, procedural safeguards, evaluation or placement procedures, or due process procedures specifically related to children's educational rights. It does, however, specify administrative requirements, complaint procedures, and consequences for noncompliance related to both services and employment, and provision of reasonable accommodations for eligible students across educational activities and settings. The determination of reasonable accommodations is specific both to individual children and to the program in question. The main test for determining the best accommodation for a child is effectiveness. In particular, the accommodation should provide the child in question with the same opportunities as children without disabilities in similar situations. The accommodation does not have to ensure the child in question equal results or benefits, however. A program does not need to provide accommodations that represent undue hardship (significant difficulty or expense) or that would fundamentally change the nature of the program. Accommodations that programs can be expected to make to support the participation of children with disabilities can include, but are not limited to, modifications of tests, equipment, and facilities; alternate location of services; assignment of aides; provision of written communication in alternative formats; and construction of new facilities. Parents who have questions about accommodations that are (or are not) planned for their child should consult with a qualified attorney.

Education for All Handicapped Children Act and Individuals with Disabilities Education Act Amendments

The Education for All Handicapped Children Act of 1975, later renamed and reauthorized as the Individuals with Disabilities Education Act of 1990 (IDEA) and subsequent amendments, is the most comprehensive law supporting the developmental and educational experiences of children with disabilities. IDEA focuses on children and young adults from birth to 21 years of age who experience physical or mental conditions that result in developmental delays in cognitive, physical, communicative, social or emotional, or adaptive development. Part C of the law provides for children under 3 years of age who need early intervention services because they either (a) are experiencing developmental delays in cognitive, physical, communicative, social or emotional, or adaptive development, or (b) have a diagnosed physical or mental condition that has a high probability of resulting in developmental delay. Delays must be determined using appropriate diagnostic instruments and procedures. For children 3 to 21 years of age, disabilities are specifically defined as mental retardation (intellectual disability); hearing, visual, or speech impairment; deafness; blindness; serious emotional disturbance; orthopedic impairment; autism; traumatic brain injury; other health impairments; specific learning disabilities; deaf–blindness; or multiple disabilities. Other conditions can be included if they are likely to result in the need for special education or related services.

     IDEA requires schools to provide children with disabilities with a FAPE that includes special education and, if needed, related services (i.e., psychological services; speech, physical, and occupational therapy; diagnostic medical services; school health services; therapeutic recreation; counseling; social work services; transportation; and parent counseling and training). Under IDEA, children have the right to be educated in the least restrictive environment (LRE). Schools should approach the education of a child with disabilities with the assumption that the child will be enrolled in the general education classroom with peers who do not have disabilities. Other program options (e.g., resource room, separate class, separate school) should be considered only when it is determined that the educational needs of the child cannot be met in the general education classroom. IDEA provides children with the right to team-based determination of eligibility and services and the development and use of an Individualized Family Service Plan (IFSP) for children younger than 3 years or an IEP for children 3 years and older. Depending on the child's age, the individualized plan should include specific supports for the transition from infant–toddler programs to preschool, preschool to kindergarten, middle school to high school, and high school to postschool opportunities. Finally, IDEA guarantees parents and their children written notice regarding identification, evaluation, and placement action; team and multisource evaluation and placement procedures; the right to participate in IFSP and IEP meetings; periodic review; and the right to impartial hearings if the parents disagree with the school on identification, evaluation, or placement of their child.

Supplemental Security Income

The Supplemental Security Income (SSI) program for children with disabilities can provide parents and children with financial support if the parents can demonstrate that (a) the child meets the standard of disability and (b) the family meets the established income and asset requirements specified by the Social Security Administration. It is important to understand that the SSI program described here and the Social Security Disability Insurance program are different programs. To meet the SSI standard of disability, a child must have a

> medically determinable physical or mental impairment which results in marked and severe functional limitations, and which can be expected to result in death or which has lasted or can be expected to last for a continuous period of not less than 12 months.

This standard is supplemented by both a listing of over 100 disabilities (e.g., blindness, deafness, cerebral palsy, mental retardation) and a description of functioning in broad developmental areas including cognition, communication, motor skills, social and personal growth, concentration, persistence, pace, and responsivity. Evidence that supports a child's "marked and severe functional limitations" includes medical and school records, reports, and letters describing the child's functional abilities. Features that can be considered in determining a child's eligibility include effects of medication, living conditions and environment, need for assistive devices, and school functioning. Information about a child's disability can be obtained from medical personnel, teachers, counselors, therapists, social workers, and others who provide services. Although no specific condition is excluded, keep in mind that a child's eligibility is based on documentation that he or she is experiencing severe functional limitations.

In addition to meeting a disability standard, parents must demonstrate that the family meets an income or asset standard. Several factors are considered in determining income or asset eligibility, including actual income, the number of dependents in the household, and the total value of certain items owned (limits of $2,000 for a single person and $3,000 for a couple). If both the disability and the income or asset standards are met, a family may be eligible for up to about $512 per month (as established by the Social Security Administration for the year 2000). This figure will vary depending on individual family circumstances. Some states supplement the SSI benefits. Families receiving SSI benefits are required to establish a dedicated bank account into which the Social Security

Administration can directly deposit SSI benefits. SSI benefits can be used in a variety of ways to support the child with a disability, including education, job-related training, personal needs assistance, specialized equipment, housing modifications, medical treatment, and therapy or rehabilitation.

All children who are determined to be eligible for SSI must undergo a periodic Continued Disability Review (CDR), or redetermination, to make sure they continue to meet SSI eligibility standards. If a child is considered eligible due to prematurity, he or she must undergo a CDR by 1 year of age. If a child's eligibility was determined for a reason other than low birth weight, he or she will undergo a CDR every 3 years until he or she is 18 years of age. When the child turns 18 years of age, eligibility will be considered in relation to the adult standards, which place an emphasis on an individual's ability to work. While a child is receiving SSI, the parent must provide evidence of the child's limitations and any interventions that are being conducted to address those limitations.

Finally, SSI eligibility may automatically qualify a child for Medicaid benefits. Depending on a family's specific circumstances, the child may or may not continue to qualify for Medicaid benefits if he or she loses SSI benefits. It is important that parents contact their local Social Security Administration office to determine the state regulations related to SSI and Medicaid eligibility.

Medicaid

The Medicaid program is a needs-based program that provides children with special access to important health services (Medicaid, 42 U.S.C. § 1396 *et seq.*). Families whose income places them at or below 133% of the poverty threshold and whose children meet the disability guidelines established for SSI just discussed can qualify for Medicaid benefits. For example, a single-parent household including two children under 18 years of age could quality for Medicaid if the family income is at or below about $17,850. A two-parent household including two children under 18 years of age could quality for Medicaid if the family income is at or below about $22,470. This example is an approximation based on the U.S. Census Bureau's 1999 projections of the poverty threshold (actual eligibility may vary). Some states have raised the standard to as high as 185%, 250%, 300%, or even 400% of the federal poverty level. In most states, a child automatically qualifies for Medicaid if the parent can establish SSI eligibility.

Children who qualify for Medicaid benefits can take advantage of the program's Early and Periodic Screening, Diagnostic, and Treatment (EPSDT) services. This group of services is designed to make sure that all children who are eligible for Medicaid receive necessary health care. EPSDT services include developmental screening services (i.e., developmental history, physical and mental assessment, immunizations, laboratory tests, health education, etc.), diagnostic services (e.g., dental, hearing, and vision services), assistive technology (e.g., hearing aids, eyeglasses, communication devices), assistance with transportation and scheduling of appointments, and preventative and corrective treatment services (i.e., optional services such as service coordination to help protect families' rights, ensure procedural safeguards, and enable access to services authorized by the state; occupational, physical, and speech therapy; rehabilitative services; and private duty nursing). A child can receive EPSDT services from physicians, nurses, pediatricians, or other qualified health care providers who are certified by the state's Medicaid program. State Medicaid agencies coordinate their efforts with a variety of other social service agencies to identify and enroll all eligible children.

Finally, there are several "safety nets" in the Medicaid program to protect families who are not able to provide necessary health care because of the child's health condition or because of the family's financial status. First, Medicaid waivers have been developed by states to allow families to provide or have access to home and community-based care that would not be covered under private insurance. In a waiver program, the state uses both federal and state money to pay for health care for people with health conditions specified in the waiver program. Waiver programs are often more flexible than the federal Medicaid program and may be different from state to state. Eligibility for Medicaid waivers is based only on a child's developmental disability, not on a family's income or assets. The health-care coverage provided by these waivers is especially critical if private insurance does not cover a child's health-care needs or the family has exceeded the limits of its private insurance. Before the development of the Medicaid waivers, the only option that many families had for accessing Medicaid was to have their children institutionalized in approved residential care facilities (e.g., nursing homes). A waiver program can allow for less costly home and community care.

The second safety net of the Medicaid program is the Presumptive Eligibility Option, through which approved health-care providers are allowed to provide temporary Medicaid enrollment for children who appear to be eligible based on age and family income. Third, the Medicaid program now includes a 12-Month Continuous Eligibility Option. Should a child's Medicaid eligibility end for any reason, the state can continue the child's coverage for as long as 12 months after the unfavorable redetermination. Finally, the State Children's Health Insurance Program (CHIP) was created to provide health-care coverage for families whose incomes are too high to allow them to qualify for Medicaid but too low to enable the family to afford adequate coverage through private insurance. Parents should contact their local Medicaid program representative to determine options related to eligibility and benefits.

Consolidated Omnibus Budget Reconciliation Act

The Consolidated Omnibus Budget Reconciliation Act of 1985 (COBRA) was written to provide health-care support to families in the event that an income earner experiences a change in employment status that would otherwise result in a loss of group health plan coverage provided by an employer. The provisions protect only certain employees on the basis of their length of service, the size of the company, and the type of health insurance the company provides. COBRA defines a number of circumstances as qualifying events that might normally result in a loss of health-care benefits for the covered employee, including a shift from full-time to part-time employment, voluntary or involuntary termination of employment, becoming eligible for Medicare, legal separation or divorce, death of the covered employee, and loss of the "dependent child" status as defined in the plan. In such circumstances, the employee is granted a 60-day period during which he or she can choose to pay for continued health-care coverage under the employer's group health plan. In short, the law is intended to provide families with a "safety net." Although an employee can only purchase continued health-care benefits for as long as 36 months (depending on the circumstance), the amount that the employee will pay for premiums during this time is typically less than the cost of purchasing private health-care insurance. The continued health-care coverage purchased by the employee should be identical to that which was available prior to the change in employment status. Employers are obligated to notify employees of the COBRA provisions when they are first employed and at the time their status changes.

ADVOCATING FOR CHILDREN'S LEGAL RIGHTS AND BENEFITS

The federal programs described above are designed to ensure that the rights of children and families are protected and that education, health care benefits, and financial support are provided. In spite of the intent of and protection offered by these programs, parents may find themselves at odds with their local, state, or federal service system at some point. Although conflict between parents and professionals can be a result of someone's (e.g., an administrator's, counselor's, teacher's, specialist's) intentional efforts to ignore federal requirements, such willful negligence is not common. More typically, conflicts are a result of honest mistakes, a lack of sensitivity to or understanding of needs, a lack of knowledge about federal requirements, different interpretations of federal requirements, or differences in opinion regarding options and strategies for meeting children's needs. All of these situations can be addressed through open communication, the sharing of information, and a willingness to learn about and explore options.

There are several things parents should consider when advocating for their children. First, parents need to understand and believe that they are the experts on their children. Does this mean that they have the technical knowledge that a professional might have? Not necessarily. But they do have the best knowledge about who their child is (his or her interests, abilities, potential, and needs). As the experts, parents not only have information that will help the professionals provide the most appropriate supports for their children, but they also have the greatest motivation to see that their children's needs are met. Parents should use that knowledge and motivation to their advantage.

Second, parents should learn about their child's disability and about the services that are available. This will not only make them informed advocates, but will also put them in a position in which they do not have to take on faith the information provided by professionals. Parents will find that they will better understand different perspectives and the full range of options available to them and their child.

Third, parents should consider carefully what they want for their child, what they are doing to meet that goal (to get what they want), whether their plan to meet that goal is working, and if it is not working, what they need to change to make it a more effective plan. Such planning enables parents to both generate alternatives and understand alternatives generated by others. The process also helps parents to consider the viability, acceptability, and potential effectiveness of alternatives as well as to become personally responsible for their child's future.

Fourth, parents should foster a positive partnership with professionals through open and honest communication. They can learn about the supports that are available to them and their child, and professionals will learn about the child's and the family's needs. As a team, parents and professionals can identify ways to support child and family needs and protect their basic rights. Communication helps everyone to learn, to share, and to clear up misunderstandings.

Fifth, parents should learn to network with other parents and professionals who are experienced and knowledgeable (Rothman & Ostrosky, 1998). They should seek information that might be useful to them and their child. They should not be afraid to ask lots of questions. Parents should establish informal relationships for the purpose of gathering information and formal relationships so that they have someone to help them advocate for their child. They should choose as an advocate a person with whom they feel comfortable and who has relevant knowledge, resources, and contacts in the community. Finally, parents should discuss expectations, roles, and responsibilities early in the relationship and document all in-person, telephone, and written communications. It is always a good idea for parents to ask for written confirmation from the person with whom they have spoken. Documentation is especially important when decisions are being made, because it helps everyone involved "stay on the same page" and avoid misunderstandings. Parents should create a file for documentation and keep that file organized in chronological order, up to date, and in a handy location.

When Rights and Needs Are Not Being Met

There will be times when parents act in good faith, demonstrate patience and proactive communication skills, and provide necessary documentation and still find that their child's rights and needs are not being met. The challenges that these parents face may be directly related to the personal views and actions of the professional with whom they are working (e.g., lack of knowledge, different interpretation of the situation or program policy, personal values and beliefs). The challenges, however, may also be a direct result of program policies or procedures. The person with whom the parents are working may agree with them but feel bound by how he or she interprets the program rules and regulations. When parents find that they cannot make progress in getting their child's needs met, they should first seek informal mediation and voluntary compliance. They should solicit the advice or assistance of a formal advocate, someone who understands the specific challenges with which they are faced. They should make sure that all stakeholders are present during mediation. If informal mediation does not work, they will need to file a formal complaint following the grievance procedures of the program or business with which they are interacting. During a formal complaint procedure, the services of a qualified and impartial mediator should be secured. During this type of hearing, parents have the right to have legal counsel present. If mediation is not successful, they can file a formal complaint with the federal agency responsible for administrative oversight of the rights being violated (e.g., the U.S. Department of Justice for civil rights discrimination, the U.S. Department of Education for IDEA violations, the Social Security Administration for SSI violations, and the Health Care Financing Administration for Medicaid violations). Parents can also file a civil action lawsuit, which may be necessary if they believe that their child's rights are being violated and they have exhausted all other options. Parents should contact local and state consumer organizations (e.g., P&As, parent training and information centers, legal aid groups, and the Commissioner's Directory of Lawyers Practicing Disability Law) for direction and advice. They could talk with an attorney they know personally and ask for a reference. It is critical that the attorney secured to represent a case involving the rights of a child with a disability is knowledgeable about disability law. Finally, parents should choose an attorney they believe they can trust.

ESTATE PLANNING

People often do not give careful consideration to planning for the future when they are investing so much energy in making sure that their child's immediate needs are met. Regardless of financial status, estate planning is critical for ensuring that their children's needs continue to be met after the parents are gone (Frolik, 1992). There are a number of issues that parents must consider as they plan their estate, including establishing a will. This document outlines the parents' wishes related to the estate and children, including guardianship, gifts and inheritance, and beneficiaries. The issue of guardianship is critical for all minor children and children over the age of 18 who are not considered fully competent to care for themselves. Parents are the natural guardians of their children, the people responsible for their children's care and welfare. In the event of the death of the parents, someone else must be appointed guardian of the children. Appointed guardians are often family members or friends whom parents trust to act in their children's best interests. There are three basic types of appointed guardians: (a) a guardian who is authorized to provide consent for a child's activities of daily living, (b) a guardian of the estate who has authority over a child's finances and property, and (c) a general guardian who would have authority over both personal activities and finances and property. If parents fail to appoint a guardian, the state can assume the responsibility of appointing one. Although the decision should be made with the best interests of the children in mind, this cannot be guaranteed; the state-appointed guardian may not be someone of whom the parents would approve. Finally, guardianship for individuals over the age of 18 may be complete or limited in scope, depending on the individual's level of competence. In the case of limited guardianship, the courts can decide the scope of the guardian's authority.

It is important to understand that wills can be modified as needed to address changes in financial circumstances and in a child's medical or financial needs. When developing the plan, parents should consider the following:

- Design the plan to meet specific circumstances and the specific needs of the child. An estate plan should be unique, based on the nature and severity of the child's disability. For example, the type and scope of guardianship will be a function of the child's needs and competence.
- Evaluate the child's current and projected circumstances and need for benefits related to health, productivity and earning potential, and independence.
- Consider the child's current government benefits (e.g., SSI and Medicaid) *and* the child's potential for needing such benefits in the future. Parents should consider how the plan they develop may affect their child's eligibility for government benefits. For instance, giving a child a gift or inheritance of more than $2,000 can make that child ineligible for SSI and Medicaid benefits. Not only could the child lose the cash and medical benefits available through these programs, but he or she could also lose benefits related to supported employment and vocational rehabilitation services, group housing, job coaches, personal attendant care, and transportation assistance.
- Consider developing a Special Needs Trust. A Special Needs Trust is put in the name of a trustee whom the parent identifies and who agrees to manage the child's resources. Because the trust is not in the child's name, he or she can remain eligible for government benefits (Fee, 1992b).
- Write a Letter of Intent to be included with the will. This document should provide the reader with a rich description of the child's history, current status, personal insights, and the parents' hopes for his or her future. The letter can include the contributions from all relevant stakeholders, including the child, and should be modified as needed. The Letter of Intent is not a legal document, but it can provide court personnel and others with guidance in understanding the child and the wishes of the parents (Fee, 1992a).

Finally, parents should seek the advice and guidance of a qualified attorney or certified estate planner who is knowledgeable about both estate planning and government programs that can provide their child with necessary supports (Frolik, 1992). The local P&A office, the Arc (formerly the Association for Retarded Citizens), and the local bar association can help parents find a qualified professional.

COMMONLY ASKED QUESTIONS

- *How do I find out what my child's rights are under the law?* In most cases, programs or agencies will provide parents with information about rights and benefits. However, it is always a good idea to become an informed consumer. Parents should ask questions, do some research, and talk with other parents. The technological revolution has made information available to parents that would have been relatively inaccessible 10 years ago. Parents who are not comfortable with computers should find a friend who is or meet with their local librarian to learn to surf the Internet.

• *Why are some professionals cooperative and others not?* People and programs are going to differ on values, attitudes, education, understanding, and interpretation. Parents' experiences will vary as a function of the people with whom they interact. Although federal programs are intended to be implemented consistently, the reality is that they are not, and some of this is a reflection of the personnel who are responsible for implementation. As noted previously, there are many reasons for different interpretations. A person might agree with a parent on one level but feel bound by program policies or regulations.

• *What do I do if my child's rights are being violated?* Parents should first assume that an honest mistake has been made and seek to clarify the situation. They should make sure that they are included in the process and that their voice is being heard. If they cannot get resolution on their own or with the help of an advocate, they may need to seek formal mediation or, if all else fails, resolution through legal channels.

• *How do I find an advocate for my child?* Parents should talk with other parents they know or parents of children who have preceded their child in the system. They should talk with professionals they trust and with whom they are comfortable. If necessary, they can contact local disability-related agencies. Finally, they can contact their local P&A office for advice.

• *I live a pretty modest lifestyle—do I really need an estate plan?* All families, regardless of financial circumstances, should take the time to develop an estate plan. Parents can leave their child with a disability vulnerable if no plan has been developed. The time taken and stress related to developing a plan are worth the peace of mind it will bring in the long run.

FINAL THOUGHTS

A number of federal programs have been developed in an effort to reduce the number and intensity of some of the challenges that children with disabilities and their families may experience. This chapter has provided an overview of some of these programs and how parents and their children can benefit from them, as well as some suggestions for advocating for children's legal rights and benefits. Finally, it is important that parents draw up a will so that their child's needs can continue to be met even after they are no longer alive.

REFERENCES

Americans with Disabilities Act of 1990, 42 U.S.C. § 12101 *et seq.*

Consolidated Omnibus Budget Reconciliation Act of 1985, 42 U.S.C. § 300 gg–41.

Developmental Disabilities Assistance and Bill of Rights Act of 2000, 42 U.S.C. § 6000 *et seq.*

Education for All Handicapped Children Act of 1975, 20 U.S.C. § 1400 *et seq.*

Fee, R. W. (1992a). The letter of intent. *News Digest, 2*(1) [Estate Planning issue, ND18]. Retrieved June 25, 2004, from National Information Center for Children and Youth with Disabilities Web site: http://www.nichcy.org/pubs/newsdig/nd18txt.htm

Fee, R. W. (1992b). The special needs trust. *News Digest, 2*(1) [Estate Planning issue, ND18]. Retrieved June 25, 2004, from National Information Center for Children and Youth with Disabilities Web site: http://www.nichcy.org/pubs/newsdig/nd18txt.htm

Frolik, L. A. (1992). Overview of estate planning issues. *News Digest, 2*(1) [Estate Planning issue, ND18]. Retrieved June 25, 2004, from National Information Center for Children and Youth with Disabilities Web site: http://www.nichcy.org/pubs/newsdig/nd18txt.htm

Individuals with Disabilities Education Act Amendments of 1997, 20 U.S.C. § 1401 (26). Retrieved June 25, 2004, from http://www.ed.gov/Offices/OSERS/IDEA/

Malone, D. M., & Orthner, D. K. (1988). Infant Care as a parent education resource: Recent trends in care issues. *Family Relations, 37,* 367–372.

Medicaid, 42 U.S.C. § 1396 *et seq.* Retrieved September 14, 2004, from www.cms.hhs.gov/medicaid/publications/overview-medicare-medicaid/default4.asp

Personal Responsibility and Work Opportunity Act of 1996 (Supplemental Security Income Program for Children), 42 U.S.C. § 211 *et seq.*

Rehabilitation Act of 1973, 29 U.S.C. § 701 *et seq.* (Amendments occurred in 1992 and 1998.) Retrieved June 25, 2004, from http://www.dol.gov/oasam/regs/statutes/sec504.htm

Rothman, S. M., & Ostrosky, M. M. (1998, August). Six recommendations to consider when choosing an advocate for your special needs child. *National Parent Information Network: Parent News, 4*(8). Retrieved from http://npin.org/pnews/1998/pnew898.htm

AUTHOR INDEX

SUBJECT INDEX

AAMR. *See* American Association on Mental Retardation (AAMR)

ABC paradigm. *See* Antecedent–behavior–consequence (ABC paradigm)

Aberrant Behavior Checklist (Aman & Singh), 298

Ability–achievement discrepancies, 328–329

Abrahamson v. Hershman, 100

Absence seizures, 276–277

Academic interventions, 300–301

Acquired megacolon, 52

Action plans, 23–24, 43–44

Active treatment, 175

ADHD. *See* Attention-deficit/hyperactivity disorder (ADHD)

Administration on Aging, 163

Adolescent Behavior Checklist (Demb, Brier, & Huron), 298

Advocacy. *See also* Self-advocacy
   consumer empowerment and, 15–16
   epilepsy, 288–289
   independent living and, 456
   legal rights and benefits and, 536–538
   protection and advocacy systems (P&As), 530

African Americans, 33, 106–107

Aggression, 186, 200, 297, 313

Aging. *See* Older individuals with lifelong disabilities

Alaska, 482

Alaska Natives, 106

Alzheimer's disease, 159–160

Amendments to the Rehabilitation Act of 1973. *See* Rehabilitation Act Amendments (P.L. 102-569)

American Association on Mental Retardation (AAMR)
   adaptive domains and, 125, 127, 136
   definition of mental retardation, 13, 190, 193, 224
   four dimensions of supports of, 193
   identification of behavior consultant guidelines of, 405
   older individuals with lifelong disabilities and, 155
   PCP and, 17

American Psychiatric Association (APA), 296

American Psychological Association, 405

Americans with Disabilities Act of 1990 (ADA; P.L. 101-336)
   case law concerning, 453–454
   employment and, 28
   epilepsy and, 284–285
   independent living and, 451–452
   individuals with severe intellectual disabilities and, 223
   nondiscrimination protections of, 434–435, 451–452
   older individuals with lifelong disabilities and, 164
   provisions of, 11, 531–532
   return-to-work policy and, 432
   supported employment and, 413, 414, 432, 434–435, 438

Analogue functional analysis, 397

Antecedent–behavior–consequence (ABC paradigm), 397

Anxiety, 61, 300

APA. *See* American Psychiatric Association (APA)

Appropriate education, 102–103

The Arc, 141, 164, 539

Arizona, 450, 482

Arkansas, 482

Asian–Pacific Islanders, 33, 106

Asperger's disorder, 313

Assessment and evaluation. *See also* Intelligence testing
   adaptive behavior and, 191
   diversity and, 101, 191
   effectiveness measures for supported employment, 417–426
   for emotional disturbances, 298–300
   IDEA Amendments and, 111
   nondiscriminatory evaluation and, 102
   for positive behavior support (PBS), 396–397, 404
   of severe intellectual disability, 225
   steps of referral and assessment process, 104–105

Assessment Center Deaf Exercise Adaptation Model, 432

Assistive technology. *See also* Technology
   cerebral palsy and, 248–249
   Idea mandates for, 99, 111, 248
   IEP and, 248–249
   independent living and, 459, 464–465
   overview of, 111–113
   for self-care, 251–254
   supported employment and, 267, 428–429, 431
   transition from school to adulthood and, 133–134

Assistive Technology Act of 1998, 464

Association for Behavior Analysis, 405

Ataxia, 242

Athetosis, 242

Attendant care. *See* Personal assistant services (PAS)

Attention, 332–333, 343–345, 399–400

Attention-deficit disorder, 350

Attention-deficit/hyperactivity disorder (ADHD), 327, 331, 336–337, 344, 350

Auras, 276

Autism
   Asperger's disorder, 313
   behavior issues, 312–313, 315–321
   case examples, 52, 317–321
   causes of, 310–311
   characteristics of, 311–313
   communication impairments and, 312
   definition of, 310
   diagnosis and assessment of, 8, 298
   employment and, 315
   genetics and, 311
   IDEA and, 98
   incidence of, 310
   medical services, 314–315
   medication for, 314
   personal perspective on, 185–188
   social relationships and, 311–312, 318

CONTRIBUTORS

Beth A. Bader, PhD, has been associated with the State Partnership and Systems Change Initiative (SPI) Project Office at Virginia Commonwealth University since the beginning of the project in 1998. SPI, a collaboration among the Social Security Administration, the Rehabilitation Services Administration, the Substance Abuse and Mental Health Services Administration, and the Department of Labor, seeks to evaluate work incentives and systems change initiatives that result in increased employment of people with disabilities being implemented in 17 different states. For the past 30 years, Dr. Bader has provided direct service, consultation, and technical assistance within health, mental health, mental retardation, rehabilitative services, social services, and other disability-related state agencies. In recent years, she has provided assistance in interpreting and analyzing state and federal policies, especially as they relate to individuals with disabilities who are seeking employment through One-Stop Career Centers. Currently, Dr. Bader is a research associate at the Rehabilitation Research and Training Center at Virginia Commonwealth University.

William N. Bender, PhD, taught in a junior high special education resource room for several years before receiving his PhD in special education from the University of North Carolina in 1983. He has published over 60 articles and 10 books on special and general education. His primary research has focused on several areas, including learning disabilities, discipline, school violence, and differentiated instruction. His easy humor and practical experience keep demand high for his workshops; he travels widely, speaking at various education conventions, and conducts over 30 workshops for school districts each year.

Mary Boat, PhD, is an assistant professor of early childhood education at the University of Cincinnati. She has worked extensively in interdisciplinary professional preparation for personnel who work with young children with and without disabilities and their families. This work has included preservice undergraduate and graduate preparation, as well as in-service training for professionals in the early childhood and early childhood special education fields. Dr. Boat has been the recipient of state and federal grants related to working directly with young children with disabilities, as well as service delivery and policy issues. She has conducted, published, and presented research related to early intervention and personnel preparation. In addition, she has provided service to early intervention programs and schools through numerous collaborative and consultative efforts. She has been extensively involved in early-intervention leadership activities, including serving as professional cochair of the North Carolina Interagency Coordinating Council.

Valerie (Vicki) Brooke, MEd, is a faculty member at Virginia Commonwealth University (VCU) and has been working in the field of employment for people with disabilities since 1979. She earned her MEd from VCU in special education with an emphasis on employment. As the director of training at the Rehabilitation Research and Training Center on Workplace Supports, funded by the U.S. Department of Education's National Institute on Disability and Rehabilitation Research, as well as project director for the Social Security

Administration's Regional Technical Assistance Center on Benefits Planning Assistance and Outreach, she is responsible for developing personnel training and technical assistance programs using innovative formats, to include distance education technologies. Vicki is interested in all aspects of employment-related issues and concerns that impact the employment rate and advancement of people with disabilities. She is a frequent speaker, consultant, and author of numerous book chapters, journal articles, newsletters, and fact sheets in all areas of employment.

Elaine Clark, PhD, is a professor in the Department of Educational Psychology at the University of Utah and training director of the School Psychology program. She has an extensive background in school, clinical, and neuropsychology. Dr. Clark received a PhD in educational psychology at Michigan State University, and a PhD in clinical psychology with a specialization in neuropsychology from Brigham Young University. Her primary research and teaching interest is in the area of genetic and neurological conditions, including mental retardation and acquired brain injuries. She is on the staff at the University Neuropsychiatric Institute and University Psychoeducational Clinic and is involved nationally on boards to promote the education of children with disabilities (e.g., Council of Directors of School Psychology Programs and the American Psychological Association's Division 16 Executive Board). She also serves on the boards of the Brain Injury Association of Utah and the state school psychology association. Dr. Clark has been actively involved in statewide training of school personnel in severe low- incidence disabilities. She has published a couple of books on issues pertaining to the education of children with brain injuries and has published numerous chapters and articles. She is the recipient of a number of federal grants and is currently the principal investigator of a U.S. Department of Education leadership grant to train doctoral students in the area of severe disabilities (e.g., autism, intellectual disabilities, and brain injuries). She is particularly interested in the psychological health of children with disabilities and is involved with research on mental illness and disability.

Sharon H. deFur, EdD, is an associate professor of special education and area coordinator of curriculum and instruction in the School of Education at the College of William and Mary. Prior to joining the faculty at William and Mary, Dr. deFur served as the coordinator of transition services for the State of Virginia. She is a past president of the Council for Exceptional Children's Division on Career Development and Transition. Her research interests include topics related to youth and young adults with disabilities and their successful transition from school to postschool environments, standards-based reform and its impact on students with disabilities, and the evaluation of effective special education personnel preparation initiatives.

Stacy Dymond, PhD, is an assistant professor of special education at the University of Illinois at Urbana-Champaign, where she teaches curriculum courses for students in the special education and elementary education programs. She currently codirects two research projects. One focuses on access to the general curriculum for high school students with significant cognitive disabilities in inclusive school and community settings. The second is an investigation of high school service learning programs that serve students with and without disabilities.

Cecil Fore III, PhD, is an assistant professor in the Department of Special Education at the University of Georgia who specializes in curriculum-based assessment, minority issues, and cultural bias in testing. He received his PhD from Southern Illinois University in 1999. For the past 2 years, Dr. Fore has worked on developing effective techniques for including students with disabilities in general education classrooms in Alabama and Georgia. He is currently collaborating on a Georgia State Improvement Grant to provide professional development and training for regular classroom teachers on inclusion issues. His other research projects involve rural and urban special education, mentoring new teachers, and the use of technology in the classroom.

Elizabeth Evans Getzel, MA, is the director of postsecondary education initiatives at the Virgina Commonwealth University Rehabilitation Research and Training Center on Workplace Supports. Ms. Getzel has over 20 years of experience conducting research, evaluation, and training in the areas of transition planning for secondary students with disabilities, postsecondary education for students with disabilities, and career planning and employment for individuals with disabilities. She has authored and coauthored several articles and book chapters on her work in the areas of transition and postsecondary education.

Ray Graesser obtained his master's degree in rehabilitation administration and services at Southern Illinois University. He worked as case manger, grant writer, and administrator for a variety of programs that serve people with disabilities at the Virginia Department of Rehabilitative Services and served as a computer analyst for the same agency. He was the parent of a child with severe autism. Ray passed away in 2004.

Lesa Nitcy Hope, MSW, lives in Atlanta with her husband, Martyn, and daughter, Nadia. She manages a family support program for people with mental retardation at the Atlanta Alliance on Developmental Disabilities. She is completing her PhD in social work at the University of Georgia. Her research interests are community practice and issues related to developmental disabilities.

Katherine Inge, PhD, OTR, is an assistant professor at Virginia Commonwealth University and has been associated with the university for 21 years. She is currently the director of instructional technology for the Rehabilitation Research and Training Center on Workplace Supports and the director of the Training and Technical Assistance to Providers Project. She has directed a number of federally funded supported-employment projects for individuals who have significant disabilities. She has also coauthored two books, one on assistive technology, and authored numerous articles on the employment of individuals with significant disabilities.

William R. Jenson, PhD, graduated from Utah State University in 1976 with a degree in applied behavior analysis and school psychology. He completed a clinical internship at Las Vegas Mental Health Center and later directed the Adolescent Residential Center there. He then assumed the directorship of the Children's Behavior Therapy Unit (CBTU) for Salt Lake Mental Health. This center is a day hospital and school for autistic and behaviorally disordered students. After directing CBTU for 8 years, Dr. Jenson joined the School Psychology Program in the Educational Psychology Department at the University of Utah. He is currently a professor in the Department of Educational Psychology and was department chair for 10 years. His research interests include autism, externalizing behavior disorders, the management of noncompliance and aggression, practical classroom behavior management, educational technology, behavioral assessment, academic interventions, and parent training. He has published numerous research papers and books, including the *Tough Kid Book; Tough Kid Tool Box: A Resource Book; Applied Behavior Analysis in Teaching; Understanding Childhood Behavior Disorders; Teaching Behaviorally Disordered Students: Preferred Practices; Best Practices: Behavioral and Educational Strategies for Teachers;* and the Homework Partners Series, as well as classroom computer products including Get'm on Task (GOT) and the Functional Assessment and Interventions Program (FAIP).

Thomas J. Kehle, PhD, is a professor at the University of Connecticut and training director of the School Psychology Program. Dr. Kehle graduated from the University of Kentucky in 1972 with a major in school psychology. Besides directing the School Psychology Program, he currently consults with school districts in Connecticut and Massachusetts. In addition to consulting and training school psychologists, he conducts research on behavior management strategies and writes extensively in this area. He is working on a book on preferred practices for teaching students with behavior problems and has written numerous articles on the topic (e.g., on behavioral contingencies and self-management). Dr. Kehle is an expert on self-modeling techniques and the theories that underlie this method. In addition, he is well known for his RICH theory and his expert knowledge about human intelligence. Some of his most recent writings have to do with ways to promote intellectual growth.

John Kregel, EdD, is professor of special education at Virginia Commonwealth University and associate director and research director of the VCU Rehabilitation Research and Training Center on Workplace Supports. He also coordinates the Urban Services Leadership track in the School of Education doctoral program. Dr. Kregel is also chairman of the VCU Department of Special Education and Disability Policy. His professional interests include supported employment and transition from school to work for individuals with disabilities. He is the author of more than 75 articles, chapters, monographs, and books on the employment of individuals with disabilities. He also served as coeditor of the journal *Focus on Autism and Other Developmental Disabilities.*

Nancy P. Kropf, MSW, PhD, is professor and chair of the doctoral program in the School of Social Work, University of Georgia. In addition, she is the current president of the Association of Gerontology Education in Social Work (AGE SW), a national organization of social work educators in aging. She also was a Hartford Geriatric Faculty Scholar, part of a program to develop leaders in social work and aging. Her area of research is late-life caregiving relationships, including those of older parents of sons and daughters with disabilities and those of grandparents who are raising grandchildren.

D. Michael Malone, PhD, is an associate professor of early childhood education at the University of Cincinnati. His background in disabilities studies crosses the lifespan, with foci in both early childhood and late life. Specific emphases include interdisciplinary teamwork and program development, personnel preparation, cognitive and social development within family contexts, observational methodology, and policy. Dr. Malone has directed and served on numerous federal and state grants designed to promote systems change through professional development, has developed and delivered a variety of courses and course lectures, presented numerous papers at professional meetings, and published his work in early childhood intervention and gerontology.

Daniel E. Olympia, PhD, is currently an assistant professor in the School Psychology Program at the University of Utah in Salt Lake City. He received his initial graduate training in school psychology and counseling and guidance at Moorhead State University in Moorhead, Minnesota, and North Dakota State University in Fargo. He received his doctorate in educational psychology from the University of Utah in 1992. He has over 17 years of experience working in public schools as a school psychologist and counselor. His research interests include school-based interventions for academic and behavioral problems, social skills training, management of aggression with children and adolescents, and home–school collaboration. He has coauthored articles and books on homework strategies for parents and teachers, home–school collaboration, academic and behavioral interventions for students with disabilities, and schoolwide behavior support.

Susan O'Mara has over 20 years' experience in providing education, work incentive counseling, and employment assistance to individuals with disabilities. Her direct counseling and education experience includes extensive work with beneficiaries and recipients, while developing and coordinating a statewide work-incentive support project , as well as benefits consultation provided in support of the Social Security Administration's Project ABLE. Susan currently serves as coordinator of training and technical assistance for Virgina Commonwealth University's (VCU) Benefits Assistance Resource Center. She is also a member of the VCU National Project Office team, providing technical assistance, monitoring, and evaluation to state projects under the SSA/RSA [Rehabilitation Services Administration] State Partnership Systems Change Initiative. Other previous experience includes serving as a regional marketing specialist for the Virginia Department of Rehabilitative Services, coordinating training and assistance on workplace supports to the business community and workforce development entities, and experience as a job coach, program manager, and consultant on Virginia's Supported Employment Systems Change Grant.

Wendy Parent, PhD, CRC, is a research associate professor and assistant director, Kansas University Center on Developmental Disabilities, a Center for Excellence in Developmental Disabilities, at the University of Kansas. She was previously with the Institute on Human Development and Disability at the University of Georgia, where she developed a disability studies program and taught graduate and undergraduate interdisciplinary education courses and supervised student internships with an emphasis on severe disability. She has served on the faculty of Rehabilitation Counseling at the University of Georgia, and on the faculties of the Rural Institute on Disability, University of Montana, and the Rehabilitation Research and Training Center on Supported Employment at Virginia Commonwealth University. Dr. Parent has 19 years experience in the area of supported employment and transition. She recently served as the principal investigator for a 5-year Workforce Action grant through the Department of Labor focusing on enhancing customized employment opportunities for individuals with disabilities through direct service, product development, and systems change. Dr. Parent has published numerous book chapters and journal articles on transition and supported employment and provided presentations and training workshops for people with disabilities, family members, job coaches, rehabilitation counselors, special educators, employers, transition coordinators, and other agency and community representatives. Her interests and research include consumer choice and satisfaction, creative job development and supports, interagency collaboration and teamwork, natural supports, leadership, job coach training, and service-delivery issues.

Elizabeth Perry-Varner, MS, CRC, CRP, LPC, has worked in the field of rehabilitation counseling for 13 years. Her professional experience includes working in an administrative and leadership capacity, being an adjunct faculty member, and providing direct service for persons with disabilities. She has worked with persons with many types of disabilities, including epilepsy, traumatic brain injury, mental illness, and spinal cord injury. In addition to the direct service she provides to clients, Ms. Perry-Varner supervises the Independent Living/ Life Skills Training program and chairs the Personal and Social Service Committee for accreditation by the Commission on Accreditation of Rehabilitation Facilities. She is published in a rehabilitative counseling journal for which she wrote a paper on One-Stop Career Centers. She has also written a chapter on epilepsy for a textbook on developmental disabilities. She has served on many boards, including the Epilepsy Association of Virginia, the Virginia Board for People with Disabilities, and the Disability Council for the United Way.

Leslie Philippen, MA, is a behavioral specialist currently working with children and adults with autism and related disorders. She consults with several organizations in Maryland. She has extensive experience implementing behavioral programming with families in crisis situations.

Valerie Postal, MSEd, is a doctoral candidate in special education at Penn State University. She is a nationally certified school psychologist and a board-certified behavior analyst. She has over 20 years of experience as a behavior specialist. She currently conducts research and provides training in her areas of interest, which include autism, ADHD, assessment, children's behavior, child development, mental health concerns of young children, and program planning for children with special needs.

Dennis H. Reid, PhD, has over 30 years of experience in managing and providing supports in developmental disabilities. He has published over 100 applied research articles and book chapters and has served on the editorial boards of 10 professional journals. His experience includes directing residential, educational, and vocational service programs, as well as providing positive behavior support services in community and school settings. Currently, Dr. Reid is director of the Carolina Behavior Analysis and Support Center in Morganton, North Carolina.

W. Grant Revell, MS, MEd, is a research associate at the Virginia Commonwealth University Rehabilitation Research and Training Center (RRTC) on Workplace Supports. He holds master's degrees in rehabilitation counseling and in special education of individuals who are mentally retarded. His primary research areas are funding, policy analysis, and systems development related specifically to competitive employment of people with significant disabilities. He has directed a variety of projects at the RRTC and most recently was project director for the National Supported Employment Consortium, a national study of supported employment in the United States, funded by the Rehabilitation Services Administration. He is actively involved in research specifically addressing the use of performance-based funding in the purchase of employment. He recently coauthored a paper that analyzed the outcome-based funding provision of the Ticket to Work; the paper is being published by the Urban Institute in the compendium titled *Paying for Results in Vocational Rehabilitation: Will Provider Incentives Work for Ticket to Work?* He has prepared and edited a variety of technical assistance guides published by the VCU RRTC on methods to encourage effective collaboration between state Vocational Rehabilitation and other agencies in the funding of supported employment services. He has published extensively in the areas of systemic development of policies and funding strategies that support improved employment supports and outcomes for persons with the most significant disabilities. Prior to his employment at the VCU RRTC, he worked for 14 years at the Virginia Department of Rehabilitative Services as a vocational rehabilitation counselor and in a variety of state-level positions in the areas of planning, developmental disabilities, and supported employment.

David A. Rotholz, PhD, has over 20 years of experience working with people who have developmental disabilities. His most recent work has involved statewide systems change in positive behavior support and person-centered planning. He has published works in the areas of positive behavior support, ecobehavioral analysis, augmentative communication, and national trends in residential setting use. He also holds leadership positions with national, state, and local disability organizations. Dr. Rotholz is currently clinical associate professor and project director at the Center for Disability Resources of the University of South Carolina School of Medicine.

Paul Sale, EdD, is professor and dean of the College of Education and Human Development at Radford University in Radford, Virginia. His experiences and research interests focus on the education of students with severe disabilities, transition of youth with disabilities to adult life, and leadership issues in education.

William R. Sharpton, PhD, is a professor on the faculty of the Department of Special Education and Habilitative Services at the University of New Orleans. He is also director of several sponsored projects and coordinates a graduate-level personnel preparation program focusing on the needs of individuals with severe disabilities. His research interests include the design of effective instructional programs that result in integrated opportunities for individuals with severe disabilities, including employment in community settings.

Marcia D. Smith, PhD, is in private practice providing psychological services to children and adults with autism and other developmental disabilities. She has extensive experience in the area of behavior management and autism in both supported employment and residential settings. She has authored books and journal articles on autism, supported employment, and behavior management and has provided training to professionals, paraprofessionals, and parents. Her areas of interest include autism, supported employment, and the management of challenging behaviors associated with developmental disabilities.

Wendy Strobel, MS, CRC, ATP, is the project director for the Demand Pull Program at the Rehabilitation Engineering Research Center on Technology Transfer, where she assists in the transfer of new assistive technologies to the consumer market. She was formerly employed as an assistive technology and transition specialist with George Mason University's Training and Technical Assistance Center and as a training associate for the Virginia Commonwealth University Rehabilitation Research and Training Center on Workplace Supports. She holds a master's degree in rehabilitation counseling, is a certified rehabilitation counselor, and an assistive technology practitioner. She has extensive experience in providing services to people with disabilities in all aspects of the rehabilitation process. She has assisted people with disabilities through supported employment, training on workplace supports, person-centered planning, independent living, and assistive technology.

Colleen A. Thoma, PhD, is an associate professor in the Department of Special Education and Disability Policy and is the coordinator of the undergraduate and graduate programs that prepare special educators to teach students with cognitive disabilities or mental retardation at Virginia Commonwealth University. She teaches courses in methods and strategies, transition planning, assistive technology, characteristics of students with cognitive disabilities, and assessment. She has conducted research in the areas of assessment, self-determination in transition planning, positive behavior supports, and teacher education. She has published articles and book chapters and made presentations on self-determined transition planning, alternative assessment, person-centered planning, assistive technology, and teacher education.

Ed Turner has 28 years of experience in the disability rights field. He has been an instructor in special education, a peer counselor for independent living, and an assistant administrator for a gubernatorial-appointed board that advocates for the rights of persons with disabilities. As a peer counselor at the Norfolk Center for Independent Living, 15% of his caseload involved people with spinal cord injures (SCI) and 85% involved persons with developmental disabilities; he supported many of these participants to overcome barriers they were facing in the process of achieving community reintegration. Mr. Turner is now serving as a training associate at the Rehabilitation Research and Training Center (RRTC) on Workplace Supports at Virginia Commonwealth University. In this role, he has developed a Self-Advocacy Training Institute to inform customers of their rights and of how to use self-advocacy to get the full benefits of those rights. For the past 4½ years, he has served as the self-advocacy/mentor sub-project director for the Medical College of Virginia RRTC SCI Model Systems Project. In this position, he develops training materials designed to assist customers with SCI to better understand their rights to employment services and programs. During this 4½-year period, 46 customers were trained in five Self-Advocacy Institutes, with 16 mentors being identified to provide support to newly injured people with SCI.

Douglas J. Usiak is the executive director of the Western New York Independent Living Project (WNYILP) family of agencies in Buffalo. He has served two terms as chairperson of New York State Independent Living Council (NYSILC) and as its interim executive director. Mr. Usiak is a member of the Advisory Committee of the Center for International Rehabilitation Research Information and Exchange (CIRRIE) and the steering committees of the Rehabilitation Engineering Research Center (RERC) on Universal Design and the RERC on Aging, at the University at Buffalo. He helped to create AZtech, a consumer-controlled primary and secondary marketing organization specializing in universal design of assistive technology to serve people with and without disabilities. He is the project director and principal investigator of the RRTC-ILM.

Paul Wehman, PhD, is professor of physical medicine and rehabilitation at Virginia Commonwealth University (VCU), with joint appointments in the Department of Curriculum and Instruction and the Department of Rehabilitation Counseling. He pioneered the development of supported employment at VCU in the early 1980s and has been heavily involved in the use of supported employment with people who have severe disabilities, such as those with severe intellectual disabilities, brain injury, spinal cord injury, or autism. Dr. Wehman is also director of the Rehabilitation Research and Training Center on Workplace Supports and chairman of the Division of Rehabilitation Research. He has written extensively on issues related to transition from school to adulthood, and special education for young adults. He has published over 150 articles and 24 book chapters, and authored or edited 33 books. He is a recipient of the Joseph P. Kennedy, Jr., Foundation International Award in Mental Retardation, was a Mary Switzer Fellow for the National Rehabilitation Association in 1985, and in October 1992 received the Distinguished Service Award from the President's Committee on Employment for Persons with Disabilities. Dr. Wehman was recognized as one of the 50 most influential special educators of the millenium by a national survey coordinated by the *Remedial and Special Education* journal (December 2000), and received the VCU Distinguished Service Award (September 2001). He testified on behalf of the President's Committee on Excellence in Special Education (April 30, 2002). He is also editor-in-chief of the *Journal of Vocational Rehabilitation*.

Therese Wehman, PhD, received her doctorate in child development from the Erikson Institute, Loyola University, Chicago. Her areas of specialization focus on young children birth to age 6 with disabilities, early childhood program administration, organizational development, and team building. She holds advanced degrees and Illinois teaching certification in educational administration, elementary education, early childhood education, and special education. She has had extensive experience designing and administering early childhood intervention programs for young children with special needs and their families in both public schools and nonprofit organizations. She has held graduate faculty positions and directed graduate research at the Erikson Institute for Advanced Study in Child Development and National Louis University prior to joining the faculty at Elmhurst College. She is currently program coordinator of and an associate professor in the Early Childhood Special Education Graduate Program at Elmhurst College. Her research interests focus on early intervention system change, building parent–professional partnerships, professional leadership development, and inclusion.

Michael D. West, PhD, is assistant professor at Virginia Commonwealth University (VCU) and is also research associate with the Rehabilitation Research and Training Center (RRTC) on Workplace Supports. Dr. West's research projects have included national surveys of supported employment policies and practices, a study of students with disabilities in higher education in Virginia, and states' use of Medicaid Home- and Community-Based Waivers to fund employment services. He also is involved in research and demonstration efforts related to Social Security disability reform at the VCU RRTC on Workplace Supports.

Pamela S. Wolfe, PhD, is an associate professor of special education at Pennsylvania State University, where she teaches and conducts research related to transition and students with severe disabilities. Specific research interests include instructional methodologies, transition planning, sexuality training, and applied behavior analysis. She is currently codirector of a grant to train graduate students for work with students having autism. Dr. Wolfe has a strong interest in fostering self-advocacy for persons with severe disabilities in integrated community settings.

Satoko Yasuda, PhD, works as a research assistant at the Rehabilitation Research and Training Center at Virginia Commonwealth University. She is involved in research regarding employment issues for individuals with disabilities and has coauthored articles related to employment of individuals with traumatic brain injury and spinal cord injury.